Merrill
Algebra Two
with Trigonometry

Foster • Rath • Winters

Charles E. Merrill Publishing Co.
A Bell & Howell Company
Columbus, Ohio

Toronto • London • Sydney

About the Cover

The cover photograph shows Tower Place, 3340 Peachtree Road, Atlanta, Georgia. The building was designed by Stevens and Wilkinson Architects and built in 1975. The building is 396 feet tall and has 29 stories, all of which are offices. It takes 6 weeks to wash its 10,400 windows. Tower Place has 68 sides, which is more than any other building in the United States.

The photographer was E. Alan McGee/Alpha.

ISBN 0-675-05205-X

ISBN 0-675-05204-1
Published by
Charles E. Merrill Publishing Co.
A Bell & Howell Company
Columbus, Ohio 43216

Printed in the United States of America

Authors

Alan G. Foster is head of the Mathematics Department at Addison Trail High School, Addison, Illinois. He has taught mathematics courses at every level of the high school curriculum. Mr. Foster obtained his B.S. from Illinois State University and his M.A. in mathematics from the University of Illinois, with additional work at University of Colorado, University of Wyoming, Northern Illinois University, Purdue, Northwestern, Princeton, Illinois Institute of Technology, and National College of Education. Mr. Foster is active in professional organizations at local, state, and national levels, frequently speaking or conducting workshops. He is a past president of the Illlinois Council of Teachers of Mathematics.

James N. Rath has 25 years of classroom experience in teaching mathematics at every level of the high school curriculum. He has also taught calculus at the college level. Mr. Rath is a former head of the Mathematics Department at Darien High School, Darien, Connecticut. He earned his B.A. in Philosophy from the Catholic University of America. He obtained both his M.Ed. and his M.A. in mathematics from Boston College. He developed a minicourse in BASIC for the Darien Public Schools. Mr. Rath is a member of various local, state, and national organizations.

Leslie J. Winters is chairperson of the Mathematics Department at John F. Kennedy High School, Granada Hills, California. He has taught mathematics at every level from junior high to college. He holds the following degrees: B.A., mathematics, Pepperdine University; B.S., secondary education, University of Dayton; M.S., secondary education, University of Southern California; M.A., mathematics, Boston College. Mr. Winters co-authored "Flow Chart Mathematics" for Victor Corporation and is a frequent speaker at local, state, and national conferences.

Consultants

Dr. F. Joe Crosswhite
Professor of Mathematics
Ohio State University
Columbus, Ohio

Lee Yunker
Head, Mathematics Department
West Chicago Community High School
West Chicago, Illinois

Reviewers

David A. Flowers
Supervisor, Instructional Computer Services
Fort Wayne Community Schools
Fort Wayne, Indiana

Carl F. Pasbjerg
Mathematics Department Chairperson
Adams High School
Rochester, Michigan

June Norman White
Mathematics Coordinator
Beaumont I.S.D.
Beaumont, Texas

Dolores Jones
Secondary Math Curriculum Director
Bibb County Schools
Macon, Georgia

Gerard J. Swanson
Department Chairman
Weymouth Secondary Schools
Weymouth, Massachusetts

Janice M. Wong
Mathematics Teacher
El Camino High School
Sacramento, California

Staff

Editorial
Project Editor: Darlene Lewis
Assistant Project Editor: Jack Witherspoon
Assistant Editors: Annamaria J. Doney,
                        Cynthia Lindsay, Michael H. Thorne
Photo Editor: Linda Hoffhines

Art
Project Artist: Lewis H. Bolen
Book Designer: Michael T. Henry
Cover Designer: Lester Shumaker
Artists: Larry Winston Collins, Jim Shough

Photo Credits

Preface

This second edition of *Merrill Algebra Two with Trigonometry* is designed for use by students in second-year high school algebra courses. The text is based on the successful first edition of *Merrill Algebra Two with Trigonometry*. The goals of the text are to develop proficiency with mathematical skills, to expand understanding of mathematical concepts, to improve logical thinking, and to promote success. To achieve these goals, the following strategies are used.

Build upon a Solid Foundation.   Review is provided for those topics generally presented in first year algebra. In this way, the student's understanding is strengthened before more difficult concepts are introduced.

Utilize Sound Pedagogy.   *Merrill Algebra Two with Trigonometry* covers in logical sequence all topics generally presented at this level. Concepts are introduced when they are needed. Each concept presented is then used within that lesson and in later lessons.

Gear Presentation for Learning.   An appropriate reading level has been maintained throughout the text. Furthermore, many photographs, illustrations, charts, graphs, and tables provide visual aids for the concepts and skills presented. Hence, students are able to read and learn with increased understanding.

Use Relevant Real-Life Applications.   Applications are provided not only for practice, but also to aid understanding in how concepts are used.

The text offers a variety of aids for the student in learning algebra.

Student Annotations	Help students identify important concepts as they study.
Skills Review	Provides students with a mini-review of skills and concepts taught previously.
Selected Answers	Allow students to check their progress as they work. These answers are provided at the back of the text.
Vocabulary	Enables students to focus on increasing their mathematical vocabulary.
Chapter Summary	Provides students with a compact listing of major concepts presented within each chapter.
Chapter Review	Permits students to review each chapter by working sample problems from each lesson.
Chapter Test	Enables students to check their own progress.
Cumulative Review	Helps students to maintain and use algebraic concepts.

The following special features, which appear periodically throughout the text, provide interesting and useful extra topics.

Careers	Depict a variety of persons in different careers using mathematics. These careers are typical of careers that students may pursue.
Reading Algebra	Provides students with the instruction needed to read and interpret mathematical symbolism.
Problem Solving	Illustrates several helpful techniques for solving mathematical problems.
Applications	Provide insights into the use of mathematics in everyday life.
Calculator	Instructs students in using a calculator. The use of the calculator is related to concepts taught within the chapter.
Excursions in Algebra	Enliven and help maintain student interest by providing interesting side trips. Topics are varied and include history, glimpses into development and uses of algebra, puzzles, and games.
BASIC	Instructs students in writing programs using the BASIC computer language. This material, provided in the Appendix, can be taught as a unit or interspersed throughout the year.

Teachers and students familiar with the earlier edition of this text will be pleased to see that the clarity of explanations and careful sequencing of topics has been retained in this new edition of *Merrill Algebra Two with Trigonometry*.

Contents

Quadratic Relations and Functions _____ 196

7

Conics _____ 222

8

Polynomial Functions _____ 258

9

Rational Polynomial Expressions _____ 292

10

Exponents _____ 320

11

Exponential and Logarithmic Functions _____ 350

12

Sequences and Series _____ 384

13

Probability _____ 422

14

Statistics _____ 452

15

chapter
1   Equations and Inequalities

Equations can be used in many areas of our everyday lives. For example, suppose an investment of $7500 in solar heating equipment results in a yearly savings of $450 on heating bills. In addition to this, the owner receives a $2100 tax credit from the government the first year only. How many years will it take for the savings to equal the investment? This problem can be solved using the equation $450y + 2100 = 7500$.

1–1 Expressions and Formulas

We often use mathematical expressions like $4(x + 2y) - 5x^3$. This expression contains the following kinds of symbols.

constants:	4 2 5 3	
variables:	x y	represent unknown quantities
operation symbols:	+ −	tell which operations are involved
grouping symbols:	( )	tell order for doing operations

The following numerical expressions all represent the number sixteen. Sixteen is called the **value** of each expression.

$$4^2 \qquad 9 + 7 \qquad (12 \div 2) + 10$$

In the expression 4^2, the **base** is 4 and the **exponent** is 2. An exponent indicates the number of times the base is used as a factor.

4^2 means $4 \cdot 4$. $\qquad$ 10^1 means 10. $\qquad$ x^5 means $x \cdot x \cdot x \cdot x \cdot x$.

What is the value of $4 + 3 \cdot 2$? You might evaluate the expression in one of the ways below.

Multiply 3 and 2. Then add 4. $\qquad$ *Add 4 and 3. Then multiply by 2.*

$$4 + 3 \cdot 2 = 4 + 6 \qquad\qquad 4 + 3 \cdot 2 = 7 \cdot 2$$
$$= 10 \qquad\qquad\qquad\qquad = 14$$

Which answer is correct?

A numerical expression should have a unique value. To find this value, you must know the order for performing operations.

> 1. **Evaluate all powers.**
> 2. **Then do all multiplications and divisions from left to right.**
> 3. **Then do all additions and subtractions from left to right.**

Order of Operations

Thus, the value of $4 + 3 \cdot 2$ is 10.

example

1 **Find the value of $4 + 8^2 \div 4 \cdot 2$.**

$$4 + 8^2 \div 4 \cdot 2 = 4 + 64 \div 4 \cdot 2 \qquad \textit{Evaluate all powers.}$$
$$= 4 + 16 \cdot 2 \qquad \textit{Do all multiplications and}$$
$$= 4 + 32 \qquad\quad \textit{divisions left to right.}$$
$$= 36 \qquad\qquad \textit{Do all additions and}$$
$$\textit{subtractions left to right.}$$

The value is 36.

Grouping symbols are used to change the order of operations. Start with the operations inside the innermost grouping symbols.

example

2 **Find the value of $[(4 + 8)^2 \div 4] \cdot 2$.**

$$\begin{aligned}[(4 + 8)^2 \div 4] \cdot 2 &= [(12)^2 \div 4] \cdot 2 &&\textit{First add 4 and 8.}\\ &= [144 \div 4] \cdot 2 &&\textit{Then find } 12^2.\\ &= [36] \cdot 2 &&\textit{Now divide 144 by 4.}\\ &= 72 &&\textit{Multiply 36 by 2.}\end{aligned}$$

The value is 72.

Mathematical expressions with at least one variable are called **algebraic expressions.** You can evaluate an algebraic expression by substituting a value for each variable.

example

3 **Evaluate $5x^2 + 3xy$ if $x = {}^-5$ and $y = 3$.**

$$\begin{aligned}5x^2 + 3xy &= 5(^-5)^2 + 3(^-5)(3) &&\textit{Replace x by } ^-5 \textit{ and y by 3.}\\ &= 5(25) + 3(^-5)(3) &&\textit{Find } (^-5)^2.\\ &= 125 + {}^-45 &&\textit{Multiply left to right.}\\ &= 80 &&\textit{Add.}\end{aligned}$$

The value is 80.

A **formula** is a mathematical sentence about the relationships among certain quantities. For example, $A = l \cdot w$ relates the area of a rectangle to its length and width.

In a formula, if you know replacements for every variable except one, you can find a replacement for that variable.

example

4 **The relationship between Celsius temperature *(C)* and Fahrenheit temperature *(F)* is given by $C = \dfrac{5(F - 32)}{9}$. Find C if $F = 68$.**

$$\begin{aligned}C &= \frac{5(F - 32)}{9} &&\textit{Write the formula.}\\ C &= \frac{5(68 - 32)}{9} &&\textit{Replace F by 68.}\\ C &= \frac{180}{9} &&\textit{Subtract 32 from 68. Multiply 5 by 36.}\\ C &= 20 &&\textit{Divide 180 by 9.}\end{aligned}$$

The Celsius temperature is 20°.

exercises

Exploratory Find the value of each expression.

1. $2 + 8 - 3$
2. $5 - 3 \cdot 2$
3. $5 - (4 + 3)^2$
4. $2(6 + 1)$
5. $2 \cdot 6 + 1$
6. $3^3 - 2^3$
7. $3(2^2 + 3)$
8. $5^2 \div 2^5$
9. $2 + 5^2$
10. $(5 - 7)^2$
11. $2(3 + 8) - 1$
12. $2(8) - 8 \div 4$
13. $5^2 - (3 + 2)^2$
14. $3 + (3 - 3)^3 - 3$
15. $3 \times 2 - 2$

Written Find the value of each expression.

1. $(6 + 5) \cdot 4 - 3$
2. $(6 + 5)(4 - 3)$
3. $12 + 8 \div 4$
4. $12 + (8 \div 4)$
5. $12 \div 8 \cdot 4$
6. $12 \div (8 \cdot 4)$
7. $(5 + 3)^2 - 16 \div 4$
8. $5 + 3^2 - 16 \div 4$
9. $2 \cdot 9 \div 6 + 7$
10. $8 - 2 \cdot 3 - 3$
11. $12 + 18 \div 6 + 7$
12. $4 + 8 \cdot 4 \div 2 - 10$

Evaluate if $a = 3$, $b = 7$, $c = {}^-2$, $d = \frac{1}{2}$, and $e = 0.3$.

13. $6a^3 - 2b$
14. $3ab - 6bc$
15. $3ad + bc$
16. $c^2 - 5d$
17. $5c + be$
18. $8e - 3bc$
19. $(a + c)^3 + d^2$
20. $(a + b - d)^2$
21. $12a^2 + bc$
22. $4a - 12cd$
23. $\dfrac{6ac}{d}$
24. $\dfrac{3ab}{cd}$
25. $\dfrac{3ce}{d^2}$
26. $\dfrac{10e^2}{3d}$
27. $\dfrac{5a + 3c}{3b}$
28. $\dfrac{3ab^2 - c^3}{a + c}$
29. $(5a + 3d)^2 - e^2$
30. $(3b - 21d)^2$

Simple *interest (I)* is calculated using the formula $I = prt$. The variable p represents the *principal* in dollars, r represents the *rate* of interest in percent, and t represents the *time* in years. Find I given the following values.

31. $p = \$1000$, $r = 6\%$, and $t = 3$ years
32. $p = \$2500$, $r = 9\%$, and $t = 30$ months
33. $p = \$5000$, $r = 8\%$, and $t = 9$ months
34. $p = \$2000$, $r = 8\%$, and $t = 9$ months
35. $p = \$20{,}000$, $r = 14\frac{1}{2}\%$, and $t = 6$ years
36. $p = \$65{,}000$, $r = 16\%$, and $t = 63$ months

The formula for the area of a trapezoid is $A = \dfrac{h}{2}(b + B)$. A represents the measure of the area, h represents the measure of the altitude, and b and B represent the measures of the bases. Calculate the measure of the area of each trapezoid given the following values.

37. $b = 12$, $B = 20$, and $h = 8$
38. $b = 4$, $B = 11$, and $h = 7$
39. $h = 10$, $b = 6$, and $B = 14$
40. $h = 8$, $B = 16$, and $b = 12$
41. $h = 8$, $b = 8.6$, and $B = 14.8$
42. $h = 12$, $B = 9.7$, and $b = 6.2$
43. $h = 9$, $B = 7\frac{2}{3}$, and $b = 4\frac{1}{6}$
44. $h = 6\frac{1}{2}$, $b = 8\frac{1}{3}$, and $B = 12$

Challenge Show that you can find at least three different answers to $4 + 8^2 \div 4 \cdot 2$ depending on how you group. Should this be allowed? If not, why not?

1–2   Properties of Addition and Multiplication

One of the basic properties of addition and multiplication is **commutativity.** This means that the order in which two numbers are added or multiplied does *not* change their sum or their product.

$$8 + 3 = 3 + 8 \qquad\qquad 24 \cdot 9 = 9 \cdot 24$$
$$4\tfrac{1}{2} + \tfrac{2}{3} = \tfrac{2}{3} + 4\tfrac{1}{2} \qquad 13.7(2.5) = 2.5(13.7)$$

> **For all numbers a and b,**
> $$a + b = b + a \text{ and,}$$
> $$a \cdot b = b \cdot a$$

Commutative Properties

Another basic property of addition and multiplication is **associativity.** To add three numbers, you add two numbers at a time. For example, to find $8 + 6 + 4$, you could add the sum of 8 and 6 to 4. Or you could add 8 to the sum of 6 and 4. Either way, the sum is 18.

$$(8 + 6) + 4 = 8 + (6 + 4)$$
$$14 + 4 = 8 + 10$$
$$18 = 18$$

The way you group, or associate, three or more numbers does *not* change their sum. The same property holds for multiplication. The way you group, or associate, three or more numbers does *not* change their product.

$$(11 \cdot 4) \cdot 3 = 11 \cdot (4 \cdot 3)$$
$$44 \cdot 3 = 11 \cdot 12$$
$$132 = 132$$

> **For all numbers a, b, and c,**
> $$(a + b) + c = a + (b + c) \text{ and,}$$
> $$(a \cdot b) \cdot c = a \cdot (b \cdot c).$$

Associative Properties

The commutative and associative properties used together make addition and multiplication easier.

example

1   **Find $1 + 2 + 3 + 4 + 5 + 6 + 7 + 8 + 9$.**

$$1 + 2 + 3 + 4 + 5 + 6 + 7 + 8 + 9$$
$$= (1 + 9) + (2 + 8) + (3 + 7) + (4 + 6) + 5$$
$$= \quad 10 \quad + \quad 10 \quad + \quad 10 \quad + \quad 10 \quad + 5$$
$$= 45$$

The sum is 45.

2 **Simplify** $6 \cdot 2 \cdot 12 \cdot 5$.

$$6 \cdot 2 \cdot 12 \cdot 5 = (6 \cdot 12) \cdot (2 \cdot 5)$$
$$= \quad 72 \quad \cdot \quad 10$$
$$= 720$$

The product is 720.

The sum of any number and zero is identical to the original number.

$$2 + 0 = 2 \qquad 0 + {}^-8 = {}^-8 \qquad 7.7 + 0 = 7.7$$

Zero is the **additive identity.**

The product of any number and one is identical to the original number.

$$6 \cdot 1 = 6 \qquad 1 \cdot {}^-9 = {}^-9 \qquad 1 \cdot 18.3 = 18.3$$

One is the **multiplicative identity.**

> **For any number a,**
> $a + 0 = a = 0 + a$ **and,**
> $a \cdot 1 = a = 1 \cdot a.$

Identity Properties

If the sum of two numbers is zero, they are called **additive inverses** of each other.

$$2 + {}^-2 = 0 \qquad {}^-85.2 + 85.2 = 0$$

If the product of two numbers is one, they are called **multiplicative inverses,** or **reciprocals** of each other.

$$2 \cdot \frac{1}{2} = 1 \qquad \frac{1}{19} \cdot 19 = 1$$

> **For any number a,**
> $a + {}^-a = 0 = {}^-a + a$ **and,**
> **if a is *not* zero,** $a \cdot \dfrac{1}{a} = 1 = \dfrac{1}{a} \cdot a.$

Inverse Properties

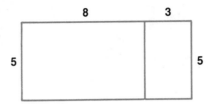

You can find the area of this rectangle in two different ways.

Method 1: Multiply the length by the width.

$A = (5)(8 + 3)$
$A = (5)(11)$
$A = 55$

Method 2: Add the areas of the smaller rectangles.

$A = 5(8) + 5(3)$
$A = 40 + 15$
$A = 55$

This example shows that $(5)(8 + 3)$ and $(5)(8) + (5)(3)$ have the same value, 55. Other similar examples lead to the following generalization.

For all numbers a, b, and c, $a(b + c) = ab + ac$ **and** $(b + c)a = ba + ca.$

Distributive Property

We say that multiplication is distributive over addition.

Since subtraction sentences can be written as addition sentences, the distributive property also applies to subtraction.

$$4(5 - 3) = 4(2) \qquad\qquad 4(5 - 3) = 4(5 + (^-3))$$
$$= 8 \qquad\qquad\qquad\qquad\quad = 4 \cdot 5 - 4 \cdot 3$$
$$= 20 - 12$$
$$= 8$$

The distributive property can be used to simplify expressions containing like terms. In $5y + 3x + 7y + 2y^2$, for example, $5y$ and $7y$ are like terms and $5y$, $3x$, and $2y^2$ are unlike terms.

examples

3 **Simplify $5y + 3x + 7y + 2y^2$.**

$$\begin{aligned} 5y + 3x + 7y + 2y^2 &= 5y + (3x + 7y) + 2y^2 & \text{\textit{Associative Property for Addition}} \\ &= 5y + (7y + 3x) + 2y^2 & \text{\textit{Commutative Property for Addition}} \\ &= (5y + 7y) + 3x + 2y^2 & \text{\textit{Associative Property for Addition}} \\ &= (5 + 7)y + 3x + 2y^2 & \text{\textit{Distributive Property}} \\ &= 12y + 3x + 2y^2 \end{aligned}$$

4 **Simplify $6(a + 2b) + 4(4a - 7b)$.**

$$\begin{aligned} 6(a + 2b) + 4(4a - 7b) &= 6a + 12b + 16a - 28b & \text{\textit{Distributive Property}} \\ &= 6a + 16a + 12b - 28b & \text{\textit{Commutative Property for Addition}} \\ &= (6 + 16)a + (12 - 28)b & \text{\textit{Distributive Property}} \\ &= 22a - 16b \end{aligned}$$

exercises

Exploratory State the property shown in each of the following.

1. $8 + (6 + 4) = (8 + 6) + 4$
2. $7(5) = 5(7)$
3. $(a + b)c = ac + bc$
4. $a(3 - 2) = a \cdot 3 - a \cdot 2$
5. $8 + (1 + 6) = 8 + (6 + 1)$
6. $3 + {}^-3 = 0$
7. $2(3 + 6) = 2(3) + 2(6)$
8. $9 - (3 + 4) = 9 - (4 + 3)$
9. $3 + 6 = 6 + 3$
10. $8(6 - 7) = (6 - 7)8$
11. $8\left(\frac{1}{8}\right) = 1$
12. $11 + (6 + 4) = (6 + 4) + 11$
13. ${}^-9 + 9 = 9 + {}^-9$
14. $3(47) = 3(40) + 3(7)$

Written State the property shown in each of the following.

1. $3(9) = 9(3)$
2. $(5 + 6) + 3 = 5 + (6 + 3)$
3. $(4 + 11) \cdot 6 = 4(6) + 11(6)$
4. $(a + b) + {}^-(a + b) = 0$
5. $11 + a = a + 11$
6. $(3 + 9) + 14 = 14 + (3 + 9)$
7. $3 + (a + b) = (a + b) + 3$
8. $7 \cdot 1 = 7$
9. $8(5 + 3) = 40 + 24$
10. $3a + 6 = 3(a + 2)$
11. $(11a + 3b) + 0 = 11a + 3b$
12. $8(4) = 4(8)$
13. $3\left(\frac{1}{3}\right) = 1$
14. $(4 + 9a)2b = 2b(4 + 9a).$
15. $a + b + 0 = a + b$
16. $\left(\frac{1}{m}\right)m = 1$
17. $11(3a + 2b) = 11(2b + 3a)$
18. $5a + {}^-5a = 0$
19. $1 = ax^2 \cdot \frac{1}{ax^2}$
20. $0 + 7 = 7$

Simplify.

21. $8 + 15 - 3$
22. $5(13 + 25)$
23. $7x + 8y + 9y - 5x$
24. $3a + 5b + 7a - 3b$
25. $3(5a + 6b) + 8(2a - b)$
26. $2(7c - 5d) - 3(d + 2c)$
27. $\frac{1}{4}(12 + 20a) + \frac{3}{4}(12 + 20a)$
28. $\frac{1}{2}(17 - 4x) - \frac{3}{4}(6 - 16x)$
29. $\frac{2}{3}\left(\frac{1}{2}a + 3b\right) + \frac{1}{2}\left(\frac{2}{3}a + b\right)$
30. $\frac{3}{4}(2x - 5y) + \frac{1}{2}\left(\frac{2}{3}x + 4y\right)$
31. $7(0.2m + 0.3n) + 5(0.6m - n)$
32. $9(0.6a - 0.2c) + 3(0.2a + 1.1c)$

33. If $a + b = a$, what is the value of b? What is b called?
34. If $ab = 1$, what is the value of a? What is a called?
35. If $ab = a$, what is the value of b? What is b called?
36. If $a + b = 0$, what is the value of a? What is a called?

Challenge Explain what is wrong with the following sentence.

$$\text{If } a\left(\frac{1}{a}\right) = 1, \text{ then } 0\left(\frac{1}{0}\right) = 1.$$

1-3 Properties of Equality

Some relations have three important properties. In your study of arithmetic, you have assumed these properties for equality.

For any number a, $a = a$.	*Reflexive Property of Equality*
For all numbers a and b, if $a = b$, then $b = a$.	*Symmetric Property of Equality*
For all numbers a, b, and c, if $a = b$ and $b = c$, then $a = c$.	*Transitive Property of Equality*

1 State the property of equality shown in each of the following.

a. $21.4 = 21.4$

b. If $36 \cdot 2 = 72$, then $72 = 36 \cdot 2$.

c. If $8 = 6 + 2$ and $6 + 2 = 5 + 3$, then $8 = 5 + 3$.

a. reflexive property

b. symmetric property

c. transitive property

An important property of equality is the substitution property.

For all numbers a and b, if $a = b$, then a may be replaced by b.	*Substitution Property of Equality*

Sentences with variables to be replaced, such as $5 = x + 4$, are called *open sentences*. The **solution set** of an open sentence is the set of all replacements for variables that make the sentence true.

An equation is a statement of equality between two mathematical expressions. Solving an equation means finding the solution set of the equation. Sometimes an equation can be solved by performing the indicated operations and using substitution.

A set of numbers is indicated by braces. $\{1, 2, 3\}$ is the set which contains the elements 1, 2, and 3.

2 Solve $y = 8(0.3) + 1.2$.

$y = 8(0.3) + 1.2$

$y = 2.4 + 1.2$ *Substitute 2.4 for 8(0.3).*

$y = 3.6$ *Substitute 3.6 for 2.4 + 1.2.*

The solution is 3.6. The solution set is $\{3.6\}$.

Sometimes an equation can be solved by adding or subtracting the same number to both sides of the equation.

example

3 **Solve $x + 28.3 = 56.0$.**

$$x + 28.3 = 56.0$$
$$x + 28.3 + {}^-28.3 = 56.0 + {}^-28.3 \qquad \textit{Add}^-28.3 \textit{ to both sides.}$$
$$x = 27.7 \qquad \textit{Substitution.}$$

The solution is 27.7. The solution set is {27.7}.

For any numbers a, b, and c, if $a = b$, then $a + c = b + c$ and $a - c = b - c$.	*Addition and Subtraction Properties of Equality*

Sometimes an equation can be solved by multiplying or dividing both sides by the same number.

examples

4 **Solve $7x = 42$.**

$$7x = 42$$
$$\frac{1}{7} \cdot 7x = \frac{1}{7} \cdot 42 \qquad \textit{Multiply both sides by } \frac{1}{7}.$$
$$x = 6 \qquad \textit{Substitution.}$$

The solution is 6. The solution set is {6}.

5 **Solve $7x = 42$.**

$$7x = 42$$
$$\frac{7x}{7} = \frac{42}{7} \qquad \textit{Divide both sides by 7.}$$
$$x = 6 \qquad \textit{Substitution.}$$

The solution is 6. The solution set is {6}.

For any numbers a, b, and c, if $a = b$, then $a \cdot c = b \cdot c$ and, if c is *not* zero, $\dfrac{a}{c} = \dfrac{b}{c}$.	*Multiplication and Division Properties of Equality*

Many equations can be solved by using the properties of equality along with the other properties you have studied.

6 **Solve $5x - 7 = 23$.**

$$5x - 7 = 23$$
$$5x - 7 + 7 = 23 + 7 \qquad \textit{Addition Property}$$
$$5x = 30 \qquad \textit{Substitution}$$
$$\frac{5x}{5} = \frac{30}{5} \qquad \textit{Division Property}$$
$$x = 6 \qquad \textit{Substitution}$$

The solution is 6. The solution set is $\{6\}$.

You may combine steps when solving equations.

7 **Solve $\frac{3}{4}(8a + 20) - 2a = \frac{2}{3} + 1\frac{1}{3}$.**

$$\frac{3}{4}(8a + 20) - 2a = \frac{2}{3} + 1\frac{1}{3}$$
$$6a + 15 - 2a = 2 \qquad \textit{Distributive and Substitution Properties}$$
$$4a + 15 = 2 \qquad \textit{Commutative, Distributive and Substitution Properties}$$
$$4a = {}^-13 \qquad \textit{Subtraction and Substitution Properties}$$
$$a = -\frac{13}{4} \qquad \textit{Division and Substitution Properties}$$

The solution is $-\frac{13}{4}$. The solution set is $\left\{ -\frac{13}{4} \right\}$.

exercises

Exploratory   State the property shown in each of the following.

1. $3 + (2 + 3) = 3 + (2 + 3)$
2. $3 + (2 + 3) = 3 + 5$
3. If $x + 3 = 7$, then $x = 4$.
4. If $5x = 40$, then $x = 8$.
5. If $7 = 2 + 5$, and $2 + 5 = \sqrt{49}$, then $7 = \sqrt{49}$.
6. If $8 + 1 = 9$ and $9 = 3 + 6$, then $8 + 1 = 3 + 6$.
7. If $3 = 2 + 1$, then $2 + 1 = 3$.
8. If $5 + 7 = 12$, then $12 = 7 + 5$.
9. If $2 + 1 = 3$, then $6 + (2 + 1) = 6 + 3$.
10. If $8 = 6 + 2$ and $6 + 2 = 5 + 3$, then $8 = 5 + 3$.
11. If $7 = n$, then $n = 7$.
12. If $\frac{2}{3}x = 6$, then $x = 9$.
13. $81 = 81$
14. $9 + 5 = (6 + 3) + 5$

Written State the property shown in each of the following.

1. If $8 + 1 = x$, then $x = 8 + 1$.

2. If $6 + 9 = 5 + 10$ and $5 + 10 = 15$, then $6 + 9 = 15$.

3. If $7 + 4 = 7 + 3 + 1$ and $7 + 3 + 1 = 10 + 1$, then $7 + 4 = 10 + 1$.

4. $9 + (2 + 10) = 9 + 12$

5. $6 + a = 6 + a$

6. If $11 - 5 = 4 + 2$, then $4 + 2 = 11 - 5$.

7. $4 + 7 + 9 = 11 + 9$

8. $4 + 7 + 9 = 4 + 7 + 9$

9. If $5x + 7x = 4$, then $(5 + 7)x = 4$.

10. If $\frac{3}{4}x = \frac{2}{3}$, then $9x = 8$.

11. If $7x = 21$, then $x = 3$.

12. If $7b + 3 = 10$, then $7b = 7$.

13. $5x + 8x = 30 - 4$
    a. $(5 + 8)x = 30 - 4$
    b. $\qquad 13x = 26$
    c. $\qquad x = 2$

14. $8a - 3 = 22$
    a. $8a = 22 + 3$
    b. $8a = 25$
    c. $a = \frac{25}{8}$

Solve each equation.

15. $4x = 30$

16. $15 = {}^-3y$

17. $a + 17 = 31$

18. $12 = 8 - r$

19. $\frac{3}{4}x = \frac{5}{7}$

20. $5q = \frac{2}{5}$

21. $\frac{2}{5}m = 1\frac{3}{4}$

22. $\frac{3}{7}x = 4\frac{1}{2}$

23. $3x + 8 = 29$

24. $4 - 8x = 36$

25. $2 + 12x = {}^-142$

26. $3 - 2x = 18$

27. $\frac{3}{4}r + 1 = 10$

28. $1 + \frac{2}{3}y = 27$

29. $9x + 4 = 2\frac{1}{2}$

30. $4x + \frac{3}{5} = 1\frac{7}{10}$

31. $\frac{8e}{9} + \frac{1}{3} = \frac{3}{5}$

32. $\frac{3}{8} - \frac{1}{4}x = \frac{1}{16}$

33. $1.2x + 3.7 = 13.3$

34. $4.5 - 3.9m = 20.1$

35. ${}^-2.1 = 37 - 0.6b$

36. $3.2a - 1.1 = 4.02$

37. $1.3 - 0.003x = 0.67$

38. $1.1x - 0.09 = 2.22$

39. $9 = 16d + 51$

40. $10r - 17 = 51$

41. $5t + 4 = 2t + 13$

42. $2y - 8 = 14 - 9y$

43. $3x + 5 = 9x + 2$

44. $3x - 4 = 7x - 11$

45. $\frac{3}{4}s - \frac{1}{2} = \frac{1}{4}s + 5$

46. $\frac{2}{3} - \frac{3}{5}x = \frac{2}{5}x + \frac{4}{3}$

47. $8 - x = 5x + 32$

48. $4 + 3p = p - 12$

49. $2(3d - 10) = 40$

50. $3 = {}^-3(y + 5)$

51. $5(3x + 5) = 4x - 8$

52. $2(6 - 7k) = 2k - 4$

53. $8x - 3 = 5(2x + 1)$

54. $2x - 4(x + 2) = {}^-2x - 8$

55. $285 - 38x = 2033$

56. $2467 - 897b = 10{,}091.5$

57. $8061 = 295a - 1084$

58. $847.6b - 3269.5 = 610.1b + 2406.75$

History

excursions in algebra

The Marquise du Châtelet (1706–1749) was born into nobility in Paris, France. She was an extremely brilliant mathematician who concentrated her studies on the works of Euclid and Isaac Newton. She was also a philosopher of considerable merit. Several of her philosophy papers were published posthumously.

1-4   Using Equations

In algebra, we often translate verbal expressions into algebraic expressions. Variables are used to represent numbers that are not known. Any letter may be used as a variable.

Verbal Expression	Algebraic Expression
a number increased by 5	$x + 5$
twice the cube of *a number*	$2n^3$
the square of *a number* increased by the cube of the *same number*	$x^2 + x^3$
product of *a number* and 9	$9n$
three times the sum of *a number* and 7	$3(b + 7)$

As shown below, equations can be used to represent verbal mathematical sentences.

Verbal Sentence	Equation
Eight is equal to five plus three.	$8 = 5 + 3$
A number decreased by 7 is ‾3.	$y - 7 = {}^-3$
Six times a number is 42.	$6n = 42$
A number divided by 3 is equal to $\frac{3}{4}$.	$\dfrac{x}{3} = \dfrac{3}{4}$

You can use equations to solve many verbal problems. First you should read the problem carefully and define a variable.

Jeff Carter bought some 20¢ stamps and twice as many 2¢ stamps. He paid 96¢ for all the stamps. How many of each did he buy?

Define a variable.   The problem asks for how many stamps of each kind. Let n represent the number of 20¢ stamps. Since he bought twice as many 2¢ stamps, $2n$ represents the number of 2¢ stamps.

After defining a variable you should write an equation that describes the relationships in the problem.

Write an equation.

$$\text{cost of 20¢ stamps} + \text{cost of 2¢ stamps} = 96¢$$
$$20n \quad + \quad 2(2n) \quad = 96$$

Next you should solve the equation.

Solve the equation.
$$20n + 2(2n) = 96$$
$$20n + 4n = 96$$
$$24n = 96$$
$$n = 4$$

Then check your solution in the words of the problem.

Check your solution. If n is 4, then Jeff bought four 20¢ stamps and $2n$ or eight 2¢ stamps.

$$4(20¢) + 8(2¢) \stackrel{?}{=} 96¢$$
$$80¢ + 16¢ \stackrel{?}{=} 96¢$$
$$96¢ = 96¢$$

Answer the problem. Jeff bought four 20¢ stamps and eight 2¢ stamps.

1. **Define a variable.**
2. **Write an equation.**
3. **Solve the equation.**
4. **Check your solution.**
5. **Answer the problem.**

Using Equations to Solve Problems

examples

1   A number increased by 17 is 41. Find the number.

Define a variable. Let n stand for the number.

Write an equation. $n + 17 = 41$

Solve the equation. $n = 24$

Check your solution. Does 24 increased by 17 equal 41?
$$24 + 17 \stackrel{?}{=} 41$$
$$41 = 41$$

Answer the problem. The number is 24.

2   Henry Takahashi drove for $1\frac{1}{2}$ hours at 50 miles per hour. He drove 55 miles per hour for the rest of the trip. If Henry drove a total of 174 miles, how long did he drive at 55 miles per hour?

Define a variable. Let t stand for the length of time Henry drove at 55 miles per hour.

Write an equation. total distance = distance at 50 mph + distance at 55 mph
$$174 \quad = \quad 50(1.5) \quad + \quad 55 \cdot t$$

Solve the equation.
$$174 = 50(1.5) + 55 \cdot t$$
$$174 = 75 + 55t$$
$$99 = 55t$$
$$1.8 = t$$

Check your solution. If Henry drives for $1\frac{1}{2}$ hours at 50 mph and for 1.8 hours at 55 mph, will he travel 174 miles?
$$1.5(50) + 1.8(55) \stackrel{?}{=} 174$$
$$75 \quad + \quad 99 \quad \stackrel{?}{=} 174$$
$$174 = 174$$

Answer the problem. Henry drove 1.8 hours at 55 miles per hour.

3 The sum of Laurie's and Peggy's ages is 34 years. In 5 years, twice Laurie's age increased by Peggy's age will be 67 years. How old is each now?

Define a variable.

Let n = Laurie's age now.
Then, $34 - n$ = Peggy's age now.
$n + 5$ = Laurie's age in 5 years
$(34 - n) + 5$ = Peggy's age in 5 years

Write an equation.

$2(n + 5) + (34 - n) + 5 = 67$

Solve the equation.

$2n + 10 + 34 - n + 5 = 67$
$n + 49 = 67$
$n = 18$

Check your solution.

$2(18 + 5) + (34 - 18) + 5 \stackrel{?}{=} 67$
$2(23) + 16 + 5 \stackrel{?}{=} 67$
$67 = 67$

Answer the problem.

Laurie is 18 years old and Peggy is $34 - 18$ or 16 years old.

exercises

Exploratory State an algebraic expression for each of the following. Use x for the variable.

1. four times a number
2. one-third of a number
3. twice a number increased by 11
4. twelve decreased by the square of a number
5. twice the sum of a number and 7
6. five times a number decreased by 4
7. the sum of twice a number and 7
8. three decreased by twice a number
9. eight increased by the square of a number
10. the product of the square of a number and six
11. one-fifth the sum of 4 and a number
12. four times the sum of 8 and a number
13. eight times the sum of a number and its square
14. the sum of 8 and four times a number
15. the square of the sum of a number and 11
16. the sum of the square of a number and 11

Written Solve each problem.

1. A number decreased by 89 is 29. Find the number.
2. The sum of twice a number and 3 is 49. Find the number.
3. Eighty-seven increased by three times a number is 165. Find the number.
4. Thirty-two decreased by twice a number is 18. Find the number.

5. Julia Blackford wants to pay about $6800 for a new car. The dealer says the car costs $8000. Julia's price is what percent of the dealer's price?

6. John Colston got $2000 trade-in on his car. The dealer is selling John's car for $1800. The dealer's selling price is what percent of the trade-in value?

7. Gunta's dad is 25 years older than Gunta. The sum of their ages is 61. How old is Gunta?

8. Greg is 3 years older than Kevin. In seven years, the sum of their ages will be 41. How old is each now?

9. Mrs. Shieh was 24 years old when Ingrid was born. In three years the sum of their ages will be 68 years. How old is each now?

10. The sum of Paul and Beth Taulman's ages now is 67 years. Eight years ago Paul was twice as old as Beth. How old is each now?

11. To estimate when to harvest her early pea crop, Dorothy Davis counts heat units. As of June 1 she has counted 835 heat units. There are usually 30 heat units per day in June. Early peas require 1165 heat units to mature. On what day can Dorothy plan to harvest her crop?

12. Ben Jackson bought a microwave oven for $60 more than half its original price. He paid $274 for the oven. What was the original price?

13. Felipe Vasquez bought some 15¢ stamps and the same number of 20¢ stamps. He paid a total of $1.75 for all the stamps. How many of each kind did he buy?

14. Jenny Johnston bought some apples for 79¢ per pound and twice as many pounds of bananas for 39¢ per pound. If her total bill was $7.85, how many pounds of bananas did she buy?

15. Neva Fannin ordered concert tickets which cost $3.50 for adults and $2.50 for students. She ordered 4 more student tickets than adult tickets. Her total bill was $58. How many of each did she order?

16. The Drama Club sold 320 adult tickets and 153 student tickets for their last performance. Adult tickets were 75¢ more than student tickets. If the total receipts were $949.50, what was the price of each ticket?

17. The width of a rectangle is 5 meters more than one-half its length. The perimeter is 286 meters. Find the length and width.

18. The width of a rectangle is 12 units less than its length. If you add 30 units to both the length and width, you double the perimeter. Find the length and width of the original rectangle.

19. Ron Dorris is on his way to San Diego, 300 miles away. He drives 45 miles per hour for 3 hours. He drives 55 miles per hour for the rest of the trip. How long does Ron drive at 55 miles per hour?

20. Two hours after a truck leaves Phoenix traveling at 45 miles per hour, a car leaves to overtake the truck. If it takes the car ten hours to catch the truck, what was the car's speed?

21. Lita Vance is driving to Lake Tahoe, a distance of 662 miles. If she drives 55 miles per hour for 5 hours, at what speed must she travel to complete the total trip in 14 hours?

22. San Francisco and Los Angeles are 470 miles apart by train. An express train leaves Los Angeles at the same time a passenger train leaves San Francisco. The express train travels 10 miles per hour faster than the passenger train. The two trains pass each other in 2.5 hours. How fast is each train traveling?

1–5   Absolute Value

Certainly ⁻5 and 5 are quite different, but they do have something in common. They are the same distance from 0 on the number line.

We say that ⁻5 and 5 have the same **absolute value.** The absolute value of a number is the number of units it is from 0 on the number line.

The absolute value of ⁻5 is 5.   The absolute value of 5 is 5.
$$\left|{}^{-}5\right| = 5$$ $$\left|5\right| = 5$$

We can also define absolute value in the following way.

> **For any number a,**
> **if $a \geq 0$, then $\left|a\right| = a$;**
> **if $a < 0$, then $\left|a\right| = {}^{-}a$.**

Definition of Absolute Value

---

examples

1 Find the absolute value of 3 and of ⁻7.

$$\left|3\right| = 3$$
$$\left|{}^{-}7\right| = {}^{-}({}^{-}7) \text{ or } 7$$

2 Find the absolute value of $x - 5$.

If x is 5 or greater, than $\left|x - 5\right| = x - 5$.
If x is less than 5, then $\left|x - 5\right| = {}^{-}(x - 5)$.

3 Find $\left|3x - 2\right| + 7.2$ if $x = {}^{-}3$.

$$
\begin{aligned}
\left|3x - 2\right| + 7.2 &= \left|3({}^{-}3) - 2\right| + 7.2 \\
&= \left|{}^{-}9 - 2\right| + 7.2 \\
&= \left|{}^{-}11\right| + 7.2 \\
&= 11 + 7.2 \\
&= 18.2
\end{aligned}
$$

The value is 18.2

Some equations contain absolute value expressions. You can use the definition of absolute value to solve the equations.

4 **Solve $|x - 7| = 12$.**

$$|x - 7| = 12$$

If x − 7 is positive or zero $\quad x - 7 = 12 \quad$ or $\quad x - 7 = {}^-12 \quad$ *If x − 7 is negative*

$$x = 19 \qquad\qquad x = {}^-5$$

Check: $\quad |x - 7| = 12$

$$|19 - 7| \overset{?}{=} 12 \quad \text{or} \quad |{}^-5 - 7| \overset{?}{=} 12$$

$$|12| \overset{?}{=} 12 \qquad\qquad |{}^-12| \overset{?}{=} 12$$

$$12 = 12 \qquad\qquad\quad 12 = 12$$

The solutions are 19 and $^-5$. The solution set is $\{19, {}^-5\}$.

5 **Solve $5|2x + 3| = 30$.**

$$5|2x + 3| = 30$$

$$|2x + 3| = 6$$

If 2x + 3 is positive or zero $\quad 2x + 3 = 6 \quad$ or $\quad 2x + 3 = {}^-6 \quad$ *If 2x + 3 is negative*

$$2x = 3 \qquad\qquad 2x = {}^-9$$

$$x = \frac{3}{2} \qquad\qquad x = -\frac{9}{2}$$

Check: $5|2x + 3| = 30$

$$5\left|2\left(\frac{3}{2}\right) + 3\right| \overset{?}{=} 30 \quad \text{or} \quad 5\left|2\left(-\frac{9}{2}\right) + 3\right| \overset{?}{=} 30$$

$$5|3 + 3| \overset{?}{=} 30 \qquad\qquad 5|{}^-9 + 3| \overset{?}{=} 30$$

$$5|6| \overset{?}{=} 30 \qquad\qquad 5|{}^-6| \overset{?}{=} 30$$

$$30 = 30 \qquad\qquad 5(6) \overset{?}{=} 30$$

$$30 = 30$$

The solutions are $\frac{3}{2}$ and $-\frac{9}{2}$. The solution set is $\left\{\frac{3}{2}, -\frac{9}{2}\right\}$.

Some absolute value equations have *no solutions*. For example, $|x| = {}^-3$ is *never* true. Since the absolute value of a number is always positive or zero, there is *no* replacement for x that will make the sentence true. The equation $|x| = {}^-3$ has no solutions. The solution set has no members at all. It is called the empty set, $\{\ \}$ or $\emptyset$.

6 **Solve $|3x + 7| + 4 = 0$.**

$$|3x + 7| + 4 = 0$$

$$|3x + 7| = {}^-4$$

This sentence is *never* true. The equation has *no solutions*. The solution set is $\emptyset$.

exercises

Exploratory Evaluate if $x = {}^-5$.

1. $|x|$
2. $|4x|$
3. $|{}^-2x|$
4. $|x + 6|$
5. $|7x - 1|$
6. $|{}^-x|$
7. $|2x + 5|$
8. $|{}^-2x + 5|$
9. $5 - |x|$
10. $5 - |{}^-x|$
11. $|x| + x$
12. $|x - 7| - 8$
13. $|3x + 10| - 7$
14. $7 - |3x + 10|$
15. $|x + 4| + |2x|$

Written Solve each open sentence.

1. $|x + 11| = 42$
2. $|x + 6| = 19$
3. $|x - 5| = 11$
4. $|x - 3| = 17$
5. $3|x + 7| = 36$
6. $5|x + 4| = 45$
7. $8|x - 3| = 88$
8. $11|x - 9| = 121$
9. $|2x + 7| = 19$
10. $|3x + 12| = 48$
11. $|3x - 7| = 18$
12. $|5x + 30| = 65$
13. $|2x + 5| = 16$
14. $|2x + 9| = 30$
15. $|2x - 37| = 15$
16. $|4x - 3| = {}^-27$
17. $|6x + 5| = 21$
18. $|2x + 7| = 0$
19. $3|5x + 2| = 51$
20. $8|4x - 3| = 64$
21. $^-6|2x - 14| = {}^-42$
22. $5|3x - 4| = 30$
23. $7|3x + 5| = 25$
24. $4|6x - 1| = 29$
25. $3|5x - 29| = {}^-3$
26. $2|6 - 5x| = 26$
27. $9|3 - 2x| = 15$
28. $2|7 - 3x| = 3$
29. $|2a + 7| = a - 4$
30. $|7 + 3a| = 11 - a$
31. $|3t - 5| = 2t$
32. $5|3x - 4| = x + 1$
33. $|x - 3| + 7 = 2$
34. $3|2x - 5| = {}^-1$
35. $9|x + 4| - 3 = {}^-8$
36. $21 + |6x + 5| = 0$

Challenge Solve each open sentence.

1. $|x + 3| = |5x - 9|$
2. $|x - 2| = |7x + 22|$
3. $|2x - 3| = |x + 7|$
4. $|3x + 2| = |5x - 12|$
5. $|3x - 1| = |5x - 2| - 4$
6. $|2x - 3| = |5x + 1| + 3$

Skills Review Simplify.

1. $5(6y)$
2. $\frac{1}{2}(2a)$
3. $(^-4y)(^-2)$
4. $8x + 11x$
5. $x + x$
6. $3b - b$
7. $5y - 11y$
8. $a + a + 2$
9. $3 + 6y + 2$
10. $8c - 3 - 2c + 2$
11. $\frac{1}{2}x + \frac{3}{2}x - 5$
12. $x + \frac{3}{2}x - 5 - x$
13. $^-(^-x + 2y)$
14. $2(3y - 5) - 7y + 4$
15. $5(2 - 3x) - 2(4x - 2)$

18 *Equations and Inequalities*

Understanding algebra depends largely on understanding the symbols used in algebra. The symbols of language are the letters of the alphabet. In English, there are just 26 letters, and most letters have one or two sounds. On the other hand, there are many symbols used in mathematics, and the meaning of these symbols frequently depends on how they are used. Notice how the symbol **4** is used in each expression.

Expression	*Translation*
4	four
40	forty
0.04	four hundredths
4^2	four squared
2^4	two to the fourth power
$\frac{1}{4}$	one-fourth

In like manner, the symbol − may be used in several ways.

Expression	*Translation*
$9 - 4$	nine minus four
$^-4$	negative four
$\frac{3}{4}$	three-fourths
$5 \times 4 = 20$	five times four equals twenty

Exercises Match each expression with the correct translation.

1. $3a$ **a.** three times a squared plus one

2. a^3 **b.** three times a

3. $3a^2 + 1$ **c.** three times a plus one, quantity squared

4. $(3a + 1)^2$ **d.** a divided by three

5. $(3a)^2 + 1$ **e.** a to the third power

6. $\frac{a}{3}$ **f.** three times a, quantity squared, plus one

Write each algebraic expression in words.

7. $3ad + bc$ **8.** $6a^3 - 2b$ **9.** $(a + b - c)^2$

10. $(a + c)^3 + d^2$ **11.** $\frac{6ac}{d}$ **12.** $\frac{5a + 3c}{3b}$

1–6   Inequalities

Jim and Leslie are jockeys. Suppose you compare their weights. You can make only one of the following statements.

Jim's weight *is less than* Leslie's weight.	Jim's weight *is the same as* Leslie's weight.	Jim's weight *is more than* Leslie's weight.

Let j stand for Jim's weight and ℓ stand for Leslie's weight. Then you can use inequalities and an equation to compare their weights.

$$j < \ell \qquad j = \ell \qquad j > \ell$$

> **For any two numbers a and b, exactly one of the following statements is true.**
> $$a < b \qquad a = b \qquad a > b$$

Trichotomy Property

Suppose Jim weighs 113 pounds and Leslie weighs 108 pounds. Then Jim's weight is more than Leslie's weight. They each have saddles that weigh 13 pounds. How do their weights plus saddle weights compare?

Jim's weight	$113 > 108$	*Leslie's weight*
Jim's weight plus saddle	$113 + 13 > 108 + 13$	*Leslie's weight plus saddle*
	$126 > 121$	

Notice that adding the same number to both sides of an inequality does *not* change the truth of the inequality.

> **For any numbers, a, b, and c,**
> 1. **if $a > b$, then $a + c > b + c$ and $a - c > b - c$;**
> 2. **if $a < b$, then $a + c < b + c$ and $a - c < b - c$.**

Addition and Subtraction Properties for Inequalities

You can use these properties to solve inequalities.

---

example

1 **Solve $9x + 7 < 8x - 2$.**

$$9x + 7 < 8x - 2$$
$$^-8x + 9x + 7 < {}^-8x + 8x - 2 \qquad \text{Add } ^-8x \text{ to both sides.}$$
$$x + 7 < {}^-2$$
$$x + 7 + {}^-7 < {}^-2 + {}^-7 \qquad \text{Add } ^-7 \text{ to both sides.}$$
$$x < {}^-9$$

Check: To check, choose several numbers less than $^-9$. Substitute those numbers, in turn, into the inequality.

The solutions are any numbers less than $^-9$.

You know that $18 > {}^-11$ is a true inequality. If you multiply both sides of this inequality by a positive number, the result is a true inequality.

$$18 > {}^-11 \qquad \text{\textit{A true inequality}}$$
$$18(3) > {}^-11(3) \qquad \text{\textit{Multiply both sides by 3.}}$$
$$54 > {}^-33 \qquad \text{\textit{Another true inequality}}$$

Suppose you multiply both sides of a true inequality by a negative number. Try $^-2$.

$$18 > {}^-11 \qquad \text{\textit{A true inequality}}$$
$$18({}^-2) > {}^-11({}^-2) \qquad \text{\textit{Multiply both sides by ${}^-2$.}}$$
$$^-36 > 22 \qquad \text{\textit{False!!!}}$$

But, *reverse the inequality sign,* and the result is true. These examples suggest the following properties.

For any numbers *a*, *b*, and *c*,

1. If $c > 0$ and $a < b$, then $ac < bc$ and $\dfrac{a}{c} < \dfrac{b}{c}$.

2. If $c > 0$ and $a > b$, then $ac > bc$ and $\dfrac{a}{c} > \dfrac{b}{c}$.

3. If $c < 0$ and $a < b$, then $ac > bc$ and $\dfrac{a}{c} > \dfrac{b}{c}$.

4. If $c < 0$ and $a > b$, then $ac < bc$ and $\dfrac{a}{c} < \dfrac{b}{c}$.

Multiplication and Divison Properties for Inequalities

The following examples show how this property is used to solve inequalities.

example

2   **Solve $-\dfrac{y}{3} < 4$.**

$$-\frac{y}{3} < 4$$
$$({}^-3)\left(-\frac{y}{3}\right) > ({}^-3)(4) \qquad \text{\textit{Reverse the inequality sign since each side is multiplied by ${}^-3$.}}$$
$$y > {}^-12$$

The solutions are any numbers greater than $^-12$.
The solution set can be written $\{y \mid y > {}^-12\}$. It is read *the set of all numbers y such that y is greater than $^-12$.*

The symbols $\neq$, $\leq$, and $\geq$ can also be used when comparing numbers. The symbol $\neq$ means *is not equal to*. The symbol $\leq$ means *is less than or equal to*. The symbol $\geq$ means *is greater than or equal to*.

example

3 Solve $9x + 4 \leq 13x - 7$.

$$9x + 4 \leq 13x - 7$$
$$^-13x + 9x + 4 \leq {}^-13x + 13x - 7 \qquad \text{Add } ^-13x \text{ to both sides.}$$
$$^-4x + 4 \leq {}^-7$$
$$^-4x + 4 + {}^-4 \leq {}^-7 + {}^-4 \qquad \text{Add } ^-4 \text{ to both sides.}$$
$$^-4x \leq {}^-11$$
$$\left(-\frac{1}{4}\right)(-4x) \geq \left(-\frac{1}{4}\right)(^-11) \qquad \text{Multiply both sides by } -\frac{1}{4}$$
$$x \geq \frac{11}{4} \qquad \text{and reverse the inequality sign.}$$

The solutions are any numbers greater than or equal to $\frac{11}{4}$. The solution set is $\left\{ x \mid x \geq \frac{11}{4} \right\}$.

exercises

Exploratory Replace each □ with <, >, or = to make each sentence true.

1. $^-7 \;\square\; ^-(6 + 2)$
2. $^-5 \;\square\; ^-3$
3. $^-5\frac{1}{3} \;\square\; ^-5$
4. $^-6 \;\square\; 7 + {}^-13$
5. $^-4 \;\square\; ^-7 + 4.$
6. $(6 + 4) - 4 \;\square\; 20 \div 5 + 1$
7. $^-15 - {}^-27 \;\square\; 12$
8. $0.12 \;\square\; 0.012$
9. $\frac{1}{3} \;\square\; \frac{3}{9}$
10. $2\frac{1}{4} + 3 \;\square\; 2\frac{1}{4}$
11. $2\frac{1}{4} - 3 \;\square\; 2\frac{1}{4}$
12. $2\frac{1}{4} - 3 \;\square\; 3$
13. $1\frac{7}{8} \;\square\; 1\frac{3}{4}$
14. $(4 + 6)^3 \;\square\; (5 + 5)^3$
15. $10^3 + 1 \;\square\; 10^3$
16. $2^4 \;\square\; 4^2$
17. $(2 + 3)^3 \;\square\; 2^3 + 3^3$
18. $x(3 + y) \;\square\; 3x + xy$

Written Solve each inequality.

1. $3x + 7 > 43$
2. $2t - 9 < 21$
3. $7n - 5 \geq 44$
4. $5x + 4 \geq 34$
5. $5r + 8 > 24$
6. $6s - 7 < 29$
7. $8 - 3x < 44$
8. $15 - 2t \geq 55$
9. $11 - 5y < {}^-77$
10. $29 - 7y < 24$
11. $5(x - 3) \geq 15$
12. $9(x + 2) < 72$
13. $5(2x - 7) > 10$
14. $3(4x + 7) < 21$
15. $3(3w + 1) \geq 48$
16. $25 \leq {}^-5(4 - p)$
17. $5(5z - 3) \leq 60$
18. $^-42 > 7(2x + 3)$
19. $^-4(13 - 6t) < 26$
20. $40 \leq {}^-6(5r - 7)$
21. $7x - 5 > 3x + 4$
22. $3x + 1 < x + 5$
23. $1 - 2x \leq 5x - 2$
24. $3 - 2x \geq 0$
25. $2(r - 3) + 5 \geq 9$
26. $3(3x + 2) > 7x - 2$
27. $1 + 2(x + 4) \geq 1 + 3(x + 2)$

28. $4(4z + 5) - 5 > 3(4z - 1)$

29. $2(3m + 4) - 2 \le 3(1 + 3m)$

30. $2(m - 5) - 3(2m - 5) < 5m + 1$

31. $3b - 2(b - 5) < 2(b + 4)$

32. $7 + 3y > 2(y + 3) - 2(^-1 - y)$

33. $0.01x - 2.32 \ge 0$

34. $x - 5 < 0.1$

35. $\dfrac{3x}{4} - \dfrac{1}{2} < 0$

36. $\dfrac{3x - 5}{2} \le 0$

37. $\dfrac{2x + 3}{5} \le 0.03$

38. $\dfrac{2x + 3}{5} \ge ^-0.03$

39. $20\left(\dfrac{1}{5} - \dfrac{w}{4}\right) \ge ^-2w$

40. $\dfrac{3x - 3}{5} < \dfrac{4x - 2}{6}$

41. $\dfrac{x + 8}{16} - 1 > \dfrac{4 - x}{12}$

42. $\dfrac{2 - 3b}{4} \le 2\left(\dfrac{2b}{3} - 4b\right)$

Challenge   Find the set of all numbers x satisfying the given conditions.

1. $x + 1 > 0$ and $x - 3 < 0$

2. $x - 1 < 0$ and $x + 2 > 0$

3. $3x - 2 \ge 0$ and $5x - 1 \le 0$

4. $2x + 1 > 0$ and $x - 1 > 0$

Basic Functions

Electronic calculators differ in the functions they perform. Most calculators have the following keys and functions.

Key	Name	Function
$+/-$	Change Sign	changes the sign of the number
x^2	Square	calculates the square of the number
$\sqrt{x}$	Square Root	calculates the square root of the number
$1/x$	Reciprocal	calculates the reciprocal of the number

First enter the number and then press the appropriate key.

The calculator features in this book assume that the calculator being used evaluates expressions in the algebraic mode. That is, the algebraic order of operations holds when the calculator performs any sequence of operations.

Example   Evaluate $3 + 5 \div 2 + 5^2$.

ENTER: 3 $\boxed{+}$ 5 $\boxed{\div}$ 2 $\boxed{+}$ 5 $\boxed{x^2}$ $\boxed{=}$

DISPLAY: 3   5   2   5.5   5   25   30.5   The answer is 30.5

If your calculator does not use the algebraic order of operations, your answer will be different. Read the manual for your calculator and adapt the order of entry accordingly.

Exercises   Use the calculator to compute each of the following.

1. $6 \cdot 2 - 4 \cdot 2$

2. $42 - 54 \div 6$

3. $24 \div 6 - 3^2 \div 3$

4. $6 \cdot 3 \div 9 - 1$

5. $8 + 5^2 + 6 \div 3 - \sqrt{2}$

6. $13 - 4(17)^2 + \sqrt{0.978}$

7. Use the change sign key to evaluate $(^-91,651)(\sqrt{21,376}) \div ^-12,878$.

8. Use the reciprocal key to evaluate $\dfrac{1}{101 + (75)(30)} + \sqrt{51}$.

1-7   Using Inequalities

The symbols of inequality may be used to represent different types of verbal sentences.

Verbal Sentence	Inequality
x is less than 14.	$x < 14$
x is less than or equal to 14. x is at most 14. x is no more than 14. The greatest value of x is 14. The maximum value of x is 14.	$x \leq 14$
x is greater than 14.	$x > 14$
x is greater than or equal to 14. x is at least 14. x is no less than 14. The least value of x is 14. The minimum value of x is 14.	$x \geq 14$

Inequalities can be used to solve many verbal problems. The procedure used to solve problems with equations can also be used to solve problems with inequalities.

example 1   Corbie Cochran wants to invest $10,000, some in bonds at 6% interest annually and the rest in stocks at 9% interest annually. If he wishes to earn at least $720 this year, what is the minimum he should invest in stocks?

The sum at least 720 means the sum is greater than or equal to 720.

Define a variable.   Let n = amount invested in stocks.
Then $10,000 - n$ = amount invested in bonds.

Write an inequality.   (rate)(amount) +   (rate)(amount) $\geq$ minimum desired
$(0.09)(n)$ $+ (0.06)(10,000 - n) \geq$ 720

Solve the inequality. $0.09n + 600 - 0.06n \geq 720$
$0.03n \geq 120$
$n \geq 4000$

Answer the problem.   Corbie must invest at least $4000 in stocks.

2 **The Clippers have won 24 baseball games and have lost 40 games. They have 60 more games to play. To win at least 50% of *all* their games, how many more games must they win?**

Define a variable. The problem asks for how many additional games the Clippers must win to win at least 50% of their games.
Let w stand for the number of additional games that they must win.

Write an inequality.
$$\% \text{ of games won} \geq 50\%$$
$$\frac{\text{number of games won}}{\text{number of games played}} \geq 50\%$$
$$\frac{24 + w}{24 + 40 + 60} \geq 0.50$$

Solve the inequality.
$$\frac{24 + w}{24 + 40 + 60} \geq 0.50$$
$$\frac{24 + w}{124} \geq 0.50$$
$$24 + w \geq 62$$
$$w \geq 38$$

Check your solution. To check, choose several numbers greater than 38. Substitute those numbers, in turn, into the inequality.

Answer the problem. The Clippers must win at least 38 more games.

3 **Kym Sutherland has 6 quarts of a 90% antifreeze solution. How much 40% antifreeze must she add to make a solution that is at most 70% antifreeze?**

Let q = quarts of 40% antifreeze to be added.

$$(0.90)(6) + (0.40)(q) \leq (0.70)(q + 6)$$
$$5.4 + 0.40q \leq 0.70q + 4.2$$
$$1.2 \leq 0.30q$$
$$4 \leq q$$

Therefore, Kym must add at least 4 quarts of 40% antifreeze.

The table at the right is for state income tax. Corinne figured her tax to be $47.38. According to the table, this means her taxable income is at least $7225, but less than $7250.

Let c stand for Corinne's taxable income. Then two inequalities, $c \geq 7225$ and $c < 7250$, describe her taxable income. The sentence, $c \geq 7225$ and $c < 7250$, is called a **compound sentence**. A compound sentence containing **and** is true only if both parts of it are true. A compound sentence containing **or** is true if at least one part of it is true.

If Ohio taxable income (Line 5) is:		The tax
At Least	But less than	liability is:
7,100	7,125	46.13
7,125	7,150	46.38
7,150	7,175	46.63
7,175	7,200	46.88
7,200	7,225	47.13
7,225	7,250	47.38
7,250	7,275	47.63
7,275	7,300	47.88
7,300	7,325	48.13
7,325	7,350	48.38
7,350	7,375	48.63

Another way of writing $c \geq 7225$ and $c < 7250$ is as follows.

$$7225 \leq c < 7250$$

The sentence is read, "c is greater than or equal to 7225 *and* less than 7250." (Inequality sentences containing **or** *cannot* be combined in this way.)

To solve a compound sentence, you must solve each part of the compound sentence.

example

4   **Solve $3 < 2x - 1 < 9$.**

First, write the compound sentence using the word *and*. Then solve each part of the sentence.

$3 < 2x - 1$ and $2x - 1 < 9$
$4 < 2x$ and $2x < 10$
$2 < x$ and $x < 5$
$\qquad 2 < x < 5$

Or both parts may be solved at the same time.

$3 < 2x - 1 < 9$
$4 < 2x < 10$
$2 < x < 5$

exercises

Exploratory   State whether each compound sentence is *true* or *false*.

1. $9 > 8$ and $9 > 7$
2. $15 \geq 14$ and $5 < 4$
3. $^-2 < 1$ and $1 > 2$
4. $5 < 10$ and $^-5 > ^-10$
5. $^-5 < ^-6$ or $3 > 0$
6. $^-3 \leq ^-3$ or $8 > 11$

Write each compound sentence with the word *and*.

7. $^-3 < x < 2$
8. $^-1 \leq b < 3$
9. $1 < 3y \leq 13$
10. $^-12 < t \leq 4$
11. $5 \leq 3 - 2g < 1$
12. $^-2 < 3(k + 2) < 6$

Write each compound sentence without the word *and*.

13. $^-2 < x$ and $x < 10$ **14.** $0 \leq b$ and $b < 5$ **15.** $x \geq {}^-2$ and $x \leq 10$

16. $y > 4$ and $y \leq 9$ **17.** $m \leq 5$ and $^-5 \leq m$ **18.** $n > {}^-15$ and $n < 7$

Written   Solve each problem.

1. Diencha has $110.37 in her checking account. The bank does not charge for checks if $50 or more is in the account. For how much can she write a check and not be charged?

2. Pataskala Municipal Garage charges $1.50 for the first hour and $0.50 for each additional hour. For how many hours can you park your car if the most you can pay is $4.50?

3. One number is twice another number. Twice the lesser number increased by the greater number is at least 85. What is the *least* possible value for the lesser number?

4. Dave Sharp has $10 to buy stamps. He wants to buy twice as many 20¢ stamps as 12¢ stamps. What is the greatest number of 20¢ stamps he can buy?

5. Chuck Piwonski wants to invest $12,000, some at 6% interest annually and the rest at 10% interest annually. If he wishes to earn at least $980 this year, what is the minimum he can invest at 10%?

6. Donna Pennycuff invested part of $8000 in stock that lost 2%. She invested the balance at 8% interest annually. If her total gain for the year was at least $400, what was the greatest amount of money that she could have invested in stock?

7. Adult tickets to a concert cost $5.50 and student tickets cost $3.50. How many tickets can be purchased for $64.50 if there must be three more student tickets than adult tickets?

8. Apples cost 10¢ per pound more than grapefruit. Carleton Foushee buys 6 pounds of grapefruit and 8 pounds of apples and pays less than $10.50. What is the highest price possible for apples per pound?

9. Susan's softball team has won 11 games and has lost 8 games. They have 11 more games to play. To win at least 50% of *all* games, how many more games must they win?

10. The Reynoldsburg Raiders play 84 games this season. At midseason they had won 30 games. To win at least 60% of *all* games, how many of the remaining games must they win?

11. Roy has 8 gallons of 40% antifreeze solution. How much 100% antifreeze must be added to make a solution that is at least 60% antifreeze?

12. A 20 gallon salt solution is 30% salt. What is the greatest number of gallons of water that can be evaporated so the solution is still less than 45% salt?

13. Jorge Acevedo begins a bike ride at 8 miles per hour. Three hours later Patsy starts after him in a car. If she wishes to overtake him within 45 minutes, what is the minimum speed that she must travel?

14. Tony starts from Boise at 9 A.M. towards Missoula, a distance of 343 miles. At 11 A.M. Pam starts from Missoula towards Boise, driving 10 miles per hour slower than Tony. If they wish to meet each other by 2:30 P.M., what is the minimum speed each must travel?

Solve each compound sentence.

15. $2 < y + 4 < 11$ **16.** $1 < x - 2 < 7$ **17.** $x - 4 < 1$ or $x + 2 > 1$

18. $y + 6 > {}^-1$ or $y - 2 < 4$ **19.** $4 < 2x - 2 < 10$ **20.** $^-1 < 3m + 2 < 14$

21. $2x - 1 < {}^-5$ or $3x + 2 \geq 5$ **22.** $5b < 9 + 2b$ or $9 - 2b > 11$

To solve many problems in mathematics, you can write an equation. Then you solve the equation and answer the problem. However, this procedure may not always be the best one to use.

There are other strategies which may be more suitable than writing an equation. One of these strategies is to solve a simpler problem. This strategy involves setting aside the original problem and solving a simpler or more familiar case of the problem. The same concepts and relationships that were used to solve the simpler problem can then be used to solve the original problem.

Example: Find the sum of the numbers 1 through 1000.

Obviously, this problem could be solved by actually adding all the numbers. But this process would be very tedious even if you used a calculator.

Consider a simpler problem. Find the sum of the numbers 1 through 10.

$$
\begin{array}{ccccc}
1 & 2 & 3 & 4 & 5 \\
+\ 10 & +\ 9 & +\ 8 & +\ 7 & +\ 6 \\
\hline
11 & 11 & 11 & 11 & 11
\end{array}
$$

Now extend this concept to the original problem.

$$
\begin{array}{ccccc}
1 & 2 & 3 & & 499 & 500 \\
+\ 1000 & +\ 999 & +\ 998 & \ldots & +\ 502 & +\ 501 \\
\hline
1001 & 1001 & 1001 & & 1001 & 1001
\end{array}
$$

sum of 1 through 1000 = 500 × 1001 or 500,500

This strategy may also involve breaking a complicated problem down into several easier problems. After these problems are solved, their solutions may be used to solve the original problem.

Exercises Solve each problem.

1. Find the total number of squares in the checkerboard shown at the right.

2. A total of 3001 digits were used to print the page numbers of the Northern College annual. How many pages are in the annual?

3. Find the sum of the first n positive integers.

4. A drain pipe is 750 cm long. A spider climbs up 100 cm during the day but falls back 80 cm during the night. If the spider begins at the bottom of the pipe, on what day will it get to the top?

1–8   Absolute Value Inequalities

The absolute value of a number represents its distance from zero on the number line. You can use this idea to help solve absolute value inequalities.

examples

1   Solve $|x| < 3$.

You can translate $|x| < 3$ in the following way.

The distance between x and 0 is less than 3 units.
$$|x| \qquad < \qquad 3$$

To make $|x| < 3$ true, you must substitute values for x that are less than 3 units from 0.

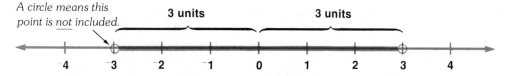

A circle means this point is <u>not</u> included.   3 units   3 units

All the numbers between ⁻3 and 3 are less than three units from zero. The solution set is $\{x \,|\, {}^-3 < x < 3\}$.

2   Solve $|x| \geq 2$.

The distance between x and 0 is equal to or greater than 2 units.
$$|x| \qquad \geq \qquad 2$$

To make this true, you must substitute values for x that are 2 or more units from 0.

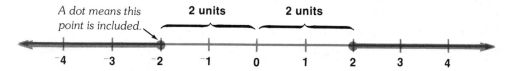

A dot means this point is included.   2 units   2 units

The solution set is $\{x \,|\, x \geq 2 \text{ or } x \leq {}^-2\}$

3   Solve $|2x - 5| > 9$.

The inequality $|2x - 5| > 9$ says that $2x - 5$ is more than 9 units from 0.

| *If $2x - 5 \geq 0$* | $2x - 5 > 9$ | or | $^-(2x - 5) > 9$ | *If $2x - 5 < 0$* |

$$2x > 14$$
$$x > 7$$

$$2x - 5 < {}^-9$$
$$2x < {}^-4$$
$$x < {}^-2$$

The solution set is $\{x \,|\, x < {}^-2 \text{ or } x > 7\}$.

4 **Solve $|2x + 3| + 4 < 5$.**

$$|2x + 3| + 4 < 5$$
$$|2x + 3| < 1 \quad \textit{Add } ^-4 \textit{ to each side to isolate the absolute value expression.}$$

The inequality $|2x + 3| < 1$ says that $2x + 3$ is less than 1 unit from 0. Thus, it can be written as follows.

$$^-1 < 2x + 3 < 1$$
$$^-4 < 2x < ^-2$$
$$^-2 < x < ^-1$$

The solution set is $\{x | ^-2 < x < ^-1\}$

Some absolute value inequalities have *no solutions*. For example, $|4x - 9| < ^-7$ is *never* true. Since the absolute value of a number is always positive or zero, there is *no* replacement for x that will make the sentence true. The inequality $|4x - 9| < ^-7$ has no solutions.

Some absolute value inequalities are *always true*. For example, $|10x + 3| > ^-5$ is *always* true. Since the absolute value of a number is always positive or zero, any replacement for x will make the sentence true. The solution set for $|10x + 3| > ^-5$ is the set of real numbers.

exercises

Exploratory **Write an absolute value inequality for each sentence. Then graph each inequality on a number line.**

1. All numbers between $^-3$ and 3.
2. All numbers less than 8 and greater than $^-8$.
3. All numbers greater than 6 or less than $^-6$.
4. All numbers less than or equal to 5, and greater than or equal to $^-5$.
5. $x > 3$ or $x < ^-3$
6. $x < 6$ and $x > ^-6$
7. $x \leq 4$ and $x \geq ^-4$
8. $x \geq 7$ or $x \leq ^-7$
9. $^-6 < x < 6$
10. $^-3 < x < 3$
11. $x > ^-2$ and $x < 2$
12. $x < 10$ and $x > ^-10$

Written **Solve each inequality.**

1. $|x| < 9$
2. $|x| \geq 2$
3. $|x + 1| > 3$
4. $|x + 1| \leq 3$
5. $|x - 4| \leq 8$
6. $|3x| < 6$

7. $|7x| \geq 21$ **8.** $|x - 9| > 5$

9. $|x| > 7$ **10.** $|5x| < 35$

11. $|2x| \leq 26$ **12.** $|2x| \geq {}^-64$

13. $|3x| < {}^-15$ **14.** $|5x| < 15$

15. $|x + 3| > 17$ **16.** $|x - 4| \leq {}^-12$

17. $|x - 12| < 42$ **18.** $|x + 9| \geq 17$

19. $|2x - 9| \leq 27$ **20.** $|3x + 11| > 1$

21. $|4x - 3| \geq 12$ **22.** $|3x + 7| \leq 26$

23. $|5x + 7| < 81$ **24.** $|3x + 11| > 42$

25. $|6x + 25| + 14 < 6$ **26.** $6 + |3x| > 0$

27. $|2x - 5| \leq 7$ **28.** $|4x| + 3 \leq 0$

29. $|x| \leq x$ **30.** $|x| > x$

31. $|x + 2| - x \geq 0$ **32.** $2 + |3 - 2x| > 0$

Challenge Solve each inequality.

1. $|x + 1| + |x - 1| \leq 2$ **2.** $|x + 3| + |x - 3| > 8$

Mathematics Contests excursions in algebra

A number of mathematics contests are available to high school students. One of the best known contests is the Annual High School Mathematics Contest. Another contest is the U.S. Mathematical Olympiad which is patterned after the International Mathematical Olympiad.

Mathematics contests are organized in a number of different ways. The International Mathematical Olympiad, for example, lasts for two days. Each day, three problems are presented with four and one-half hours allowed to solve them. The problems are assigned points according to difficulty. Some contests provide short-answer questions with time limits like six minutes.

In one contest the following question appeared. The time limit for this question and another paired with it was 11 minutes. Eighty-six percent of the contestants answered the question correctly. Time yourself as you work the problem.

> A club found that it could achieve a membership ratio of 2 adults for each minor either by inducting 24 adults or by expelling x minors. Find x.

In another contest the following question appeared.

> Two boys, A and B, start at the same time to ride from Port Jervis to Poughkeepsie, 60 miles away. A travels 4 miles an hour slower than B. B reaches Poughkeepsie and at once turns back meeting A 12 miles from Poughkeepsie. Find the rate that A traveled.

Chapter Summary

1. Order of Operations: 1. Evaluate all powers.   2. Then do all multiplications and divisions from left to right.   3. Then do all additions and subtractions from left to right.   (1)

2. In a formula, if you know replacements for every variable, except one, you can find a replacement for that variable.   (2)

3. Properties of Operations: (4 − 6)

For any numbers a, b, and c		
	Addition	Multiplication
Commutative	$a + b = b + a$	$a \cdot b = b \cdot a$
Associative	$(a + b) + c = a + (b + c)$	$(a \cdot b) \cdot c = a \cdot (b \cdot c)$
Identity	$a + 0 = a = 0 + a$	$a \cdot 1 = a = 1 \cdot a$
Inverse	$a + {}^-a = 0 = {}^-a + a$	If a is *not* zero, then $a \cdot \dfrac{1}{a} = 1 = \dfrac{1}{a} \cdot a.$
Distributive of multiplication over addition: $a(b + c) = ab + ac$ and $(b + c)a = ba + ca$		

4. Properties of Equality: (8 − 9)

For any numbers a, b, and c	
Reflexive:	$a = a$
Symmetric:	If $a = b$, then $b = a$.
Transitive:	If $a = b$ and $b = c$, then $a = c$.
Substitution:	If $a = b$, then a may be replaced by b.
Addition and Subtraction:	If $a = b$, then $a + c = b + c$, and $a - c = b - c$.
Multiplication and Division:	If $a = b$, then $a \cdot c = b \cdot c$, and if c is not zero, $\dfrac{a}{c} = \dfrac{b}{c}$.

5. Solving an equation means finding replacements for variables in the equation so that a true sentence results. (8)

6. Problem Solving Procedure Using Equations: 1. Define a variable. 2. Write an equation. 3. Solve the equation. 4. Check your solution. 5. Answer the problem. (13)

7. The absolute value of a number is the number of units it is from zero on the number line. For any number a, if $a \geq 0$, then $|a| = a$. If $a < 0$, then $|a| = {}^-a$. (16)

8. Trichotomy Property: For any two numbers a and b, exactly one of the following statements is true. $a < b$, $a = b$, or $a > b$. (20)

9. Properties of Inequalities: (20 − 21)

For any numbers a, b, and c	
Addition and Subtraction:	1. If $a > b$, then $a + c > b + c$ and $a - c > b - c$. 2. If $a < b$, then $a + c < b + c$ and $a - c < b - c$.
Multiplication and Division:	1. If $c > 0$ and $a < b$, then $ac < bc$ and $\dfrac{a}{c} < \dfrac{b}{c}$. 2. If $c > 0$ and $a > b$, then $ac > bc$ and $\dfrac{a}{c} > \dfrac{b}{c}$. 3. If $c < 0$ and $a < b$, then $ac > bc$ and $\dfrac{a}{c} > \dfrac{b}{c}$. 4. If $c < 0$ and $a > b$, then $ac < bc$ and $\dfrac{a}{c} < \dfrac{b}{c}$.

Chapter Review

1–1 **Find the value of each expression.**

1. $(4 + 6)^2 - 24 \div 3$

2. $4 + 6^2 - 24 \div 3$

3. $(3 - 9)^2 \times 2 - 10 \div 6$

Evaluate if $a = -\dfrac{1}{2}$, $b = 4$, $c = 5$, and $d = {}^-3$.

4. $\dfrac{3ab}{cd}$

5. $\dfrac{4a + 3c}{3b}$

6. $\dfrac{3ab^2 - d^3}{a}$

1–2 **State the property shown in each of the following.**

7. $3 + (a + b) = (a + b) + 3$

8. $(3 + a) + b = 3 + (a + b)$

9. $(a + b) + 0 = (a + b)$

10. $(a + b) + {}^-(a + b) = 0$

Simplify.

11. $(9 + 48)7 + 3$

12. $15r + 18s + 16r - 8s$

13. $7p + 9q - 10p + 4q$

14. $(14y + 7z)\dfrac{1}{7} - (7z + 14y)\dfrac{2}{7}$

1–3 **State the property shown in each of the following.**

15. $3r + (7 - 1)s = 3r + 6s$

16. $5x + 3y = 5x + 3y$

17. If $12 - 7 = 3 + 2$, then
$3 + 2 = 12 - 7$.

18. If $12 - 7 = 10 - 5$ and $10 - 5 = 5$,
then $12 - 7 = 5$.

Solve each equation.

19. $15x + 25 = 2(x - 4)$

20. $3(6 - 4x) = 4x + 2$

21. $2(3x - 1) = 3(x + 2)$

22. $9 = \dfrac{3y - 6}{2}$

23. $\dfrac{2}{7}a = \dfrac{16}{5}$

24. $\dfrac{3}{4}y + \dfrac{3}{4} = \dfrac{5}{2}$

1–4 **Solve each problem.**

25. The width of a rectangle is 4 meters more than one-third its length. The perimeter is 64 meters. Find the length and width.

26. Maureen's dad is 32 years older than Maureen. Six years ago, the sum of their ages was 52. How old is Maureen now?

27. To estimate when to harvest his snap bean crop, a South Carolina farmer counts heat units. As of May 1, he has counted 1022 heat units. There are usually 19 heat units per day in May. Snap beans require 1250 heat units to mature. The farmer can plan to harvest his crop in how many more days?

28. Rockford and Chicago are 126 miles apart by train. An express train leaves Chicago at the same time a passenger train leaves Rockford. The express train travels 15 miles per hour faster than the passenger train. The two trains pass each other in 0.7 hours. How fast is each train traveling?

1–5 **Solve each open sentence.**

29. $|2x - 37| = 15$

30. $|p - 3| + 7 = 2$

31. $8|2a - 3| = 64$

1–6 **Solve each inequality.**

32. $8(2x - 1) > 11x + 31$

33. $3 - 4x \leq 6x + 5$

34. $4(3x + 2) + 6 \geq 7x - 9$

1–7 **Solve each problem.**

35. Tania has 10 gallons of a 50% antifreeze solution. How much 100% antifreeze must she add to make a solution that is at least 80% antifreeze?

36. Roxie has $8.40 to spend on gasoline. Where Roxie lives gasoline costs between $1.40 and $1.60 per gallon. How many gallons of gasoline can Roxie buy?

Solve each compound sentence.

37. $^-1 < 3(y - 2) \leq 9$

38. $2x - 5 < {}^-5$ or $3x + 2 \geq 5$

1–8 **Solve each inequality.**

39. $7 + |9 - 2x| > 4$

40. $|6 + 7x| + 11 \leq 2$

41. $|2x + 5| \leq 4$

42. $|3x + 7| \geq 26$

Chapter Test

State the property shown in each of the following.

1. $(5 \cdot r) \cdot s = 5 \cdot (r \cdot s)$

2. $(5 \cdot r) \cdot s = s \cdot (5 \cdot r)$

3. $\left(4 \cdot \frac{1}{4}\right) \cdot 3 = \left(4 \cdot \frac{1}{4}\right) \cdot 3$

4. $(6 - 2)a - 3b = 4a - 3b$

5. If $2(7) + 3 = 14 + 3$ and $14 + 3 = 17$, then $2(7) + 3 = 17$.

6. If $(a + b)c = ac + bc$, then $ac + bc = (a + b)c$.

Find the value of each expression.

7. $(2 + 3)^3 - 4 \div 2$

8. $[2 + 3^3 - 4] \div 2$

9. $(2^5 - 2^3) + 2^3$

10. $[5(19 - 4) \div 3] - 4^2$

Evaluate if $a = {}^-9$, $b = \frac{2}{3}$, $c = 8$, and $d = {}^-6$.

11. $\frac{a}{b^2} + c$

12. $\frac{db + 4c}{a}$

13. $2b(4a + d^2)$

14. $\frac{4a + 3c}{3b}$

Solve each open sentence.

15. $2x - 7 - (x - 5) = 0$

16. $5y - 3 = {}^-2y + 10$

17. $\frac{a}{4} + 3 = \frac{5}{2}$

18. $2 + 9x - 105 = {}^-x - 3$

19. $5t + 7 = 5t + 3$

20. $5r - (5 + 4r) = (3 + r) - 8$

21. $\left|5x + 10\right| - 3 = 0$

22. $\left|5x + 10\right| + 3 = 0$

23. $\left|4x - 8\right| + x = 12$

24. $\left|4x - 5\right| + 4 = 7x + 8$

25. $4 > m + 1$

26. $4p + 8 \geq 12$

27. $3(2 + 3r) + r < 2(9 - r)$

28. ${}^-12 < 7x - 5 \leq 9$

29. $\left|5 + t\right| \leq 8$

30. $\left|9x - 4\right| + 8 > 4$

Solve each problem.

31. San Francisco and Los Angeles are 470 miles apart by train. An express train leaves San Francisco at the same time a passenger train leaves Los Angeles. The express train travels 10 miles per hour faster than the passenger train. If the passenger train travels 89 miles per hour, in how many hours will the trains pass each other?

32. Gloria's softball team has won 13 games and lost 7 games. They have 12 more games to play. To win at least 50% of *all* games, how many more games must they win?

chapter
2 Linear Relations and Functions

Certain trees in a reforested area are marked with special tags so that they can be used for sample measurement. After five years, one of the sample trees is 2 meters tall. Six years later the tree is 3.2 meters tall. The trees are harvested when the sample trees are 7 meters tall. Assuming the trees grow at a constant rate, a linear function can be used to determine in what year the trees can be harvested.

2–1 The Coordinate Plane

The graph of all real numbers is the entire number line.

Unless stated otherwise, the word numbers means real numbers.

Completeness Property of Real Numbers

The graph of an open sentence is the graph of the solution set of that open sentence. The number line can be used to graph open sentences in one variable.

examples

1 **Graph $7x = 42$.**

$7x = 42$
$x = 6$

2 **Graph $2t - 9 < 21$.**

$2t - 9 < 21$
$2t < 30$
$t < 15$

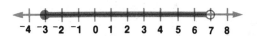

3 **Graph $^-3 \le x < 7$.**

$^-3 \le x$ and $x < 7$

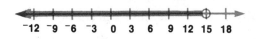

4 **Graph $|x + 3| \le 2$.**

Recall that $|x + 3| \le 2$ means
that $x + 3 \le 2$ and $^-(x + 3) \le 2$.
$x + 3 \le 2$ and $^-x - 3 \le 2$
$x \le ^-1$ and $x \ge ^-5$

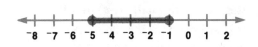

The graph of all **ordered pairs** of real numbers is the entire plane.

Two perpendicular number lines separate the plane into four parts, called **quadrants**. The horizontal number line usually is called the **x-axis**. The vertical number line usually is called the **y-axis**. The plane determined by the perpendicular axes is called a **coordinate plane**.

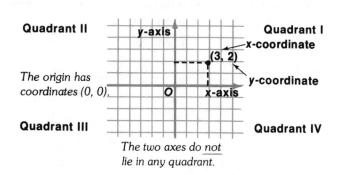

Each point in the coordinate plane corresponds to exactly one or-dered pair of numbers. These numbers are called the **coordinates** of the point. The coordinates of a point are given in a particular order. For example, ($^-$2, 3) and (3, $^-$2) do *not* represent the same point.

Each ordered pair of numbers corresponds to exactly one point in the coordinate plane. The point is the **graph** for the ordered pair.

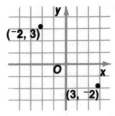

example

5   **Graph point *A* at (3, $^-$2), *B* at ($^-$1.5, $^-$4), and *C* at ($^-$2, 0).**

A (3, $^-$2)   Start at the origin, 0. Move 3 units to the right and 2 units down.

B ($^-$1.5, $^-$4)   Start at 0. Move 1.5 units to the left and 4 units down.

C ($^-$2, 0)   Start at 0. Move 2 units to the left.

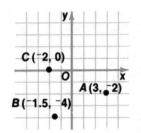

---

exercises

Exploratory   **Graph each set on a number line.**

1. {7, 5}   **2.** {6}   **3.** {2, 3}   **4.** $\left\{-\dfrac{3}{5}\right\}$

Graph the solution set for each open sentence on a number line.

5. $x > {}^-3$ **6.** $a \le 0$ **7.** $p \ge 4\frac{1}{2}$

8. $x < {}^-7.5$ **9.** $^-4 \le s < 2$ **10.** $^-0.04 \le t \le 0.04$

11. $r > 6$ or $r < 1$ **12.** $q < {}^-2.5$ or $q \ge 2.5$ **13.** $x \le 5$ or $x > 2$

In which quadrant will (*x*, *y*) lie given the following conditions?

14. x is positive and y is positive   **15.** x is positive and y is negative
16. x is negative and y is negative   **17.** x is negative and y is positive
18. x is negative and y is 0

Graph each ordered pair on the same coordinate plane.

19. (7, 4)   **20.** ($^-$7, 4)   **21.** (7, $^-$4)   **22.** ($^-$7, $^-$4)
23. (2.5, 0)   **24.** (0, 2.5)   **25.** (1.5, 3)   **26.** (3, 1.5)

Written   **Graph the solution set for each open sentence on a number line.**

1. $\frac{2}{3}m = 26$ **2.** $\frac{1}{4}s - 1 = \frac{3}{4}$ **3.** $2k + 7 = k + 7$

4. $12q - 24 = 45 + 9q$ **5.** $3(u - 2) + 1 = u + 7$ **6.** $2(x + 1) - 3 = 8 - x$

7. $\frac{1}{2}(y + 1) = 3$ **8.** $\frac{1}{3}(x - 3) = 5$ **9.** $3w - (10 - w) = w + 2$

10. $3(n - 3) - n = n + 1$ **11.** $\left|v - 1\right| + 2 = 4$ **12.** $\left|3e + 7\right| + 6 = 1$

13. $2(x - 6) > 3(x - 2)$
14. $50(c - 3) \geq 25 + 15c$
15. $5(r - 3) \leq 6(r - 3)$
16. $y - 5 > 3(y - 9)$
17. $2(1 + 2b) > 5b - (3 - 2b)$
18. $(x + 1) + 2(3 - 2x) \leq 3(2 + x) - 5$
19. $6(1 - x) - 4(2 - x) \leq x + 7$
20. $5(w - 1) - (2w + 1) < 5(w + 2)$
21. $\left| x + 4 \right| < 3$
22. $\left| 2a + 3 \right| > 6$
23. $5 \geq \left| 2r + 3 \right|$
24. $1 - \left| h + 3 \right| < 5$
25. $\left| 3(x + 4) \right| \geq 48$
26. $\left| 3(1 - s) \right| < 27$
27. $\left| 1 + 2(x - 3) \right| > 7$
28. $\left| 2 - 3(2x - 1) \right| \leq 7$

Graph each of the following sets of ordered pairs. Then, state whether the points graphed are the vertices of a rectangle.

29. $\{(0, 0), (0, 3), (7, 0), (7, 3)\}$
30. $\{(^-4, 0), (^-2, 5), (1, 5), (^-1, 0)\}$
31. $\{(2, 5), (7, 4), (8, 3), (1, 2)\}$
32. $\{(0, 1), (7, 1), (0, ^-3), (7, ^-3)\}$
33. $\{(^-1, ^-1), (^-1, ^-5), (3, ^-1), (3, ^-5)\}$
34. $\{(^-4, 6), (^-2, 6), (^-3, 7), (^-1, 7)\}$

Each of the following are the coordinates of three vertices of a rectangle. Graph them. Then, find each fourth vertex.

35. $(3, 1), (3, ^-3), (^-5, ^-3)$
36. $(2, 0), (0, 2), (^-4, ^-2)$
37. $(1, 0), (3, 0), (3, 3)$
38. $(^-1, 0), (1, 1), (0, 3)$
39. $(^-3, 4), (5, 4) (5, ^-3)$
40. $(4, ^-1), (1, ^-4), (0, ^-3)$

History

René Descartes (1596–1650) was a French mathematician and philosopher. He is credited with the invention of a branch of mathematics called analytic geometry. Analytic geometry is a combination of ideas from algebra and geometry. Analytic geometry uses the following.

1. The coordinate plane
2. Each point in a coordinate plane corresponds to exactly one ordered pair of numbers, and vice versa.
3. Graphs of expressions like $f(x) = 2x + 1$

Descartes, in 1637, became the first mathematician to put the three steps together.

Sometimes, ordered pairs are referred to as Cartesian coordinates. The word Cartesian is taken from the name Descartes.

2-2 Relations and Functions

The amount of electricity used in recent years in the U.S. can be written as a set of ordered pairs. The first number is the year, and the second number is the amount in billions of kilowatt hours.

{(1970, 1500), (1972, 1750), (1974, 1820), (1976, 2050),
(1978, 2200), (1980, 2500)}

A set of ordered pairs is called a **relation.** The set of first coordinates, in this case years, is called the **domain** of the relation. The set of second coordinates, billion kilowatt hours, is called the **range** of the relation.

Year	Kilowatt Hours
1970	1500
1972	1750
1974	1820
1976	2050
1978	2200
1980	2500

> **A relation is a set of ordered pairs. The domain is the set of all first coordinates of the ordered pairs. The range is the set of all second coordinates of the ordered pairs.**

Definition of Relation, Domain, and Range

A **mapping** illustrates how each element in the domain of a relation is paired with an element in the range. The following diagrams are mappings of the given relations.

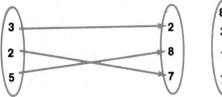

{(3, 2), (2, 7), (5, 8)}

{(8, 4), (3, 9), (1, 2), (7, 4)}

example

1 **State a relation shown by the graph. Then state the domain and range of the relation.**

The relation is
{(⁻3, 7), (⁻2, 4) (⁻1, 1), (0, 2), (1, 5), (2, 8)}.

The domain is {⁻3, ⁻2, ⁻1, 0, 1, 2}.

The range is {7, 4, 1, 2, 5, 8}.

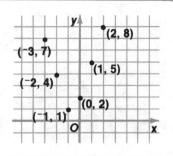

The graph on the left shows how the amount of electricity consumed compares with the cost of the electricity. The graph on the right shows the amount of electricity used in a certain area at different hours in an average weekday.

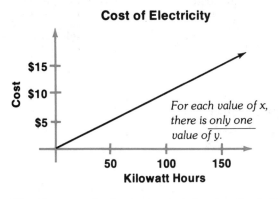

Cost of Electricity

For each value of x, there is only one value of y.

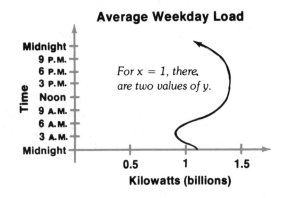

Average Weekday Load

For x = 1, there, are two values of y.

The first graph shows a special type of relation called a **function**.

> **A function is a relation in which each element of the domain is paired with exactly one element of the range.**

Definition of Function

2 **Is {(2, 3), (3, ⁻4), (4, 1), (1, 3)} a function?**

This relation is a function since each element of the domain is paired with exactly one element of the range.

3 **Is {(4, 4) (⁻2, 3), (4, 2), (3, 4), (1, 1)} a function?**

This relation is *not* a function. The element 4 of the domain is paired with two different elements of the range, 4 and 2.

4 **Which of the following mappings represent functions?**

a.

1 → 2
2 → 3
4 → 4

yes

b.

1 → 2
3 → 8
7 → 6

yes

c.

5 → 8
⁻2 → ⁻1
4 → 3
  → 7

no

⁻2 is paired with two elements of the range.

5 **Does y = 4x represent a function?**

Suppose the value of x is 3. What is the corresponding value of y? Is there more than one value for y? When x is 3, y is 12. There is only one value for y. If you try other values of x you will see that they are always paired with exactly one value of y. The equation y = 4x does represent a function.

The graph on the right represents the following relation.

$$\{(^-2, 3), (^-1, 1), (1, 2), (1, ^-1), (3, 1)\}$$

Suppose you drew a vertical line through each point on the graph. The vertical line through $(1, 2)$ would also pass through $(1, ^-1)$. This shows that the relation is *not* a function. There are two elements of the range, 2 and $^-1$, that pair with the domain element 1.

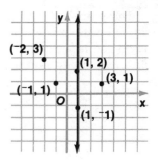

> **If any vertical line drawn on the graph of a relation passes through no more than one point of that graph, then the relation is a function.**

Vertical Line Test for a Function

 example

6 **Use the vertical line test to determine if the relation graphed is a function.**

The vertical line whose equation is $x = 2$ intersects the graph at $(2, 2)$ and $(2, ^-2)$. Therefore, the relation is *not* a function.

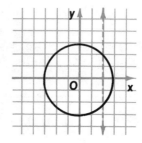

Equations that represent functions often are written in a special way. The equation $y = 2x + 1$ can be written $f(x) = 2x + 1$. The symbol $f(x)$ is read "f of x." Likewise, the symbol $f(3)$ is read "f of 3." If 3 is an element of the domain of the function, then $f(3)$ is the corresponding element of the range. To show that the value of $f(3)$ is 7, you write $f(3) = 7$.

Letters other than f can be used to represent a function. For example, the equation $y = 4x + 3$ can be written $g(x) = 4x + 3$.

example

7 **Find $f(15)$ if $f(x) = 100x - 5x^2$.**

$f(x) = 100x - 5x^2$
$f(15) = 100(15) - 5(15)^2$ *Substitute 15 for x.*
$\quad\quad = 1500 - 5(225)$
$\quad\quad = 1500 - 1125$
$\quad\quad = 375$ Therefore, $f(15) = 375$.

Often we give only the equation for a function without naming the domain. In this book, we mean the domain is all real numbers. The corresponding range values are also real numbers.

42   *Linear Relations and Functions*

exercises

Exploratory   State the domain and range of each relation. Then state if the relation is a function.

1. $\{(4, 4), (1, 1), (3, 3)\}$
2. $\{(6, 4)\}$
3. $\{(4, 3), (8, {}^-2), ({}^-17, 4), ({}^-17, 8)\}$
4. $\{(1, 5), (5, 1)\}$
5. $\{({}^-3, {}^-3), ({}^-2, {}^-2), (2, 2), (4, 4)\}$
6. $\{({}^-3, 3), ({}^-2, 2), (2, {}^-2), (4, {}^-4)\}$
7. $\{(5, {}^-3), ({}^-3, 5)\}$
8. $\{({}^-3, 3), ({}^-2, 3), (2, 3), (4, 3)\}$

State the relation shown by each of the following mappings. Then state if the relation is a function.

9.
10.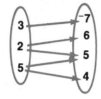
11.
12.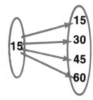

Written   State a relation shown by the graph. Then state the domain and range of the relation.

1.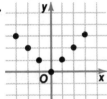
2.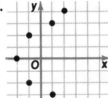
3.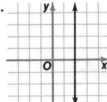
4.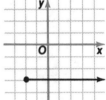

Use the vertical line test to determine if each relation is a function. Write yes or no.

5.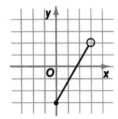
6.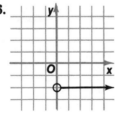
7.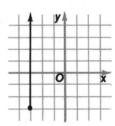
8.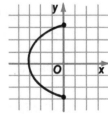

9.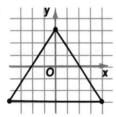
10.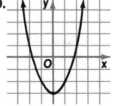
11.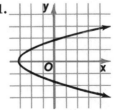
12.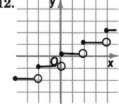

Given $f(x) = \dfrac{7}{x-2}$, find each value.

13. $f(12)$ **14.** $f(3)$ **15.** $f(^-1)$ **16.** $f(5.5)$

17. $f\left(\dfrac{1}{2}\right)$ **18.** $f\left(\dfrac{2}{3}\right)$ **19.** $f(a)$ **20.** $f(u+2)$

Given $g(x) = 4x^3 + 2x^2 + x - 7$, find each value.

21. $g(0)$ **22.** $g(1)$ **23.** $g(2)$ **24.** $g(^-4)$

25. $g\left(-\dfrac{1}{2}\right)$ **26.** $g\left(\dfrac{1}{2}\right)$ **27.** $g(t)$ **28.** $g(2s)$

Given $h(x) = \dfrac{x^2 + 5x - 6}{x+3}$, find each value.

29. $h(4)$ **30.** $h(6)$ **31.** $h(^-4)$ **32.** $h(^-6.3)$

33. $h\left(\dfrac{1}{3}\right)$ **34.** $h\left(\dfrac{1}{2}\right)$ **35.** $h(a+1)$ **36.** $h(2m+3)$

Challenge   State the domain of each relation.

> **Sample:** $f(x) = \dfrac{14}{x+4}$ The relation is undefined when the denominator is 0.
> $$x + 4 = 0 \text{ or } x = {}^-4$$
> Thus, the domain is all real numbers except $^-4$.

1. $f(x) = \dfrac{3}{x-5}$ **2.** $f(x) = \dfrac{3}{|2x-7|}$ **3.** $g(x) = \dfrac{3}{x^2}$ **4.** $g(x) = \dfrac{2x+3}{2x-1}$

5. $x = |y|$ **6.** $y = |x| - 1$ **7.** $x = |^-y|$ **8.** $x = {}^-|y+4|$

Sets of Numbers   excursions in algebra

Some important sets of numbers are listed below.

The set of natural or counting numbers, **N**
  N $= \{1, 2, 3, 4, 5, \ldots\}$

The set of integers, **Z**
  Z $= \{\ldots, {}^-2, {}^-1, 0, 1, 2, \ldots\}$

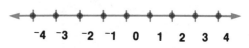

The set of rational numbers, **Q**
  Q $= \left\{\dfrac{m}{n},\ m \text{ and } n \text{ are integers and } n \text{ is } not \text{ zero}\right\}$
    $= \{$all terminating and repeating decimals$\}$

Numbers like $-\dfrac{2}{3}$, *1.1, 2, and 0 are rational.*

The set of irrational numbers, **I**
  I $= \{$all nonterminating, nonrepeating decimals$\}$

Numbers like $\sqrt{2}$ *and* π *are irrational.*

The set of all real numbers, **R**
  R $= \{$all decimals$\}$

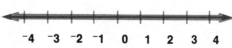

Taken together, the sets of rational and irrational numbers make up the real numbers.

Simulation games are games that resemble real life processes. The game called LIFE, created by John Horton Conway, is one example. It shows, in a simple way, the evolution of a society of *living* organisms as it ages with time.

You can play LIFE using a grid of squares and counters in two different colors, say black and green. The counters are placed on the grid, one to a square. Then you change the positions of the counters according to the following *genetic laws*, or rules, for births, deaths, and survivals.

SURVIVALS Every counter with 2 or 3 neighboring counters survives for the next generation. *Neighboring counters have common sides or corners.*

DEATHS Every counter with 4 or more neighbors dies from overpopulation. Every counter with only one neighbor or none dies from isolation.

BIRTHS Every empty cell with exactly 3 neighbors is a birth cell. A counter is placed on the cell for the next generation.

To help eliminate mistakes in play, the following procedure is suggested.

1. Start with a pattern of black counters.
2. Put a green counter where each birth cell will occur.
3. Put a second black counter on top of each death cell. Ignore the green counters when determining death cells.
4. Check the new pattern. Then, remove all dead counters, and replace the newborn green counters with black counters.

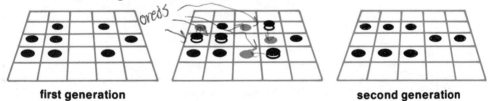

first generation   **second generation**

Notice that births and deaths occur simultaneously. Together, they are a move to the next generation.

When you play this game, you will find that many patterns either die, reach a stable repeating pattern or become blinkers, alternating between two patterns.

Computers are very helpful in simulations because they can display the changes, and a number of patterns can be observed in a short period of time.

Exercises Find the next six generations for each of the following.

1. 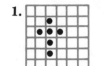   2.   3.   4.   5.

2–3   Linear Functions

You can write the solutions to open sentences in two variables as sets of ordered pairs. These solutions can be graphed in the coordinate plane. The following graph represents the solutions to $3x - y = 1$.

An infinite number of ordered pairs will satisfy $3x - y = 1$. The graph of these ordered pairs is a straight line. An equation whose graph is a straight line is called a **linear equation** in two variables.

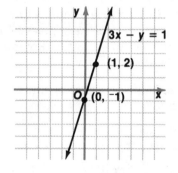

In a linear equation each term is a constant, like 7, or a constant times a variable to the first power, like $7x$. Thus, $4x + 3y = 7$, $2x = 8 + y$, $5m - n = 1$, and $y = 7$ are linear equations in two variables. But $3x + y^2 = y$ and $\dfrac{1}{x} + y = 4$ are *not*.   *Why?*

When variables other than x and y are used, assume that the letter coming first in the alphabet represents the domain or horizontal coordinate.

Any linear equation can be written in **standard form**.

> The standard form of a linear equation is
> $$ax + by = c$$
> where a, b, and c are real numbers, and a and b are *not both* zero.

Standard Form of a Linear Equation

Usually a, b, and c are given as integers that have greatest common factor 1.

example

1 **Write the equation $x = \dfrac{2}{3}y - 1$ in standard form.**

$$x = \frac{2}{3}y - 1$$
$$3x = 2y - 3 \qquad \textit{Multiply both sides by 3 to eliminate the fraction.}$$
$$3x - 2y = {}^-3 \qquad \textit{Add } {}^-2y \textit{ to both sides.}$$

To graph a linear equation, it is helpful to make a table of ordered pairs that satisfy the equation. These ordered pairs can then be graphed and connected with a straight line. Since two points determine a line, you need only two points to graph a linear equation in two variables. In checking your work it is helpful to use a third point.

2 **Graph $3y = {}^-2x - 6$.**

Transform the equation so that
y is on one side by itself.

$$3y = {}^-2x - 6$$
$$y = -\frac{2}{3}x - 2$$

Next, find three ordered pairs that satisfy the equation. Then, graph the ordered pairs and connect the points with a line.

x	$-\frac{2}{3}x - 2$	y	(x, y)
$^-3$	$-\frac{2}{3}(^-3) - 2$	0	$(^-3, 0)$
0	$-\frac{2}{3}(0) - 2$	$^-2$	$(0, ^-2)$
3	$-\frac{2}{3}(3) - 2$	$^-4$	$(3, ^-4)$

Why were the values of $^-3$, 0, and 3 chosen for x?

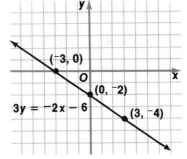

3 **Graph $2a = 3b - 4$.**

Transform the equation so that
b is isolated.

$$2a = 3b - 4$$
$$^-3b = ^-2a - 4$$
$$b = \frac{2}{3}a + \frac{4}{3}$$

Next, find three ordered pairs that satisfy the equation. Then, graph the ordered pairs and connect the points with a line.

a	$\frac{2}{3}a + \frac{4}{3}$	b	(a, b)
$^-2$	$\frac{2}{3}(^-2) + \frac{4}{3}$	0	$(^-2, 0)$
1	$\frac{2}{3}(1) + \frac{4}{3}$	2	$(1, 2)$
4	$\frac{2}{3}(4) + \frac{4}{3}$	4	$(4, 4)$

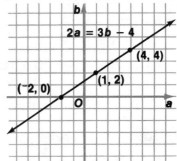

Not all linear equations in two variables represent functions. For example, consider the equation $x = 3$. Its graph is a vertical line. Any vertical line drawn on the graph of the equation passes through every point of that graph. The relation is *not* a function.

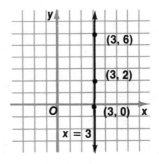

The equation $x = 3$ means that y can be any number as long as x is 3.

Any function whose ordered pairs satisfy a linear equation in two variables is called a **linear function.**

> **A linear function can be defined by $f(x) = mx + b$ where m and b are real numbers.**

Definition of Linear Function

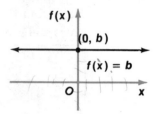

In the definition of a linear function, m or b may be zero.

If $m = 0$, then $f(x) = b$. The graph is a horizontal line. This function is called a **constant function.**

4 **Which of the following are linear functions?**

a. $f(x) = x^3 + 4$

This cannot be written in the form $f(x) = mx + b$. Thus, it is *not* a linear function.

b. $g(x) = 4 - x$

This can be written in the form $f(x) = mx + b$ where $m = {}^-1$ and $b = 4$. Thus, it is a linear function.

exercises

Exploratory   State whether each equation is a linear equation.

1. $x^2 + y^2 = 7$
2. $x + y = 4$
3. $x - 2y = 5$
4. $x^2 = 9$
5. $a + 3b = 7$
6. $5m^2 = n^2$
7. $y = {}^-4x$
8. $7 = 2y$

State whether each of the following is a linear function.

9. $f(x) = x^2 + 3$
10. $g(x) = 7$
11. $3\,g(x) = x$
12. $g(x) = x - 4$
13. $5\,f(x) = 5x^2 - 5$
14. $4\,f(b) = 2 - b$
15. $f(x) = \frac{2}{3}(6 - 9x)$
16. $g(x) = x(2 - x)$

Written   Write each equation in standard form.

1. $y = 2x - 6$
2. $y = {}^-4x + 1$
3. $x = 5$
4. $y - 7 = 0$
5. $y = \frac{5}{8}x + 1$
6. $x = \frac{1}{3}y - 4$
7. $y = 3x$
8. $x = \frac{3}{5} + \frac{y}{4}$

Graph each equation.

9. $y = x$
10. $y = x + 1$
11. $y = 2x + 3$
12. $y = 5x - 4$
13. $b = 2a - 3$
14. $p = 5q + 1$
15. $x + y = 7$
16. $x - y = 4$
17. $4x + 3y = 12$
18. $2x - 5y = 10$
19. $2a + 3b = 6$
20. $5 = 5x$
21. $f(x) = 2x + 1$
22. $f(x) = 3x - 1$
23. $3s - 2t = 6$
24. $2r - 3s = 6$
25. $5x = 4$
26. $3y = 5$
27. $x + 1 = 2y$
28. $3x - 4 = 2y$
29. $\frac{1}{3}x + \frac{1}{2}y = 1$
30. $\frac{2}{3}x + \frac{1}{4}y = 2$
31. $\frac{x}{4} - \frac{y}{3} = 2$
32. $\frac{x}{3} + \frac{y}{2} = 3$
33. $a = \frac{2}{3}$
34. $4g(x) = 4$
35. $h(y) = 3 - 2y$
36. $3p(x) = x - 6$

2–4 Slopes and Intercepts

A ramp installed to give handicapped people access to a certain building has a base 12 meters long and an elevation of 2 meters. The steepness or **slope** of the ramp is found by using the following ratio.

$$\text{slope} = \frac{\text{change in vertical units}}{\text{change in horizontal units}}$$

Thus, the slope of the ramp is $\frac{2}{12}$ or $\frac{1}{6}$.

In the graph of $f(x) = 4x$ shown at the right, the y-coordinates increase 8 units for each 2 units increase in the corresponding x-coordinates. The slope of the line whose equation is $f(x) = 4x$ is $\frac{8}{2}$ or 4. The vertical change is the difference of the y-coordinates. The horizontal change is the difference of the corresponding x-coordinates.

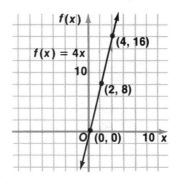

x	$4x$
0	0
2	8
4	16

The slope, m, of a line passing through points (x_1, y_1) and (x_2, y_2) is given by the following equation.

$$m = \frac{y_1 - y_2}{x_1 - x_2}$$

Definition of Slope

---

example

1 Determine the slope of the line that passes through $(0, {}^-5)$ and $(1, {}^-3)$.

$$\begin{aligned}
\text{slope} &= \frac{y_1 - y_2}{x_1 - x_2} \\
&= \frac{{}^-5 - {}^-3}{0 - 1} \\
&= \frac{{}^-2}{{}^-1} \\
&= 2 \qquad \text{The slope of the line is 2.}
\end{aligned}$$

2 **Determine the slope of each of the following lines.**

a.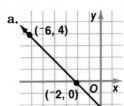

b.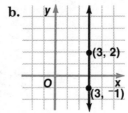

c.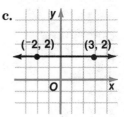

a. slope $= \dfrac{4 - 0}{-6 - (-2)}$

$= \dfrac{4}{-4}$ or -1

The slope is -1.

b. slope $= \dfrac{2 - (-1)}{3 - 3}$

$= \dfrac{3}{0}$

The slope is undefined.

c. slope $= \dfrac{2 - 2}{-2 - 3}$

$= \dfrac{0}{-5}$ or 0

The line has a slope of 0.

3 **Graph the line that passes through $(-1, -2)$ and whose slope is $\dfrac{3}{4}$.**

First graph the ordered pair $(-1, -2)$. Since the slope is $\dfrac{3}{4}$, the vertical change is 3 and the horizontal change is 4. From $(-1, -2)$ move 3 units up and 4 units to the right. This point is $(3, 1)$. Connect these two points with a straight line.

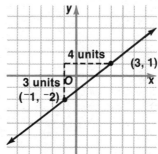

The previous examples suggest the following statements about the slope of a line.

If the line rises to the right, then the slope is positive.

If the line is horizontal, then the slope is zero.

If the line falls to the right, then the slope is negative.

If the line is vertical, then the slope is *undefined*.

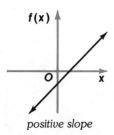

positive slope

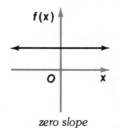

zero slope

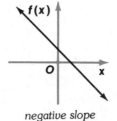

negative slope

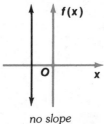

no slope

The graphs of $f(x) = 3x + 2$, $g(x) = 3x$, and $h(x) = 3x - 5$ are lines with the same slope. But, these lines do *not* pass through the same points.

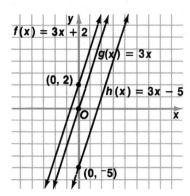

Consider the points where each line crosses the y-axis.

$$f(x) = 3x + 2 \quad \text{crosses at } (0, 2).$$
$$g(x) = 3x \quad \text{crosses at } (0, 0).$$
$$h(x) = 3x - 5 \quad \text{crosses at } (0, {}^-5).$$

The x-coordinate of each point is 0.

The y-coordinates at these points are called the **y-intercepts** of the lines. The y-intercept is the value of y when x is zero.

$f(x) = 3x + 2$ has y-intercept 2.
$g(x) = 3x$ or $g(x) = 3x + 0$ has y-intercept 0.
$h(x) = 3x - 5$ or $h(x) = 3x + {}^-5$ has y-intercept ${}^-5$.

The **x-intercept** of a line is the value of x when y is zero. What are the x-intercepts of the lines described above?

---

example

4 **Find the slope, y-intercept, and x-intercept of the line whose equation is $5x + 3y = 9$.**

To find the slope and y-intercept, solve the equation for y.
$$5x + 3y = 9$$
$$3y = 9 - 5x$$
$$y = -\frac{5}{3}x + 3 \qquad \text{Thus, the slope is } -\frac{5}{3} \text{ and the y-intercept is 3.}$$

To find the x-intercept, let $y = 0$ and solve for x.
$$0 = -\frac{5}{3}x + 3$$
$${}^-3 = -\frac{5}{3}x$$
$${}^-9 = {}^-5x$$
$$\frac{9}{5} = x \qquad \text{The x-intercept is } \frac{9}{5}.$$

exercises

Exploratory State the slope, y-intercept, and x-intercept for each graph.

1.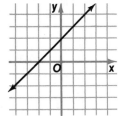

2.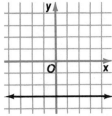

3.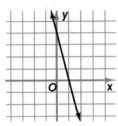

4.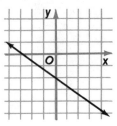

5.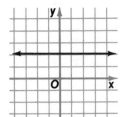

6.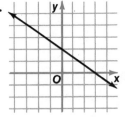

7.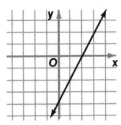

8.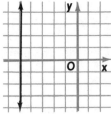

Written Find the slope, y-intercept, and x-intercept of each line whose equation is given below.

1. $y = 5x - 9$
2. $y = {}^-3x - 5$
3. $y - 1 = 7x$
4. $y + 6 = 5x$
5. $3y = {}^-2x - 15$
6. $3y = x + 4$
7. $y = {}^-2$
8. $x = 4$
9. $f(x) = x - 2$
10. $g(x) = 4x - 1$
11. $x + 2y = 5$
12. $2x + 3y = 6$
13. $3x - 2y = 12$
14. $5x + 3y = 30$
15. $x + 2y = 7$
16. $3x + y = 6$
17. $2x - 3y = 12$
18. $5x - 2y = 20$

Determine the slope of the line passing through each pair of points.

19. $(6, 1)$ and $(8, {}^-4)$
20. $(5, 7)$ and $(4, {}^-6)$
21. $({}^-3, 0)$ and $(8, 2)$
22. $({}^-6, {}^-3)$ and $(4, 1)$
23. $({}^-8, {}^-2)$ and $({}^-4, 8)$
24. $(6, 1)$ and $(6, 7)$
25. $(2.5, 3)$ and $(1, {}^-9)$
26. $(0, 0)$ and $\left(\frac{3}{2}, \frac{1}{4}\right)$
27. $\left(1\frac{3}{4}, \frac{1}{3}\right)$ and $\left(2, \frac{1}{3}\right)$

A line has slope 7. For each pair of points on the line, find the missing coordinate.

28. $(0, 0)$ and $(x, 7)$
29. $(6, y)$ and $(2, {}^-13)$
30. $({}^-2, {}^-7)$ and $(0, y)$
31. $(x, {}^-1)$ and $(3, 6)$
32. $\left({}^-17\frac{1}{2}, {}^-35\right)$ and $(x, 0)$
33. $\left({}^-10\frac{2}{3}, y\right)$ and $\left({}^-8\frac{1}{3}, 16\right)$

Graph the equation of the line that passes through the given point and has the given slope.

34. $({}^-3, 2)$, $m = {}^-2$
35. $(0, 0)$, $m = 3$
36. $(3, 4)$, $m = {}^-1$
37. $({}^-1, 1)$, $m = \frac{1}{4}$
38. $(2, {}^-1)$, $m = 0$
39. $({}^-4, 1)$, $m = -\frac{5}{3}$

2–5 Finding Linear Equations

In the figure at the right, $\overleftrightarrow{AB}$ passes through points $A(0, b)$ and $B(x, y)$. Notice that b is the y-intercept of $\overleftrightarrow{AB}$.

Suppose you want to find an equation for $\overleftrightarrow{AB}$. Let m represent the slope of the line.

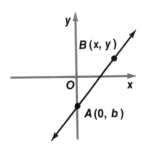

$m = \dfrac{y - b}{x - 0}$ *Definition of slope*

$m = \dfrac{y - b}{x}$ *Solve for y.*

$mx = y - b$

$y = mx + b$

This equation of a line, $y = mx + b$, is called the **slope-intercept form.**

> **The slope-intercept form of the equation of a line is $y = mx + b$. The slope is m and the y-intercept is b.**

Slope-Intercept Form of a Linear Equation

Suppose you are given the slope and y-intercept of a line. You can find the slope-intercept form of the equation of the line by substitution. For example, if the slope of a line is $-\frac{2}{3}$ and its y-intercept is 14, an equation of the line is $y = -\frac{2}{3}x + 14$. The standard form of this equation is $2x + 3y = 42$.

The form $y = mx + b$ is often written as $f(x) = mx + b$.

example

1 **Find the slope-intercept form of the equation of a line with slope $\frac{2}{3}$ passing through (4, 7).**

First, substitute the slope and coordinates of the point into the slope-intercept form and solve for b.

$y = mx + b$

$7 = \left(\dfrac{2}{3}\right)(4) + b$ *Substitute 7 for y, $\frac{2}{3}$ for m, and 4 for x.*

$7 = \dfrac{8}{3} + b$

$\dfrac{13}{3} = b$

Write the equation in slope-intercept form.

$y = \dfrac{2}{3}x + \dfrac{13}{3}$ *Substitute $\frac{2}{3}$ for m and $\frac{13}{3}$ for b.*

2 **Find the slope-intercept form of the equation of a line passing through $(^-2, 5)$ and $(3, 0)$.**

First find the slope.

$$\text{slope} = \frac{5 - 0}{^-2 - 3}$$

$$= \frac{5}{^-5}$$

$$= ^-1$$

Next, substitute the slope and coordinates of one point in the slope-intercept form and solve for b.

$y = mx + b$
$5 = (^-1)(^-2) + b$ *Substitute 5 for y, ⁻1 for m, and ⁻2 for x. Using the other*
$5 = 2 + b$ *point would give the same results.*
$3 = b$

The slope-intercept form of the equation of the line is $y = ^-x + 3$.

3 **Find the slope and y-intercept of a line with equation in standard form.**

Recall that the standard form of the equation of a line is $ax + by = c$.
If b is not zero, the slope and y-intercept are found by solving the equation for y.

$ax + by = c$
$\quad by = ^-ax + c$
$\qquad y = -\frac{a}{b}x + \frac{c}{b}$ The slope is $-\frac{a}{b}$ and the y-intercept is $\frac{c}{b}$.

Consider the line with equation $y = ^-2x + 4$. The standard form of this equation is $2x + y = 4$. The following calculations use the information from Example 3 to find the slope and y-intercept.

$$\text{slope} = -\frac{a}{b} \qquad\qquad y\text{-intercept} = \frac{c}{b}$$

$$= -\frac{2}{1} \text{ or } ^-2 \qquad\qquad = \frac{4}{1} \text{ or } 4$$

Notice that these values are the same as the values you would obtain from the slope-intercept form of the equation.

exercises

Exploratory Find the slope-intercept form of the equation of each line which has slope m and y-intercept b.

1. $m = 5, b = ^-3$

2. $m = ^-1, b = 3$

3. $m = ^-1, b = 4$

4. $m = 8, b = 1$

5. $m = \frac{2}{3}, b = ^-7$

6. $m = \frac{1}{4}, b = 6$

7. $m = 2.5, b = 0$

8. $m = ^-4.1, b = ^-9$

9. $m = 0, b = 0$

State the slope and y-intercept of the graph of each of the following.

10. $y = {}^-2x + 5$

11. $y = {}^-4x + 6$

12. $\frac{1}{2}y = 7x - 1$

13. $y = x - 8$

14. $y = -\frac{3}{4}x - 3$

15. $y = \frac{1}{3}x$

16. $^-y = 0.2x + 6$

17. $^-y = x$

18. $y = cx + t$

Find the slope-intercept form of each equation.

19. $2x + 5y = 10$

20. $3x - y = 6$

21. $2x + 3y = 4$

22. $4x + 8y = 11$

23. $2x - 2y = 4$

24. $2x = 11$

Written   **State the slope and y-intercept of the graph of each of the following.**

1. $^-2x + y = 15$

2. $0.4x - 0.4y = 0.4$

3. $5x - 3y = 0.6$

4. $3x - 4y = 1$

5. $8x = 1$

6. $8x - y = {}^-1$

7. $x - \frac{1}{2}y = 2$

8. $2x - \frac{1}{3}y = {}^-5$

9. $\frac{1}{5}x - \frac{1}{3}y = \frac{1}{7}$

Find the slope-intercept form of the equation of the line satisfying each of the following conditions.

10. slope $= \frac{1}{2}$ and passes through (6, 4)

11. slope $= \frac{3}{4}$ and passes through (8, $^-1$)

12. slope $= \frac{2}{3}$ and passes through (6, $^-2$)

13. slope $= -\frac{4}{5}$ and passes through (2, $^-3$)

14. slope $= 4$ and passes through (2, $^-3$)

15. slope $= 5$ and passes through the origin

16. slope $= -\frac{3}{2}$ and passes through (6, 1)

17. slope $= -\frac{8}{3}$ and passes through (0, 6)

18. passes through (5, 7) and (4, $^-6$)

19. passes through (6, 1) and (8, $^-4$)

20. passes through ($^-6$, $^-3$) and (4, 1)

21. passes through ($^-3$, 0) and (8, 2)

22. passes through (6, 1) and (6, 7)

23. passes through ($^-8$, $^-2$) and ($^-4$, 8)

24. passes through (4, 6) and (0, 0)

25. passes through (4, 3) and (6, 3)

26. x-intercept $= {}^-3$, y-intercept $= 6$

27. x-intercept $= 6$, y-intercept $= 4$

28. x-intercept $= 6$, y-intercept $= 8$

29. x-intercept $= 5$, y-intercept $= 6$

30. x-intercept $= \frac{3}{5}$, y-intercept $= 6$

31. x-intercept $= \frac{1}{3}$, y-intercept $= -\frac{1}{4}$

32. x-intercept $= 0$, y-intercept $= 2$

33. x-intercept $= {}^-7$, y-intercept $= 0$

Find the standard form of the equation of the line satisfying each of the following conditions.

34. slope $= 1$ and passes through (2, 3)

35. slope $= 2$ and passes through (4, 6)

36. slope $= {}^-2$ and passes through ($^-1$, 4)

37. slope $= {}^-3$ and passes through (2, 5)

38. slope $= \frac{4}{3}$ and passes through (4, 3)

39. slope $= -\frac{2}{3}$ and passes through ($^-3$, 5)

40. passes through (2, 3) and (1, 5)

41. passes through (2, 5) and (3, 6)

42. passes through (1, $^-2$) and (3, 7)

43. passes through (1, 0) and (2, $^-5$)

44. passes through ($^-1$, 5) and (2, 3)

45. passes through ($^-1$, $^-1$) and ($^-1$, 8)

46. x-intercept $= 4$, y-intercept $= 3$

47. x-intercept $= 9$, y-intercept $= 1$

48. x-intercept $= {}^-6$, y-intercept $= 5$

49. x-intercept $= {}^-1$, y-intercept $= 1$

50. x-intercept $= 0$, y-intercept $= {}^-5$

51. x-intercept $= 0$, y-intercept $= 7$

2-6   Special Functions

Recall that a linear function can be described by $y = mx + b$ or $f(x) = mx + b$ where m and b are real numbers. There are some kinds of linear functions which have special names.

If $m = 0$, the function is called a **constant function**. Its graph is a horizontal line.

If $b = 0$ and $m = 1$, the function is called the **identity function.** Its graph passes through the origin and forms congruent angles with the axes.

If $b = 0$ and $m \neq 0$, the function is called a **direct variation.** Its graph passes through the origin.

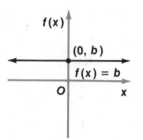

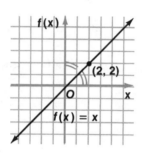

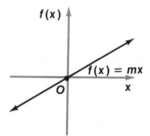

A linear function described by $y = b$ or $f(x) = b$ is called a constant function.

Definition of Constant Function

A linear function described by $y = x$ or $f(x) = x$ is called the identity function.

Definition of Identity Function

A linear function described by $y = mx$ or $f(x) = mx$ where $m \neq 0$ is called a direct variation. The constant m is called the constant of variation or constant of proportionality.

Definition of Direct Variation

A special language often is used with direct variation. The cost of electricity (c) *varies directly with* the amount of electricity (k) used means $c = mk$. You could also say the cost of electricity *is directly proportional to* the amount of electricity used.

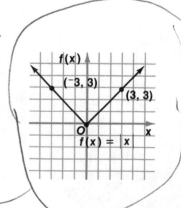

Several other functions are closely related to linear functions. Absolute value functions are one example.

Consider $f(x) = |x|$ or $y = |x|$. When x is positive or zero the function is like $y = x$. When x is negative the function is like $y = ^-x$. The graph of $f(x) = |x|$ is shown on the right.

All of the following graphs represent absolute value functions.

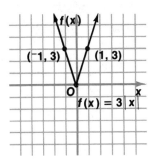

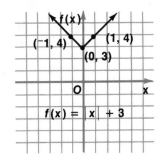

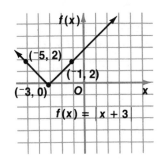

The domain is $\{x \mid x \text{ is real}\}$.
The range is $\{y \mid y \geq 0\}$.

The domain is $\{x \mid x \text{ is real}\}$.
The range is $\{y \mid y \geq 3\}$.

The domain is $\{x \mid x \text{ is real}\}$.
The range is $\{y \mid y \geq 0\}$.

Step functions like the ones graphed below are also related to linear functions.

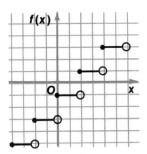

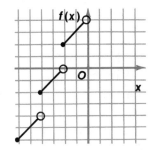

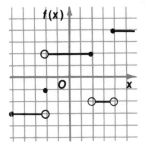

One type of step function is called **greatest integer function.** The *greatest integer of* x is written $[x]$ and means the greatest integer *not* greater than x. For example, $[6.2]$ is 6 and $[^-1.8]$ is $^-2$.

1 **Graph $f(x) = [x] + 1$.**

x	$[x]$	$[x] + 1$
0	0	1
0.2	0	1
0.6	0	1
1.0	1	2
1.5	1	2
2.0	2	3
2.5	2	3

The domain is all real numbers.

The range is all integers.

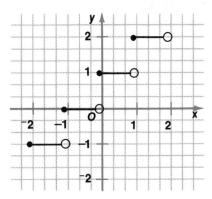

exercises

Exploratory Identify each function as *C* for *constant*, as *I* for *identity*, as *D* for *direct variation*, as *A* for *absolute value*, or as *G* for *greatest integer function*.

1. $f(x) = |3x - 2|$
2. $f(x) = [^-x]$
3. $g(x) = 3x$
4. $g(x) = [2x]$
5. $y = |2x|$
6. $f(x) = |2x + 1|$
7. $f(x) = |x - \frac{2}{3}|$
8. $g(x) = 19$
9. $g(x) = [2x + 1]$
10. $h(x) = {}^-2x$
11. $f(x) = \frac{1}{2}x$
12. $p(x) = x$
13. $h(x) = [x - 3]$
14. $f(x) = {}^-3x$
15. $g(x) = |x + 3|$
16. $h(x) = {}^-7$
17. $m(x) = |{}^-3x|$
18. $f(x) = [x - \frac{1}{2}]$
19. $f(x) = [x - 2\frac{1}{2}]$
20. $f(x) = [3x - 5]$
21. $m(x) = \frac{2}{3}$
22. $g(x) = {}^-x$
23. $k(x) = |x - 8|$
24. $f(x) = 0$

Written Graph each function.

1. $f(x) = x$
2. $g(x) = 3x$
3. $h(x) = {}^-2x$
4. $f(x) = \frac{1}{2}x$
5. $p(x) = |x|$
6. $r(x) = |2x|$
7. $g(x) = |{}^-3x|$
8. $f(x) = |x + 3|$
9. $f(x) = |x - \frac{2}{3}|$
10. $f(x) = |2x + 1|$
11. $f(x) = [x]$
12. $g(x) = [^-x]$
13. $h(x) = {}^-[x]$
14. $p(x) = [2x]$
15. $f(x) = 2[x]$
16. $r(x) = [x] - 3$
17. $h(x) = |3x| - 2$
18. $g(x) = {}^-|x| + 3$
19. $r(x) = 2|x| - 3$
20. $f(x) = |x - 3| + 2$
21. $f(x) = [x - \frac{1}{2}]$
22. $m(x) = [3x - 5]$
23. $p(x) = 3 - [x]$
24. $f(x) = {}^-[x - 2]$

Explain how the graphs of each pair of equations differ.

25. $y = 2[x]$ and $y = [2x]$
26. $y = [x + 5]$ and $y = [x] + 5$
27. $y = |x - 3|$ and $y = |x| - 3$
28. $y = |3x|$ and $y = 3|x|$
29. $y = |2x + 5|$ and $y = |2x| + 5$
30. $y = [2x + 5]$ and $y = [2x] + 5$
31. $y = |ax|$ and $y = a|x|$
32. $y = |x + b|$ and $y = |x| + b$
33. $y = {}^-3[x]$ and $y = [^-3x]$
34. $y = {}^-2|x|$ and $y = |{}^-2x|$

Skills Review Solve each of the following.

1. $3x + 1 = 10$
2. $7 - 3y = 20$
3. $8 = \frac{2y + 2}{5}$
4. $\frac{3y - 6}{2} = 9$
5. $4x - 3 = 7x + 18$
6. $6 - x = {}^-3x + 10$
7. $\frac{1}{2}(x + 4) = x - 2$
8. ${}^-3(2 - x) = 2(x - 4)$
9. ${}^-2(3x - 1) - (x + 5) = 11$
10. $2y + 1 \le {}^-7$
11. $3(y - 2) \ge 9$
12. $2x > 7(x - 5)$
13. $2y + 7(1 - y) < {}^-8$
14. $10y < 6(2y + 4)$
15. $\frac{2}{3}x - 2 \ge \frac{5}{6}x + 2$

58   *Linear Relations and Functions*

Another strategy which may help you solve a problem is to look for a pattern. Sometimes a pattern may be obvious, but many times it is not. You may have to "play" with the facts and figures until you arrive at a pattern. Then you can solve the problem by generalizing and applying the pattern.

Example: Write an equation showing the relationship between the variables in the chart below.

x	1	2	3	4	5
y	17	21	25	29	33

Look for a pattern by finding differences between successive values of x and successive values of y.

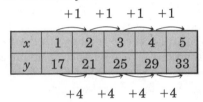

$$+1 \quad +1 \quad +1 \quad +1$$

x	1	2	3	4	5
y	17	21	25	29	33

$$+4 \quad +4 \quad +4 \quad +4$$

Notice that the changes in x are 1 while the changes in y are 4. This suggests that $y = 4x$ since the changes in y are 4 times the changes in x. Try $x = 1$ in $y = 4x$.

$$y = 4 \cdot 1 \text{ or } 4$$

But when x is 1, y is 17 not 4. To make y equal to 17 when x is equal to 1, you need to add 13. The equation becomes $y = 4x + 13$. This equation checks for each value of x.

Exercises Write an equation showing the relationship between the variables in each chart. Then complete the chart.

1.

x	1	2	3			6
y	8	16		32	40	

2.

a	1	2	3	4	5	6
b	5	7	9			

3. The Worthington City Council has 12 members. After their last session, each member shook hands with each other member. How many handshakes were there in all?

4. At Dublin High School, there are 500 students and 500 lockers, numbered 1 through 500. Suppose the first student opens each locker. Then the second student closes every second locker. The third student closes every third locker if it is open or opens it if it is closed. The fourth student changes the state of every fourth locker. This process continues until the five-hundredth student changes the state of the five-hundredth locker. After this process is completed, state which lockers are open.

2–7   Using Linear Functions

Geothermal energy is generated wherever water comes into contact with heated underground rocks. This heat turns the water into steam which is used to make electricity.

The underground temperature of rocks varies with their depth below the surface. The temperature at the surface is about 20° C. At a depth of 2 km, the temperature is about 90° C. This information can be used to find an equation for the relationship. (Assume the relationship is linear.)

Let t represent the temperature at a certain depth.
Let d represent the depth given in kilometers.
Let c represent the constant of variation.

$t = cd + 20$ *20° C is the surface temperature.*
$90 = c(2) + 20$
$70 = c(2)$
$35 = c$

Thus, the relationship between the underground temperature and its depth can be described as follows.

$t = 35d + 20$

1   **Find the underground temperature 3600 meters below the surface.**

$t = 35d + 20$
$t = 35(3.6) + 20$ *3600 m = 3.6 km*
$t = 146$

The temperature is 146° C.

2 Ace Repair Shop has the following chart for its employees to use in computing customers' bills. Write an equation to describe the relationship between the number of labor hours and the charge. (Assume the relationship is linear.)

Labor Hours	0.5	0.75	1	1.25	1.5	2
Charge	$29	$33.50	$38	$42.50	$47	$56

First draw a graph to show the relationship.

Using two points on the line, find the slope of the line.

$$m = \frac{56 - 38}{2 - 1}$$
$$= \frac{18}{1} \text{ or } 18$$

Then, substitute the slope and coordinates of one point in the general slope-intercept form and solve for b.

$$y = mx + b$$
$$38 = (18)(1) + b$$
$$20 = b$$

Thus, the equation which describes the relationship is $c = 18h + 20$.

exercises

Exploratory Solve each problem.

1. Inches of snowfall varies directly with inches of rainfall. Thirty-five inches of snow is about the same as 3.5 inches of rain. Write an equation to describe the relationship between inches of snowfall and inches of rainfall.

2. Twelve inches of snowfall is equivalent to how much rainfall?

3. Forty-eight inches of snowfall is equivalent to how much rainfall?

4. Eleven inches of rainfall is equivalent to how much snowfall?

5. Four and one-half inches of rainfall is equivalent to how much snowfall?

6. Frontier Auto Shop has a standard $12 shop charge for every job it takes. In addition, the mechanic working on the job charges $20 per hour. Write an equation to describe the relationship between time spent on a job and total charge for the job.

7. Cindy Baker worked 4 hours on a car. How much will Frontier Auto Shop charge?

8. Joshua Levy worked 2.5 hours on a car. How much will Frontier Auto Shop charge?

9. Frontier Auto Shop charged $47 for a job. How much time did the mechanic work?

10. Frontier Auto Shop charged $100 for a job. How much time did the mechanic work?

11. Light travels faster than sound. If you count the number of seconds between when you see lightning and when you hear it, you can estimate how far away it is. The distance d in kilometers between you and the lightning is estimated by $d = 0.32s - 0.4$ where s is the number of seconds. Complete the chart for estimating the distance.

Time (seconds)	2	3	4	5	10	15	20	25	30	40	50	60
Distance (kilometers)												

12. Crickets vary their number of chirps with the temperature. If you count the number of chirps in a minute, you can tell the temperature. The temperature t in degrees Celsius is estimated by $t = 0.2(n + 32)$ where n is the number of chirps in one minute. Complete the chart for estimating the temperature.

Chirps	50	60	70	80	90	100	110	120	130
Temperature (Celsius)									

Written   Write an equation to describe the relationship in each of the following.

1. The present population of Whitehall is 47,000. The population increases by 550 each year. What is the population y years from now?

2. A telephone company charges $12 per month plus 10¢ for each local call. What is the monthly bill if c local calls are made?

3. A ranger calculates there are 6,000 deer in a preserve. She also estimates that 75 more deer die than are born each year. How many deer will be in the preserve x years from now?

4. The RD Rug Company produced 600 oriental rugs its first year of business. Each year after that, production increased by 100. What was the total number of oriental rugs produced yearly after y years?

5. The ABC Car Rental Agency rents cars for $23 a day plus 18¢ a mile. How much does it cost to rent a car for a week and drive it t miles?

6. Emilio earns a flat salary of $150 per week for selling records. He receives an extra 30¢ for each record over 100 that he sells. How much will he make if he sells r records?

For each of the following, write an equation to describe the relationship. Then, use the equation to complete each table. Assume each relationship is linear.

7. Cost of bowling at Bingo's Bowling Lanes

Number of Games	1	2	3	4	5	6
Cost	$1.25	$2.50	$3.75			

8. Cost of Repair Work at Acme Auto Repair

Hours of Labor	1	2	3	4	6	8	12	15	20	25	30
Total Bill	$44	$56	$68	$80							

9. Cost of Long Distance Phone Call

Minutes	3	4	5	6	8	10	15	20	30	45	60
Cost	$1.38	$1.72	$2.06								

10. Number of Luncheon Specials sold at Open Hearth Restaurant

Number of Customers	20	30	40	50	75	100	150	200
Number of Luncheon Specials	10	16	22	28				

Memory/Parentheses

The memory feature of a calculator can be used to store intermediate results.

Many calculators have the following memory keys.

STO	Store	Stores the number displayed in the memory.
RCL	Recall	Retrieves the stored number from the memory to the display.

Example: Evaluate $\dfrac{6.1}{^-7.6 + 2.3}$.

ENTER: 7.6 [+/−] [+] 2.3 [=] [STO] 6.1 [÷] [RCL] [=]

DISPLAY: 7.6   −7.6   2.3 −5.3   6.1   −5.3 −1.1509434

The answer is -1.1509434.

The parentheses keys on a calculator can be used to change the order of operations.

Example: Evaluate $\dfrac{3(4b + a)}{9}$ if $a = 42$ and $b = 5$.

ENTER: 3 [×] [(] 4 [×] 5 [+] 42 [)] [÷] 9 [=]

DISPLAY: 3   4   5 20 42 62 186 9 20.666667

The answer is 20.666667

Exercises
Use either the memory keys or parentheses keys on your calculator to evaluate each of the following.

1. $(13 - 2) - (^-7 + 8)$

2. $(15 \div 2 + 3) \div 4$

3. $\left(\frac{1}{3} + 2\right)\left(6 - \frac{4}{5}\right)$

4. $3.4 - \left(\frac{9}{13} + 5 - \frac{4}{7}\right)^2$

5. $\dfrac{8(5) - 65 \div 7}{^-12 - (^-34)}$

6. $\left(\left(\frac{5}{8} - 3\right)^2 + \sqrt{17}\,\right)^2$

**Graphing Linear Inequalities
in Two Variables**

The graph of $y = -\frac{2}{3}x + \frac{5}{3}$ is a line which separates the coordinate plane into two regions.

The graph of $y > -\frac{2}{3}x + \frac{5}{3}$
is the region *above* the line.
In that region the value of
y is greater than $-\frac{2}{3}x + \frac{5}{3}$.

The graph of $y < -\frac{2}{3}x + \frac{5}{3}$
is the region *below* the line.
In that region the value of
y is less than $-\frac{2}{3}x + \frac{5}{3}$.

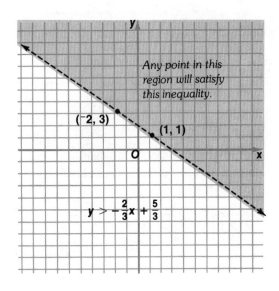

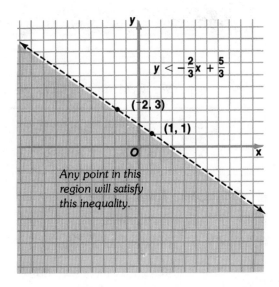

The line described by $y = -\frac{2}{3}x + \frac{5}{3}$ is called the *boundary* of each region. If the boundary is part of a graph, it is drawn as a solid line. If the boundary is *not* part of a graph, it is drawn as a broken line.

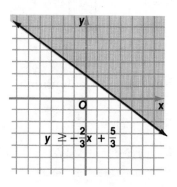

Note that $\geq$ tells you the boundary is included.

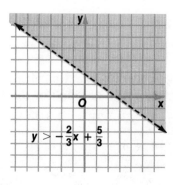

Note that $>$ tells you the boundary is *not* included.

1 Graph $2y - 5x \le 1$.

$2y - 5x \le 1$
$\qquad 2y \le 5x + 1$
$\qquad y \le \frac{5}{2}x + \frac{1}{2}$

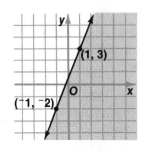

Note that the boundary is included.

$(1, 3)$
$(^-1, ^-2)$

2 Graph $y \ge |x| - 1$.

To determine which region should be shaded, test two points, one on each side of the graph. Substitute these values into the inequality.

Note that the boundary is included.

$(1, 0)$
$(^-1, 0)$
$(0, ^-1)$

$\qquad (1, 1)$ $\qquad\qquad\qquad\qquad (1, ^-1)$
$\quad y \ge |x| - 1$ $\qquad\qquad\quad\; y \ge |x| - 1$
$\quad 1 \ge |1| - 1$ $\qquad\qquad\quad\; ^-1 \ge |1| - 1$
$\quad 1 \ge 0$ _True_ $\qquad\qquad\quad\; ^-1 \ge 0$ _Not true_

exercises

Exploratory Name which points, $(0, 0)$, $(2, ^-3)$, or $(^-1, 2)$ lie on the graph of each inequality.

1. $x + 2y < 7$ 2. $3x - y \ge 2$ 3. $3x + 2y \le 0$ 4. $x + y \ge 7$
5. $4x + 2y \ge 7$ 6. $5x - y > 2$ 7. $y < 0$ 8. $4x \ge ^-12$

Written Draw the graph of each inequality.

1. $y < 3$ 2. $x < 1$ 3. $y > 5x - 3$ 4. $y \ge x - 7$
5. $y \le ^-3x + 1$ 6. $y < 2x + 3$ 7. $2x - 5y \ge 4$ 8. $2x + 5y \ge 3$
9. $y > \frac{1}{3}x + 7$ 10. $y > \frac{1}{2}x - 3$ 11. $x - 2y \le 2$ 12. $^-2x + 5 \le 3y$
13. $y \ge |x|$ 14. $y \ge |x| - 3$ 15. $|x| + y \ge 3$ 16. $y + |x| < 2$
17. $y < |x| + 2$ 18. $y < |x| - 2$ 19. $y > |2x|$ 20. $y \ge |3x|$
21. $|y| < x$ 22. $|y| \ge 2x$ 23. $|x| \le |y|$ 24. $|x| > |y|$

25. Graph all points to the right of $x = 4$.
26. Graph all points in the second quadrant between $x = ^-2$ and $x = ^-5$.
27. Graph all points in the first quadrant bounded by the two axes and $x + 2y = 4$.
28. Graph all points in the fourth quadrant bounded by the two axes and the lines $3x - y = 4$ and $x - y = 5$.

Challenge Draw the graph of each of the following.

1. $|x| + |y| = 1$ 2. $|x| - |y| = 1$ 3. $|x| + |y| \le 1$ 4. $|x| + |y| > 1$

ordered pairs (37)
quadrants (37)
x-axis (37)
y-axis (37)
origin (37)
coordinate plane (37)
coordinate (38)
graph (38)
relation (40)
domain (40)
range (40)
mapping (40)
function (41)

vertical line test (42)
linear equation (46)
standard form (46)
linear function (48)
slope (49)
y-intercept (51)
x-intercept (51)
slope-intercept form (53)
constant function (56)
identity function (56)
direct variation (56)
greatest integer function (57)
linear inequalities (64)

Chapter Summary

1. **Completeness Property of Real Numbers:** Each real number corresponds to exactly one point on a number line. Each point on a number line corresponds to exactly one real number. (37)
2. The graph of an open sentence is the graph of the solution set of that open sentence. (37)
3. Each point in a coordinate plane corresponds to exactly one ordered pair of numbers. Each ordered pair of numbers corresponds to exactly one point in a coordinate plane. (38)
4. **Definition of Relation, Domain, and Range:** A relation is a set of ordered pairs. The domain is the set of all first coordinates of the ordered pairs. The range is the set of all second coordinates of the ordered pairs. (40)
5. **Definition of Function:** A function is a relation in which each element of the domain is paired with exactly one element of the range. (41)
6. **Vertical Line Test for a Function:** If any vertical line drawn on the graph of a relation passes through no more than one point of that graph, then the relation is a function. (42)
7. An equation whose graph is a straight line is called a **linear equation** in two variables (46)
8. **Standard Form of a Linear Equation:** The standard form of a linear equation is $ax + by = c$ where a, b, and c are real numbers, and a and b are *not both* zero. (46)
9. **Definition of Linear Function:** A linear function can be defined by $f(x) = mx + b$ where m and b are real numbers. (48)

10. Definition of Slope: The slope, m, of a line passing through points (x_1, y_1) and (x_2, y_2) is given by the following equation.

$$m = \frac{y_1 - y_2}{x_1 - x_2} \quad (49)$$

11. The y-intercept is the value of a function when x is zero. The x-intercept is the value of a function when y is zero.   (51)
12. Slope-Intercept Form of a Linear Equation: The slope-intercept form of the equation of a line is $y = mx + b$. The slope is m and the y-intercept is b.   (53)
13. Definition of Constant Function: A linear function described by $y = b$ or $f(x) = b$ is called a constant function.   (56)
14. Definition of Identity Function: A linear function described by $y = x$ or $f(x) = x$ is called the identity function.   (56)
15. Definition of Direct Variation: A linear function described by $y = mx$ or $f(x) = mx$ where $m \neq 0$ is called a direct variation. The constant m is called the constant of variation or constant of proportionality.   (56)
16. The greatest integer of x is written $[x]$ and means the greatest integer not greater than x.   (57)
17. An inequality describes the set of points above or below the boundary line.   (64)

Chapter Review

2–1 **Graph the solution set for each open sentence on a number line.**

1. $b > {}^-1$
2. ${}^-5 \leq x < 0$
3. $n > \frac{1}{2}$ or $n \leq {}^-3$
4. $7r - 5 = 3r - 5$
5. $|3p + 2| - 6 = 7$
6. $9y + 4.3 = 2.5$
7. $6(1 - x) - 4(2 - x) \leq x + 7$
8. $|q + 7| < 5$

Graph each ordered pair on the same coordinate axes.

9. $(5, 2)$
10. $({}^-1, 4)$
11. $(0, {}^-3)$

2–2 **State the domain and range of each relation. Then state if the relation is a function.**

12. $\{(4.5, 1), ({}^-4.5, 2), (4.5, 3), ({}^-3.5, 4)\}$
13. $\{(1, 4.5), (2, {}^-4.5), (3, 4.5), (4, {}^-3.5), (5, {}^-3.5)\}$
14. $\{(13, {}^-8), (14, {}^-9), (15, {}^-9), (16, {}^-8)\}$

Use the vertical line test to determine if each relation is a function.

15.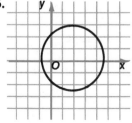
16.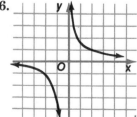
17.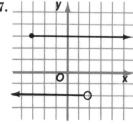

Given $f(x) = 2x^3 + 4x^2 + 4x + 1$, find each value.

18. $f(0)$ **19.** $f(^-3)$ **20.** $f(a)$

2–3   State whether each equation is a linear equation.

21. $x^2 + y^2 = 4$ **22.** $xy = 12$
23. $y = 5$ **24.** $x + y = 9$

Graph each equation.

25. $y = \frac{1}{3}x$ **26.** $y = 3x$
27. $y = 2x - 1$ **28.** $3y = 2x + 1$

2–4   Find the slope, y-intercept, and x-intercept of the graph of each of the following.

29. $3x + 7y = 2$ **30.** $4x - 3y = 7$
31. $\frac{1}{3}x - \frac{2}{3}y = 5$ **32.** $\frac{1}{2}x + \frac{3}{4}y = 1$

Determine the slope of the line passing through each pair of points.

33. $(5, 1)$ and $(3, 7)$ **34.** $(^-4, 2)$ and $(1, 0)$ **35.** $(^-3, ^-2)$ and $(0, 4)$

A line has slope $\frac{2}{3}$. For each pair of points on the line, find the missing coordinate.

36. $(0, 6)$ and $(^-6, y)$ **37.** $(^-9, 0)$ and $(x, 10)$

Graph the line that passes through the given point and has the given slope.

38. $(^-3, 2)$, $m = 3$ **39.** $(3, 4)$, $m = \frac{1}{4}$ **40.** $(2, ^-1)$, $m = -\frac{5}{3}$

2–5   Find the slope-intercept form of the equation of the line satisfying each of the following conditions.

41. slope 5 and y-intercept $^-7$ **42.** slope $\frac{2}{3}$ and passes through $(1, ^-4)$
43. passes through $(^-3, 0)$ and $(4, ^-6)$ **44.** x-intercept $^-2$ and y-intercept 5

Find the standard form of the equation of the line satisfying each of the following conditions.

45. slope 4 and passes through $(5, ^-2)$ **46.** slope $-\frac{3}{2}$ and y-intercept 7
47. x-intercept 2 and y-intercept $^-6$ **48.** passes through $(5, 3)$ and $(^-2, 1)$

2–6   Graph each function.

49. $g(x) = |^-x|$ **50.** $q(x) = |x - 3|$ **51.** $f(x) = |2x| - 1$
52. $p(x) = [^-x]$ **53.** $f(x) = ^-[x]$ **54.** $f(x) = [3x]$

2–7   **55.** The Lewis Parcel Service charges $2.50 per pound for the first three pounds and $1.00 for each pound thereafter. Write an equation to find the cost of sending a package that weighs p pounds. Assume $p \geq 3$.
        56. Use the equation in exercise 55 to find the cost of sending packages which weigh 6 lb, 8 lb, 15 lb, and 42 lb.

2–8   Graph each inequality.

57. $3x + 4y < 9$ **58.** $2x - 5y > 4$
59. $y \geq |x| + 5$ **60.** $y \leq |x + 5|$

Chapter Test

Graph the solution set for each open sentence on a number line.

1. $^-2r - 3(r - 2) = r - 6$

2. $2(m - 4) + 3(m + 2) = 8$

3. $1 + 3(x - 2) \geq ^-2(2x - 1)$

4. $5(3t + 2) < 4(3t + 4)$

5. $\left| 5p + 6 \right| - p = 2$

6. $\left| 4a + 2 \right| + 5 > 5$

7. The points $(^-6, 4)$, $(^-4, 6)$, and $(^-2, 4)$ are three vertices of a rectangle. Graph them. Then, find the fourth vertex.

State the domain and range of each relation. Then state if the relation is a function.

8. $\{(1, 2), (7, 2), (9, ^-3), (2, 7)\}$

9. $\{(1.4, 1.4), (1.4, 1.5)\}$

10. $\{(3, ^-2), (5, 4), (7, ^-2)\}$
    yes

Use the vertical line test to determine if each relation is a function.

11.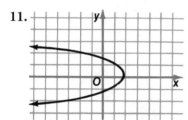

12.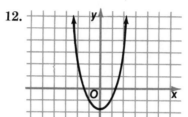

13.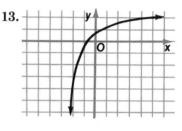

Given $f(x) = 2x^3 + 3x^2 - 5x - 4$, **find each value.**

14. $f(^-3)$

15. $f(1)$

16. $f(c)$

Graph each equation or inequality.

17. $y = \dfrac{12}{5}x$

18. $y = 7$

19. $y = ^-7x + 3$

20. $y = 3x - \dfrac{1}{2}$

21. $5x + 2y = 12$

22. $3y - 3x = 10$

23. $5y + 3x - 10 = 0$

24. $4x + 12y = ^-15$

25. $2x + 3y > 7$

26. $4x + 6y \leq 9$

27. $f(x) = \left| x + 2 \right|$

28. $f(x) = ^-[x]$

29. $y < 3\left| x \right| - 1$

30. $y \geq \left| 3x - 1 \right|$

31. $y = \left| 4x + 3 \right| + 2$

32. $y = 2[x] - 7$

Determine the slope of the line passing through each pair of points.

33. $(7, 4)$ and $(^-2, 5)$

34. $(0, 6)$ and $(1, ^-1)$

Find the slope-intercept form of the equation of the line satisfying each of the following conditions.

35. slope 4 and passes through $\left(\dfrac{2}{3}, \dfrac{2}{3} \right)$

36. passes through $(0, 7)$ and $(5, 2)$

Find the standard form of the equation of the line satisfying each of the following conditions.

37. slope $\dfrac{1}{3}$ and y-intercept 7

38. x-intercept $^-6$ and y-intercept $^-6$

A line has a slope $-\dfrac{2}{5}$. **For each pair of points on the line, find the missing coordinate.**

39. $(5, 1)$ and $(15, y)$

40. $(x, 2)$ and $(^-5, 5)$

41. As a waiter, Ryan earns an average of $28.00 a day in tips. If he also earns $3.00 per hour, write an equation to determine the total amount he earns in an h hour day.

chapter
3 Systems of Equations and Inequalities

One of the most practical applications of mathematics to business is the branch of mathematics called linear programming. A company can use it to schedule production to meet sales requirements at a minimum cost to the company. Linear programming depends on the graphs of linear equations and inequalities.

3-1 Parallel and Perpendicular Lines

The graphs of $y = -\frac{3}{4}x - 3$, $y = -\frac{3}{4}x$, and $y = -\frac{3}{4}x + 3$ are straight lines that have the same slope. They are called **parallel lines**.

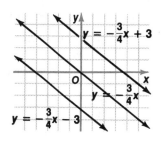

> **In a plane, lines with the same slope are called parallel lines. Also, vertical lines are parallel.**

Definition of Parallel Lines

examples

1 **Find the slope of a line *parallel* to the line whose equation is $3y - 5x = 15$.**

Parallel lines have the same slope.

Find the slope of the line whose equation is $3y - 5x = 15$. To do so, write the equation in slope-intercept form. $y = mx + b$

$$3y - 5x = 15$$
$$3y = 5x + 15$$
$$y = \frac{5}{3}x + 5$$

The slope of any line parallel to the given line is $\frac{5}{3}$.

2 **Find an equation of the line that passes through (4, 6) and is *parallel* to the line whose equation is $y = \frac{2}{3}x + 5$.**

First, find the slope.

$y = \frac{2}{3}x + 5$ is in slope-intercept form.

The slope is $\frac{2}{3}$.

Next use (4, 6) and the slope $\frac{2}{3}$ to find the *y*-intercept.

$$y = mx + b$$
$$6 = \left(\frac{2}{3}\right)(4) + b \qquad \textit{Substitution.}$$
$$6 = \frac{8}{3} + b$$
$$\frac{10}{3} = b \qquad \textit{The y-intercept is } \frac{10}{3}.$$

An equation of the line is $y = \frac{2}{3}x + \frac{10}{3}$.

The graphs of $y = \frac{5}{3}x + 2$ and $y = -\frac{3}{5}x + 6$ are straight lines that are perpendicular. Notice how their slopes are related.

$$\left(\frac{5}{3}\right)\left(-\frac{3}{5}\right) = {}^-1$$

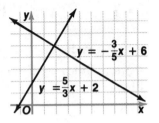

The product of their slopes is $^-1$. This is true for any two nonvertical perpendicular lines.

Two nonvertical lines are perpendicular if and only if the product of their slopes is $^-1$. Any vertical line is perpendicular to any horizontal line.	*Definition of Perpendicular Lines*

examples

3 **Find the slope of a line perpendicular to the line whose equation is $3y - x = 2$.**

$3y - x = 2$
$^-x + 3y = 2$ *This equation is in standard form.*

Recall that the slope of a line whose equation is in standard form is $-\frac{a}{b}$.

The slope of the given line is $-\left(\frac{-1}{3}\right)$ or $\frac{1}{3}$.

$\frac{1}{3} \cdot m = {}^-1$ *Let m stand for the slope of the perpendicular line.*

$m = {}^-3$ The slope of any line perpendicular to the given line is $^-3$.

4 **Find an equation of the line that passes through (4, 6) and is perpendicular to the line whose equation is $y = \frac{2}{3}x + 5$.**

The slope of the given line is $\frac{2}{3}$. $y = \frac{2}{3}x + 5$ is in slope-intercept form.

$\frac{2}{3} \cdot m = {}^-1$ *Let m stand for the slope of the perpendicular line.*

$m = -\frac{3}{2}$

The slope of the perpendicular line is $-\frac{3}{2}$.

$y = mx + b$ *Let b stand for the y-intercept of the perpendicular line.*

$6 = \left(-\frac{3}{2}\right)(4) + b$ *The line passes through (4, 6) and has slope $-\frac{3}{2}$.*

$12 = b$ *The y-intercept is 12.*

An equation of the line is $y = -\frac{3}{2}x + 12$.   *This could be written $3x + 2y = 24$.*

Exploratory Find the slope of a line that is parallel to each line whose equation is given.

1. $y = 4x + 2$

2. $y = 5 - 2x$

3. $2y = 3x - 8$

4. $6y - 5x = 0$

5. $\frac{1}{3}x - \frac{3}{8}y = 11$

6. $x = 4y + 7$

Find the slope of a line that is perpendicular to each line whose equation is given.

7. $y = 2x + 4$

8. $y = 2 - 5x$

9. $3y = 8x - 2$

10. $5y - 6x = 0$

11. $3x - 8y = 11$

12. $4x = 7y + 1$

Written State whether the graphs of the following equations are parallel, perpendicular or neither.

1. $x + y = 5$
   $x + y = {}^-10$

2. $x + y = 5$
   $x - y = 5$

3. $y = 2x$
   $y = 2x - 4$

4. $2y + 3x = 5$
   $3y - 2x = 5$

5. $\frac{1}{3}x + \frac{2}{3}y = \frac{3}{5}$
   $2x + 4y = 7$

6. $2y + 3x = 5$
   $3y + 3x = 5$

7. $3x - 8y = 11$
   $3x - 6y = 10$

8. $\frac{1}{2}x + \frac{1}{3}y = 2$

   $2x - 3y = 4$

9. $7x - 5y = 2$

   $\frac{1}{7}x - \frac{1}{5}y = 2$

Find an equation of the line that passes through each given point and is parallel to the line with the given equation.

10. $(4, 2)$; $y = 2x - 4$

11. $(3, 1)$; $y = \frac{1}{3}x + 6$

12. $\left(\frac{1}{2}, \frac{1}{3}\right)$; $x + 2y = 5$

13. $(0, 0)$; $3x - y = 4$

14. $(4, {}^-2)$; $\frac{x}{3} - \frac{y}{5} = 2$

15. $\left(\frac{1}{2}, \frac{1}{3}\right)$; $x + y = 4$

16. $({}^-3, {}^-1)$; $y + x = 6$

17. $(7, {}^-1)$; $2y - 3x = 1$

18. $(3, 7)$; $\frac{2}{3}x = \frac{1}{2}y$

Find an equation of the line that passes through each given point and is perpendicular to the line with the given equation.

19. $({}^-2, 0)$; $y = {}^-3x + 7$

20. $({}^-3, 4)$; $y = \frac{2}{3}x + 1$

21. $(2, 5)$; $3x + 5y = 7$

22. $(3, 6)$; $4x - y = 2$

23. $(0, {}^-4)$; $6x - 3y = 5$

24. $(5, {}^-3)$; $4x + 7y = 11$

25. $(12, 6)$; $\frac{3}{4}x + \frac{1}{2}y = 2$

26. $({}^-10, 3)$; $\frac{2}{3}x + y = 6$

27. $(6, {}^-5)$; $3x - \frac{1}{5}y = 3$

Find the value of a for which the graph of the first equation is perpendicular to the graph of the second equation.

28. $y = ax - 5$; $2y = 3x$

29. $y = ax + 2$; $3y - 4x = 7$

30. $y = \frac{a}{3}x - 6$; $4x + 2y = 6$

31. $3y + ax = 8$; $y = \frac{3}{4}x + 2$

32. Show that $(1, 3)$, $(4, 1)$, and $(5, 9)$ are vertices of a right triangle.

33. Show that $({}^-6, 5)$, $({}^-2, 7)$, $(5, 3)$ and $(1, 1)$ are vertices of a parallelogram.

34. Write a computer program to find the equation of a line passing through (p, q) and parallel to a line whose equation is $ax + by = c$.

35. Write a computer program to find the equation of a line passing through (p, q) and perpendicular to a line whose equation is $ax + by = c$.

3–2　Solving Systems of Equations Graphically

The cost of renting a car from ACE is $18 per day plus 30¢ per mile driven. The cost of renting a similar car from QUALITY is $20 per day plus 25¢ per mile driven. Caroline needs to rent a car for one day. Should she rent from ACE or QUALITY?

Let d = cost of renting car for one day.
Let m = number of miles driven in one day.

You can write the following equations.

$d = 18 + 0.30m$ 　　*Cost of renting car from ACE for one day*

$d = 20 + 0.25m$ 　　*Cost of renting car from QUALITY for one day*

Graphing these two equations shows how the costs compare. The graphs show that the QUALITY car costs more if less than 40 miles are driven. The QUALITY and ACE cars cost the same if 40 miles are driven. The ACE car costs more if more than 40 miles are driven.

Each point on a line satisfies the equation of the line. Since (40, 30) is on both lines graphed above, it satisfies both equations.

Together the equations $d = 18 + 0.30m$ and $d = 20 + 0.25m$ are called a **system of equations.** The solution of the system is (40, 30).

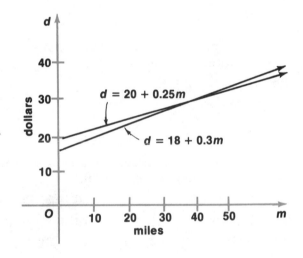

---

example

1　**Solve the system of equations by graphing.**

$3x - y = 1$
$2x + y = 4$

The slope-intercept form of $3x - y = 1$ is $y = 3x - 1$.
The slope-intercept form of $2x + y = 4$ is $y = -2x + 4$.
The two lines have different slopes. The graphs of the equations are intersecting lines.

The solution of the system is (1, 2).

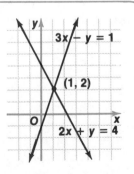

A system of equations that has *one* ordered pair as its solution is said to be **consistent** and **independent**. However, not all systems have one ordered pair as the solution.

2 **Solve the system of equations by graphing.**

$y = {}^-3x - 2$
$y = {}^-3x + 3$

Both lines have the same slope but different y-intercepts. The graphs of the equations are parallel lines. Since they do not intersect, there is *no solution* to this system of equations. Such a system is said to be **inconsistent.**

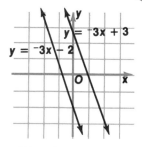

The solution set is empty, $\emptyset$.

3 **Solve the system of equations by graphing.**

$2y + 3x = 6$
$4y + 6x = 12$

The slope-intercept form of $2y + 3x = 6$ is $y = -\dfrac{3}{2}x + 3$.

The slope-intercept form of $4y + 6x = 12$ is $y = -\dfrac{3}{2}x + 3$.

Both lines have the same slope and the same y-intercept. The graphs of the equations are the same line. Any ordered pair on the graph satisfies both equations. So, there is an *infinite number* of solutions to this system of equations. Such a system is said to be **consistent** and **dependent**.

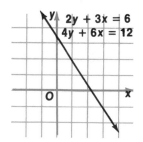

The solution set is $\{(x, y) \mid 2x + 3y = 6\}$.

The following chart gives a summary of the possibilities for the graphs of two linear equations in two variables.

Graphs of Equations	Slopes of Lines	Name of System of Equations
lines intersect	different slopes	consistent and independent
lines parallel	same slope, different intercepts	inconsistent
lines coincide	same slope, same intercepts	consistent and dependent

important

exercises

Exploratory State the ordered pair which is the intersection of each pair of lines.

1. a, b
2. a, e
3. a, d
4. b, c
5. c, d
6. e, d
7. b, f
8. f, d

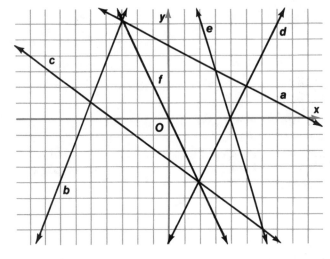

Written Graph each system of equations and state its solution. Then state whether the system is *consistent and independent, consistent and dependent,* or *inconsistent.*

1. $x + y = 4$
   $2x + 3y = 9$

2. $x + y = 6$
   $x - y = 2$

3. $x + y = 6$
   $3x + 3y = 3$

4. $x + 1 = y$
   $2x - 2y = 8$

5. $x + 2y = 5$
   $3x - 15 = {}^-6y$

6. $2x + 4y = 8$
   $x + 2y = 4$

7. $y = {}^-3x$
   $6y - x = {}^-38$

8. $\frac{1}{2}x + \frac{1}{3}y = 2$
   $x - y = {}^-1$

9. $\frac{3}{4}x - y = 0$
   $\frac{y}{3} + \frac{x}{2} = 6$

10. $x + y = 1$
    $3x + 5y = 7$

11. $x + 5y = 10$
    $x + 5y = 15$

12. $3x - 8y = 4$
    $6x - 42 = 16y$

13. $x + y = {}^-6$
    $2x - y = 2$

14. $3x + 6 = 7y$
    $x + 2y = 11$

15. $2x + 3y = 5$
    ${}^-6x - 9y = {}^-15$

16. $\frac{2}{3}x = \frac{5}{3}y$
    $2x - 5y = 0$

17. $y = \frac{x}{2}$
    $2y = x + 4$

18. $9x + 8y = 8$
    $\frac{3}{4}x + \frac{2}{3}y = 8$

19. $2x + 3y = {}^-4$
    ${}^-3x + y = {}^-5$

20. ${}^-2x + 5y = {}^-14$
    $x - y = 1$

21. $9x - 5 = 7y$
    $4\frac{1}{2}x - 3\frac{1}{2}y = 2\frac{1}{2}$

22. Write an equation of the line passing through $(5, {}^-1)$ that is inconsistent with $5x - 3y = 2$.

23. Find a and b so that $ax + 5y = b$ and $6x + 10y = 16$ will be consistent and dependent equations.

Write a system of equations for each problem and solve by graphing.

24. George bought 7 quarts of cleaning fluid: x quarts at $3.00 per quart and y quarts at $2.00 per quart. Find x and y if the total cost was $16.00.

25. Kenneth mixes r cups of cashews with s cups of peanuts. This yields 12 cups of a mixture having one part cashews to three parts peanuts. Find r and s.

Jeanne Cezanne is an archeologist. Her specific job is identifying ancient documents, paintings, and art. Often, she must translate writings from a language that has not been used for several centuries. In this work she not only must understand the language, but the numeration system as well.

One ancient Greek system used the symbols shown below for powers of ten.

symbol	I	△	H	X	M
word	ena	deka	heka	chilioi	mynioi
meaning	1	10	100	1000	10,000

The system also had a unique way of showing five times each of the powers.

	meant	5
	meant	5 × 10 or 50
	meant	5 × 100 or 500

This pattern was probably one of the first attempts to express numbers concisely. Follow the same pattern to find Greek numerals for 5000 and 50,000.

Exercises   Find the meaning for each of the following numerals.

1. ⌈||

2. ⌐△||

3. ⌐H ⌐△ |||

4. X ⌐△ ||

5. ⌐X ⌐△ ⌈

6. XX△

7. MXH△||

8. XX⌐△△

3-3   Solving Systems of Equations Algebraically

Usually a system of equations is easier to solve by algebraic methods rather than by graphing. Two such methods are the **substitution method** and the **elimination method**.

examples

1 **Use the substitution method to solve the system of equations.**

$y = 3x - 1$
$3x + 2y = 16$

The first equation says that y is equal to $3x - 1$. Therefore, $3x - 1$ can be *substituted* for y in the second equation.

$$3x + 2y = 16$$
$$3x + 2(3x - 1) = 16 \qquad \text{Substitute } 3x - 1 \text{ for } y.$$
$$3x + 6x - 2 = 16 \qquad \text{The resulting equation has only one}$$
$$9x - 2 = 16 \qquad \text{variable now, x.}$$
$$9x = 18$$
$$x = 2$$

Now find y by substituting 2 for x in the equation $y = 3x - 1$.

$$y = 3x - 1$$
$$y = 3(2) - 1 \qquad \text{Substitute 2 for x.}$$
$$y = 5$$

The solution is $(2, 5)$

2 **Use the elimination method to solve the system of equations.**

$4x + 2y = {}^-8$
$x - 2y = {}^-7$

Add the second equation to the first equation.

$$\begin{array}{l} 4x + 2y = {}^-8 \qquad \text{Add.}\\ \underline{x - 2y = {}^-7} \\ 5x \quad\ \ = {}^-15 \qquad \text{The variable } y \text{ is eliminated.}\\ \quad\ x = {}^-3 \qquad \text{Solve for x.} \end{array}$$

To find y, substitute $^-3$ for x in $x - 2y = {}^-7$.

$$x - 2y = {}^-7$$
$$({}^-3) - 2y = {}^-7 \qquad \text{Substitute } ^-3 \text{ for x.}$$
$${}^-2y = {}^-4$$
$$y = 2$$

The solution is $({}^-3, 2)$.

3   Use the elimination method to solve the system of equations.

$2x + 3y = 2$
$3x - 4y = {}^-14$

Adding the two equations does *not* eliminate either of the variables. However, if the first equation is multiplied by 4 and the second equation is multiplied by 3, the variable y can be eliminated by addition.

$2x + 3y = 2$ Multiply by 4. $8x + 12y = 8$

$3x - 4y = {}^-14$ Multiply by 3. $9x - 12y = {}^-42$

Now add to eliminate y. Then solve for x.

$$8x + 12y = 8$$
$$\underline{9x - 12y = {}^-42} \quad \textit{Add.}$$
$$17x \qquad = {}^-34 \quad \textit{The variable y is eliminated.}$$
$$x \qquad = {}^-2 \quad \textit{Solve for x.}$$

Finally, substitute $^-2$ for x and solve for y. Use the original first equation.

$$2x + 3y = 2$$
$$2(^-2) + 3y = 2$$
$$^-4 + 3y = 2$$
$$3y = 6$$
$$y = 2$$

The solution is $(^-2, 2)$.

exercises

Exploratory   For each system, state the multipliers you would use to eliminate each of the variables by addition.

1. $2x + 3y = 7$
   $3x - 4y = 2$

2. $x - y = 1$
   $3x - y = 3$

3. $6x - 4y = 20$
   $4x + y = 6$

4. $x + 2y = 3$
   $5x - 3y = 2$

5. $3x + 4y = 6$
   $2x + 5y = 11$

6. $x + 8y = 12$
   $^-3x + 7y = {}^-5$

7. $3x + 4y = 7$
   $4x - 3y = 1$

8. $2x - 3y = 0$
   $6x + 5y = 7$

9. $x + y = 6$
   $^-2x + y = {}^-3$

10. $3x - 5y = {}^-13$
    $4x + 3y = 2$

Written Solve each system of equations by the substitution method.

1. $y = 3x$
   $x + 2y = {}^-21$

2. $6x - 4y = {}^-6$
   $3x + y = 3$

3. $2x + 2y = 4$
   $x - 2y = 0$

4. $2m + n = 1$
   $m - n = 8$

5. $x - 2y = 5$
   $3x - 5y = 8$

6. $3x + 4y = {}^-7$
   $2x + y = {}^-3$

Solve each system of equations by the elimination method.

7. $4x + y = 9$
   $3x - 2y = 4$

8. $x - y = 4$
   $x + 2y = 1$

9. $2x + y = 0$
   $5x + 3y = 1$

10. $3x + 2y = 9$
    $2x - 3y = 19$

11. $4x - 3y = {}^-4$
    $3x - 2y = {}^-4$

12. $8x + 3y = 4$
    $4x - 9y = {}^-5$

Solve each system of equations. (Use either method.)

13. $3x + 2y = 40$
    $x - 7y = {}^-2$

14. $2x + 3y = 8$
    $x - y = 2$

15. $x + y = 6$
    $x - y = 4.5$

16. $2x - y = 36$
    $3x - \frac{1}{2}y = 26$

17. $3y - 2x = 4$
    $\frac{1}{6}(3y - 4x) = 1$

18. $3x + \frac{1}{3}y = 10$
    $2x - 5 = \frac{1}{3}y$

19. $5m + 2n = {}^-8$
    $4m + 3n = 2$

20. $2a + 2b = {}^-3$
    $5a + 3b = 6$

21. $3x - 5y = {}^-13$
    $4x + 3y = 2$

22. ${}^-9x - 6y = {}^-15$
    $13x + 7y = 18\frac{1}{3}$

23. $3m + 7n = 5$
    $2m = {}^-7 - 3n$

24. $2y - 3x = 0$
    $x - y + 2 = 0$

25. $\frac{2x + y}{3} = 15$
    $\frac{3x - y}{5} = 1$

26. $\frac{1}{4}x + y = \frac{7}{2}$
    $\frac{1}{2}x - \frac{1}{4}y = 1$

27. $\frac{x}{2} - \frac{2y}{3} = 2\frac{1}{3}$
    $\frac{3x}{2} + 2y = {}^-25$

28. $2x + 3y - 8 = 0$
    $3x + 2y - 17 = 0$

29. $0.2a = 0.3b$
    $0.4a - 0.2b = 0.2$

30. $\frac{1}{3}x + \frac{1}{3}y = 5$
    $\frac{1}{6}x - \frac{1}{9}y = 0$

31. $\frac{1}{3}x + 5 = \frac{2}{3}y$
    $\frac{1}{2}x + \frac{1}{3}y = \frac{1}{2}$

32. $\frac{a}{2} + \frac{b}{3} = 4$
    $\frac{2a}{3} + \frac{3b}{2} = \frac{35}{3}$

33. $\frac{m}{3} + \frac{n}{5} = {}^-\frac{1}{5}$
    $\frac{2m}{3} - \frac{3n}{4} = {}^-5$

34. $34x - 63y = {}^-1063$
    $14x + 43y = 2251$

35. $108x + 537y = {}^-1395$
    ${}^-214x - 321y = 535$

36. $93a + 17b = {}^-157.1$
    $74a - 75b = {}^-4392$

Solve each problem.

37. The sum of two numbers is 42. Their difference is 12. What are the numbers?

38. The sum of Kari's age and her mother's age is 52. Kari's mother is 20 years older than Kari. How old is each?

39. The perimeter of a rectangle is 86 cm. Twice the width exceeds the length by 2 cm. Find the dimensions of the rectangle.

40. Write a computer program to solve the system $ax + by = c$ and $dx + ey = f$. Input the value of a, b, c, d, e, and f. Print out the system and its solution, if it exists.

3–4   Solving Systems of Equations in Three Variables

The equation $2x + 3y + z = 10$ is an equation in three variables, $x, y,$ and z. The solution to such an equation is an ordered triple.

The system below has three equations and three variables.

$$2x + 3y + z = 10$$
$$4x + 2y - z = 13$$
$$x + y + z = 5$$

Each equation is satisfied when x is 3, y is 1, and z is 1.

$$2(3) + 3(1) + (1) = 6 + 3 + 1 = 10$$
$$4(3) + 2(1) - (1) = 12 + 2 - 1 = 13$$
$$(3) + (1) + (1) = 3 + 1 + 1 = 5$$

Thus, the solution to this system is the ordered triple (3, 1, 1).

Systems of equations in three variables are solved using the same methods as when solving systems of equations in two variables.

---

example

1   **Solve the following system of equations.**

$$2x + y + z = 11$$
$$3y - z = {}^-1$$
$$2z = 8$$

Solve the third equation for z.

$$2z = 8$$
$$z = 4$$

Substitute 4 for z in the second equation.

$$3y - (4) = {}^-1$$
$$3y = 3$$
$$y = 1$$

Substitute 4 for z and 1 for y in the first equation.

$$2x + (1) + (4) = 11$$
$$2x = 6$$
$$x = 3$$

The solution is (3, 1, 4).

Check: First equation $2(3) + 1 + 4 = 11$
Second equation $3(1) - 4 = {}^-1$
Third equation $2(4) = 8$

2 **Solve the following system of equations.**

$2x + 3y + 2z = 14$
$4x + 2y - z = 15$
$x + y + 3z = 8$

Use elimination to make a system of two equations in two variables.

$2x + 3y + 2z = 14$
$4x + 2y - z = 15$ **Multiply by 2.**

$2x + 3y + 2z = 14$
$8x + 4y - 2z = 30$
$10x + 7y \quad\quad = 44$ *Add to eliminate z.*

$4x + 2y - z = 15$
$x + y + 3z = 8$ **Multiply by 3.**

$12x + 6y - 3z = 45$
$x + y + 3z = 8$
$13x + 7y \quad\quad = 53$ *Add to eliminate z.*

The result is two equations with the same two variables.

$$10x + 7y = 44$$
$$13x + 7y = 53$$

Solve this system for x and y.

$10x + 7y = 44$
$13x + 7y = 53$ **Multiply by ⁻1.**

$^-10x - 7y = ^-44$
$13x + 7y = \quad 53$ *Add to eliminate y.*
$3x \quad\quad = \quad 9$
$x \quad\quad = \quad 3$

Now substitute 3 for x in $10x + 7y = 44$ to find y.

$10(3) + 7y = 44$ *Substitute 3 for x.*
$30 + 7y = 44$
$7y = 14$
$y = 2$

Then substitute the values for x and y in one of the original equations. Solve the equation for z.

$x + y + 3z = 8$
$(3) + (2) + 3z = 8$
$3z = 3$
$z = 1$

The solution is (3, 2, 1).

exercises

Exploratory A possible solution for each system of equations is given in color. Check to see if it is the correct solution.

1. $x + y + z = 6$ $(2, 2, 2)$
$x - 3y + 2z = 1$
$2x - y + 2z = 0$

2. $2x + 3y - z = 0$ $(0, 0, 0)$
$x + 2y + z = 0$
$x - y + z = 0$

3. $x + y + z = 3$ $(3, ^-2, 2)$
$x - z = 1$
$y - z = ^-4$

4. $4x + y - 2z = 0$ $(3, 0, 6)$
$^-2x + y + z = 0$
$x - 2y = 0$

5. $3x + 2y + z = 5$ $(8, ^-11, 3)$
$2x + y - z = 2$
$x + y + z = 0$

6. $x + y = ^-6$ $(^-4, ^-2, 2)$
$x + z = ^-2$
$y + z = 2$

Written Solve each system of equations.

1. $a - 2b + c = {}^-9$
   $2b + 3c = 16$
   $4b = 8$

2. $x + y + z = {}^-1$
   $2x + y = 2$
   ${}^-3x = {}^-9$

3. $2x + 4y - z = {}^-3$
   $y + z = 4$
   $2y = {}^-2$

4. $x + y - z = {}^-1$
   $x + y + z = 3$
   $3x - 2y - z = {}^-4$

5. $a + b + c = 0$
   $2a + b - c = 2$
   $2a + 2b + c = 5$

6. $x + y + z = 15$
   $x + z = 12$
   $y + z = 10$

7. $x - 2y + z = 3$
   $2x + y - 2z = 31$
   ${}^-x + 2y + 3z = {}^-23$

8. $x + y + z = 4$
   $x - y + z = 0$
   $x - y - z = {}^-2$

9. $a + b - 2c = 4$
   $2a + b + 2c = 0$
   $a - 3b - 4c = {}^-2$

10. $2x + 3y + z = 7$
    $x + y + z = 4$
    $3x + 4y - 2z = 6$

11. $x + y + z = {}^-1$
    $2x - y + z = 19$
    $3x - 2y - 4z = 16$

12. $2x - y + 4z = 7$
    $x - 3y + z = {}^-2$
    $3x - 2y + 2z = {}^-2$

13. $x + 2y - 3z = 10$
    ${}^-4x + y - z = {}^-10$
    $3x - 7y + 2z = 5$

14. $x + 8y + 2z = {}^-24$
    $3x + y + 7z = {}^-3$
    $4x - 3y + 6z = 9$

15. $2a + b + c = 7$
    $12a - 2b - 2c = 2$
    $\frac{2a}{3} - b + \frac{c}{3} = -\frac{1}{3}$

Solve each problem.

16. The sum of three numbers is 20. The first number is the sum of the second and the third, and the third number is three times the first. Find the numbers.

17. The sum of three numbers is 16. One of the numbers is the sum of the other two numbers. It is also four times the difference of the other two numbers. Find the numbers.

18. The perimeter of a triangle is 18 feet. The longest side is twice as long as the shortest side. The length of the remaining side is the average of the lengths of the longest and shortest sides. Find the lengths of the three sides.

19. Books cost x dollars each, records cost y dollars each, and tapes cost z dollars each. Bart orders 3 books, 1 record, and 2 tapes for $43. Bebe orders 1 book, 1 record, and 2 tapes for $31. Deidre orders 1 book, 3 records, and 1 tape for $36. Find x, y, and z.

Challenge Solve the system of equations.

$$w + x + y + z = 2$$
$$2w - x - y + 2z = 7$$
$$2w + 3x + 2y - z = {}^-2$$
$$3w - 2x - y - 3z = {}^-2$$

Skills Review Solve each inequality.

1. $3x - 5 > 2x + 1$

2. $3x + 13 > 3 - 2x$

3. $2(a + 4) \geq 8$

4. $3(b + 1) - b \geq 2b$

5. $7x > 3(1 + 2x)$

6. $5(x - 1) \leq 3(3 + x)$

7. $\frac{x - 3}{5} < \frac{2}{5}$

8. $\frac{n + 5}{3} < \frac{n - 1}{6}$

9. $\frac{x - 2}{3} + \frac{x + 3}{3} \geq 3$

10. $\frac{3}{2}x - 12 < 0$

11. $\frac{x - 4}{5} > \frac{x}{10} + 4$

12. $\frac{t}{3} + 5 < \frac{t}{6} - 1$

3-5   Solving Systems of Equations Using Matrices

A rectangular arrangement of terms in rows and columns enclosed in brackets or large parentheses is called a **matrix**. The following matrix has two rows and four columns.

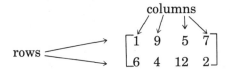

A system of equations may be represented by a matrix.

System of Equations	Matrix

$$3x + 4y - 2z = 5$$
$$2x + y - z = 1$$
$$^-x - y - 2z = ^-9$$

$$\begin{bmatrix} 3 & 4 & ^-2 & 5 \\ 2 & 1 & ^-1 & 1 \\ ^-1 & ^-1 & ^-2 & ^-9 \end{bmatrix}$$

Each row in the matrix corresponds to an equation. Each column corresponds to the coefficient of a given variable or the constant term.

The system of equations can be solved by using the matrix rather than the equations themselves. Each change of the matrix represents a corresponding change of the system.

$$\begin{bmatrix} 3 & 4 & ^-2 & 5 \\ ^-4 & ^-2 & 2 & ^-2 \\ ^-1 & ^-1 & ^-2 & ^-9 \end{bmatrix}$$ *Multiply Row 2 by ⁻2.*

$$\begin{bmatrix} ^-1 & 2 & 0 & 3 \\ ^-5 & ^-3 & 0 & ^-11 \\ ^-1 & ^-1 & ^-2 & ^-9 \end{bmatrix}$$ *Replace Row 1 by sum of Row 1 and Row 2.*
Replace Row 2 by sum of Row 2 and Row 3.

$$\begin{bmatrix} ^-3 & 6 & 0 & 9 \\ ^-10 & ^-6 & 0 & ^-22 \\ ^-1 & ^-1 & ^-2 & ^-9 \end{bmatrix}$$ *Multiply Row 1 by 3.*
Multiply Row 2 by 2.

$$\begin{bmatrix} ^-13 & 0 & 0 & ^-13 \\ ^-10 & ^-6 & 0 & ^-22 \\ ^-1 & ^-1 & ^-2 & ^-9 \end{bmatrix}$$ *Replace by sum of Row 1 and Row 2.*

The last matrix represents the following system.

$$^-13x \qquad\qquad = ^-13$$
$$^-10x - 6y \qquad = ^-22$$
$$^-x - y - 2z = ^-9$$

This system has the same solution as the original system. Use algebra to solve the system.

$$^-13x = ^-13$$
$$x = 1 \qquad \text{Solve for x.}$$

To find y, substitute 1 for x in the second equation.
$$^-10(1) - 6y = ^-22$$
$$^-6y = ^-12$$
$$y = 2$$
To find z, substitute the values for x and y in the third equation.
$$^-(1) - (2) - 2z = ^-9$$
$$^-2z = ^-6$$
$$z = 3 \qquad \text{The solution is } (1, 2, 3).$$

In general, you may use any of the following **row operations** on a matrix.

---

1. **Interchange any two rows.**
2. **Replace any row with a nonzero multiple of that row.**
3. **Replace any row with the sum of that row and another row.**

Row Operations on Matrices

The goal of the matrix method of solution is to obtain all zeros in either of the following "triangles."

$$\begin{bmatrix} a & b & c & d \\ e & f & g & h \\ i & j & k & l \end{bmatrix} \quad \text{or} \quad \begin{bmatrix} a & b & c & d \\ e & f & g & h \\ i & j & k & l \end{bmatrix}$$

exercises

Exploratory State the row operations you would use so that a zero occurs in the second column of row one.

1. $\begin{bmatrix} ^-3 & 2 & 1 \\ 4 & 2 & 6 \end{bmatrix}$

2. $\begin{bmatrix} 2 & 4 & 3 \\ ^-2 & ^-3 & 1 \end{bmatrix}$

3. $\begin{bmatrix} ^-6 & ^-2 & ^-3 \\ 4 & 3 & 1 \end{bmatrix}$

4. $\begin{bmatrix} 2 & ^-1 & 3 \\ 4 & 2 & ^-6 \end{bmatrix}$

5. $\begin{bmatrix} ^-9 & ^-1 & 6 \\ 0 & ^-4 & ^-8 \end{bmatrix}$

6. $\begin{bmatrix} 1 & ^-6 & 0 \\ ^-2 & 4 & ^-3 \end{bmatrix}$

Written Solve each system of equations using row operations on matrices.

1. $6x + y = 9$
   $3x + 2y = 0$

2. $^-2x - 3y = ^-11$
   $3x + y = ^-1$

3. $3x + 2y = 5$
   $4x - 3y = 1$

4. $x + y + z = ^-2$
   $2x - 3y + z = ^-11$
   $^-x + 2y - z = 8$

5. $2x + 6y + 8z = 5$
   $^-2x + 9y - 12z = ^-1$
   $4x + 6y - 4z = 3$

6. $4x + 2y + 3z = 6$
   $2x + 7y - 3z = 0$
   $^-3x - 9y + 2z = ^-13$

7. $x + y + z = 6$
   $2x - 3y + 4z = 3$
   $4x - 8y + 4z = 12$

8. $4x + 3y + z = ^-10$
   $x - 12y + 2z = ^-5$
   $x + 18y + z = 4$

9. $x + 2y + z = 24$
   $2x - 3y + z = ^-1$
   $x - 2y + 2z = 7$

10. $x + y + z + w = 10$
    $2x - y + 3z - w = 5$
    $3x + y + z + w = 12$
    $^-x - y + z + w = 4$

11. $x + y + z + w = 0$
    $2x + 3y - z + w = 7$
    $3x + 2y - 3z + 2w = 9$
    $4x - y - z - w = ^-5$

Matrices with the same dimensions can be added. For example, the sum of two 3×2 matrices is a 3×2 matrix in which the terms are the sums of the corresponding terms of the given matrices.

$$\begin{bmatrix} 5 & ^-2 \\ 9 & 4 \\ ^-7 & 0 \end{bmatrix} + \begin{bmatrix} 1 & ^-9 \\ ^-3 & 6 \\ 2 & ^-8 \end{bmatrix} = \begin{bmatrix} 5 + 1 & ^-2 + ^-9 \\ 9 + ^-3 & 4 + 6 \\ ^-7 + 2 & 0 + ^-8 \end{bmatrix}$$

$$= \begin{bmatrix} 6 & ^-11 \\ 6 & 10 \\ ^-5 & ^-8 \end{bmatrix}$$

A matrix can be multiplied by a constant called a **scalar.** For example, the product of a 2×3 matrix and a scalar is a 2×3 matrix in which the terms are the product of the scalar and the corresponding terms of the given matrix.

$$6 \times \begin{bmatrix} 3 & ^-2 & 4 \\ 7 & ^-9 & ^-2 \end{bmatrix} = \begin{bmatrix} 6(3) & 6(^-2) & 6(4) \\ 6(7) & 6(^-9) & 6(^-2) \end{bmatrix}$$

$$= \begin{bmatrix} 18 & ^-12 & 24 \\ 42 & ^-54 & ^-12 \end{bmatrix}$$

A matrix can also be multiplied by another matrix, provided that the first matrix has the same number of columns as the second matrix has rows. The product of the two matrices is found by multiplying rows and columns.

$$\begin{bmatrix} 3 & 0 & ^-4 \\ 9 & ^-8 & 2 \end{bmatrix} \times \begin{bmatrix} 7 \\ ^-1 \\ ^-5 \end{bmatrix} = \begin{bmatrix} 3(7) + 0(^-1) + ^-4(^-5) \\ 9(7) + ^-8(^-1) + 2(^-5) \end{bmatrix}$$

$$= \begin{bmatrix} 21 + 0 + 20 \\ 63 + 8 + ^-10 \end{bmatrix}$$

$$= \begin{bmatrix} 41 \\ 61 \end{bmatrix}$$

Notice that the product has as many rows as the first matrix and as many columns as the second matrix.

Exercises   Refer to exercises 13–21 on page 567. Solve them using your own computations.

3–6   Determinants

A matrix that has the same number of rows as columns is called a **square matrix.** A matrix of nth order has n rows and n columns.

$$\begin{bmatrix} 4 & 1 & 2 \\ {}^-3 & 0 & 1 \\ 5 & 2 & 6 \end{bmatrix} \text{ is a 3 by 3 square matrix.}$$

Associated with each square matrix is a **determinant.**

The determinant of $\begin{bmatrix} 2 & 1 \\ 3 & 4 \end{bmatrix}$ is denoted by $\det \begin{bmatrix} 2 & 1 \\ 3 & 4 \end{bmatrix}$ or $\begin{vmatrix} 2 & 1 \\ 3 & 4 \end{vmatrix}$.

The quantities in a determinant are called elements.

The value of a second order determinant is defined as follows.

$$\begin{vmatrix} a & b \\ c & d \end{vmatrix} = ad - bc$$

Value of a Second Order Determinant

Note that the value of a second order determinant is found using diagonals.

$$ad - bc$$

example

1 Find the value of $\begin{vmatrix} 2 & 1 \\ 3 & 4 \end{vmatrix}$.

$$= 2 \cdot 4 - 3 \cdot 1$$
$$= 5$$

Diagonals can also be used to find the value of a third order determinant. The first two columns are written next to the determinant. The value of the determinant is the sum of the products of the elements in each diagonal. Note which products have negative signs and which products have positive signs in the diagram below.

$${}^-gec \; {}^-hfa \; {}^-idb$$

$$\begin{array}{ccc|cc} a & b & c & a & b \\ d & e & f & d & e \\ g & h & i & g & h \end{array} \qquad = aei + bfg + cdh - gec - hfa - idb$$

$${}^+aei \; {}^+bfg \; {}^+cdh$$

$$\begin{vmatrix} a & b & c \\ d & e & f \\ g & h & i \end{vmatrix} = aei + bfg + cdh - gec - hfa - idb$$

2 Find the value of $\begin{vmatrix} 1 & 2 & 3 \\ 6 & 5 & 4 \\ 7 & 8 & 9 \end{vmatrix}$.

$$\begin{vmatrix} 1 & 2 & 3 \\ 6 & 5 & 4 \\ 7 & 8 & 9 \end{vmatrix} = 1 \cdot 5 \cdot 9 + 2 \cdot 4 \cdot 7 + 3 \cdot 6 \cdot 8 - 7 \cdot 5 \cdot 3 - 8 \cdot 4 \cdot 1 - 9 \cdot 6 \cdot 2$$

$$= 45 + 56 + 144 - 105 - 32 - 108 \text{ or } 0$$

In a determinant, the **minor** of an element is the determinant formed when the row and column containing the element are deleted. Consider the determinant $\begin{vmatrix} 1 & 3 & 7 \\ 4 & 8 & 2 \\ 9 & 5 & 6 \end{vmatrix}$. The minor of 1 is

$\begin{vmatrix} 1 & 3 & 7 \\ 4 & 8 & 2 \\ 9 & 5 & 6 \end{vmatrix}$ or $\begin{vmatrix} 8 & 2 \\ 5 & 6 \end{vmatrix}$. The minor of 5 is $\begin{vmatrix} 1 & 3 & 7 \\ 4 & 8 & 2 \\ 9 & 5 & 6 \end{vmatrix}$ or $\begin{vmatrix} 1 & 7 \\ 4 & 2 \end{vmatrix}$.

A method called **expansion by minors** may be used to find the value of any third or higher order determinant. The expansion of a third order determinant is shown below. Each element in a row is multiplied by its minor. Notice that the signs of the terms alternate with the first term being positive.

$$\begin{vmatrix} a & b & c \\ d & e & f \\ g & h & i \end{vmatrix} = a\begin{vmatrix} e & f \\ h & i \end{vmatrix} - b\begin{vmatrix} d & f \\ g & i \end{vmatrix} + c\begin{vmatrix} d & e \\ g & h \end{vmatrix}$$

3 Find the value of $\begin{vmatrix} 2 & 3 & 4 \\ 6 & 5 & 7 \\ 1 & 2 & 8 \end{vmatrix}$ using expansion by minors.

$$\begin{vmatrix} 2 & 3 & 4 \\ 6 & 5 & 7 \\ 1 & 2 & 8 \end{vmatrix} = 2\begin{vmatrix} 5 & 7 \\ 2 & 8 \end{vmatrix} - 3\begin{vmatrix} 6 & 7 \\ 1 & 8 \end{vmatrix} + 4\begin{vmatrix} 6 & 5 \\ 1 & 2 \end{vmatrix}$$

$$= 2(40 - 14) - 3(48 - 7) + 4(12 - 5)$$

$$= 52 - 123 + 28 \text{ or } {}^-43$$

exercises

Exploratory Find the value of each determinant.

1. $\begin{vmatrix} 3 & 1 \\ 4 & 6 \end{vmatrix}$

2. $\begin{vmatrix} 7 & ^-3 \\ 0 & 1 \end{vmatrix}$

3. $\begin{vmatrix} 0 & 1 \\ 0 & 1 \end{vmatrix}$

4. $\begin{vmatrix} 11 & ^-2 \\ ^-3 & ^-5 \end{vmatrix}$

5. $\begin{vmatrix} 1 & 0 \\ 0 & 1 \end{vmatrix}$

6. $\begin{vmatrix} ^-8 & ^-7 \\ ^-4 & ^-6 \end{vmatrix}$

7. $\begin{vmatrix} 2 & 4 \\ ^-3 & 1 \end{vmatrix}$

8. $\begin{vmatrix} ^-5 & 3 \\ 1 & 2 \end{vmatrix}$

9. $\begin{vmatrix} 7 & 8 \\ ^-9 & 0 \end{vmatrix}$

10. $\begin{vmatrix} 5 & 5 \\ 5 & 5 \end{vmatrix}$

11. $\begin{vmatrix} ^-6 & ^-2 \\ 2 & 6 \end{vmatrix}$

12. $\begin{vmatrix} 8 & ^-1 \\ 13 & 0 \end{vmatrix}$

Written Find the value of each determinant.

1. $\begin{vmatrix} 24 & 6 \\ ^-13 & ^-4 \end{vmatrix}$

2. $\begin{vmatrix} 18 & ^-5 \\ ^-9 & 11 \end{vmatrix}$

3. $\begin{vmatrix} ^-13 & ^-11 \\ 17 & ^-12 \end{vmatrix}$

4. $\begin{vmatrix} ^-6 & 7 \\ ^-9 & 10 \end{vmatrix}$

5. $\begin{vmatrix} 2 & 0 & 2 \\ 0 & 3 & ^-3 \\ ^-3 & ^-2 & 0 \end{vmatrix}$

6. $\begin{vmatrix} 2 & 3 & 4 \\ 3 & 2 & ^-1 \\ 4 & 3 & 7 \end{vmatrix}$

7. $\begin{vmatrix} 1 & 3 & ^-2 \\ 2 & ^-1 & 1 \\ ^-2 & 2 & 3 \end{vmatrix}$

8. $\begin{vmatrix} ^-1 & 1 & 2 \\ 2 & 1 & 0 \\ 3 & 6 & ^-2 \end{vmatrix}$

9. $\begin{vmatrix} 1 & ^-1 & 1 \\ 4 & 3 & 1 \\ 0 & 5 & 2 \end{vmatrix}$

10. $\begin{vmatrix} 3 & ^-1 & 2 \\ 0 & 4 & 1 \\ 5 & ^-2 & ^-3 \end{vmatrix}$

11. $\begin{vmatrix} 1 & 2 & ^-3 \\ 3 & ^-5 & ^-1 \\ 4 & 4 & 1 \end{vmatrix}$

12. $\begin{vmatrix} 3 & 2 & 5 \\ ^-1 & 1 & 1 \\ 4 & 3 & 3 \end{vmatrix}$

13. $\begin{vmatrix} 4 & 0 & 1 \\ 2 & ^-3 & 3 \\ 5 & 4 & ^-6 \end{vmatrix}$

14. $\begin{vmatrix} 76 & 31 & ^-3 \\ 22 & 49 & 60 \\ 14 & 98 & 31 \end{vmatrix}$

15. $\begin{vmatrix} 471 & 318 & 219 \\ 21 & 37 & ^-4 \\ 66 & 77 & 88 \end{vmatrix}$

16. $\begin{vmatrix} 44 & 41 & 46 \\ 32 & ^-59 & 36 \\ 72 & ^-61 & 84 \end{vmatrix}$

Challenge Find the value of a that makes each statement true.

1. $\begin{vmatrix} 3 & 0 & 1 \\ 5 & a & 2a \\ 2 & 3 & 7 \end{vmatrix} = 2$

2. $\begin{vmatrix} 3 & ^-6 & 6 \\ 2 & 5 & 6 \\ 2 & 4 & 6 \end{vmatrix} = a \begin{vmatrix} 1 & ^-2 & 2 \\ 2 & 5 & 6 \\ 1 & 2 & 3 \end{vmatrix}$

3. $\begin{vmatrix} 5 & a & 2 \\ a & 1 & ^-2 \\ ^-4 & a & 7 \end{vmatrix} = 52$

Sample: The following calculation shows how to expand a 4 by 4 determinant by minors.

$$\begin{vmatrix} 2 & 3 & 4 & 5 \\ 6 & 7 & 8 & 9 \\ 10 & 11 & 12 & 13 \\ 14 & 15 & 16 & 17 \end{vmatrix} = 2 \begin{vmatrix} 7 & 8 & 9 \\ 11 & 12 & 13 \\ 15 & 16 & 17 \end{vmatrix} - 3 \begin{vmatrix} 6 & 8 & 9 \\ 10 & 12 & 13 \\ 14 & 16 & 17 \end{vmatrix} + 4 \begin{vmatrix} 6 & 7 & 9 \\ 10 & 11 & 13 \\ 14 & 15 & 17 \end{vmatrix} - 5 \begin{vmatrix} 6 & 7 & 8 \\ 10 & 11 & 12 \\ 14 & 15 & 16 \end{vmatrix}$$

4. Find the value of the determinant in the sample above.

Find the value of each determinant using expansion by minors.

5. $\begin{vmatrix} 1 & 2 & 3 & 1 \\ 4 & 3 & ^-1 & 0 \\ 2 & ^-5 & 4 & 4 \\ 1 & ^-2 & 0 & 2 \end{vmatrix}$

6. $\begin{vmatrix} 3 & 3 & 3 & 3 \\ 2 & 1 & 2 & 1 \\ 4 & 3 & ^-1 & 5 \\ 2 & 5 & 0 & 1 \end{vmatrix}$

7. $\begin{vmatrix} 1 & 4 & 3 & 0 \\ ^-2 & ^-3 & 6 & 4 \\ 5 & 1 & 1 & 2 \\ 4 & 2 & 5 & ^-1 \end{vmatrix}$

3–7　Cramer's Rule

Determinants can be used to solve a system of linear equations. Consider solving the following system of two equations in two variables.

$$ax + by = c$$
$$dx + ey = f$$

Solve for y using the elimination method.

$$adx + bdy = cd \qquad \text{\textit{Multiply the first equation by d.}}$$
$$\underline{{}^-adx - aey = {}^-af} \qquad \text{\textit{Multiply the second equation by }}{}^-\textit{a.}$$
$$bdy - aey = cd - af \qquad \text{\textit{Add.}}$$
$$(bd - ae)y = cd - af \qquad \text{\textit{Factor.}}$$

$$y = \frac{cd - af}{bd - ae} \text{ or } y = \frac{af - cd}{ae - bd} \qquad \text{\textit{Assume }}(bd - ae) \neq 0. \text{ \textit{Why?}}$$

Then solve for x in the same manner.

$$x = \frac{ce - bf}{ae - bd}$$

Thus, the solution to the system is $\left(\dfrac{ce - bf}{ae - bd}, \dfrac{af - cd}{ae - bd} \right)$.

Notice that the denominator of each fraction is the same. It can be written as a determinant.

$$ae - bd = \begin{vmatrix} a & b \\ d & e \end{vmatrix}$$

Each numerator also may be written as a determinant.

$$ce - bf = \begin{vmatrix} c & b \\ f & e \end{vmatrix} \text{ and } af - cd = \begin{vmatrix} a & c \\ d & f \end{vmatrix}$$

Therefore, the solution to a system of two linear equations in two variables can be found using determinants. This method is known as **Cramer's Rule.**

The solution to the system of equations $\begin{array}{l} ax + by = c \\ dx + ey = f \end{array}$ is (x, y)

where $x = \dfrac{\begin{vmatrix} c & b \\ f & e \end{vmatrix}}{\begin{vmatrix} a & b \\ d & e \end{vmatrix}}$ and $y = \dfrac{\begin{vmatrix} a & c \\ d & f \end{vmatrix}}{\begin{vmatrix} a & b \\ d & e \end{vmatrix}}$ and $\begin{vmatrix} a & b \\ d & e \end{vmatrix} \neq 0.$

Cramer's Rule

---

1 Use Cramer's rule to solve the following system of equations.

$$3x - 5y = {}^-7$$
$$x + 2y = 16$$

$$x = \frac{\begin{vmatrix} {}^-7 & {}^-5 \\ 16 & 2 \end{vmatrix}}{\begin{vmatrix} 3 & {}^-5 \\ 1 & 2 \end{vmatrix}}$$

$$= \frac{{}^-7 \cdot 2 - 16 \cdot {}^-5}{3 \cdot 2 - 1 \cdot {}^-5}$$

$$= \frac{66}{11}$$

$$= 6$$

$$y = \frac{\begin{vmatrix} 3 & {}^-7 \\ 1 & 16 \end{vmatrix}}{\begin{vmatrix} 3 & {}^-5 \\ 1 & 2 \end{vmatrix}}$$

$$= \frac{3 \cdot 16 - 1 \cdot {}^-7}{3 \cdot 2 - 1 \cdot {}^-5}$$

$$= \frac{55}{11}$$

$$= 5$$

The solution is $(6, 5)$.

important

Cramer's Rule may be extended to solve a system of n linear equations in n variables. The determinant in each denominator contains the coefficients of the variables. The determinant in each numerator is the same determinant except for the column of the coefficients of the variable to be found. This column is replaced by the column of constants.

2 Use Cramer's Rule to solve the following system of equations.

$$a + 2b - c = {}^-7$$
$$2a + 3b + 2c = {}^-3$$
$$a - 2b - 2c = 3$$

$$a = \frac{\begin{vmatrix} {}^-7 & 2 & {}^-1 \\ {}^-3 & 3 & 2 \\ 3 & {}^-2 & {}^-2 \end{vmatrix}}{\begin{vmatrix} 1 & 2 & {}^-1 \\ 2 & 3 & 2 \\ 1 & {}^-2 & {}^-2 \end{vmatrix}}$$

$$= \frac{17}{17} \text{ or } 1$$

$$b = \frac{\begin{vmatrix} 1 & {}^-7 & {}^-1 \\ 2 & {}^-3 & 2 \\ 1 & 3 & {}^-2 \end{vmatrix}}{\begin{vmatrix} 1 & 2 & {}^-1 \\ 2 & 3 & 2 \\ 1 & {}^-2 & {}^-2 \end{vmatrix}}$$

$$= \frac{{}^-51}{17} \text{ or } {}^-3$$

$$c = \frac{\begin{vmatrix} 1 & 2 & {}^-7 \\ 2 & 3 & {}^-3 \\ 1 & {}^-2 & 3 \end{vmatrix}}{\begin{vmatrix} 1 & 2 & {}^-1 \\ 2 & 3 & 2 \\ 1 & {}^-2 & {}^-2 \end{vmatrix}}$$

$$= \frac{34}{17} \text{ or } 2$$

The solution is $(1, {}^-3, 2)$.

exercises

Exploratory
Name the determinants you would use to solve each system by Cramer's Rule.

1. $3x + 2y = 5$
$4x - y = 3$

2. $4x + 2y = 8$
$6x - 3y = 0$

3. $2a - 4b = 16$
$3a - 5b = 21$

4. $r - s = 0$
$2r + 5s = {}^-3$

5. $3x + y = {}^-8$
$4x - 2y = {}^-14$

6. $x + y = 6$
$x - y = 2$

7. $x + 11 = 8y$
$8(x - y) = 3$

8. $3m - n = 2$
$m + n = 5$

9. $3x + 2y = 5$
$5x - 6y = 11$

10. $a - 2b + 3c = {}^-4$
$2a - b + 4c = {}^-1$
$2a + 3b + 5c = 1$

11. $2x + 4y - z = {}^-6$
$x - 2y + 3z = 2$
$x + 2y - 4z = {}^-10$

12. $2x - y + z = {}^-2$
$x + 2y + 6z = 3$
$3x - y + 2z = {}^-1$

13. $4r + s + 3t = 1$
$2r + 6t = 3$
$4r - 3s = 8$

Written

1–13. Solve each system of equations in the Exploratory Exercises using Cramer's Rule.

14. Explain why Cramer's rule will not work if a system of equations is dependent or inconsistent.

Write a system of equations for each problem and solve using Cramer's Rule.

15. Floyd has 16 coins in pennies, nickels, and dimes. The number of dimes is equal to the sum of the number of pennies and number of nickels. If the total value of the coins is $1.08, how many of each kind does he have?

16. Meiko bought 97 cans of soft drink for a party. The number of root beers exceeded the number of colas by 15. The total number of colas and orange drinks was 23 less than twice the number of root beers. How many cans of each did she buy?

History
excursions in algebra

Gabriel Cramer was a Swiss mathematician of the 18th century. He was a professor of mathematics at the University of Geneva at the age of twenty. Although Cramer's Rule is named after him, he was not the first person to originate that result. Colin Maclaurin, a British mathematician, wrote the rule for solving systems of equations by determinants in his *Treatise of Algebra*. It was published in 1748, two years before Cramer published Cramer's Rule. Often in mathematics, the person who popularized a result had his name attached to it, although later it was learned that someone else had originally discovered the same result.

3–8   Graphing Systems of Inequalities

Consider the following system of inequalities.

$$y \geq 2x - 1$$
$$y \leq {}^-2x - 2$$

To solve this system, find the ordered pairs that satisfy *both* inequalities. One way is to graph each inequality and find the intersection of the two graphs.

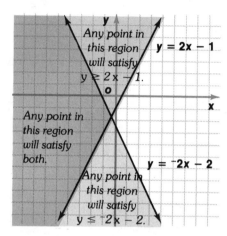

Some systems of inequalities have *no* solutions.

example

1 **Solve the following system by graphing.**

$$y > x + 1$$
$$y < x - 4$$

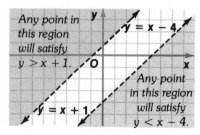

The graphs of the two inequalities have *no* points in common. So *no* ordered pair will satisfy both inequalities.

Systems of more than two inequalities can also be graphed.

2 Solve the following system by graphing.

$y \leq 3$
$x \geq {}^-2$
$y > x$

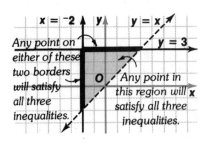

$x = {}^-2$ $y = x$

Any point on either of these two borders will satisfy all three inequalities.

$y = 3$

O   Any point in this region will satisfy all three inequalities.

x

exercises

Exploratory   Does the point given in color satisfy the system of inequalities?

1. $y < \frac{1}{2}x + 2$ $(0, 0)$
   $y > 3x - 2$

2. $y < x - 2$ $(1, 2)$
   $y > {}^-x$

3. $y > {}^-2$ $(1, 1)$
   $x \leq 1$

4. $y < 3$ $(4, 4)$
   $x \geq {}^-1$

5. $y + 2x > 6$ $(4, 0)$
   $x < 5$

6. $3y - x < 3$ $(9, 3)$
   $y > 2$

7. $y > x + 3$ $(3, 2)$
   $y < {}^-x$

8. $y > x + 3$ $(2, {}^-3)$
   $y < {}^-x$

Written   Solve each system of inequalities by graphing.

1. $y > 3$
   $x \leq 1$

2. $y \leq 5$
   $x \geq {}^-1$

3. $y > 3$
   $y + x > 2$

4. $y < {}^-2$
   $y - x > 1$

5. $y \geq 2x - 2$
   $y \leq {}^-x + 2$

6. $y \geq x - 3$
   $y \geq {}^-x + 1$

7. $y > x + 1$
   $y < x - 3$

8. $y - x \leq 3$
   $y \geq x + 2$

9. $y < {}^-x - 3$
   $x + 2 > y$

10. $x + y > 5$
    $x - y \leq 3$

11. $x + y \geq 3$
    $2x - 3y \leq 6$

12. $x + 2y \geq 7$
    $3x - 4y < 12$

13. $^-4y - 3x > 10$
    $2y - 3x < 5$

14. $|x| > 5$
    $x + y < 6$

15. $|x + 2| < 3$
    $x + y \geq 1$

16. $x \geq 1$
    $y < {}^-1$
    $y > x$

17. $y \leq 2$
    $y \geq 2x$
    $y \geq x + 1$

18. $x \geq {}^-1$
    $x \leq 1$
    $y > 2$

19. $x \geq {}^-2$
    $2y \geq 3$
    $x - y \leq {}^-5$

20. $2y \leq x$
    $3x + 5y \leq 10$
    $x \leq 3$

21. $y < 2x + 1$
    $y > 2x - 2$
    $3x + y > 8$

3-9   Linear Programming

The Blair Company makes two types of pianos, spinets and consoles. The equipment in the factory allows for making at most 450 spinets and 200 consoles in one month.

The following chart shows the cost of making each type of piano and the profit.

Piano	Cost per Unit	Profit per Unit
Spinet	$600	$125
Console	$900	$200

During the month of June, the company can spend $360,000 to make these pianos. To make the greatest profit, how many of each type should be made in June?

First, write a system of inequalities and graph them to show the *possible* solutions to this problem.

Let s = the number of spinets made.
Let c = the number of consoles made.

$0 \le s \le 450$ The number of spinets made is between 0 and 450 inclusive.

$0 \le c \le 200$ The number of consoles made is between 0 and 200 inclusive.

$600s + 900c \le 360,000$ The cost of spinets plus the cost of consoles does not exceed $360,000.

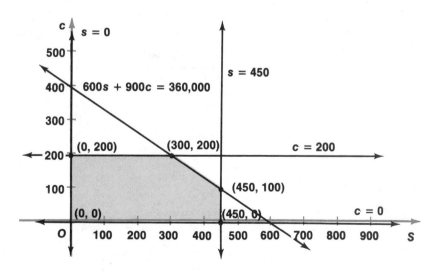

Any point in the region shown will satisfy the conditions.

Now, write an expression for profit.

Profit = *Profit on spinets + profit on consoles*

$$\text{Profit} = 125s + 200c$$

To solve the problem, find which ordered pair on the graph yields the greatest profit.

Mathematicians have shown that a maximum or minimum value is always at one of the vertices of the polygon. In this case there are five points to try:

(s, c)	$(0, 0)$	$(0, 200)$	$(300, 200)$	$(450, 100)$	$(450, 0)$
$125s + 200c$	$0	$40,000	$77,500	$76,250	$56,250

The Blair Company will make the greatest profit by building 300 spinets and 200 consoles in June.

Finding a maximum or minimum value with given conditions is called **linear programming.** Use the following method to solve linear programming problems.

1. **Define variables.**
2. **Write a system of inequalities.**
3. **Graph the system. Find vertices of the polygon formed.**
4. **Write an expression to be maximized or minimized.**
5. **Substitute values from vertices into the expression.**
6. **Select the greatest or least result.**

Linear Programming Procedure

examples

1 The area of a parking lot is 600 square meters. A car requires 6 square meters and a bus requires 30 square meters of space. The attendant can handle no more than 60 vehicles. If a car is charged $2.50 and a bus $7.50, how many of each should be accepted to maximize income?

Define variables.   Let c = the number of cars accepted.
Let b = the number of buses accepted.

Write inequalities. $c + b \le 60$ The attendant can handle no more than 60 vehicles.

$6c + 30b \le 600$ The maximum space for the cars and buses is 600 square meters.

Graph the system.

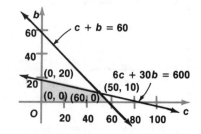

Write the expression to be maximized.	*Income = Car Income + Bus Income* Income = $\quad 2.50c \quad + \quad 7.50b$	

Substitute values into the expression.

(c, b)	$(0, 0)$	$(0, 20)$	$(50, 10)$	$(60, 0)$
$2.5c + 7.5b$	$0	$150	$200	$150

Answer the problem.   The attendant should accept 50 cars and 10 buses to maximize income.

2 **Raw Materials A and B are used to make one of the Target Company's products. The product must contain no more than 9 units of A and at least 18 units of B. It must cost no more than \$300. The following chart shows how much each unit of raw material costs and weighs.**

Material	Cost per Unit	Weight per Unit
A	$4	10 pounds
B	$12	20 pounds

How much of each raw material should be used to maximize the weight?

Define variables.   Let a stand for amount of material A used.
Let b stand for amount of material B used.

Write inequalities. $0 \le a \le 9$ The product contains no more than 9 units of A.
$b \ge 18$ The product contains at least 18 units of B.
$4a + 12b \le 300$

Graph the system.

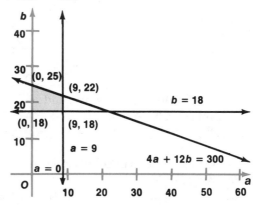

Write expression to be maximized.   *Weight = Weight material A + Weight material B*
Weight = $\quad 10a \quad + \quad 20b$

Substitute values into the expression.

(a, b)	$(0, 18)$	$(0, 25)$	$(9, 22)$	$(9, 18)$
$10a + 20b$	360	500	530	450

Answer the problem.   The Target Company should use 9 units of material A and 22 units of material B for each unit of product.

exercises

Exploratory Graph each system of inequalities. Name the vertices of the polygon formed.

1. $1 \le y \le 3$
$y \le 2x + 1$
$y \le -\frac{1}{2}x + 6$

2. $x \ge 0$
$y \ge 3$
$y \ge 2x + 1$
$y \le -\frac{1}{2}x + 6$

3. $y \ge 1$
$y \le 2x + 1$
$x \le 6$

4. $0 \le x \le 50$
$0 \le y \le 70$
$60 \le x + y \le 80$

Written Graph each system of inequalities. Name the vertices of the polygon formed. Find the maximum and minimum values of the expression given in color.

1. $y \ge 2$ $\qquad$ $3x - 2y$
$1 \le x \le 5$
$y \le x + 3$

2. $x + y \ge 2$ $\qquad$ $4x + 3y$
$4y \le x + 8$
$y \ge 2x - 5$

3. $y \le 7$ $\qquad$ $2x - 3y$
$y \le x + 4$
$y \ge {}^-x + 6$
$x \le 5$

4. $y \le x + 5$ $\qquad$ $x - 2y$
$y \ge x$
$x \ge {}^-3$
$y + 2x \le 5$

5. $y \le x + 6$ $\qquad$ $3x + y$
$y + 2x \ge 6$
$2 \le x \le 6$

6. $x + y \ge 2$ $\qquad$ $3y + x$
$4y \le x + 8$
$2y \ge 3x - 6$

7. $y \ge 0$ $\qquad$ $5x - 3y$
$0 \le x \le 5$
$^-x + y \le 2$
$x + y \le 6$

8. $x \ge 0$ $\qquad$ $3x - 5y$
$y \ge 0$
$x + 2y \le 6$
$2y - x \le 2$
$x + y \le 5$

9. A painter has exactly 32 units of yellow dye and 54 units of green dye. He plans to mix as many gallons as possible of color A and color B. Each gallon of color A requires 4 units of yellow dye and 1 unit of green dye. Each gallon of color B requires 1 unit of yellow dye and 6 units of green dye.
   a. Let x be the number of gallons of color A and let y be the number of gallons of color B. Write the inequalities.
   b. Graph the system of inequalities and name the vertices of the polygon formed.
   c. Find the maximum number of gallons, $x + y$, possible.

10. A farmer has 20 days in which to plant corn and beans. The corn can be planted at a rate of 10 acres per day and the beans at a rate of 15 acres per day. The farm has 250 acres available.
   a. Let x be the number of acres of corn and let y be the number of acres of beans. Write the inequalities that represent the situation.
   b. Graph the system of inequalities and name the vertices of the polygon formed.
   c. If corn profits $30 per acre and beans profit $25 per acre, find the values of x and y that maximize the profit.
   d. If corn profits $29 per acre and beans profit $30 per acre, find the values of x and y that maximize the profit.

11. A dressmaking shop makes dresses and pantsuits. The equipment in the shop allows for making at most 30 dresses and 20 pantsuits in a week. It takes 10 worker-hours to make a dress and 20 worker-hours to make a pantsuit. There are 500 worker-hours available per week in the shop.
    a. If the profit on a dress and the profit on a pantsuit are the same, how many of each should be made to maximize the profit?
    b. If the profit on a pantsuit is three times the profit on a dress, how many of each should be made to maximize the profit?

12. A builder has 60 lots on which he can build houses with one house on each lot. He builds two types of houses, colonial and ranch. Sales experience has taught him that he should plan to build at least 3 times as many ranch-style houses as colonial. If he makes a profit of $5000 on each colonial and $4500 on each ranch, how many of each kind should he build to maximize profit?

13. Fashion Furniture makes two kinds of chairs, rockers and swivels. Two operations A and B, are used. Operation A is limited to 20 hours a day. Operation B is limited to 15 hours per day. The following chart shows the amount of time each operation takes for one chair. It also shows the profit made on each chair.

Chair	Operation A	Operation B	Profit
Rocker	2 hr	3 hr	$12
Swivel	4 hr	1 hr	$10

How many chairs of each kind should Fashion Furniture make each day to maximize profit?

14. Recreation Unlimited produces footballs and basketballs. Producing a football requires 4 hours on machine A and 2 hours on machine B. Producing a basketball requires 6 hours on machine A, 6 hours on machine B, and 1 hour on machine C. Machine A is available 120 hours per week, machine B is available 72 hours per week, and machine C is available 10 hours per week. If the company profits $3 on each football and $2 on each basketball, how many of each should be produced to maximize the company's profit?

15. The table gives the amounts of ingredient A and ingredient B in two types of dog foods: X and Y.

Food Type	Amount of Ingredient A	Amount of Ingredient B
X	1 unit per pound	$\frac{1}{2}$ unit per pound
Y	$\frac{1}{3}$ unit per pound	1 unit per pound

The dogs in a kennel must get *at least* 40 pounds of food per day. The food may be a mixture of type X and type Y. The daily diet must contain at least 20 units of ingredient A and at least 30 units of ingredient B. The dogs must not get more than 100 pounds of food per day.
    a. Type X costs $0.80 per pound and type Y costs $0.40 per pound. What is the least possible cost per day for feeding the dogs?
    b. If the price on type X is raised to $1.00 per pound and the price on type Y remains the same, should the mixture be changed?

parallel lines   (71)
perpendicular lines   (72)
system of equations   (74)
consistent system   (75)
independent system   (75)
inconsistent system   (75)
dependent system   (75)
substitution method   (78)

elimination method   (78)
matrix   (84)
row operations   (85)
square matrix   (87)
determinant   (87)
expansion by minors   (88)
Cramer's Rule   (90)
linear programming   (96)

Chapter Summary

1. Definition of Parallel Lines: In a plane, lines with the same slope are called parallel lines. Also, vertical lines are parallel.   (71)
2. Definition of Perpendicular Lines: Two nonvertical lines are perpendicular if and only if the product of their slopes is $^-1$. Any vertical line is perpendicular to any horizontal line.   (72)
3. Possibilities for the graphs of two linear equations in two variables: (75)

Graphs of Equations	Slopes of Lines	Name of System of Equations
lines intersect	different slopes	consistent and independent
lines parallel	same slope, different intercepts	inconsistent
lines coincide	same slope, same intercepts	consistent and dependent

4. The substitution method and the elimination method can be used to solve systems of equations.   (78)
5. A rectangular arrangement of terms in rows and columns is called a matrix.   (84)
6. Row Operations on Matrices:
    1. Interchange any two rows.
    2. Replace any row with a nonzero multiple of that row.
    3. Replace any row with the sum of that row and another row.   (85)
7. A square matrix has the same number of rows as columns.   (87)
8. A determinant is associated with each square matrix. The value of a second order determinant is defined as follows.

$$\begin{vmatrix} a & b \\ c & d \end{vmatrix} = ad - bc \quad (87)$$

9. The value of a third order determinant is defined as follows.

$$\begin{vmatrix} a & b & c \\ d & e & f \\ g & h & i \end{vmatrix} = aei + bfg + cdh - gec - hfa - idb \quad (88)$$

10. Expansion by minors can be used to find the value of a third order determinant.

$$\begin{vmatrix} a & b & c \\ d & e & f \\ g & h & i \end{vmatrix} = a\begin{vmatrix} e & f \\ h & i \end{vmatrix} - b\begin{vmatrix} d & f \\ g & i \end{vmatrix} + c\begin{vmatrix} d & e \\ g & h \end{vmatrix} \quad (88)$$

11. Cramer's Rule: The solution to the system $\begin{matrix} ax + by = c \\ dx + ey = f \end{matrix}$ is (x, y)

where $x = \dfrac{\begin{vmatrix} c & b \\ f & e \end{vmatrix}}{\begin{vmatrix} a & b \\ d & e \end{vmatrix}}$ and $y = \dfrac{\begin{vmatrix} a & c \\ d & f \end{vmatrix}}{\begin{vmatrix} a & b \\ d & e \end{vmatrix}}$ and $\begin{vmatrix} a & b \\ d & e \end{vmatrix} \neq 0$.   (90)

12. To solve a system of inequalities, find the ordered pairs that satisfy both inequalities.   (93)
13. Linear Programming Procedure:
    1. Define variables.
    2. Write a system of inequalities.
    3. Graph the system. Find vertices of the polygon formed.
    4. Write an expression to be maximized or minimized.
    5. Substitute values from vertices into the expression.
    6. Select the greatest or least result.   (96)

Chapter Review

3–1 Find an equation of the line that passes through each given point and is parallel to the line with the given equation.

1. $(4, 6)$; $y = 3x - 2$
2. $(1, 1)$; $y = {}^-3x - 1$
3. $({}^-1, {}^-1)$; $y = 6x - 8$
4. $(7, 7)$; $2x + 3y = 6$

Find an equation of the line that passes through each given point and is perpendicular to the line with the given equation.

5. $(3, 5)$; $y = 2x - 5$
6. $(1, 4)$; $y = 3x - 1$
7. $({}^-1, {}^-1)$; $2y + 3x = 10$
8. $(0, 10)$; $y = 4x$

3–2 Graph each system of equations and state its solution. Then, state whether the system is *consistent and independent, consistent and dependent,* or *inconsistent.*

9. $x + y = {}^-8$
   $2x - y = 2$
10. $x + y = 6$
    $x - y = 2$
11. $x + y = 11$
    $3x - 3y = 3$
12. $x + y = 6$
    $2x + 2y = 12$

3–3 **Solve each system of equations algebraically.**

13. $x + y = 6$

$x - y = 4\frac{1}{2}$

14. $3x - 5y = {}^-13$

$4x + 3y = 2$

15. $2x + 3y = 8$

$x - y = 2$

16. $\frac{1}{3}x + \frac{1}{3}y = 5$

$\frac{1}{6}x - \frac{1}{9}y = 0$

3–4 **17.** $x + y + z = 6$

$2x - y + z = 3$

$3x - y - 2z = {}^-5$

18. $x + y - z = 4$

$2x - 3y + z = 1$

$4x - y + 2z = 12$

3–5 **Solve each system of equations using row operations on matrices.**

19. $2x + y = 5$

$3x - 2y = 4$

20. $x + y + z = 2$

$4x + 2y + 3z = 9$

${}^-2x + y - 3z = {}^-9$

3–6 **Find the value of each determinant.**

21. $\begin{vmatrix} 2 & 3 \\ 4 & 5 \end{vmatrix}$

22. $\begin{vmatrix} 6 & {}^-1 \\ 3 & {}^-2 \end{vmatrix}$

23. $\begin{vmatrix} 2 & 1 & 0 \\ 3 & 2 & 6 \\ {}^-1 & {}^-3 & {}^-4 \end{vmatrix}$

24. $\begin{vmatrix} 4 & 8 & 2 \\ 3 & 0 & 6 \\ {}^-1 & {}^-2 & {}^-3 \end{vmatrix}$

3–7 **Solve each system of equations using Cramer's rule.**

25. $7x - 8y = 11$

$9x - 2y = 3$

26. $x + 2y = 5$

$x - y = 6$

27. $4x + 3y + z = {}^-10$

$x - 12y + 2z = {}^-5$

$x + 18y + z = 4$

28. $a + b + c = {}^-1$

$2a + 4b + c = 1$

$3a - b - c = {}^-15$

3–8 **Solve each system of inequalities by graphing.**

29. $x + y < 2$

$x + 2y > {}^-3$

30. $y < {}^-2$

$y - x > 1$

31. $y \geq x - 3$

$y \geq {}^-x + 1$

32. $x + y < 4$

$y \geq {}^-3x + 1$

3–9 **Graph each system of inequalities. Name the vertices of the polygon formed. Find the maximum and minimum values of the expression given in color.**

33. $x \geq 0$ $2x + 4y$

$y \geq 0$

$x + y \leq 3$

$3x + y \leq 6$

34. $0 \leq x \leq 5$ $2x + 3y$

$0 \leq y \leq 6$

$x + y \leq 9$

35. A farmer has 90 acres on which he may raise peanuts and corn. He has accepted orders requiring at least 10 acres of peanuts and 5 acres of corn. He also must follow a regulation that the acreage for corn must be at least twice the acreage for peanuts. If the profit is \$100 per acre of corn and \$200 per acre of peanuts, how many acres of each will give him the greatest profit?

Find an equation of the line that passes through each given point and is parallel to the line with the given equation.

1. $(2, 4)$; $y = 3x - 5$

2. $(7, {}^-4)$; $y = {}^-x + 6$

Find an equation of the line that passes through each given point and is perpendicular to the line with the given equation.

3. $(3, 4)$; $y = 2x + 1$

4. $(6, {}^-1)$; $y + 2x = 5$

Graph each system of equations. Then state the solution to the system.

5. $x + y = 7$
   $x - y = 1$

6. $2x + 3y = 5$
   ${}^-3x + 6y = 12$

Solve each system of equations algebraically.

7. $3x + 8y = {}^-6$
   $4x - 2y = 11$

8. $7x + 2y = 11$
   $3x + 16 = {}^-8y$

9. $x + y + z = {}^-1$
   $2x + 4y + z = 1$
   $3x - y - z = {}^-15$

Solve each system of equations using row operations on matrices.

10. $4x + y = 9$
    ${}^-3x + 2y = {}^-4$

11. $x + 2y + z = 4$
    $3x - 2y + z = 2$
    $4x + 2y - 3z = 3$

Find the value of each determinant.

12. $\begin{vmatrix} 3 & 1 \\ {}^-2 & 4 \end{vmatrix}$

13. $\begin{vmatrix} 7 & 1 & 6 \\ 3 & {}^-1 & 4 \\ {}^-2 & 3 & 0 \end{vmatrix}$

Solve each system of equations using Cramer's rule.

14. ${}^-2x + 3y = 5$
    $x + 4y = 14$

15. $r + s + t = 7$
    $3r - 7s + 2t = 11$
    ${}^-9r + 21s + 3t = {}^-3$

Solve each system of inequalities by graphing.

16. $y > 2x + 1$
    $y \le {}^-3x + 4$

17. $x + y \le 6$
    $x - y \ge 4$

Graph each system of inequalities. Name the vertices of the polygon formed. Find the maximum and minimum values of the expression given in color.

18. $0 \le x \le 6$ $2x + y$
    $0 \le y \le 2$
    $x + y \le 4$

19. $0 \le x \le 4$ $3x - 2y$
    $y + x \le 6$
    $y \ge 0$

cumulative review

Evaluate if $a = 4$, $b = {}^-7$, $c = \frac{1}{3}$, and $d = {}^-3$.

1. $\frac{a}{c^2} + b$

2. $\frac{ab + 4c}{d}$

3. $2a(4c + b^2) + |d|$

Simplify.

4. $(9 - 29)7 - 12$

5. $7x + 18y - 10x + 3y$

6. $\frac{2}{3}(15 - 9a) - (6a - 21)\frac{1}{3}$

Solve each open sentence.

7. $4 - 7a = 25$

8. $\frac{8}{9}x + \frac{1}{3} = \frac{3}{5}$

9. $2(6 - 7x) = 2x - 4$

10. $5|b + 4| = 45$

11. $|2r + 9| = 0$

12. $|7 + 3x| = 11 - x$

13. $5x + 8 > 24$

14. $3(4m + 7) < 21$

15. $1 - 2y \le 5y - 2$

16. $|b + 1| > 3$

17. $|x - 4| \le {}^-8$

18. $|2n - 5| < 7$

Graph each equation or inequality on the number line.

19. $x + 5 = 5(x + 5)$

20. $3(a - 3) - a = a + 1$

21. $5(n - 3) \le 6(n - 3)$

22. $5(y - 1) - (2y + 1) < 5(y + 2)$

Given $f(x) = 2x^3 + 4x^2 - x + 2$, find each value.

23. $f(3)$

24. $f({}^-4)$

25. $f\left(\frac{1}{2}\right)$

Graph each equation.

26. $y - 3x = 2$

27. $y + 6 = {}^-x$

28. $y = {}^-5$

29. $y = x$

30. $y = \frac{1}{2}x$

31. $y = |x - 7|$

32. $y = [2x]$

33. $x = 3\frac{1}{2}$

34. $y = 3|x| - 2$

35. $y + 2x = {}^-3$

36. $y = -[x - 1]$

37. $y = |x - 2| + 3$

Find the slope-intercept form of lines satisfying the following conditions.

38. x-intercept $= 5$, y-intercept $= 4$

39. passes through $(6, 1)$ and $({}^-4, 8)$

40. slope $= \frac{4}{5}$ and passes through $(6, {}^-2)$

Find the standard form of lines satisfying the following conditions.

41. x-intercept $= {}^-3$, y-intercept $= 8$

42. passes through $({}^-6, {}^-3)$ and $(4, {}^-6)$

43. slope $= -\frac{2}{3}$ and passes through $(5, 1)$

Find the slope of a line perpendicular to the line whose equation is given.

44. $y = \frac{4}{5}x + 3$

45. $2x + 3y = 1$

Solve each system of equations.

46. $x + y = 7$
$x - y = 9$

47. $2a + 3b = 6$
$2a - 5b = 22$

48. $2x - 5y = 1$
$3x - 4y = {}^-2$

49. $3x + 4y = {}^-25$
$2x - 3y = 6$

50. $\frac{4}{3}r + s = 2$
${}^-2r + 6s = 7$

51. $\frac{2a + b}{3} = 5$
$3a = b + 5$

Find the value of each determinant.

52. $\begin{vmatrix} 3 & 1 \\ 4 & 7 \end{vmatrix}$

53. $\begin{vmatrix} 1 & 2 & {}^-2 \\ 2 & {}^-1 & 1 \\ 3 & {}^-3 & 4 \end{vmatrix}$

Solve each system of inequalities by graphing.

54. $y > x$
$y < x - 3$

55. $2x + 3y < 6$
$y > {}^-x + 4$

Solve each problem.

56. Leon bought a 10-speed bicycle on sale for 75% of its original price. The sale price was $41 less than the original price. Find the original price and the sale price.

57. Mindy wants to earn at least $13 this week. Her father has agreed to pay her $5 to mow the lawn and $2 an hour to weed the garden. Suppose Mindy mows the lawn once. What is the minimum number of hours she will have to spend weeding the garden to earn at least $13?

58. A certain telephone call costs $1.38 for the first three minutes and $0.34 for each minute thereafter. Write an equation to describe the relationship between the length of the telephone call and the cost of the telephone call.

59. Using the equation in exercise 58, find the cost of a 15-minute telephone call.

60. The Marinacci family has invested $10,000. Part of the money is invested at 5% and part at 7%. If the total income from these investments is $540, how much is invested at each rate?

61. Randa wishes to prepare 50 pounds of blended coffee to sell at $3.50 a pound. How many pounds of coffee selling at $5 a pound and how many pounds of coffee selling at $3 a pound should she use?

chapter
4 Polynomials

The paddleboat, *The Golden Conifer,* is rented to take 100 campers to Pine Hill Camp. The fare is $5 per camper. The owner of the paddleboat agrees to reduce the fare by two cents for every camper beyond the first 60. The formula $r = 6.2n - 0.02n^2$, where n is the number of passengers, can be used to determine r, the total rental fee. The expression $6.2n - 0.02n^2$ is an example of a polynomial.

4–1   Monomials

A **monomial** is an expression that is a number, a variable, or the product of a number and one or more variables. Expressions like -3, y, m^7, $-4x^2$, and $\frac{3}{5}ab^3$ are monomials. Expressions like $2x + 1$, $\frac{3}{x}$, and $\sqrt{x}$ are *not* monomials.

A monomial that contains no variable is called a **constant.** The numerical factor of a monomial is called the **coefficient.** For example, the coefficient of $-4x^2$ is -4. The **degree** of a monomial is the sum of the exponents of its variables. The degree of a nonzero constant is 0. The constant 0 has no degree.

Monomial	Coefficient	Variables	Exponents	Degree
y	1	y	1	1
$-4x^2$	-4	x	2	2
m^7	1	m	7	7
$\frac{3}{5}ab^3$	$\frac{3}{5}$	a and b	1 and 3	4

Recall that $y = 1 \cdot y^1$.

If two monomials are the same or differ only by their coefficients, they are called **like terms.**

Like $6x^3y$ and $17x^3y$ Unlike $3a^2b$ and $4ab^2$

examples

1   Simplify $6x^3y - 17x^3y$.

$$6x^3y - 17x^3y = (6 - 17)x^3y \qquad \text{Distributive Property}$$
$$= -11x^3y$$

2   Simplify $3n^4p^5 - 7n^4p^5 + 8n^4p^5$.

$$3n^4p^5 - 7n^4p^5 + 8n^4p^5 = (3 - 7 + 8)n^4p^5 \qquad \text{Distributive Property}$$
$$= 4n^4p^5$$

The expression x^3 means $x \cdot x \cdot x$. You can use the meaning of exponents to discover how to multiply powers.

example

3   Simplify $(s^2t^3)(s^4t^5)$.

$$(s^2t^3)(s^4t^5) = (s \cdot s \cdot t \cdot t \cdot t)(s \cdot s \cdot s \cdot s \cdot t \cdot t \cdot t \cdot t \cdot t)$$
$$= s \cdot s \cdot s \cdot s \cdot s \cdot s \cdot t \cdot t \cdot t \cdot t \cdot t \cdot t \cdot t \cdot t$$
$$= s^6t^8 \qquad \text{Notice that } 2 + 4 = 6 \text{ and } 3 + 5 = 8. \text{ Also, } s^2 \cdot s^4 = s^6 \text{ and } t^3 \cdot t^5 = t^8.$$

Example **3** suggests the following property.

> **For all numbers *a*, and positive integers *m* and *n*,**
> $$a^m \cdot a^n = a^{m+n}.$$

Multiplying Powers

examples

4   **Simplify $(4^2)^3$.**

$$(4^2)^3 = 4^2 \cdot 4^2 \cdot 4^2$$
$$= 4^{2+2+2}$$
$$= 4^6$$

5   **Simplify $(h^4)^5$.**

$$(h^4)^5 = h^4 \cdot h^4 \cdot h^4 \cdot h^4 \cdot h^4$$
$$= h^{4+4+4+4+4}$$
$$= h^{20}$$

Examples **4** and **5** suggest the following property.

> **For all numbers *a*, and positive integers *m* and *n*,**
> $$(a^m)^n = a^{m \cdot n}.$$

Raising a Power to a Power

Example **6** shows how to raise a power to a power. Example **7** shows one way to find the power of a product.

examples

6   **Simplify $(r^5)^6$.**

$$(r^5)^6 = r^{5 \cdot 6}$$
$$= r^{30}$$

7   **Simplify $(ab)^4$.**

$$(ab)^4 = a \cdot b \cdot a \cdot b \cdot a \cdot b \cdot a \cdot b$$
$$= a \cdot a \cdot a \cdot a \cdot b \cdot b \cdot b \cdot b$$
$$= a^4 b^4$$

The power of a product is the product of the powers.

> **For all numbers *a*, *b*, and positive integer *m*,**
> $$(ab)^m = a^m b^m.$$

Finding a Power of a Product

You can simplify many kinds of expressions using the properties of exponents along with the commutative and associative properties.

8 **Simplify $(4x^2y)(^-3x^3y^4)$.**

$$(4x^2y)(^-3x^3y^4) = 4 \cdot {}^-3 \cdot x^2 \cdot x^3 \cdot y \cdot y^4$$
$$= {}^-12 \cdot x^{2+3} \cdot y^{1+4}$$
$$= {}^-12x^5y^5$$

9 **Simplify $(^-2r^2s^3)^3$.**

$$(^-2r^2s^3)^3 = (^-2)^3(r^2)^3(s^3)^3$$
$$= {}^-8 \cdot r^{(2 \cdot 3)} \cdot s^{(3 \cdot 3)}$$
$$= {}^-8r^6s^9$$

exercises

Exploratory State whether each of the following expressions is a monomial. If it is, then name its coefficient.

1. $7x$
2. y^2
3. $3xy + y$
4. ^-5ab
5. $\dfrac{11xy}{7}$
6. $\sqrt{cd}$
7. $\dfrac{3}{x}$
8. $^-8$

State the degree of each of the following monomials.

9. $5x^3$
10. $11m$
11. $5x^3y^2z^4$
12. $4xy$
13. 17
14. 0
15. $^-24p^4q$
16. ^-b

Written Simplify.

1. $4m + 7m + {}^-3m$
2. $2x^3 + 3x^3 + {}^-6x^3$
3. $4d^3 - d^3 + 2d^3$
4. $4ab^2 - 3ab^2$
5. $27x^2 - 3y^2 + 12x^2$
6. $3x^2y + 4 - 3x^2y$
7. $y^5 \cdot y^7$
8. $n^4 \cdot n^3 \cdot n^2$
9. $2^3 \cdot 2^4$
10. $t^{13} \cdot t^{15} \cdot t^{18}$
11. $8^6 \cdot 8^4 \cdot (8^2)^2$
12. $(m^3)^2$
13. $(y^5)^2$
14. $(2a)^3$
15. $(3a)^4$
16. $(rs^3)(^-5r^2s^3)$
17. $(5m^2k^2)(4mk^3)$
18. $(x^2y^2)^2x^3y^3$
19. $(3x^2y)^2(5xy^2z)^4$
20. $(^-2ab^2)^3(6a^2)^4$
21. $\left(\dfrac{3}{5}c^2f\right)\left(\dfrac{4}{3}cd\right)^2$
22. $\left(-\dfrac{3}{4}x^2y^3\right)^2\left(\dfrac{8}{9}xy^4\right)$
23. $(4rs^2t)^2\left(-\dfrac{1}{2}r^2t\right)^3(3st^3)^4$
24. $(^-4a)(a^2)(^-a^3) + 3a^2a^4$
25. $^-2r(rk^2)(^-5rm^2) + (^-r^2)(2rk)(4km^2)$
26. $(5a)(6a^2b)(3ab^3) + (4a^2)(3b^3)(2a^2b)$
27. $(5mn^2)(m^3n)(^-3p^2) + (8np)(3mp)(m^3n^2)$
28. $(2xy^2)^3 + (2xy^2)^2(6xy^2)$
29. $(3a)(a^2b)^3 + (2a)^2(^-a^5b^3)$

4-2   Dividing Monomials

If you add exponents when you multiply powers, then it seems reasonable to subtract exponents when you divide powers.

$$\frac{x^5}{x^3} = \frac{x \cdot x \cdot x \cdot x \cdot x}{x \cdot x \cdot x} \qquad \begin{array}{l} \leftarrow 5 \text{ factors} \\ \leftarrow 3 \text{ factors} \end{array}$$

$$= x \cdot x \qquad \leftarrow 2 \text{ or } (5 - 3) \text{ factors}$$

$$= x^{5-3} \text{ or } x^2.$$

This and other similar examples suggest the following property.

For all numbers a, and positive integers m and n,

$\dfrac{a^m}{a^n} = a^{m-n}$ if $a \neq 0$ and $m > n$.

Dividing Powers

examples

1 Simplify $\dfrac{p^9}{p^4}$.

$\dfrac{p^9}{p^4} = p^{9-4}$ *To divide powers, subtract the exponents.*

$\quad = p^5$

2 Simplify $\dfrac{(2xy)^5}{(x^2y)^2}$.

$\dfrac{(2xy)^5}{(x^2y)^2} = \dfrac{(2)^5(x)^5(y)^5}{(x^2)^2(y)^2}$

$\quad = \dfrac{32x^5y^5}{x^4y^2}$

$\quad = 32x^{(5-4)}y^{(5-2)}$

$\quad = 32x^1y^3 \text{ or } 32xy^3$

3 Simplify $\dfrac{(x^3y^4z^2)(y^5z^3)^2}{m^2y^3}$.

$\dfrac{(x^3y^4z^2)(y^5z^3)^2}{m^2y^3} = \dfrac{(x^3y^4z^2)(y^{10}z^6)}{m^2y^3}$

$\quad = \dfrac{x^3y^{14}z^8}{m^2y^3}$

$\quad = \dfrac{x^3y^{11}z^8}{m^2}$

The following pattern extends the properties of exponents to include zero as an exponent.

$$\frac{3^5}{3^1} = 3^{5-1} \text{ or } 3^4$$

$$\frac{3^4}{3^1} = 3^{4-1} \text{ or } 3^3 \qquad \frac{a^m}{a^n} = a^{m-n} \text{ if } a \neq 0.$$

$$\frac{3^3}{3^1} = 3^{3-1} \text{ or } 3^2 \qquad \textit{Notice that the exponent decreases}$$
$$\textit{by one in each step.}$$

$$\frac{3^2}{3^1} = 3^{2-1} \text{ or } 3^1$$

What number does $\frac{3^1}{3^1}$ represent? The pattern suggests that $\frac{3^1}{3^1} = 3^{1-1}$ or 3^0. But, you also know that $\frac{3^1}{3^1} = \frac{3}{3}$ or 1. Therefore, the value of 3^0 must be 1.

The example above and other similar examples suggest the following.

For any number a, except $a = 0$,
$a^0 = 1.$

Zero Exponent

The symbol 0^0 is not defined because 0^0 could stand for 0^{m-m} or $\frac{0^m}{0^m}$. The expression $\frac{0^m}{0^m}$ implies division by zero since $0^m = 0$. Division by zero is not defined. Thus, 0^0 is not defined.

examples

4 **Simplify $\frac{3^4 x^3}{3^4}$.**

$$\frac{3^4 x^3}{3^4} = (3^{4-4})x^3$$
$$= 3^0 x^3$$
$$= 1 \cdot x^3 \text{ or } x^3$$

5 **Evaluate $2^3 \cdot 7^0$.**

$$2^3 \cdot 7^0 = 2^3 \cdot 1$$
$$= 8 \cdot 1 \text{ or } 8$$

exercises

Exploratory Evaluate.

1. 2^0

2. $\left(\frac{10}{9}\right)^0$

3. $\left(\frac{3}{4}\right)^0$

4. $2(4^0)$

5. $(0.5)^0$

6. $(1.7)^0 + 3$

Simplify.

7. $\dfrac{r^4}{r}$

8. $\dfrac{m^{10}}{m^7}$

9. $\dfrac{x^6}{x^2}$

10. $\dfrac{y^7}{y^2}$

11. $\dfrac{a^6}{a^4}$

12. $\dfrac{m^6}{m^5}$

13. $\dfrac{n^5}{n^5}$

14. $k^{12}xm^0$

15. $p^3x\,(z^2r^3m^5)^0$

Written Evaluate.

1. $5^2 \cdot 6^0$

2. $7^0 \cdot 3^3$

3. $\left(\dfrac{3}{2}\right)^0 \cdot 2^0 \cdot 3^2$

4. $4(5a)^0$

5. $\dfrac{6 \cdot 3^0}{4}$

6. $(10^0)^2$

Simplify.

7. $\dfrac{12n^8}{4n^3}$

8. $\dfrac{-24s^8}{2s^5}$

9. $\dfrac{an^6}{n^5}$

10. $\dfrac{xy^7}{x^4}$

11. $\dfrac{48a^8}{12a}$

12. $\dfrac{15b^9}{3b^2}$

13. $\dfrac{4x^3}{28x}$

14. $\dfrac{12b^4}{60b}$

15. $\dfrac{-20y^5}{40y^2}$

16. $\dfrac{10m^4}{-30m}$

17. $\dfrac{4a^2b^3}{2ab^2}$

18. $\dfrac{16b^6c^5}{4b^4c^2}$

19. $\dfrac{1}{m^0 + n^0}$

20. $\dfrac{4}{x^0 + y^0}$

21. $\dfrac{-15r^5s^8}{5r^5s^2}$

22. $\dfrac{-27w^5t^7}{-3w^3t^2}$

23. $\dfrac{-2a^3b^6}{24a^2b^2}$

24. $\dfrac{-9c^4d^5}{-45c^3d^3}$

25. $\left(\dfrac{7^2p^4}{2^3p^{10}}\right)^0$

26. $\dfrac{3(a + 7)^4}{12(a + 7)^2}$

27. $\dfrac{-66m^{10}p^{13}}{33m^2p^2}$

28. $\dfrac{48w^{14}z^{10}}{-16w^{10}z^9}$

29. $\dfrac{60s^{10}t^{12}}{-12s^9t^{11}}$

30. $\dfrac{20n^5m^9}{20nm^7}$

31. $\dfrac{16b^6c^5}{(2b^2c)^2}$

32. $\dfrac{-39c^3d^4}{13(cd)^2}$

33. $\dfrac{-15r^5s^8(r^3s^2)}{45r^4s}$

34. $\dfrac{-3w^6t^7}{(-27w^3t^2)(wt)^2}$

35. $\dfrac{(x^3y^4z^5)^2}{(xyz)(x^2y^3z^4)}$

36. $\dfrac{16(a^4b^3c)^6 \cdot 2a^2(bc)^3}{a^4b^2c^6 + 7(a^2bc^3)^2}$

Skills Review Given $f(x) = x^2 + 2x - 3$, find each value.

1. $f(1)$

2. $f(^-3)$

3. $f\left(\dfrac{1}{2}\right)$

4. $f(^-0.8)$

5. $f(c)$

6. $f(c + 1)$

Given $g(x) = 2x^3 - x^2 + 4x + 6$, find each value.

7. $g(0)$

8. $g(2.5)$

9. $g(^-2)$

10. $g\left(-\dfrac{3}{4}\right)$

11. $g(a)$

12. $g(3 - a)$

Miki Merlin wants to take out a loan to buy a car. The bank loans Miki $600 at 10% interest for 1 year.

$$interest = principal \cdot rate \cdot time$$
$$i = p \cdot r \cdot t$$
$$= 600 \cdot 0.10 \cdot 1$$
$$= 60$$

The interest for 1 year is $60.

Miki's credit union also makes auto loans. They charge 1% interest on the *unpaid* balance each month. The interest is $600 · 1% or $6 the first month.

At first glance, Miki thought this would be more than the bank charges since $6 · 12 is $72.

But the interest is to be on the unpaid balance each month. Since the loan would be for 1 year, $600 ÷ 12 or $50 principal would be repaid the first month. The interest the second month is found as follows.

$$(\$600 - 50) \cdot 1\% = \$550 \cdot 0.01$$
$$= \$5.50$$

The interest for the second month is $5.50.

To find the total interest, continue to find each month's interest. Then find the sum. However, there is an easier way to find the total interest.

$$total\ interest = \frac{average}{principal} \cdot \frac{rate\ per}{month} \cdot \frac{number\ of}{months}$$
$$= \frac{600 + 50}{2} \cdot 1\% \cdot 12$$
$$= 325 \cdot 0.01 \cdot 12$$
$$= 39$$

The average principal is
$$\frac{\left(\begin{array}{c}first\ month's \\ principal\end{array} + \begin{array}{c}last\ month's \\ principal\end{array}\right)}{2}.$$

How can you find the last month's principal quickly?

The interest at the credit union would be $39.

Exercises   **Find the total interest at the bank for the following loans.**

1. $900 for 1 year at 12%

2. $1200 for 2 years at 14%

3. $1800 for $1\frac{1}{2}$ years at $13\frac{1}{2}\%$

4. $600 for $2\frac{1}{2}$ years at $15\frac{3}{4}\%$

Find the total interest at the credit union for the following loans. Assume the credit union charges $1\frac{1}{2}\%$ interest on the unpaid balance each month.

5. $950 for 1 year

6. $1800 for 2 years

7. $1200 for 15 months

8. $2500 for $2\frac{1}{2}$ years

4–3   Polynomials

A **polynomial** is either a monomial or the sum or difference of monomials. For example, $8x + y$, $3x^2 + 2x + 4$, and $5 - 3y + 5xy^2$ are polynomials. The expression $x^2 + \dfrac{2}{x}$ is *not* a polynomial since $\dfrac{2}{x}$ is not a monomial.

Each monomial in a polynomial is called a **term** of the polynomial. A polynomial with two unlike terms is called a *binomial*. A polynomial with three unlike terms is called a *trinomial*.

The degree of a polynomial is the degree of the monomial of greatest degree.

1   Find the degree of $5x^3 + 3x^2y^2 + 4xy^2 + 3x - 2$.

$5x^3$ has degree 3
$3x^2y^2$ has degree 4
$4xy^2$ has degree 3
$3x$ has degree 1
$^-2$ has degree 0

The terms of polynomials are usually arranged so that the powers of a variable are in ascending or descending order.

The degree of the polynomial is 4.

You can simplify polynomials by adding like terms as in Example **2**. Examples **3** and **4** show how to add or subtract polynomials by adding or subtracting like terms.

2   Simplify $6x^2y + 3xy^4 + 7y + 5xy^4 - 9x^2y + 8y$.

$$6x^2y + 3xy^4 + 7y + 5xy^4 - 9x^2y + 8y = (6x^2y - 9x^2y) + (3xy^4 + 5xy^4) + (7y + 8y)$$
$$= (6 - 9)x^2y + (3 + 5)xy^4 + (7 + 8)y$$
$$= {}^-3x^2y + 8xy^4 + 15y$$

3   Add $7m^2k - 8mk^2 + 19k$ and $18mk^2 - 3k$.

$$(7m^2k - 8mk^2 + 19k) + (18mk^2 - 3k) = \underline{7m^2k} - \underline{8mk^2 + 18mk^2} + \underline{19k - 3k}$$
$$= 7m^2k + \qquad 10mk^2 \qquad + \qquad 16k$$

4   Find $(2x^2 - 3xy + 5y^2) - (4x^2 - 3xy - 2y^2)$.

$$(2x^2 - 3xy + 5y^2) - (4x^2 - 3xy - 2y^2) = \underline{2x^2 - 4x^2} - \underline{3xy + 3xy} + \underline{5y^2 + 2y^2}$$
$$= \quad {}^-2x^2 \quad + \quad 0xy \quad + \quad 7y^2$$
$$= \quad {}^-2x^2 \quad + \qquad\quad 7y^2$$

The distributive property is used to multiply polynomials.

5 **Find $3x(4xy^3 - 7x^2y - 3y)$.**

$$3x(4xy^3 - 7x^2y - 3y) = 3x \cdot 4xy^3 - 3x \cdot 7x^2y - 3x \cdot 3y$$
$$= 12x^2y^3 - 21x^3y - 9xy$$

6 **Find $(2a - 3b)(3a + 4ab + b)$.**

$$(2a - 3b)(3a + 4ab + b)$$
$$= 2a(3a + 4ab + b) - 3b(3a + 4ab + b)$$
$$= 2a(3a) + 2a(4ab) + 2a(b) - 3b(3a) - 3b(4ab) - 3b(b)$$
$$= 6a^2 + 8a^2b + 2ab - 9ab - 12ab^2 - 3b^2$$
$$= 6a^2 + 8a^2b - 7ab - 12ab^2 - 3b^2$$

7 **Find $(x + 4)(x + 11)$.**

$$(x + 4)(x + 11) = (x + 4) \cdot x + (x + 4) \cdot 11$$
$$= (x \cdot x) + (4 \cdot x) + (x \cdot 11) + (4 \cdot 11)$$
$$= x^2 + 4x + 11x + 44$$
$$= x^2 + 15x + 44$$

The following process can be used to multiply binomials.

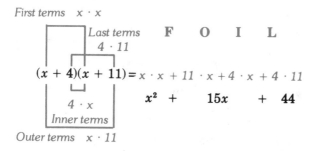

This process is called the **FOIL** rule.

The product of two binomials is the sum of the products of

F	the *first* terms,
O	the *outer* terms,
I	the *inner* terms, and
L	the *last* terms.

*FOIL Rule for
Multiplying Binomials*

8 Find $(2x + 3)(x - 5)$.

$$
\begin{array}{lcccc}
& \text{F} & \text{O} & \text{I} & \text{L} \\
(2x + 3)(x - 5) = & 2x \cdot x + & 2x \cdot {}^-5 + & 3 \cdot x + & 3 \cdot {}^-5 \\
= & 2x^2 + & 10x + & 3x - & 15 \\
= & 2x^2 - & & 7x & - 15
\end{array}
$$

9 Find $(5x - 3)(2x - 7)$.

$$
\begin{array}{lcccc}
& \text{F} & \text{O} & \text{I} & \text{L} \\
(5x - 3)(2x - 7) = & 5x \cdot 2x + & 5x \cdot {}^-7 + & {}^-3 \cdot 2x + & {}^-3 \cdot {}^-7 \\
= & 10x^2 - & 35x - & 6x + & 21 \\
= & 10x^2 - & & 41x & + 21
\end{array}
$$

exercises

Exploratory Find the degree of each polynomial.

1. $3x^2 + 27xy$

2. $x^2 + 2x + 3$

3. $a^8 + a^7b + a^6b^2 - a^2b^6 - ab^7 - b^8$

4. $3x^4y^2 - 5x^2y + 3$

5. $3r^5 - 3r^4 - 7r - 5$

6. $z^5 + 5z^4 + 9z^3 + 9z^2$

7. $m^3 + 2mn^2 + 4n^3$

8. $5xy - 2x^2 - 3y^2$

9. $13xy^7 + 36x^3y^5 - 2x^4y^5 - xy$

10. $16x^4yz + 12x^2y^3z - 24x^3y^2z - 18xy^4z$

Written Simplify each expression by performing the indicated operations.

1. $(7x - 2y) + (9x + 4y)$

2. $(^-12y - 6y^2) + (^-7y + 6y^2)$

3. $(3a + 5b) - (9a + b)$

4. $(^-5x - 6x^2) - (4x + 5x^2)$

5. $(^-3x + 5y - 10z) + (^-6x + 8z - 6y)$

6. $(7t + 4m + a) + (^-3a - 7t + m)$

7. $(7m^2 + 9m + 3) - (3m^2 + 8m + 2)$

8. $(3a^2 - 5d + 17) - (^-a^2 + 5d - 3)$

9. $(2x^2 + x + 5) + (3x^2 - x - 4)$

10. $(3y^2 + 5y - 7) + (2y^2 - 7y + 10)$

11. $^-4(a + 2b) + 7(a + b)$

12. $4(a^2 - b^2) + 3(a^2 + b^2)$

13. $(8r^2 + 5r + 14) - (7r^2 + 6r + 8)$

14. $(4k^2 + 10k - 14) - (3k^2 + 7k - 5)$

15. $(4x + 11) - (3x^2 + 7x - 3)$

16. $(10n^2 - 3nt + 4t^2) - (3n^2 + 5nt)$

17. $(4x^4 + 3x^3 + x - 7) + (3x^4 - 5x^3 + 7x^2 - 3x + 8)$

18. $(8b^5 + 4b^3 + 7b^2 - 15) + (3b^5 + 7b^3 - b + 14)$

19. $(2m^7 + 3m^5 + 2m^3 - 18) - (m^7 + 3m^4 + m^3 + 2m^2)$

20. $(x^3 - 3x^2y + 4xy^2 + y^3) - (7x^3 + x^2y - 9xy^2 + y^3)$

21. $(^-1 + x^3y - 5x^2y^2) - (xy^3 - 5x^2y^2 - 7 + 4x^3y)$

22. $^-7a^2(a^3 - ab)$

23. $4f(gf^2 - bh)$

24. $3a^3b^2(^-2ab^2 + 4a^2b - 7a)$

25. $^-5mn^2(^-3m^2n + 6m^3n - 3m^4n^4)$

26. $4ax^2(^-9a^3x^2 + 8a^2x^3 + 6a^4x^4)$

27. $17b^3d^2(^-4b^2d^2 - 11b^3d^3 - 5bd^4)$

28. $2y^4\left(\dfrac{3}{y} + \dfrac{8}{y^2} - \dfrac{1}{y^3}\right)$

29. $8x^2\left(3x^2 + \dfrac{1}{4} - \dfrac{1}{2x} + \dfrac{1}{x^2}\right)$

30. $(x + 7)(x + 2)$

31. $(m - 7)(m + 5)$

32. $(m^2 + 5)(m^2 - 4)$

33. $(y^2 + y)(y^2 + 5)$

34. $(3y - 8)(2y + 7)$

35. $(2x + 7)(3x + 5)$

36. $(2r^2 + 3)(r^2 - 5)$

37. $(2x + 3y)(3x - 5y)$

38. $(6a - 5)(7a - 9)$

You can use the **FOIL** method to find the following products.

$$(a + b)^2 = a^2 + 2ab + b^2 \qquad (a - b)^2 = a^2 - 2ab + b^2 \qquad (a + b)(a - b) = a^2 - b^2$$

Use the patterns shown above to find each product.

39. $(m + 4)^2$
40. $(x - 8)^2$
41. $(y - 2)^2$
42. $(k + 6)^2$
43. $(y - 5)(y + 5)$
44. $(2p + q^3)^2$
45. $(x - 3y)^2$
46. $(a + 6b)(a - 6b)$
47. $(4m - 3n)^2$
48. $(5r - 2)^2$
49. $(1 + 4r)^2$
50. $(6a + 2)^2$
51. $(4a - 2b)(4a + 2b)$
52. $(5x + 12)(5x - 12)$
53. $(x^3 - y)(x^3 + y)$

Find each product.

54. $(a - 1)(a^2 - 2a - 1)$
55. $(2x - 3)(x^2 - 3x - 8)$
56. $(x - y)(x^2 + xy + y^3)$
57. $(a + b)(a^2 - ab + b^2)$
58. $(m - 4)(3m^2 + 5m - 4)$
59. $(2t - 5)(t^2 + 7t + 8)$
60. $r(r - 2)(r - 3)$
61. $p(p + 5)(p - 1)$
62. $(b + 1)(b - 2)(b + 3)$
63. $(2x - 3)(x + 1)(3x - 2)$
64. $(2a + 1)(a - 2)^2$
65. $(a - 2b)^2(2a + 3b)$
66. $(a - b)(a^2 + ab + b^2)$
67. $(2k + 3)(k^2 - 7k + 21)$
68. $(x^2 + y)(x^2 + xy + y^2)$
69. $(z^2 + r)(z + zr + r^2)$
70. $(a - 2)(a^2 + 6a + 9)$
71. $(y + 4)(y^2 - 7y + 12)$

Challenge   Find each product.

1. $(x^2 + 2x - 3)(5x^2 + 3x - 7)$
2. $(3r^2 + 2d + 1)(5r^2 - 2r - 6)$
3. $(a^2 - ab + b^2)(a^2 + ab + b^2)$
4. $(4m^2 - m + 8)(m^3 + 2m^2 + 3m + 4)$

Special Products   excursions in algebra

You know that $(x - y)(x + y) = x^2 - y^2$. This fact can be used to multiply numbers in your head. Suppose you want to find $36 \cdot 44$. Notice that $36 = 40 - 4$ and $44 = 40 + 4$.

$$\begin{aligned} 36 \cdot 44 &= (40 - 4)(40 + 4) \\ &= 40^2 - 4^2 \\ &= 1600 - 16 \\ &= 1584 \end{aligned}$$

Let $x = 40$ and $y = 4$ in
$(x - y)(x + y) = x^2 - y^2$.

Try this method to calculate $27 \cdot 33$, $19 \cdot 21$, and $53 \cdot 67$ mentally.

Here is another method to find some products mentally. You know the following.

$$(x + 1)^2 = x^2 + 2x + 1$$

Suppose you want to find $(101)^2$.

$$\begin{aligned} (101)^2 &= (100)^2 + 2(100) + 1 \\ &= 10000 + 200 + 1 \\ &= 10,201 \end{aligned}$$

Let $x = 100$ in the expression
$(x + 1)^2 = x^2 + 2x + 1$.
Here $2x + 1 = 201$ and $100^2 = 10000$
can be calculated mentally.

Use this method to find the square of a number $(x + 1)$ when you already know the square of x. Can you find 31^2, 13^2, and 201^2 mentally?

4–4   Factoring

Suppose you wish to write $10x^2 + 6x$ in factored form. First find the greatest common factor (GCF) of $10x^2$ and $6x$.

$$10x^2 = 2 \cdot 5 \cdot x \cdot x$$

$$6x = 2 \cdot 3 \cdot x$$

GCF is the greatest factor that a set of terms has in common.

The greatest common factor (GCF) of $10x^2$ and $6x$ is $2x$.

Now use the distributive property to factor the expression.

$$10x^2 + 6x = (2x \cdot 5x) + (2x \cdot 3)$$
$$= 2x(5x + 3)$$

$10x^2 + 6x$ written in factored form is $2x(5x + 3)$.

examples

1 **Factor $12xy^2 - 8x^2y$.**

$$12xy^2 - 8x^2y = (2 \cdot 2 \cdot 3 \cdot x \cdot y \cdot y) - (2 \cdot 2 \cdot 2 \cdot x \cdot x \cdot y)$$
$$= (4xy \cdot 3y) - (4xy \cdot 2x) \qquad \textit{4xy is the GCF.}$$
$$= 4xy(3y - 2x)$$

2 **Factor $2m^2y + 3my^2 - 5m^2y^2 + 7my^3$.**

$$2m^2y + 3my^2 - 5m^2y^2 + 7my^3$$
$$= (2 \cdot m \cdot m \cdot y) + (3 \cdot m \cdot y \cdot y) - (5 \cdot m \cdot m \cdot y \cdot y) + (7 \cdot m \cdot y \cdot y \cdot y)$$
$$= (my \cdot 2m) + (my \cdot 3y) - (my \cdot 5my) + (my \cdot 7y^2) \qquad \textit{my is the GCF.}$$
$$= my(2m + 3y - 5my + 7y^2)$$

You have found products like $(x - 7)(x + 7)$.

$$(x - 7)(x + 7) = x \cdot x + 7 \cdot x - 7 \cdot x - 7 \cdot 7$$
$$= x^2 \qquad\qquad - 7^2$$
$$= x^2 - 49$$

To factor $x^2 - 49$, reverse the steps.

$$x^2 - 49 = x^2 - 7^2$$
$$= x^2 + 7x - 7x - 7^2$$
$$= x(x + 7) - 7(x + 7)$$
$$= (x - 7)(x + 7)$$

Factoring $x^2 - 49$ shows the following pattern.

For any numbers a and b, $a^2 - b^2 = (a - b)(a + b)$.

Factoring Difference of Two Squares

3 **Factor $16a^2 - 4$.**

$16a^2 - 4 = 4(4a^2 - 1)$ *4 is the GCF.*

$\qquad\qquad = 4[(2a)^2 - (1)^2]$

$\qquad\qquad = 4(2a - 1)(2a + 1)$

4 **Factor $4x^2 - \dfrac{1}{9}$.**

$4x^2 - \dfrac{1}{9} = (2x)^2 - \left(\dfrac{1}{3}\right)^2$

$\qquad\qquad = \left(2x - \dfrac{1}{3}\right)\left(2x + \dfrac{1}{3}\right)$

You know how to factor the difference of two squares. Can you factor the difference of two cubes? Consider $a^3 - b^3$.

$a^3 - b^3 = a^3 - a^2b + a^2b - b^3$ *Notice that $^-a^2b + a^2b = 0$.*

$\qquad\quad = a^2(a - b) + b(a^2 - b^2)$ *Distributive Property*

$\qquad\quad = a^2(a - b) + b(a - b)(a + b)$ *Factor.*

$\qquad\quad = (a - b)[a^2 + b(a + b)]$ *Distributive Property*

$\qquad\quad = (a - b)(a^2 + ab + b^2)$ *Multiply.*

A similar method can be used to show how to factor the sum of two cubes. That is, $a^3 + b^3 = (a + b)(a^2 - ab + b^2)$.

> **For any numbers a and b,**
> $a^3 + b^3 = (a + b)(a^2 - ab + b^2)$ **and,**
> $a^3 - b^3 = (a - b)(a^2 + ab + b^2)$.

Factoring Sum or Difference of Cubes

5 **Factor $m^3 + 27$.**

$m^3 + 27 = m^3 + 3^3$

$\qquad\quad = (m + 3)(m^2 - m \cdot 3 + 3^2)$

$\qquad\quad = (m + 3)(m^2 - 3m + 9)$

6 **Factor $27y^3 - 8x^3$.**

$27y^3 - 8x^3 = (3y)^3 - (2x)^3$

$\qquad\qquad = (3y - 2x)[(3y)^2 + 3y \cdot 2x + (2x)^2]$

$\qquad\qquad = (3y - 2x)(9y^2 + 6xy + 4x^2)$

exercises

Exploratory Factor.

1. $6a + 6b$
2. $8m - 2n$
3. $ab + ac$
4. $y^3 - y^2$
5. $r^2 - 9$
6. $x^2 - 49$
7. $100 - m^2$
8. $y^2 - 81z^2$
9. $2x^2 + 6y + 8b$
10. $x^2 + xy + 3x$
11. $3a^2 + 6a + 9y$
12. $r^4 + r^3s + r^2s^2$
13. $25a^2 - b^2$
14. $36s^2 - 100$
15. $5x^2y - 10xy^2$
16. $^-15x^2 - 5x$
17. $8m^2 + 4am + 16my$
18. $7pm + 2p^2 - 14px$
19. $x^3 + 8$
20. $b^3 - 27$
21. $r^3 - 1$

Written Factor.

1. $b^2 - 144$
2. $y^3 - 1$
3. $1 + r^3$
4. $m^2 - 121$
5. $8 - x^3$
6. $8a^3 + 1$
7. $3d^2 - 48$
8. $b^3 - 8a^3$
9. $27 + x^3$
10. $2y^3 - 98y$
11. $8 + x^3$
12. $a^3b^3 - 27$
13. $4a^2 - 9$
14. $2r^3 - 16s^3$
15. $9y^2 - 64$
16. $3m^3 + 24p^3$
17. $8b^3 - 27x^3$
18. $9p^2 - 4q^2$
19. $ab - a^4b$
20. $16s^2 - 81r^2$
21. $r^4 - s^4$
22. $r^3s^3 - 8s^3$
23. $64y^3 - 1$
24. $m^6 - 27$
25. $y^6 + 125$
26. $16y^4 - k^4$
27. $1 - 8m^6$
28. $16x^4 - 196y^4$
29. $(a + b)^2 - m^2$
30. $(x - y)^2 - z^2$

Power Key

Many calculators have a key that can be used to find the powers of a number other than 2. This key, , is called the "y to the x power key." To use this key, first enter y, press the key, and then enter x.

Example: If $f(x) = 4x^4 - 3x^3$, find $f(2.6)$.

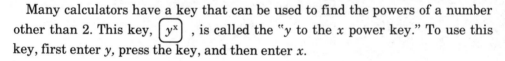

ENTER: 4 $\times$ 2.6 y^x 4 $-$ 3 $\times$ 2.6 y^x 3 $=$

DISPLAY: 4   2.6   4 182.7904 3   2.6   3 130.0624

Exercises Use the y to the x power key to find each of the following.

1. $(4.9)^5$
2. $7.7^3 + \sqrt{9.09}$
3. $91.6^3 - 13.5^4$
4. $\sqrt{(1102 - 932)^3}$
5. $(1.017^{15} + \sqrt{12.8})^3$
6. $\left(\frac{1}{219}\right)^2 - \left(\frac{7}{68}\right)^4$
7. Show that $45^3 + 13^3$ is equal to $(45 + 13)(45^2 - 45 \cdot 13 + 13^2)$.
8. Show that $45^3 - 13^3$ is equal to $(45 - 13)(45^2 + 45 \cdot 13 + 13^2)$.
9. Which is larger, 4^{10} or 10^4?
10. If $f(x) = x^5 - 3x^4 + 2x^3 - 1$, find $f\left(1\frac{213}{365}\right)$. (*Hint:* Store the value $1\frac{213}{365}$ in memory.)

4-5 Factoring Trinomials

When factoring trinomials, first look for the common monomial factors.

$$18x^3 - 48x^2y + 32xy^2 = 2x \cdot 9x^2 - 2x \cdot 24xy + 2x \cdot 16y^2$$
$$= 2x(9x^2 - 24xy + 16y^2)$$

The trinomial $9x^2 - 24xy + 16y^2$ can be factored further. Use one of the following patterns.

> **For any numbers a and b,**
> $$a^2 + 2ab + b^2 = (a + b)^2 \text{ and,}$$
> $$a^2 - 2ab + b^2 = (a - b)^2$$

Factoring Perfect Squares

example

1 Factor $9x^2 - 24xy + 16y^2$.

$$9x^2 - 24xy + 16y^2 = (3x)^2 - 2(12xy) + (4y)^2$$
$$= (3x)^2 - 2(3x)(4y) + (4y)^2$$
$$= (3x - 4y)^2$$

Use the pattern
$a^2 - 2ab + b^2 = (a - b)^2.$

Thus, $9x^2 - 24xy + 16y^2$ in factored form is $(3x - 4y)^2$.

Many trinomials like $x^2 - 5x + 6$ are *not* perfect squares. They can be factored by reversing the following pattern.

$$(x + r)(x + s) = \underline{x \cdot x} + \underline{x \cdot s + r \cdot x} + \underline{r \cdot s}$$
$$= x^2 + (r + s)x + rs$$

For $x^2 - 5x + 6$, the middle coefficient $^-5$ corresponds to $r + s$. The 6 corresponds to rs. You must find two numbers, r and s, whose sum is $^-5$ and whose product is 6.

Factors of 6	Sum of Factors
1, 6	7
$^-1, ^-6$	$^-7$
2, 3	5
$^-2, ^-3$	$^-5$

The two numbers are $^-2$ and $^-3$.

$$x^2 - 5x + 6 = (x - 2)(x - 3)$$

2 Factor $x^2 - 3x - 18$.

Factors of $^-18$	Sum of Factors
$^-1, 18$	17
$1, ^-18$	$^-17$
$^-3, 6$	3
$3, ^-6$	$^-3$
$^-2, 9$	7
$2, ^-9$	$^-7$

The two numbers are 3 and $^-6$. The product of 3 and $^-6$ is $^-18$ and the sum of 3 and $^-6$ is $^-3$.

$$x^2 - 3x - 18 = (x + 3)(x - 6)$$

Consider $2x^2 + 7x + 6$. The coefficient of x^2 is *not* 1. The factors of $2x^2 + 7x + 6$ can be found by reversing the following pattern.

$$(ax + b)(cx + d) = (ax + b)cx + (ax + b)d$$
$$= acx^2 + bcx + adx + bd$$
$$= acx^2 + (bc + ad)x + bd$$

Notice that the product of the coefficient of the x^2 term and the constant term is $abcd$. The product of the two coefficients of the x term, bc and ad, is also $abcd$.

For $2x^2 + 7x + 6$, the product of the x^2 coefficient and the constant is 12.

$$2x^2 + 7x + 6$$

The two coefficients of x must have a sum of 7 and a product of 12. The only possibility is 3 and 4 because $3 + 4 = 7$ and $3 \cdot 4 = 12$.

$$2x^2 + (4x + 3x) + 6$$

Consider the factors of 12 which have a sum of 7.

$$
\begin{aligned}
2x^2 + 7x + 6 &= 2x^2 + (4x + 3x) + 6 \\
&= (2x^2 + 4x) + (3x + 6) &&\text{\textit{Associative Property}} \\
&= 2x(x + 2) + 3(x + 2) &&\text{\textit{Distributive Property}} \\
&= (2x + 3)(x + 2) &&\text{\textit{Distributive Property}}
\end{aligned}
$$

3 Factor $6m^2 + 19m + 10$.

The product of the m^2 coefficient and the constant is $6 \cdot 10$ or 60. Thus, the coefficients of m must have a sum of 19 and a product of 60. The only possibility is 4 and 15, because $4 + 15 = 19$ and $4 \cdot 15 = 60$.

$$6m^2 + 19m + 10 = 6m^2 + (4m + 15m) + 10$$
$$= (6m^2 + 4m) + (15m + 10)$$
$$= 2m(3m + 2) + 5(3m + 2)$$
$$= (2m + 5)(3m + 2)$$

4 Factor $8z^2 - 27z - 20$.

$8(^-20) = {}^-160$

$$8z^2 - 27z - 20 = 8z^2 + (^-32z + 5z) - 20 \qquad \textit{Notice that } {}^-32 + 5 = {}^-27 \textit{ and}$$
$$= (8z^2 - 32z) + (5z - 20) \qquad (^-32)(5) = {}^-160.$$
$$= 8z(z - 4) + 5(z - 4)$$
$$= (8z + 5)(z - 4)$$

exercises

Exploratory Factor each expression.

1. $y^2 + 6y + 9$

2. $r^2 + 16r + 64$

3. $k^2 - 8k + 16$

4. $n^2 - 10n + 25$

5. $a^2 + 5a + 6$

6. $b^2 + 7b + 6$

7. $p^2 - 5p + 4$

8. $s^2 - 6s + 8$

9. $m^2 - 7m + 10$

10. $2y^2 + 7y + 3$

Written Factor each expression.

1. $a^2 + 12a + 35$

2. $d^2 + 4d - 21$

3. $f^2 - 18f + 81$

4. $r^2 - 6r + 9$

5. $k^2 + 12k + 36$

6. $p^2 + 14p + 49$

7. $3y^2 + 5y + 2$

8. $4x^2 + 11x + 6$

9. $4z^2 - 20z + 21$

10. $3t^2 + 13t + 12$

11. $a^2 + 4ab + 4b^2$

12. $m^2 - 6mk + 9k^2$

13. $p^2 - 4bp + 4b^2$

14. $9a^2 - 12ab + 4b^2$

15. $4r^2 - 20rs + 25s^2$

16. $x^3 + 2x^2 - 35x$

17. $4k^2 + 26k + 30$

18. $6d^2 + 33d - 63$

19. $4h^2 + 8h - 96$

20. $2a^3 - 7a^2 - 15a$

21. $2y^3 - 8y^2 - 42y$

22. $3m^3 + 21m^2 + 36m$

23. $18d^2 - 19d - 12$

24. $9g^2 - 12g + 4$

25. $20x^2 + 17xy - 24y^2$

26. $15a^2 - 13ab + 2b^2$

4–6   More Factoring

Sometimes several kinds of factoring may be used to completely factor a polynomial. Rearranging and grouping terms may be helpful.

1 **Factor $a^2 - 2ab + a - 2b$.**

$$a^2 - 2ab + a - 2b = a(a - 2b) + 1(a - 2b) \qquad \text{Group the terms in pairs and factor.}$$
$$= (a + 1)(a - 2b) \qquad \text{(a − 2b) is the GCF.}$$

These factors could be found another way.

$$a^2 - 2ab + a - 2b = a^2 + a - 2ab - 2b \qquad \text{Commutative Property}$$
$$= a(a + 1) - 2b(a + 1)$$
$$= (a - 2b)(a + 1) \qquad \text{(a + 1) is the GCF.}$$

Example **2** groups and factors the difference of two squares.

2 **Factor $x^3 + 2x^2 - x - 2$.**

$$x^3 + 2x^2 - x - 2 = x^2(x + 2) - 1(x + 2) \qquad \text{Group the terms in pairs and factor.}$$
$$= (x^2 - 1)(x + 2) \qquad \text{(x + 2) is the GCF.}$$
$$= (x - 1)(x + 1)(x + 2) \qquad \text{Factor } x^2 - 1.$$

These factors could be found another way.

$$x^3 + 2x^2 - x - 2 = x^3 - x + 2x^2 - 2 \qquad \text{Commutative Property}$$
$$= x(x^2 - 1) + 2(x^2 - 1) \qquad \text{Group and factor.}$$
$$= (x^2 - 1)(x + 2) \qquad \text{(x² − 1) is the GCF.}$$
$$= (x - 1)(x + 1)(x + 2) \qquad \text{Factor } x^2 - 1.$$

The next example groups, finds a perfect square trinomial, and then factors the difference of two squares.

3 **Factor $a^2 + 4ab - 9x^2 + 4b^2$.**

$$a^2 + 4ab - 9x^2 + 4b^2 = (a^2 + 4ab + 4b^2) - 9x^2 \qquad \text{Group the terms of the trinomial square.}$$
$$= [(a)^2 + 2(a \cdot 2b) + (2b)^2] - (3x)^2$$
$$= \qquad (a + 2b)^2 \qquad\qquad - (3x)^2$$
$$= [(a + 2b) - 3x][(a + 2b) + 3x] \qquad \text{Factor the difference of squares.}$$
$$= (a + 2b - 3x)(a + 2b + 3x)$$

The following checklist can be used to help you factor a given polynomial.

1. Check for the greatest common monomial factor.

2. Check for special products.
   a. If there are *two terms,* look for difference of squares, sum of cubes, difference of cubes.
   b. If there are *three terms,* look for perfect squares.

3. Try other factoring methods.
   a. If there are *three terms,* try the trinomial pattern.
   b. If there are *four or more terms,* try grouping.

examples

4 **Factor $14aby + 14amy + 7b^2y - 7m^2y$.**

$$14aby + 14amy + 7b^2y - 7m^2y = 7y[2ab + 2am + b^2 - m^2] \quad \text{7y is the GCF.}$$
$$= 7y[2a(b + m) + (b - m)(b + m)]$$
$$= 7y(2a + b - m)(b + m)$$

5 **Factor $m^3 - 3m^2a + 3ma^2 - a^3$.**

$$m^3 - 3m^2a + 3ma^2 - a^3 = (m^3 - a^3) - (3m^2a - 3ma^2)$$
$$= (m^2 + ma + a^2)(m - a) - 3ma(m - a)$$
$$= (m^2 + ma + a^2 - 3ma)(m - a)$$
$$= (m^2 - 2ma + a^2)(m - a)$$
$$= (m - a)^2(m - a) \quad (m - a)(m - a)$$
$$= (m - a)^3 \quad m^2 - 2ama \quad a^2$$

6 **Factor $6a^2 + 27a - 15$.**

$$6a^2 + 27a - 15 = 3(2a^2 + 9a - 5) \quad \text{3 is the GCF.}$$
$$= 3(2a - 1)(a + 5)$$

7 **Factor $r^3 - r^2 - 30r$.**

$$r^3 - r^2 - 30r = r(r^2 - r - 30) \quad \text{r is the GCF.}$$
$$= r(r - 6)(r + 5)$$

8 **Factor $5y^6 - 5y^2$.**

$$5y^6 - 5y^2 = 5y^2(y^4 - 1)$$
$$= 5y^2(y^2 + 1)(y^2 - 1)$$
$$= 5y^2(y^2 + 1)(y + 1)(y - 1)$$

exercises

Exploratory Complete each factorization.

1. $y(3y - 2) + 4k(3y - 2)$
2. $3x(a - 2b) - 4(a - 2b)$
3. $a(y - b) - c(y - b)$
4. $3m(m - 7) + k(m - 7)$
5. $a(a + b) - 2(a + b)$
6. $r(r - 4) - p(r - 4)$
7. $2x^2(x - 3) + (x - 3)$
8. $b(3b - 2y) - (3b - 2y)$
9. $(x + y)^2 - \frac{1}{4}$
10. $(2a + b)^2 - \frac{1}{16}$
11. $m^2 - (k - 3)^2$
12. $4a^2 - (3b + 1)^2$
13. $k^2(k + 4) - 9(k + 4)$
14. $a^2(x + y) - b^2(x + y)$
15. $(x + y)(x - y) - 4(x - y)$
16. $(a + b) + 3(a - b)(a + b)$
17. $6x(a + b) + 4y(a + b) + 7(a + b)$
18. $7a(x + y - z) + 8b(x + y - z)$

Written Factor.

1. $3y^2 + 12yk - 2y - 8k$
2. $3ax - 6bx - 4a + 8b$
3. $ay - ab - cy + cb$
4. $3m^2 - 21m + mk - 7k$
5. $a^2 + ab - 2a - 2b$
6. $r^2 - 4r - rp + 4p$
7. $2x^3 - 6x^2 + x - 3$
8. $3b^2 - 2by - 3b + 2y$
9. $x^2 + 2xy + y^2 - r^2$
10. $4a^2 + 4ab - y^2 + b^2$
11. $m^2 - k^2 + 6k - 9$
12. $4a^2 - 6b - 9b^2 - 1$
13. $k^3 + 4k^2 - 9k - 36$
14. $a^2x - b^2x + a^2y - b^2y$
15. $x^2 - y^2 + 4y - 4x$
16. $a + b + 3a^2 - 3b^2$
17. $a^2 - b^2 + 8b - 16$
18. $a^2 - 4a + 4 - 25x^2$
19. $2ab + 2am - b - m$
20. $y^3 + y^2 - y - 1$
21. $x^2 + 6x + 9 - a^2$
22. $n^2 + 2nx - 1 + x^2$
23. $a^2 - a + \frac{1}{4} - y^2$
24. $\frac{1}{16} - 9x^2 + 12xy - 4y^2$
25. $x^3 + x^2y - xyz - x^2z$
26. $p^2 - q^2 - 2p - 2q$
27. $18x^2 - 21x - 9$
28. $2y^3 - 10y^2 - 72y$
29. $b^2 - y^2 - 2yp - p^2$
30. $a^2 + 2ab + b^2 - 9$
31. $2ab + 2am + b^2 - m^2$
32. $3pq + 3ps + q^2 - s^2$
33. $8a^3 + 27$
34. $16m^3 - 2$
35. $3r - 81r^4$
36. $7p^3 + 56s^3$
37. $x^3 + y^3 - x^2y - xy^2$
38. $t^3 + 125 + 5t^2 + 25t$
39. $x^4 - 13x^2 + 36$
40. $y^4 - 14y^2 + 45$
41. $(r - p)^3 + 4rp(r - p)$
42. $a(a + 1)(a + 2) - 3a(a + 1)$
43. $4ax + 14ay - 10bx - 35by$
44. $r^2 - rt - rt^2 + t^3$
45. $8ax - 6x - 12a + 9$
46. $10x^2 - 14xy - 15x + 21y$

Challenge Factor.

1. $a^4 - 12a^3b + 24a^2b^2 - 8ab^3$
2. $a^4 - 16a^2 + 3a^3 - 48a$
3. $x^3y - 3x^2y - 6xy + 8y$
4. $m^3n + m^2n - mn^3 - mn^2$
5. $4x^2 + 12xy + 9y^2 - z^2$
6. $m^2 - 8m + 16 - 4a^2 + 28ab - 49b^2$
7. $25x^2 - y^2 - 12y - 36$
8. $4x^2 - 12x + 9 - 9x^4$

Beth Merritt is a heating analyst. She examines heating systems and recommends how they can be made more efficient. These recommendations may range from more or better insulation to a change in fuel.

A small hotel has a hot water system that is heated by fuel oil. Assume that the heating is 70% efficient. The following shows how to find the amount of oil needed to heat 1000 pounds of water from 52°F to 212°F.

heat required = weight × specific heat × temperature change
$$= 1000 \text{ lb} \times 1 \text{ Btu/lb°F} \times (212 - 52)°F$$
$$= 1000 \cdot 1 \cdot 160 \text{ Btu}$$
$$= 160{,}000 \text{ Btu}$$

Btu stands for British thermal unit. It is the amount of heat required to raise the temperature of water 1 °F.

But the heating is only 70% efficient.

160,000 ÷ 70% or 228,571 Btu are needed.   *Divide by the efficiency of the heating.*

Assume the oil provides 19,000 Btu per pound and weighs about 7 pounds per gallon.

228,571 ÷ 19,000 or 12 pounds of oil are needed.

12 ÷ 7 or 1.71 gallons of oil are needed.

Exercises
Find the amount of fuel oil needed if one of the conditions described above is changed as follows. Water weighs 8.34 pounds per gallon.

1. 1000 gallons of water are heated.
2. The water temperature is 42°F.
3. The heating is 75% efficient.
4. The oil provides 18,500 Btu per pound.
5. The oil weighs 7.2 pounds per gallon.

4–7   Dividing Polynomials

You can use the properties of exponents to divide a monomial by a monomial. You also use these properties to divide a polynomial by a monomial.

examples

1 **Divide $16x^4$ by $8x^3$.**

$$16x^4 \div 8x^3 = \frac{16x^4}{8x^3}$$
$$= \frac{16}{8} \cdot x^{4-3}$$
$$= 2x$$

2 **Find $\dfrac{-49r^3s^5}{7rs^2}$.**

$$\frac{-49r^3s^5}{7rs^2} = \frac{-49}{7} \cdot r^{3-1}s^{5-2}$$
$$= -7r^2s^3$$

3 **Find $\dfrac{36m^4y^4 - 18m^3y}{6m^2y}$.**

$$\frac{36m^4y^4 - 18m^3y}{6m^2y} = \frac{36m^4y^4}{6m^2y} - \frac{18m^3y}{6m^2y}$$
$$= \frac{36}{6} \cdot m^{4-2}y^{4-1} - \frac{18}{6} \cdot m^{3-2}y^{1-1}$$
$$= 6m^2y^3 - 3m \qquad y^{1-1} = y^0 \text{ or } 1.$$
$$= 3m(2my^3 - 1)$$

Dividing a polynomial by a polynomial is similar to long division. The following example reviews long division with numbers.

example

4 **Divide 883 by 21.**

$$
\begin{array}{r}
42 \\
21\overline{)883} \\
840 \\
\hline
43 \\
42 \\
\hline
1
\end{array}
$$

Subtract $40 \cdot 21$.

Subtract $2 \cdot 21$.

Stop when remainder is less than 21. $\dfrac{883}{21} = 42\dfrac{1}{21}$

You use a similar process to divide polynomials. Remember, you can only add or subtract like terms.

examples

5 **Divide $8y^2 + 8y + 3$ by $2y + 1$.**

$$
\begin{array}{r}
4y + 2 \\
2y + 1 \overline{)8y^2 + 8y + 3} \\
\end{array}
$$

$8y^2 + 4y$ *Subtract $4y(2y + 1)$.*

$4y + 3$

$4y + 2$ *Subtract $2(2y + 1)$.*

1 *Stop when degree of remainder is less than degree of $2y + 1$.*

Before dividing one polynomial by another, it is helpful to arrange the terms in descending powers of the variable.

$$\frac{8y^2 + 8y + 3}{2y + 1} = 4y + 2 + \frac{1}{2y + 1}$$

6 **Divide $x^3 + 5x^2 + 5x + 16$ by $x^2 + 3$.**

$$
\begin{array}{r}
x + 5 \\
x^2 + 3 \overline{)x^3 + 5x^2 + 5x + 16} \\
\end{array}
$$

$x^3 \quad\quad + 3x$

$5x^2 + 2x + 16$

$5x^2 \quad\quad + 15$

$2x + 1$

$$\frac{x^3 + 5x^2 + 5x + 16}{x^2 + 3} = x + 5 + \frac{2x + 1}{x^2 + 3}$$

If the remainder upon division is zero, then the divisor is a factor of the polynomial.

example

7 **Show that $a + 2$ is a factor of $a^3 + 3a^2 - 2a - 8$.**

$$
\begin{array}{r}
a^2 + a - 4 \\
a + 2 \overline{)a^3 + 3a^2 - 2a - 8} \\
\end{array}
$$

$a^3 + 2a^2$

$a^2 - 2a$

$a^2 + 2a$

$^-4a - 8$

$^-4a - 8$

0

Thus, $a^3 + 3a^2 - 2a - 8 = (a + 2)(a^2 + a - 4)$.

exercises

Exploratory Use division to simplify each expression.

1. $\dfrac{7^4}{7^5}$
2. $\dfrac{12^6}{12^4}$
3. $\dfrac{g^6}{g^3}$
4. $\dfrac{h^{16}}{h^2}$
5. $\dfrac{a^{10}}{a^{10}}$
6. $\dfrac{14r^{11}}{2r^{10}}$

7. $\dfrac{8a^2b^4}{2b}$
8. $\dfrac{3^3r^3s^3}{9r^2}$
9. $\dfrac{36x^3y^5}{12x^2y^2}$

10. $\dfrac{6xy^2 - 3xy + 2x^2y}{xy}$
11. $\dfrac{a^3b^2 - a^2b + 2a}{-ab}$
12. $\dfrac{6r^2s^2 + 3rs^2 - 9r^2s}{3rs}$

Written Find each solution.

1. $\dfrac{6p^4q^2 + 4p^2q + 5pq^3}{pq}$
2. $\dfrac{12mz^3 + 9m^2z^2 - 15m^2z}{-3mz}$

3. $\dfrac{28k^3py - 42kp^2y^2 + 56kp^3y^2}{14kpy}$
4. $\dfrac{18k^3lm^2 + 27k^2lm + 45k^2l^2m^2}{9klm}$

5. $\dfrac{15r^2s + 23rs^2 + 6s^3}{3rs}$
6. $\dfrac{4a^2b^3c^4 + 13ab - 12a^4b^2c}{2abc}$

7. $(x^2 - 12x - 45) \div (x + 3)$
8. $(a^2 + 7a - 60) \div (a + 12)$

9. $(6y^2 + 7y - 3) \div (2y + 3)$
10. $(15b^2 + 14b - 8) \div (5b - 2)$

11. $(8a^2 + 34a + 19) \div (2a + 7)$
12. $(20b^2 - 17b - 61) \div (5b + 7)$

13. $(28y^2 + 23y - 12) \div (7y - 3)$
14. $(80x^2 + 6x - 4) \div (10x - 3)$

15. $(a^2 - 5a - 84) \div (a + 7)$
16. $(x^2 + 20x + 91) \div (x + 7)$

17. $(a^2 - 5ab + 6b^2) \div (a - 3b)$
18. $(12x^2 - 4xy - y^2) \div (2x - y)$

19. $(6z^2 + 2z - 28) \div (3z + 7)$
20. $(3b^2 - 7ba - 20a^2) \div (3b + 5a)$

21. $(a^2 + 4a - 16) \div (a - 6)$
22. $(y^2 + y - 8) \div (y - 3)$

23. $(8x^2 - 4x + 11) \div (x + 5)$
24. $(126k^2 + 113k - 26) \div (14k - 3)$

25. $(56m^2 - 113m + 59) \div (8m - 7)$
26. $(20r^2 + 7r - 10) \div (5r - 2)$

27. $(6y^3 + 11y^2 - 4y - 4) \div (3y - 2)$
28. $(8x^3 - 22x^2 - 5x + 12) \div (4x + 3)$

29. $(6a^3 + 5a^2 + 9) \div (2a + 3)$
30. $(8b^2 - 4b + 1) \div (2b - 1)$

31. $(m^3 - 1) \div (m - 1)$
32. $(a^3 - 8) \div (a - 2)$

33. $(y^3 - 9y^2 + 27y - 28) \div (y - 3)$
34. $(x^3 + 6x^2 + 12x + 12) \div (x + 2)$

35. $(6a^3 - 5a^2 - 12a - 4) \div (3a + 2)$
36. $(2p^3 + 7p^2 - 29p + 29) \div (2p - 3)$

37. $(m^3 - 7m + 3m^2 - 21) \div (m^2 - 7)$
38. $(48p^3 - 15 + 6p^2 - 40p) \div (6p^2 - 5)$

39. $(x^3 + 4x - 4) \div (x + 2)$
40. $(2t^3 - 2t - 3) \div (t - 1)$

41. $(x^4 + 4) \div (x^2 - 2x + 2)$
42. $(y^4 + 4y^3 + 10y^2 + 12y + 9) \div (y^2 + 2y + 3)$

43. $(a^4 - 3a^2 + 1) \div (a^2 + a - 1)$
44. $(x^4 - 4x^2 + 12x - 9) \div (x^2 + 2x - 3)$

45. Is $3y - 2$ a factor of $6y^3 - y^2 - 5y + 2$? Write yes or no.

46. Is $4x + 5$ a factor of $4x^3 + x^2 + 10$? Write yes or no.

47. One factor of $a^3 - 2a^2 - a + 2$ is $a - 2$. Find the other factors.

48. One factor of $2m^3 - 11m^2 + 18m - 9$ is $m - 3$. Find the other factors.

49. Find the remainder when dividing $x^2 + 3x + 5$ by $x - 2$. If $f(x) = x^2 + 3x + 5$, find $f(2)$. Compare the answers.

50. Find the remainder when dividing $x^3 - 5x^2 + 6x - 4$ by $x - 3$. If $f(x) = x^3 - 5x^2 + 6x - 4$, find $f(3)$. Compare the answers.

4-8   Synthetic Division

There is another method for finding $3x^3 - 4x^2 - 3x - 2$ divided by $x - 3$ called **synthetic division.** These steps show how to use the method.

Step 1   Write the terms of the polynomial in descending order. Then write the coefficients as shown.

$$3 \quad {}^-4 \quad {}^-3 \quad {}^-2$$

Step 2   The divisor is $x - 3$. Since 3 is being subtracted, write 3 to the left.

$$\underline{3} \mid 3 \quad {}^-4 \quad {}^-3 \quad {}^-2$$

Step 3   Bring down the first coefficient.

$$\underline{3} \mid 3 \quad {}^-4 \quad {}^-3 \quad {}^-2$$
$$\overline{3 }\big|$$

Step 4 $3 \cdot 3 = 9$

$$\underline{3} \mid 3 \quad {}^-4 \quad {}^-3 \quad {}^-2$$
$$9$$
$$\overline{3 }\big|$$

Step 5 $^-4 + 9 = 5$

$$\underline{3} \mid 3 \quad {}^-4 \quad {}^-3 \quad {}^-2$$
$$9$$
$$\overline{3 \quad 5 }\big|$$

Step 6 $3 \cdot 5 = 15$

$$\underline{3} \mid 3 \quad {}^-4 \quad {}^-3 \quad {}^-2$$
$$9 \quad 15$$
$$\overline{3 \quad 5 }\big|$$

Step 7 $^-3 + 15 = 12$

$$\underline{3} \mid 3 \quad {}^-4 \quad {}^-3 \quad {}^-2$$
$$9 \quad 15$$
$$\overline{3 \quad 5 \quad 12 }\big|$$

Step 8 $3 \cdot 12 = 36$

$$\underline{3} \mid 3 \quad {}^-4 \quad {}^-3 \quad {}^-2$$
$$9 \quad 15 \quad 36$$
$$\overline{3 \quad 5 \quad 12 }\big|$$

Step 9 $^-2 + 36 = 34$

$$\underline{3} \mid 3 \quad {}^-4 \quad {}^-3 \quad {}^-2$$
$$9 \quad 15 \quad 36$$
$$\overline{3 \quad 5 \quad 12 \mid 34}$$

Step 10   Write the result.

$$3x^2 + 5x + 12 + \frac{34}{x - 3}$$

Compare this process to the long division process.

$$
\begin{array}{r}
3x^2 + 5x + 12 \\
x - 3 \overline{)3x^3 - 4x^2 - 3x - 2} \\
\underline{3x^3 - 9x^2} \\
5x^2 - 3x \\
\underline{5x^2 - 15x} \\
12x - 2 \\
\underline{12x - 36} \\
34
\end{array}
$$

$$
\begin{array}{r}
\underline{3} \mid 3 \quad {}^-4 \quad {}^-3 \quad {}^-2 \\
9 \quad 15 \quad 36 \\
\overline{3 \quad 5 \quad 12 \mid 34}
\end{array}
$$

1 Find $(y^2 + 6y - 7) \div (y - 2)$.

$$\begin{array}{r|rrr} 2 & 1 & 6 & {}^-7 \\ & & 2 & 16 \\ \hline & 1 & 8 & 9 \end{array}$$

The result is $y + 8 + \dfrac{9}{y - 2}$.

2 Find $(2y^3 - 3y^2 - 8y + 4) \div (y + 2)$.

$$\begin{array}{r|rrrr} {}^-2 & 2 & {}^-3 & {}^-8 & 4 \\ & & {}^-4 & 14 & {}^-12 \\ \hline & 2 & {}^-7 & 6 & {}^-8 \end{array}$$

y + 2 is the same as y − ⁻2.

The result is $2y^2 - 7y + 6 - \dfrac{8}{y + 2}$.

The coefficient of a is zero in $2a^3 + a^2 + 12$. Zero coefficients must be included when you do synthetic division.

3 Find $(2a^3 + a^2 + 12) \div (a + 2)$.

$$\begin{array}{r|rrrr} {}^-2 & 2 & 1 & 0 & 12 \\ & & {}^-4 & 6 & {}^-12 \\ \hline & 2 & {}^-3 & 6 & 0 \end{array}$$

The result is $2a^2 - 3a + 6$.

Check:
$$(a + 2)(2a^2 - 3a + 6) \overset{?}{=} 2a^3 + a^2 + 12$$
$$2a^3 - 3a^2 + 6a + 4a^2 - 6a + 12 \overset{?}{=} 2a^3 + a^2 + 12$$
$$2a^3 + a^2 + 12 = 2a^3 + a^2 + 12$$

4 Find $(2t^5 - 3t^4 - 50t^3 - 24t^2) \div (t - 6)$.

$$\begin{array}{r|rrrrrr} 6 & 2 & {}^-3 & {}^-50 & {}^-24 & 0 & 0 \\ & & 12 & 54 & 24 & 0 & 0 \\ \hline & 2 & 9 & 4 & 0 & 0 & 0 \end{array}$$

The result is $2t^4 + 9t^3 + 4t^2$.

Check:
$$(t - 6)(2t^4 + 9t^3 + 4t^2) \overset{?}{=} 2t^5 - 3t^4 - 50t^3 - 24t^2$$
$$2t^5 + 9t^4 + 4t^3 - 12t^4 - 54t^3 - 24t^2 \overset{?}{=} 2t^5 - 3t^4 - 50t^3 - 24t^2$$
$$2t^5 - 3t^4 - 50t^3 - 24t^2 = 2t^5 - 3t^4 - 50t^3 - 24t^2$$

Some divisors like $2x - 1$ have leading coefficients other than one. For example, suppose you want to divide $4x^3 + x - 1$ by $2x - 1$. You can display the intended division in the following manner, factoring the leading coefficient of the divisor from the divisor and dividend.

$$\frac{4x^3 + x - 1}{2x - 1} = \frac{2\left(2x^3 + \frac{1}{2}x - \frac{1}{2}\right)}{2\left(x - \frac{1}{2}\right)}$$

Factor 2 from both the divisor and the dividend.

$$= \frac{2x^3 + \frac{1}{2}x - \frac{1}{2}}{x - \frac{1}{2}}$$

Now, use synthetic division to divide $2x^3 + \frac{1}{2}x - \frac{1}{2}$ by $x - \frac{1}{2}$.

examples

5 **Divide $4x^3 + x - 1$ by $2x - 1$.**

$$\frac{4x^3 + x - 1}{2x - 1} = \frac{2\left(2x^3 + \frac{1}{2}x - \frac{1}{2}\right)}{2\left(x - \frac{1}{2}\right)}$$

$$= \frac{2x^3 + \frac{1}{2}x - \frac{1}{2}}{x - \frac{1}{2}}$$

$$\begin{array}{c|cccc}
\frac{1}{2} & 2 & 0 & \frac{1}{2} & -\frac{1}{2} \\
 & & 1 & \frac{1}{2} & \frac{1}{2} \\
\hline
 & 2 & 1 & 1 & 0
\end{array}$$

The result is $2x^2 + x + 1$.

Check the solution.
Does $(2x - 1)(2x^2 + x + 1) = 4x^3 + x - 1$?

6 **Divide $3a^4 - 2a^3 + 5a^2 - 4a - 2$ by $3a + 1$.**

$$\frac{3a^4 - 2a^3 + 5a^2 - 4a - 2}{3a + 1} = \frac{3\left(a^4 - \frac{2}{3}a^3 + \frac{5}{3}a^2 - \frac{4}{3}a - \frac{2}{3}\right)}{3\left(a + \frac{1}{3}\right)}$$

$$= \frac{a^4 - \frac{2}{3}a^3 + \frac{5}{3}a^2 - \frac{4}{3}a - \frac{2}{3}}{a + \frac{1}{3}}$$

$$\begin{array}{c|ccccc}
-\frac{1}{3} & 1 & -\frac{2}{3} & \frac{5}{3} & -\frac{4}{3} & -\frac{2}{3} \\
 & & -\frac{1}{3} & \frac{1}{3} & -\frac{2}{3} & \frac{2}{3} \\
\hline
 & 1 & -1 & 2 & -2 & 0
\end{array}$$

The result is $a^3 - a^2 + 2a - 2$.

Exploratory Match the division problem with the correct synthetic division.

1. $(a^3 + 6a^2 + 3a + 1) \div (a - 2) = a^2 + 8a + 19 + \dfrac{39}{a - 2}$

a. $\underline{2}\ \begin{array}{rrrr} 3 & 0 & ^-5 & 10 \\ & 6 & 12 & 14 \\ \hline 3 & 6 & 7 & | 24 \end{array}$

2. $(z^3 + 2z^2 - 3z + 4) \div (z - 5) = z^2 + 7z + 32 + \dfrac{164}{z - 5}$

b. $\underline{^-3}\ \begin{array}{rrrr} 1 & 3 & ^-4 & 1 \\ & ^-3 & 0 & 12 \\ \hline 1 & 0 & ^-4 & | 13 \end{array}$

3. $(2y^3 - 5y + 1) \div (y + 1) = 2y^2 - 2y - 3 + \dfrac{4}{y + 1}$

c. $\underline{^-3}\ \begin{array}{rrrr} 1 & 0 & ^-11 & 10 \\ & ^-3 & 9 & 6 \\ \hline 1 & ^-3 & ^-2 & | 16 \end{array}$

4. $(x^3 - 11x + 10) \div (x + 3) = x^2 - 3x - 2 + \dfrac{16}{x + 3}$

d. $\underline{2}\ \begin{array}{rrrr} 1 & 6 & 3 & 1 \\ & 2 & 16 & 38 \\ \hline 1 & 8 & 19 & | 39 \end{array}$

5. $(3y^3 - 5y + 10) \div (y - 2) = 3y^2 + 6y + 7 + \dfrac{24}{y - 2}$

e. $\underline{^-1}\ \begin{array}{rrr} 2 & 0 & ^-5 & 1 \\ & ^-2 & 2 & 3 \\ \hline 2 & ^-2 & ^-3 & | 4 \end{array}$

6. $(b^3 + 3b^2 - 4b + 1) \div (b + 3) = b^2 - 4 + \dfrac{13}{b + 3}$

f. $\underline{^-1}\ \begin{array}{rrrr} 5 & ^-3 & 2 & ^-5 \\ & ^-5 & 8 & ^-10 \\ \hline 5 & ^-8 & 10 & | ^-15 \end{array}$

7. $(5y^3 - 3y^2 + 2y - 5) \div (y + 1) = 5y^2 - 8y + 10 - \dfrac{15}{y + 1}$

g. $\underline{5}\ \begin{array}{rrrr} 1 & 2 & ^-3 & 4 \\ & 5 & 35 & 160 \\ \hline 1 & 7 & 32 & | 164 \end{array}$

Written Divide using synthetic division.

1. $(2x^3 - 3x^2 + 3x - 4) \div (x - 2)$

2. $(3y^3 + 2y^2 - 32y + 2) \div (y - 3)$

3. $(2a^3 + a^2 - 2a + 3) \div (a + 1)$

4. $(3m^3 - 2m^2 + 2m - 1) \div (m - 1)$

5. $(x^4 - 2x^3 + x^2 - 3x + 2) \div (x - 2)$

6. $(3y^4 - 6y^3 - 2y^2 + y - 6) \div (y + 1)$

7. $(6k^3 - 19k^2 + k + 6) \div (k - 3)$

8. $(z^4 - 3z^3 - z^2 - 11z - 4) \div (z - 4)$

9. $(2b^3 - 11b^2 + 12b + 9) \div (b - 3)$

10. $(x^3 + 2x^2 - 5x - 6) \div (x - 2)$

11. $(y^4 - 16y^3 + 86y^2 - 176y + 105) \div (y - 5)$

12. $(a^4 - 5a^3 - 13a^2 + 53a + 60) \div (a + 1)$

13. $(2x^4 - 5x^3 - 10x + 8) \div (x - 3)$

14. $(2a^4 - 5a^3 + 2a - 3) \div (a - 1)$

15. $(y^4 + 6y^3 - 7y^2 + 7y - 1) \div (y + 3)$

16. $(h^5 - 6h^3 + 4h^2 - 3) \div (h - 2)$

17. $(4x^4 - 5x^2 + 2x + 3) \div (2x - 1)$

18. $(2b^3 - 3b^2 - 8b + 4) \div (2b + 1)$

19. $(6x^3 - 28x^2 + 19x + 3) \div (3x - 2)$

20. $(4y^4 - 5y^2 - 8y - 10) \div (2y - 3)$

21. $(x^5 + 32) \div (x + 2)$

22. $(x^5 - 3x^2 - 20) \div (x - 2)$

Challenge Divide using synthetic division.

1. $(x^4 - 2x^3 - 34x^2 + 41x - 12) \div (x^2 + 5x - 3)$

2. $(x^5 + 3x^4 - 7x^3 + 11x^2 - 14x + 3) \div (x^3 - x^2 + 2x - 2)$

Chapter Summary

1. Properties of Exponents: For any numbers a and b, and nonnegative integers m and n, the following hold.
   1. $a^m \cdot a^n = a^{m+n}$ (108)
   2. $(a^m)^n = a^{m \cdot n}$ (108)
   3. $(ab)^m = a^m b^m$ (108)
   4. $\dfrac{a^m}{a^n} = a^{m-n}$ if $a \neq 0$ and $m > n$ (110)
   5. $a^0 = 1$ if $a \neq 0$ (111)

2. The degree of a monomial is the sum of the exponents of its variables. The degree of a polynomial is the degree of the monomial of greatest degree.   (114)

3. The product of two binomials is the sum of the product of
   F   the first terms,
   O   the outer terms,
   I   the inner terms, and
   L   the last terms.   (115)

4. Factoring Difference of Two Squares: For any numbers a and b,
   $a^2 - b^2 = (a - b)(a + b)$ (118)

5. Factoring Sum or Difference of Cubes: For any numbers a and b,
   $a^3 + b^3 = (a + b)(a^2 - ab + b^2)$ and,
   $a^3 - b^3 = (a - b)(a^2 + ab + b^2)$.   (119)

6. Factoring Perfect Squares: For any numbers a and b,
   $a^2 + 2ab + b^2 = (a + b)^2$ and,
   $a^2 - 2ab + b^2 = (a - b)^2$ (121)

7. Checklist for factoring polynomials.
   1. Check for the greatest common monomial factor.
   2. Check for special products.
      a. If there are *two terms*, look for difference of squares, sum of cubes, difference of cubes.
      b. If there are *three terms*, look for perfect squares.
   3. Try other factoring methods.
      a. If there are *three terms*, try the trinomial pattern.
      b. If there are *four or more terms*, try grouping.   (125)

4–1 **Simplify each expression.**

1. $y^9 \cdot y^2$
2. $(xy^4)(^-5x^2y^3)$
3. $(x^3)^2$
4. $(4a^2)^3$
5. $(5a)(6a^2b)(3ab^3) + (4a^2)(3b^3)(2a^2b)$
6. $(3a)(a^2b)^3 + (2a)^2(^-a^5b^3)$

4–2 **Simplify each expression.**

7. $\dfrac{a^6}{a^2}$
8. $\dfrac{14a^4b^3}{(7ab)^2}$
9. $\dfrac{m^3n^2}{2m^3n}$
10. $3x^0$
11. $(3x)^0$
12. $\dfrac{^-3x^3yz^4}{12x^2y}$

4–3 **Simplify each expression by performing the indicated operations.**

13. $(4b^3 + 7b^2 - 3b + 5) + (^-3b^3 + 8b^2 - 7)$
14. $(p^4 + 5p^2 - 3p + 7) - (p^3 + p^2 - 3p + 5)$
15. $(4a - 5)(a + 7)$
16. $(3m - 7)^2$
17. $(y + 7)(y^2 - 3y + 5)$
18. $(2x - 5)(x^2 + 8x - 7)$
19. $(m + 1)(2m + 7)(m + 3)$
20. $(2z - 5)(2z + 5)(z - 6)$

4–4 **Factor.**

21. $y^2 - 25$
22. $3a^2s - 6as^2 + 3s^3$
23. $m^3 + 8$
24. $x^4 - y^4$
25. $8m^3 - 27$
26. $p^3q^3 - 27q^3$

4–5 **Factor.**

27. $x^2 - 7x + 10$
28. $2x^2 + 7xy + 3y^2$
29. $9p^2 - 30pt + 25t^2$
30. $r^3 + 6r^2s + 8rs^2$
31. $5b^2 - 19ab - 4a^2$
32. $6x^2 + 11xy + 4y^2$
33. $21b^2 + 13b - 20$
34. $10m^2 + 19m + 6$

4–6 **Factor.**

35. $x^2 - 2xy + x - 2y$
36. $3a^2 + 12ab - 2a - 8b$
37. $^-b^2 + 8b + a^2 - 16$
38. $4a^2 + 4ab - a^2 + b^2$

4–7 **Find each solution using long division. Show your work.**

39. $(8y^3 - 22y^2 - 5y + 15) \div (4y + 3)$
40. $(2r^3 + 11r^2 - 9r - 18) \div (2r + 3)$
41. Show that $x + 1$ is *not* a factor of $2x^3 + x^2 - 11x - 30$.
42. Show that $x - 3$ is a factor of $2x^3 - 11x^2 + 12x + 9$.

4–8 **Find each solution using synthetic division. Show your work.**

43. $(2m^3 - 3m^2 - 8m + 1) \div (m - 4)$
44. $(2r^3 + r^2 - 13r + 6) \div (2r - 1)$
45. Show that $2x + 1$ is a factor of $2x^3 - 11x^2 + 12x + 9$.

Simplify each expression.

1. $(m^2)^5$

2. $\dfrac{16b^7}{2b^5}$

3. $(4a^2b^2)(5ab^3)$

4. $(5x)(6x^2y^3) + (2xy)^3 - x^2y^0$

5. $3x^2y + 4 - 3x^2y$

6. $(3y^4 + 5y^3 + y - 7) + (4y^4 - 3y^3 + 7y^2 - 3y + 8)$

7. $(4b^3 + 7b^2 - 3b + 5) - (2b^3 - 5b^2 + 2b + 7)$

8. $(2y + 7)(y - 3)$

9. $(3m + 5)^2$

10. $(y - 4)(3y^2 - 5y + 4)$

11. $(x + 3)(2x - 5)(3x + 4)$

Factor.

12. $a^2 - 121$

13. $k^2 + 3k - 40$

14. $a^2 + 6am + 9m^2$

15. $y^3 + 125$

16. $3y^2 + 15y + 18$

17. $64a^3 - 1$

18. $8a^3 - 12a^2b + 6ab^2 - b^3$

19. $6y^2 + 17y + 10$

20. $2m^3 - 6m^2 + m - 3$

21. $8m^2 - 14m - 15$

22. $r^2 + 4rs + 4s^2 - 9y^2$

23. $3y^2 - 19y + 28$

24. Use long division to find $(6y^3 - 5y^2 - 12y - 17) \div (3y + 2)$. Show your work.

25. Use synthetic division to find $(5m^3 - 3m^2 + 2m - 5) \div (m + 2)$. Show your work.

26. Show that $a - 3$ is a factor of $a^4 - a^3 + a^2 - 25a + 12$.

27. One factor of $2y^3 + y^2 - 13y + 6$ is $y + 3$. Find the other factors.

28. One factor of $4b^3 + 6b^2 + 40b - 22$ is $2b - 1$. Find the other factors.

29. do. $(6x^3 - 28x^2 + 19x + 3) \div (3x - 2)$

chapter
5 Roots

How long will the thunderstorm last? If the diameter, d, in miles, of the storm system is known, weather forecasters have an answer. The time, t, in hours is found using the formula, $t^2 = \dfrac{d^3}{216}$. Solving this equation for t involves finding roots. In this chapter, you will learn about roots.

5–1   Roots

Squaring a number means using that number as a factor two times. Cubing a number means using that number as a factor three times.

$6^2 = 6 \cdot 6$ or 36 *6 is used as a factor two times.*
$6^3 = 6 \cdot 6 \cdot 6$ or 216 *6 is used as a factor three times.*

Raising a number to the nth power means using that number as a factor n times.

$5^4 = 5 \cdot 5 \cdot 5 \cdot 5$ or 625 *5 is used as a factor four times. $n = 4$*

$2^8 = 2 \cdot 2 \cdot 2 \cdot 2 \cdot 2 \cdot 2 \cdot 2 \cdot 2$ *2 is used as a factor eight times. $n = 8$*

$6^n = \underbrace{6 \cdot 6 \cdot 6 \cdot \ldots \cdot 6}_{n \text{ factors}}$ *6 is used as a factor n times.*

The inverse of raising a number to the nth power is finding the **nth root** of that number. For example, the inverse of squaring is finding the **square root.**

To find the square root of 36, you must find two equal factors whose product is 36.

$$x^2 = 36 \qquad x \cdot x = 36$$

Since 6 times 6 is 36, one square root of 36 is 6. Since ⁻6 times ⁻6 is 36, another square root of 36 is ⁻6.

Any number which is the square of an integer is called a perfect square.

> **For any numbers a and b,**
> **if $a^2 = b$, then a is a square root of b.**

Definition of Square Root

To find the cube root of 125, you must find three equal factors whose product is 125.

$$x^3 = 125 \qquad x \cdot x \cdot x = 125$$

Since 5 times 5 times 5 is 125, the cube root of 125 is 5.

> **For any numbers a and b, and any positive integer n, if $a^n = b$, then a is an nth root of b.**

Definition of nth Root

The symbol $\sqrt[n]{}$ indicates an nth root.

index ⟶ ┐   ┌ ⟵ radical sign
$\sqrt[n]{256}$ ⟵ radicand

When *no* index appears, the **radical** sign $\sqrt{}$ indicates a square root.

Some numbers have more than one real root. For example, 36 has two real square roots, 6 and ⁻6.

The symbol $\sqrt[n]{b}$ indicates the principal nth root of b. The principal nth root of b is a positive number *unless* n is odd and b is negative. In this case the principal root is negative.

$\sqrt{36} = 6$ $\sqrt{36}$ indicates the principal square root of 36.

$^-\sqrt{36} = {}^-6$ $^-\sqrt{36}$ indicates the negative of the principal square root of 36.

$\pm\sqrt{36} = \pm6$ $\pm\sqrt{36}$ indicates both square roots of 36.   *$\pm$ means positive or negative.*

$\sqrt[3]{^-27} = {}^-3$ $\sqrt[3]{^-27}$ indicates the principal cube root of ⁻27.

$^-\sqrt[4]{16} = {}^-2$ $^-\sqrt[4]{16}$ indicates the negative of the principal fourth root of 16.

The following chart gives a summary of the real nth roots of a number b.

The Real nth Roots of b, $\sqrt[n]{b}$

	$b > 0$	$b < 0$	$b = 0$
n even	one positive root one negative root	no real roots	one real root, 0
n odd	one positive root no negative roots	no positive roots one negative root	one real root, 0

1 Find $\pm\sqrt{64b^2}$.

$\pm\sqrt{64b^2} = \pm\sqrt{(8b)^2}$
$\qquad\quad = \pm8b$ *The square roots of 8b² are ±8b.*

2 Find $^-\sqrt{(x + 3)^4}$.

$^-\sqrt{(x + 3)^4} = {}^-\sqrt{[(x + 3)^2]^2}$
$\qquad\qquad\quad = {}^-(x + 3)^2$ *The principal square root of (x + 3)⁴ is (x + 3)².*

3 Find $\sqrt[3]{27x^6}$.

$\sqrt[3]{27x^6} = \sqrt[3]{(3x^2)^3}$
$\qquad\quad = 3x^2$ *The principal cube root of 27x⁶ is 3x².*

4 Find $\sqrt[6]{c^6}$.

Since $(c)^6 = c^6$, c is a sixth root of c^6.   *6 is an even number, so the principal*
Thus, $\sqrt[6]{c^6} = |c|$.   *sixth root of c⁶ is a positive number.*

From similar examples, you can make this generalization.

For any number a, and any integer n greater than one,
1. if n is even, then $\sqrt[n]{a^n} = |a|$.   *Property of nth Roots*
2. if n is odd, then $\sqrt[n]{a^n} = a$.

Expressions such as $\sqrt{64}$ and $\sqrt[3]{-\frac{1}{8}}$ name rational numbers.

$$\sqrt{64} = 8 \qquad\qquad \sqrt[3]{-\frac{1}{8}} = -\frac{1}{2}$$

Numbers such as $\sqrt{2}$ and $\sqrt{3}$ are irrational. Real numbers that cannot be written as terminating or repeating decimals are irrational numbers. To compute with irrational numbers, decimal approximations are often used. The tables of roots and powers on pages 573 and 574 give approximations.

5 **Find a decimal approximation for $\sqrt[3]{28}$.**

Cubes and Cube Roots

n	n^3	$\sqrt[3]{n}$	$\sqrt[3]{10n}$	$\sqrt[3]{100n}$
1.0	1.000	1.000	2.154	4.642
1.1	1.331	1.032	2.224	4.791
1.2	1.728	1.063	2.289	4.932
1.3	2.197	1.091	2.351	5.066
2.5	15.625	1.357	2.924	6.300
2.6	17.576	1.375	2.962	6.383
2.7	19.683	1.392	3.000	6.463
2.8	21.952	1.409	3.037	6.542
2.9	24.389	1.426	3.072	6.619

Let $n = 2.8$.
Then $10n = 10(2.8)$ or 28.

So $\sqrt[3]{28} = \sqrt[3]{10(2.8)}$
$\qquad\quad = 3.037$

Check: $(3.037)^3 = 28.01137165$

Square roots can be approximated using a divide-and-average method.

6 **Find a decimal approximation for $\sqrt{8}$ to four places.**

Locate 8 between consecutive perfect squares.

$$4 < 8 < 9$$
$$(2)^2 < 8 < (3)^2$$
$$2 < \sqrt{8} < 3$$

Choose 3 as the first approximation since it appears closer to $\sqrt{8}$ than 2.

Divide 8 by 3 to two digits.
$$\frac{8.0}{3} = 2.6$$

Average.
$$\frac{3 + 2.6}{2} = 2.8$$

Divide 8 by 2.8 to four digits.
$$\frac{8.000}{2.8} = 2.857$$

Average.
$$\frac{2.8 + 2.857}{2} = 2.8285$$

$\sqrt{8}$ is approximately 2.8285.

Exploratory Find the value of each expression.

1. 7^2
2. 11^2
3. 3^3
4. 4^3
5. 2^4
6. 3^4
7. 13^2
8. 5^3
9. 10^5

Simplify.

10. $\sqrt{121}$
11. $^-\sqrt{144}$
12. $\sqrt[3]{8}$
13. $\sqrt[4]{16}$
14. $\sqrt[3]{y^3}$
15. $^-\sqrt[4]{y^4}$
16. $\sqrt[4]{y^8}$
17. $\sqrt[3]{^-64}$
18. $\sqrt[5]{32n^5}$
19. $\sqrt{16a^2b^4}$
20. $\sqrt{(x-2)^2}$
21. $\sqrt{x^2+6x+9}$

Use the tables of powers and roots to find each value.

22. $\sqrt{47}$
23. 51^2
24. 19^3
25. $\sqrt[3]{18}$
26. $\sqrt[3]{30}$
27. 53^3

Written Simplify.

1. $^-\sqrt{81}$
2. $\sqrt{169}$
3. $\sqrt{225}$
4. $^-\sqrt[3]{27}$
5. $\sqrt[4]{81}$
6. $\sqrt[3]{64}$
7. $\sqrt[5]{^-1}$
8. $\sqrt[3]{^-1000}$
9. $\sqrt{0.49}$
10. $\sqrt[3]{0.125}$
11. $\sqrt{121n^2}$
12. $\sqrt{144x^6}$
13. $\sqrt{(3s)^4}$
14. $\sqrt{(5b)^4}$
15. $\sqrt{576}$
16. $\sqrt{676}$
17. $\sqrt{64a^2b^4}$
18. $^-\sqrt{121b^2c^6}$
19. $\sqrt[3]{^-8b^3m^3}$
20. $\sqrt[3]{^-27r^3s^3}$
21. $\sqrt[3]{64a^6b^3}$
22. $\sqrt{(x+y)^2}$
23. $\sqrt{(3p+q)^2}$
24. $\sqrt[3]{(2m+n)^3}$
25. $\sqrt[3]{(z+a)^3}$
26. $\sqrt[4]{(r+s)^4}$
27. $\sqrt[5]{(2m-3)^5}$
28. $\sqrt{x^2+10x+25}$
29. $\sqrt{y^2+6y+9}$
30. $\sqrt{4r^2+12r+9}$
31. $\sqrt{9x^2+6x+1}$
32. $\sqrt{x^2-6xy+9y^2}$
33. $\sqrt{4x^2+12xy+9y^2}$

Use the tables of powers and roots to find each value. *pg. 573*

34. 64^2
35. $\sqrt{83}$
36. $\sqrt{9.5}$
37. 4.9^2
38. $\sqrt[3]{23}$
39. $\sqrt[3]{8.1}$
40. 9.8^3
41. 48^3
42. $\sqrt[3]{300}$

Using the divide-and-average method, find a decimal approximation to four places for each of the following.

43. $\sqrt{7}$
44. $\sqrt{11}$
45. $\sqrt{21}$
46. $\sqrt{12}$
47. $\sqrt{19}$
48. $\sqrt{30}$

Challenge

1. Does $\sqrt[4]{(^-x)^4} = x$ no matter what value x represents? Explain.
2. Does $\sqrt[5]{(^-x)^5} = x$ no matter what value x represents? Explain.
3. Under what circumstances is $\sqrt[n]{(^-x)^n} = x$?

5-2   Multiplying Radicals

The following examples show an important property of radicals.

$$\sqrt{4} \cdot \sqrt{9} = 2 \cdot 3 \text{ or } 6 \qquad \sqrt[3]{-8} \cdot \sqrt[3]{27} = {}^-2 \cdot 3 \text{ or } {}^-6$$
$$\sqrt{4 \cdot 9} = \sqrt{36} \text{ or } 6 \qquad \sqrt[3]{-8 \cdot 27} = \sqrt[3]{-216} \text{ or } {}^-6$$

> **For any numbers a and b, and any integer n greater than one.**
> 1. if n is even, then $\sqrt[n]{ab} = \sqrt[n]{a} \cdot \sqrt[n]{b}$ as long as a and b are positive or zero.
> 2. if n is odd, then $\sqrt[n]{ab} = \sqrt[n]{a} \cdot \sqrt[n]{b}$.

Product Property of Radicals

To simplify a square root, find any factors of the radicand that are perfect squares. Use prime factorization and the product property of radicals.

examples

1 Simplify $\sqrt{63}$.

$$\begin{aligned}
\sqrt{63} &= \sqrt{3^2 \cdot 7} & &\text{The prime factorization of 63 is } 3^2 \cdot 7. \\
&= \sqrt{3^2} \cdot \sqrt{7} & &\text{Product Property of Radicals} \\
&= 3\sqrt{7}
\end{aligned}$$

2 Simplify $\sqrt{45x^3y^2}$.

$$\begin{aligned}
\sqrt{45x^3y^2} &= \sqrt{3^2 \cdot 5 \cdot x^2 \cdot x \cdot y^2} \\
&= \sqrt{3^2} \cdot \sqrt{5} \cdot \sqrt{x^2} \cdot \sqrt{x} \cdot \sqrt{y^2} \\
&= 3x|y|\sqrt{5x} \quad \text{\textit{If } } x < 0, \text{\textit{ then } } \sqrt{x^3} \text{ \textit{has no real roots. Therefore, you must assume}} \\
& \qquad\qquad\qquad \text{\textit{that } } x \geq 0. \text{ \textit{Thus, it is not necessary to write } } \sqrt{x^3} = |x|\sqrt{x}.
\end{aligned}$$

To simplify nth roots, find the factors that are nth powers and use the product property.

example

3 Simplify $\sqrt[4]{2m} \cdot \sqrt[4]{5m^3}$.

$$\begin{aligned}
\sqrt[4]{2m} \cdot \sqrt[4]{5m^3} &= \sqrt[4]{2m \cdot 5m^3} & &\text{Product Property of Radicals} \\
&= \sqrt[4]{10m^4} \\
&= \sqrt[4]{10} \cdot \sqrt[4]{m^4} & &\text{Product Property of Radicals} \\
&= m\sqrt[4]{10}
\end{aligned}$$

4 Simplify $\sqrt[3]{54x^3y^5}$.

$$\sqrt[3]{54x^3y^5} = \sqrt[3]{3^3 \cdot 2 \cdot x^3 \cdot y^3 \cdot y^2}$$
$$= \sqrt[3]{3^3} \cdot \sqrt[3]{2} \cdot \sqrt[3]{x^3} \cdot \sqrt[3]{y^3} \cdot \sqrt[3]{y^2}$$
$$= 3 \cdot \sqrt[3]{2} \cdot x \cdot y \cdot \sqrt[3]{y^2}$$
$$= 3xy\sqrt[3]{2y^2}$$

When multiplying rational numbers and radicals, multiply each separately and then simplify.

$$2\sqrt{2} \cdot 4\sqrt{6} = 2 \cdot 4 \cdot \sqrt{2} \cdot \sqrt{6}$$
$$= 8\sqrt{12}$$
$$= 8 \cdot 2 \cdot \sqrt{3} \text{ or } 16\sqrt{3}$$

You can use the distributive property to help simplify radicals.

5 Simplify $\sqrt{6}(\sqrt{3} + 2\sqrt{15})$.

$$\sqrt{6}(\sqrt{3} + 2\sqrt{15}) = \sqrt{6} \cdot \sqrt{3} + \sqrt{6} \cdot 2\sqrt{15}$$
$$= \sqrt{18} + 2\sqrt{90}$$
$$= \sqrt{3^2 \cdot 2} + 2\sqrt{3^2 \cdot 2 \cdot 5}$$
$$= 3\sqrt{2} + 2 \cdot 3\sqrt{10} \text{ or } 3\sqrt{2} + 6\sqrt{10}$$

exercises

Exploratory Simplify.

1. $\sqrt{8}$
2. $\sqrt{32}$
3. $\sqrt{50x^2}$
4. $\sqrt{98y^4}$

5. $\sqrt[3]{16}$
6. $\sqrt[3]{54}$
7. $\sqrt[4]{48}$
8. $\sqrt[4]{32}$

9. $\sqrt{b^3}$
10. $\sqrt{y^5}$
11. $\sqrt[4]{a^5}$
12. $\sqrt[3]{m^4}$

13. $\sqrt[5]{r^7}$
14. $\sqrt[4]{k^6}$
15. $\sqrt{3} \cdot \sqrt{15}$
16. $\sqrt{6} \cdot \sqrt{3}$

17. $\sqrt[3]{3} \cdot \sqrt[3]{54}$
18. $\sqrt[3]{9} \cdot \sqrt[3]{6}$
19. $\sqrt{5}(\sqrt{5} - \sqrt{3})$
20. $\sqrt{5}(\sqrt{7} + \sqrt{5})$

Written Simplify.

1. $5\sqrt{54}$
2. $4\sqrt{50}$
3. $\sqrt[3]{24}$
4. $\sqrt[3]{56}$

5. $\sqrt{162}$
6. $\sqrt{450}$
7. $\sqrt[3]{-192}$
8. $\sqrt[3]{88}$

9. $3\sqrt{242}$
10. $6\sqrt{216}$
11. $\sqrt[4]{112}$
12. $\sqrt[4]{405}$

13. $(4\sqrt{18})(2\sqrt{14})$
14. $(-3\sqrt{24})(5\sqrt{20})$
15. $\sqrt[3]{121}\sqrt[3]{88}$

16. $(7\sqrt[3]{16})(5\sqrt[3]{20})$
17. $\sqrt{3}(\sqrt{6} - 2)$
18. $\sqrt{7}(3 + \sqrt{7})$

19. $\sqrt{7}(\sqrt{14} + \sqrt{21})$
20. $-\sqrt{2}(\sqrt{3} + \sqrt{2})$
21. $\sqrt[3]{2}(3\sqrt[3]{4} + 2\sqrt[3]{32})$

22. $\sqrt[3]{9}(4\sqrt[3]{9} + 2\sqrt[3]{6})$
23. $\sqrt[3]{8a^4b^7}$
24. $\sqrt{8m^2b^3}$
25. $\sqrt{50r^3p^4}$

26. $\sqrt[4]{81m^4p^5}$
27. $\sqrt[3]{3x^4y^4}$
28. $\sqrt{8x^2y} \cdot \sqrt{2xy}$
29. $\sqrt{3x^2z^3} \cdot \sqrt{15x^2z}$

30. $\sqrt[3]{3ab^5} \cdot \sqrt[3]{24a^2b^2}$
31. $\sqrt[4]{5m^3b^5} \cdot \sqrt[4]{125m^2b^3}$
32. $\sqrt[4]{3b^6r^7} \cdot \sqrt[4]{81b^2r^2}$

33. $\sqrt[3]{54r^4s^3} \cdot \sqrt[3]{16rs}$
34. $\sqrt{125m^2n} \cdot \sqrt{32m^4n^6}$
35. $\sqrt[4]{32a^5b^3} \cdot \sqrt[4]{162a^3b^2}$

5-3 Computing with Radicals

Two radical expressions are called **like radical expressions** if the indexes are alike and the radicands are alike.

$7\sqrt[3]{2}$ and $6\sqrt[3]{2}$ are like expressions.   *Both the indexes and radicands are alike.*

$\sqrt[3]{9}$ and $\sqrt[5]{9}$ are *not* like expressions.   *The indexes are not alike.*

$5\sqrt{3x}$ and $^-5\sqrt{3y}$ are *not* like expressions.   *The radicands are not alike.*

$\sqrt[3]{2a}$ and $\sqrt[4]{2b}$ are *not* like expressions.   *Neither the indexes nor the radicands are alike.*

Radicals are added or subtracted the same way monomials are added or subtracted.

Combine like terms.

$$3x + 2x + 4y = (3 + 2)x + 4y$$
$$= 5x + 4y$$

Combine like radicals.

$$3\sqrt{6} + 2\sqrt{6} + 4\sqrt{7} = (3 + 2)\sqrt{6} + 4\sqrt{7}$$
$$= 5\sqrt{6} + 4\sqrt{7}$$

example

1 **Simplify $3 + 4\sqrt{7} + 5 + 6\sqrt{7}$.**

$$3 + 4\sqrt{7} + 5 + 6\sqrt{7} = 3 + 5 + 4\sqrt{7} + 6\sqrt{7}$$
$$= (8) + (4 + 6)\sqrt{7}$$
$$= 8 + 10\sqrt{7}$$

In some cases, radicals can be simplified and then added or subtracted.

examples

2 **Simplify $5\sqrt{27} + 2\sqrt{3} - 7\sqrt{48}$.**

$$5\sqrt{27} + 2\sqrt{3} - 7\sqrt{48} = 5\sqrt{3^2 \cdot 3} + 2\sqrt{3} - 7\sqrt{4^2 \cdot 3}$$
$$= 5\sqrt{3^2}\sqrt{3} + 2\sqrt{3} - 7\sqrt{4^2}\sqrt{3}$$
$$= 5 \cdot 3\sqrt{3} + 2\sqrt{3} - 7 \cdot 4\sqrt{3}$$
$$= {}^-11\sqrt{3}$$

3 **Simplify $\sqrt[3]{40} + \sqrt[3]{135}$.**

$$\sqrt[3]{40} + \sqrt[3]{135} = \sqrt[3]{2^3 \cdot 5} + \sqrt[3]{3^3 \cdot 5}$$
$$= \sqrt[3]{2^3} \cdot \sqrt[3]{5} + \sqrt[3]{3^3} \cdot \sqrt[3]{5}$$
$$= 5\sqrt[3]{5}$$

Expressions such as $(5 + 3\sqrt{2})(3 + \sqrt{2})$ can be simplified using the FOIL method.

$$(5 + 3\sqrt{2})(3 + \sqrt{2}) = \overset{\text{F}}{5 \cdot 3} + \overset{\text{O}}{5 \cdot \sqrt{2}} + \overset{\text{I}}{3\sqrt{2} \cdot 3} + \overset{\text{L}}{3\sqrt{2} \cdot \sqrt{2}}$$
$$= 15 + 5\sqrt{2} + 9\sqrt{2} + 6$$
$$= 21 + 14\sqrt{2}$$

4 Simplify $(6 + \sqrt{2})(\sqrt{10} + \sqrt{5})$.

$$
\begin{array}{llll}
\quad\quad\quad\quad\quad\ \ \text{F} & \text{O} & \text{I} & \text{L}
\end{array}
$$

$$
\begin{aligned}
(6 + \sqrt{2})(\sqrt{10} + \sqrt{5}) &= 6\sqrt{10} + 6\sqrt{5} + \sqrt{2}\sqrt{10} + \sqrt{2}\sqrt{5} \\
&= 6\sqrt{10} + 6\sqrt{5} + \sqrt{2}\sqrt{2}\sqrt{5} + \sqrt{10} \\
&= 6\sqrt{10} + 6\sqrt{5} + 2\sqrt{5} + \sqrt{10} \\
&= 6\sqrt{10} + \sqrt{10} + 6\sqrt{5} + 2\sqrt{5} \\
&= 7\sqrt{10} + 8\sqrt{5}
\end{aligned}
$$

Binomials that are of the form $a + b\sqrt{c}$ and $a - b\sqrt{c}$ are called **conjugates** of each other. Notice that the product of conjugates is a rational number.

5 Simplify $(7 + \sqrt{2})(7 - \sqrt{2})$.

$$
\begin{array}{llll}
\quad\quad\quad\quad\quad\ \ \text{F} & \text{O} & \text{I} & \text{L}
\end{array}
$$

$$
\begin{aligned}
(7 + \sqrt{2})(7 - \sqrt{2}) &= 7 \cdot 7 - 7\sqrt{2} + 7\sqrt{2} - \sqrt{2} \cdot \sqrt{2} \\
&= 49 - \sqrt{2^2} \\
&= 49 - 2 \\
&= 47
\end{aligned}
$$

6 Simplify $(18 - 7\sqrt{3})(18 + 7\sqrt{3})$.

$$
\begin{array}{llll}
\quad\quad\quad\quad\quad\ \ \text{F} & \text{O} & \text{I} & \text{L}
\end{array}
$$

$$
\begin{aligned}
(18 - 7\sqrt{3})(18 + 7\sqrt{3}) &= 18^2 + 126\sqrt{3} - 126\sqrt{3} - 49(\sqrt{3})^2 \\
&= 18^2 - 49 \cdot 3 \\
&= 177
\end{aligned}
$$

exercises

Exploratory Simplify.

1. $3\sqrt{7} - 4\sqrt{7}$
2. $8\sqrt[3]{6} + 3\sqrt[3]{6}$
3. $3\sqrt[4]{5} - 10\sqrt[4]{5}$
4. $7\sqrt{y} + 4\sqrt{y}$
5. $5\sqrt[3]{x} + 4\sqrt[3]{x} - 6\sqrt[3]{x}$
6. $7\sqrt[3]{2} - 3\sqrt[3]{2}$
7. $\sqrt[5]{3} + 4\sqrt[5]{3}$
8. $2\sqrt{2} + \sqrt{8}$
9. $6\sqrt{3} - \sqrt{27}$
10. $8\sqrt{5} + \sqrt{75}$
11. $\sqrt[3]{40} - 2\sqrt[3]{5}$
12. $7\sqrt[3]{3} - \sqrt[3]{24}$

Multiply.

13. $(3 + \sqrt{5})(4 + \sqrt{5})$
14. $(5 + \sqrt{3})(3 - \sqrt{3})$
15. $(7 - \sqrt{2})(5 - \sqrt{2})$
16. $(3 + \sqrt{5})(3 - \sqrt{5})$
17. $(6 + \sqrt{2})(6 - \sqrt{2})$
18. $(2 + \sqrt{7})(2 - \sqrt{7})$
19. $(4 + \sqrt{3})^2$
20. $(1 - \sqrt{5})^2$
21. $(7 + \sqrt{6})^2$

Written Simplify.

1. $5\sqrt{2} + 3\sqrt{2} - 8$
2. $^{-}4\sqrt{2} + 6 + 10\sqrt{2}$
3. $^{-}3\sqrt{5} + 5\sqrt{2} + 4\sqrt{20} - 3\sqrt{50}$
4. $8\sqrt{3} - 3\sqrt{75}$
5. $3\sqrt{7} - 5\sqrt{28}$
6. $5\sqrt{20} + \sqrt{24} - \sqrt{180} + 7\sqrt{54}$
7. $7\sqrt[3]{5} + 4\sqrt[3]{5}$
8. $8\sqrt[3]{2} + 3\sqrt[3]{2} - 8\sqrt[3]{2}$
9. $\sqrt[3]{48} - \sqrt[3]{6}$
10. $\sqrt[3]{54} - \sqrt[3]{128}$
11. $7\sqrt[3]{2} + 6\sqrt[3]{150}$
12. $5\sqrt[3]{135} - 2\sqrt[3]{81}$
13. $7\sqrt{24} + \sqrt[3]{24}$
14. $\sqrt[3]{16} - \sqrt{32}$
15. $\sqrt{98} - \sqrt{72} + \sqrt{32}$
16. $\sqrt{108} - \sqrt{48} + (\sqrt{3})^2$
17. $7\sqrt[4]{2} + 8\sqrt[4]{2}$
18. $\sqrt[4]{5} + 6\sqrt[4]{5} - 2\sqrt[4]{5}$
19. $\sqrt[4]{x^2} + \sqrt[4]{x^6}$
20. $^{-}\sqrt{2x^2y^4} + \sqrt{8x^2y^4}$
21. $\sqrt[4]{y^4z^6} + \sqrt[4]{16y^4z^6}$
22. $\sqrt[3]{27m^5n^6} + \sqrt[3]{8m^8n^3}$
23. $\sqrt[4]{z^4} + \sqrt[3]{z^6} + \sqrt{z^8}$
24. $\sqrt{100m^3n} - \sqrt{64mn^3}$
25. $(5 + \sqrt{2})(3 + \sqrt{2})$
26. $(4 + \sqrt{3})(3 + \sqrt{6})$
27. $(5 + \sqrt{6})(5 - \sqrt{2})$
28. $(8 - \sqrt{3})(6 + \sqrt{3})$
29. $(7 + \sqrt{11})(2 - \sqrt{11})$
30. $(\sqrt{3} + \sqrt{2})(\sqrt{15} - \sqrt{3})$
31. $(\sqrt{3} + \sqrt{5})(\sqrt{12} - \sqrt{5})$
32. $(4 + \sqrt{5})^2$
33. $(1 - \sqrt{3})^2$
34. $(4\sqrt{5} - 3\sqrt{2})(2\sqrt{5} + 2\sqrt{2})$
35. $(5 - 3\sqrt{5})(3 + \sqrt{5})$
36. $(3 - \sqrt[3]{4})(\sqrt[3]{2} + \sqrt[3]{16})$
37. $(4 - \sqrt[3]{9})(\sqrt[3]{3} + \sqrt[3]{81})$
38. $(y + \sqrt[3]{4})(y^2 - y\sqrt[3]{4} + \sqrt[3]{16})$
39. $(x - \sqrt[3]{3})(x^2 + x\sqrt[3]{3} + \sqrt[3]{9})$

Factor over the real numbers.

> **Sample:** $x^2 - 3 = x^2 - (\sqrt{3})^2$
> $= (x - \sqrt{3})(x + \sqrt{3})$

40. $x^2 - 5$
41. $m^2 - 11$
42. $y^2 - 6$
43. $a^2 + 4a\sqrt{5} + 20$
44. $b^2 - 10b\sqrt{2} + 50$
45. $r^3 - 2r$

Radical Expressions

The calculator can be used to show that two radical expressions have the same value.

Example The expression $(\sqrt{3} - 2\sqrt{2})(\sqrt{2} - 5\sqrt{3})$ can be simplified to $^{-}19 + 11\sqrt{6}$. Show that the two expressions have the same value.
First evaluate $(\sqrt{3} - 2\sqrt{2})(\sqrt{2} - 5\sqrt{3})$.

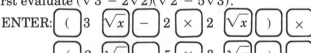

ENTER: (3 √x − 2 × 2 √x) ×
(2 √x − 5 × 3 √x) =

DISPLAY: 7.9443872

Then evaluate $^{-}19 + 11\sqrt{6}$.

ENTER: 19 +/− + 11 × 6 √x =

DISPLAY: 7.9443872

Exercises Show that the given expressions have the same value.

1. $8\sqrt{24} - 3\sqrt{54} + 5\sqrt{25}$; $7\sqrt{6} + 25$
2. $(2\sqrt{6} - 5\sqrt{3})(3\sqrt{3} + 4\sqrt{6})$; $3 - 42\sqrt{2}$
3. $(2\sqrt{5} - 8\sqrt{32})(6\sqrt{2} - 11\sqrt{5})$; $^{-}494 + 364\sqrt{10}$

5–4   Dividing Radicals

The following examples show an important property of radicals.

$$\frac{\sqrt{100}}{\sqrt{4}} = \frac{10}{2} \text{ or } 5 \qquad\qquad \frac{\sqrt[3]{216}}{\sqrt[3]{-27}} = \frac{6}{-3} \text{ or } ^-2$$

$$\sqrt{\frac{100}{4}} = \sqrt{25} \text{ or } 5^- \qquad\qquad \sqrt[3]{\frac{216}{-27}} = \sqrt[3]{-8} \text{ or } ^-2$$

> For any numbers a and b, $b \neq 0$, and any integer n greater than one,
>
> $\sqrt[n]{\dfrac{a}{b}} = \dfrac{\sqrt[n]{a}}{\sqrt[n]{b}}$ as long as all roots are defined.

Quotient Property of Radicals

The quotient property of radicals can be used in simplifying radicals.

examples

1 **Simplify** $\sqrt[3]{\dfrac{3}{8}}$.

$$\sqrt[3]{\frac{3}{8}} = \frac{\sqrt[3]{3}}{\sqrt[3]{8}} \qquad \textit{Quotient Property of Radicals}$$

$$= \frac{\sqrt[3]{3}}{2}$$

2 **Simplify** $\dfrac{6\sqrt{15}}{2\sqrt{3}}$.

$$\frac{6\sqrt{15}}{2\sqrt{3}} = \frac{6}{2}\sqrt{\frac{15}{3}} \qquad \textit{Quotient Property of Radicals}$$

$$= 3\sqrt{5}$$

Fractions are usually written without radicals in the denominator. Similarly, radicands are not left in fraction form. The process of eliminating radicals from the denominator or fractions from the radicand is called **rationalizing the denominator.**

example

3 **Simplify** $\dfrac{3}{2\sqrt{5}}$.

$$\frac{3}{2\sqrt{5}} = \frac{3}{2\sqrt{5}} \cdot \frac{\sqrt{5}}{\sqrt{5}} \qquad \textit{Why is } \frac{\sqrt{5}}{\sqrt{5}} \textit{ used?}$$

$$= \frac{3\sqrt{5}}{2\sqrt{5} \cdot 5}$$

$$= \frac{3\sqrt{5}}{10}$$

4 Simplify $\sqrt{\dfrac{5}{2}}$.

$$\sqrt{\dfrac{5}{2}} = \dfrac{\sqrt{5}}{\sqrt{2}} \cdot \dfrac{\sqrt{2}}{\sqrt{2}} \qquad \textit{Why is } \dfrac{\sqrt{2}}{\sqrt{2}} \textit{ used?}$$

$$= \dfrac{\sqrt{5 \cdot 2}}{\sqrt{2 \cdot 2}}$$

$$= \dfrac{\sqrt{10}}{2}$$

5 Simplify $\sqrt[3]{\dfrac{5}{3}}$.

$$\sqrt[3]{\dfrac{5}{3}} = \dfrac{\sqrt[3]{5}}{\sqrt[3]{3}} \cdot \dfrac{\sqrt[3]{3^2}}{\sqrt[3]{3^2}} \qquad \textit{Why is } \dfrac{\sqrt[3]{3^2}}{\sqrt[3]{3^2}} \textit{ used?}$$

$$= \dfrac{\sqrt[3]{5 \cdot 3^2}}{\sqrt[3]{3^3}}$$

$$= \dfrac{\sqrt[3]{45}}{3}$$

6 Simplify $\dfrac{1 - \sqrt{3}}{5 + 2\sqrt{3}}$.

$$\dfrac{1 - \sqrt{3}}{5 + 2\sqrt{3}} = \dfrac{1 - \sqrt{3}}{5 + 2\sqrt{3}} \cdot \dfrac{5 - 2\sqrt{3}}{5 - 2\sqrt{3}} \qquad \textit{Conjugates can be used to rationalize the denominator.}$$

$$= \dfrac{5 - 2\sqrt{3} - 5\sqrt{3} + 2\sqrt{3^2}}{25 - 10\sqrt{3} + 10\sqrt{3} - 4\sqrt{3^2}}$$

$$= \dfrac{5 - 2\sqrt{3} - 5\sqrt{3} + 6}{25 - 10\sqrt{3} + 10\sqrt{3} - 12}$$

$$= \dfrac{11 - 7\sqrt{3}}{13}$$

In general, a radical expression is simplified when the following conditions are met.

1. The index n is as small as possible.
2. The radicand contains no factor (other than one) which is the nth power of an integer or polynomial.
3. The radicand contains no fractions.
4. No radicals appear in the denominator.

Conditions for Simplified Radicals

Simplifying radicals makes it easier to approximate the value of an expression.

example

7 **Approximate the value of $\dfrac{\sqrt[3]{45}}{\sqrt[3]{2}}$ to three decimal places.**

$$\frac{\sqrt[3]{45}}{\sqrt[3]{2}} = \frac{\sqrt[3]{45}}{\sqrt[3]{2}} \cdot \frac{\sqrt[3]{2^2}}{\sqrt[3]{2^2}} \qquad \textit{Why is } \frac{\sqrt[3]{2^2}}{\sqrt[3]{2^2}} \textit{ used?}$$

$$= \frac{\sqrt[3]{45 \cdot 4}}{\sqrt[3]{2^3}}$$

$$= \frac{\sqrt[3]{180}}{2} \qquad \textit{This expression is simplified.}$$

$$\approx \frac{5.646}{2} \qquad \textit{Use the table on page 574}$$
$$\qquad\qquad \textit{to obtain 5.646.}$$

$$\approx 2.823$$

exercises

Exploratory **Simplify.**

1. $\dfrac{\sqrt{6}}{\sqrt{3}}$ **2.** $\dfrac{\sqrt{10}}{\sqrt{2}}$ **3.** $\dfrac{\sqrt[3]{18y}}{\sqrt[3]{6}}$ **4.** $\dfrac{\sqrt[4]{35x^5}}{\sqrt[4]{7}}$

5. $\sqrt{\dfrac{5}{4}}$ **6.** $\sqrt{\dfrac{7}{9}}$ **7.** $\sqrt[3]{\dfrac{5}{8}}$ **8.** $\sqrt[3]{\dfrac{4}{27}}$

State the fraction that each of the following expressions should be multiplied by to rationalize the denominator.

9. $\dfrac{2}{\sqrt{3}}$ **10.** $\dfrac{4}{\sqrt{2}}$ **11.** $\dfrac{1}{\sqrt{5}}$ **12.** $\dfrac{3}{\sqrt{7}}$

13. $\sqrt{\dfrac{6}{7}}$ **14.** $\sqrt{\dfrac{5}{8}}$ **15.** $\sqrt{\dfrac{3}{5}}$ **16.** $\sqrt{\dfrac{8}{3}}$

17. $\dfrac{3}{\sqrt[3]{4}}$ **18.** $\dfrac{4}{\sqrt[3]{2}}$ **19.** $\dfrac{7}{\sqrt[3]{9}}$ **20.** $\dfrac{4}{\sqrt[3]{16}}$

Name the conjugate of each expression.

21. $1 + \sqrt{3}$ **22.** $4 - \sqrt{5}$ **23.** $1 - \sqrt{2}$

24. $4 + \sqrt{3}$ **25.** $3 + \sqrt{5}$ **26.** $5 - \sqrt{2}$

27. $5 + 3\sqrt{3}$ **28.** $5 + 2\sqrt{5}$ **29.** $2\sqrt{2} - 3$

30. $2\sqrt{7} - 5$ **31.** $\sqrt{2} - 5\sqrt{3}$ **32.** $\sqrt{7} + \sqrt{2}$

Written Simplify.

1. $\dfrac{\sqrt{10}}{\sqrt{2}}$
2. $\dfrac{\sqrt{12}}{\sqrt{3}}$
3. $\dfrac{\sqrt{14}}{\sqrt{2}}$
4. $\dfrac{\sqrt{21}}{\sqrt{7}}$

5. $\dfrac{\sqrt[3]{81}}{\sqrt[3]{9}}$
6. $\dfrac{\sqrt[3]{54}}{\sqrt[3]{6}}$
7. $\sqrt{\dfrac{5}{4}}$
8. $\sqrt{\dfrac{7}{16}}$

9. $\sqrt{\dfrac{8}{9}}$
10. $\sqrt{\dfrac{21}{12}}$
11. $\sqrt[3]{\dfrac{5}{8}}$
12. $\sqrt[3]{\dfrac{2}{27}}$

13. $\sqrt[3]{\dfrac{54}{125}}$
14. $\sqrt[3]{\dfrac{16}{27}}$
15. $\sqrt[4]{\dfrac{5}{16}}$
16. $\sqrt[4]{\dfrac{7}{81}}$

17. $\sqrt{\dfrac{1}{3}}$
18. $\sqrt{\dfrac{1}{5}}$
19. $\sqrt{\dfrac{2}{3}}$
20. $\sqrt{\dfrac{3}{5}}$

21. $\sqrt{\dfrac{5}{12}}$
22. $\sqrt{\dfrac{5}{32}}$
23. $\sqrt[3]{\dfrac{5}{9}}$
24. $\sqrt[3]{\dfrac{9}{4}}$

25. $\sqrt[4]{\dfrac{2}{3}}$
26. $\sqrt[4]{\dfrac{3}{2}}$
27. $\dfrac{1}{3+\sqrt{5}}$
28. $\dfrac{3}{5-\sqrt{2}}$

29. $\dfrac{2}{3-\sqrt{5}}$
30. $\dfrac{7}{4-\sqrt{3}}$
31. $\dfrac{1+\sqrt{2}}{3-\sqrt{2}}$
32. $\dfrac{2+\sqrt{6}}{2-\sqrt{6}}$

33. $\dfrac{2-\sqrt{3}}{5+3\sqrt{3}}$
34. $\dfrac{3+4\sqrt{5}}{5+2\sqrt{5}}$
35. $\dfrac{1+3\sqrt{2}}{2\sqrt{2}-3}$
36. $\dfrac{2+\sqrt{7}}{2\sqrt{7}-5}$

37. $\sqrt{\dfrac{2}{5}}+\sqrt{40}+\sqrt{10}$
38. $\sqrt{\dfrac{1}{5}}+\sqrt{24}+\sqrt{20}-\sqrt{\dfrac{2}{3}}$

39. $\sqrt[3]{\dfrac{1}{4}}+\sqrt[3]{54}-\sqrt[3]{16}$
40. $\sqrt[3]{32}+\sqrt[3]{4}-\sqrt[3]{\dfrac{1}{2}}$

Approximate the values of each expression to three decimal places.

41. $\sqrt{\dfrac{5}{4}}$
42. $\sqrt{\dfrac{7}{16}}$
43. $\sqrt{\dfrac{8}{9}}$
44. $\sqrt{\dfrac{21}{12}}$

45. $\sqrt[3]{\dfrac{5}{8}}$
46. $\sqrt[3]{\dfrac{2}{27}}$
47. $\sqrt[3]{\dfrac{54}{125}}$
48. $\sqrt[3]{\dfrac{16}{27}}$

Solve each problem. Round all answers to the nearest hundredth.

49. Find the time, T, in seconds for a complete swing (back and forth) of a pendulum whose length is 6 feet.

Let $T = 2\pi\sqrt{\dfrac{L}{32}}$, where $\pi \approx 3.14$.

50. Find the time, T, in seconds for a complete swing of a pendulum whose length is 98 centimeters.

Let $T = 2\pi\sqrt{\dfrac{L}{980}}$, where $\pi \approx 3.14$.

51. Find the radius, r, of a sphere whose surface area S is 616 square inches.

Let $r = \dfrac{1}{2}\sqrt{\dfrac{S}{\pi}}$, where $\pi \approx \dfrac{22}{7}$.

52. Find the time, t, in seconds required for a freely falling body to fall a distance s of 150 feet. Let $t = \dfrac{1}{4}\sqrt{s}$.

Challenge Simplify.

1. $\dfrac{3}{\sqrt{2}+\sqrt{3}+\sqrt{5}}$
2. $\dfrac{2}{\sqrt{3}+\sqrt{7}+\sqrt{10}}$
3. $\dfrac{4}{\sqrt{3}+\sqrt{5}-\sqrt{2}}$

In mathematics, many words have specific definitions. However, when these words are used in everyday language, they frequently have a different meaning. Study each pair of sentences. How does the meaning of the word in boldface differ?

A. Plants receive nourishment and water from their **roots.**
B. The square **roots** of 36 are 6 and ⁻6.

A. The United States is a major world **power.**
B. Raising a number to the nth **power** means using that number as a factor n times.

A. I am **positive** I left my homework in my locker.
B. For any numbers a and b, and any **positive** integer n, if $a^n = b$, then a is an nth root of b.

A. The **principal** will speak at the school assembly.
B. The symbol $\sqrt[n]{b}$ indicates the **principal** nth root of b.

A. The soup tastes a little **odd.**
B. For any number a and any integer n greater than one, if n is **odd,** then $\sqrt[n]{a^n} = a$.

Read the following. Which words are mathematical words? Which words are ordinary words? Which mathematical words have another meaning in everyday language?

For any nonnegative number a and b and any integer n greater than one, $\sqrt[n]{ab} = \sqrt[n]{a} \cdot \sqrt[n]{b}$.

Product Property of Radicals

Simplifying a square root means finding the square root of the greatest perfect square factor of the radicand. You use the product property of radicals to simplify square roots.

Exercises
Write two sentences for each word. First, use the word in everyday language. Then use the word in a mathematical context.

1. index
2. negative
3. even
4. rational
5. irrational
6. like
7. rationalize
8. coordinates
9. real
10. degree
11. absolute
12. identity

5-5 Equations with Radicals

The properties of radicals can be used to solve equations.

1 Solve $x + 2 = x\sqrt{3}$.

$$x + 2 = x\sqrt{3}$$
$$x - x\sqrt{3} = -2$$
$$x(1 - \sqrt{3}) = -2 \qquad \textit{Distributive Property}$$
$$x = \frac{-2}{1 - \sqrt{3}}$$
$$x = \frac{-2}{1 - \sqrt{3}} \cdot \frac{1 + \sqrt{3}}{1 + \sqrt{3}} \qquad \textit{The conjugate of } 1 - \sqrt{3} \textit{ is } 1 + \sqrt{3}.$$
$$x = \frac{-2(1 + \sqrt{3})}{1 + \sqrt{3} - \sqrt{3} - 3}$$
$$x = \frac{-2(1 + \sqrt{3})}{-2}$$
$$x = 1 + \sqrt{3}$$

Check:
$$x + 2 = x\sqrt{3}$$
$$(1 + \sqrt{3}) + 2 \overset{?}{=} (1 + \sqrt{3})\sqrt{3}$$
$$\sqrt{3} + 3 = \sqrt{3} + 3$$

The solution is $1 + \sqrt{3}$.

Variables may appear in the radicand of a radical. Equations containing such radicals are called **radical equations.**

2 Solve $3 - \sqrt{x - 2} = 0$.

$$3 - \sqrt{x - 2} = 0$$
$$3 = \sqrt{x - 2} \qquad \textit{Isolate the radical.}$$
$$3^2 = (\sqrt{x - 2})^2 \qquad \textit{Square both sides.}$$
$$9 = x - 2$$
$$11 = x$$

Check:
$$3 - \sqrt{x - 2} = 0$$
$$3 - \sqrt{11 - 2} \overset{?}{=} 0$$
$$3 - \sqrt{9} \overset{?}{=} 0$$
$$3 - 3 \overset{?}{=} 0$$
$$0 = 0$$

The solution is 11.

Squaring both sides of an equation *may* produce results that do *not* satisfy the equation.

$$x = 2$$ This equation has *one* solution, 2.

$$(x)^2 = (2)^2$$ Square both sides.

$$x^2 = 4$$ This equation has *two* solutions, 2 and ‾2.

examples

3 **Solve $7 + \sqrt{a - 3} = 1$.**

$$7 + \sqrt{a - 3} = 1$$
$$\sqrt{a - 3} = {}^-6$$
$$(\sqrt{a - 3})^2 = ({}^-6)^2$$
$$a - 3 = 36$$
$$a = 39$$

Check: $\quad 7 + \sqrt{a - 3} = 1$
$$7 + \sqrt{39 - 3} \overset{?}{=} 1$$
$$7 + \sqrt{36} \overset{?}{=} 1$$
$$13 \neq 1$$

The answer does *not* check.
The equation has *no* solutions.

4 **Solve $\sqrt[3]{3y - 1} - 2 = 0$.**

$$\sqrt[3]{3y - 1} - 2 = 0$$
$$\sqrt[3]{3y - 1} = 2$$
$$(\sqrt[3]{3y - 1})^3 = 2^3$$
$$3y - 1 = 8$$
$$3y = 9$$
$$y = 3$$

Check: $\quad \sqrt[3]{3y - 1} - 2 = 0$
$$\sqrt[3]{3(3) - 1} - 2 \overset{?}{=} 0$$
$$\sqrt[3]{8} - 2 \overset{?}{=} 0$$
$$2 - 2 \overset{?}{=} 0$$
$$0 = 0$$

The solution is 3.

5 **Solve $r = \sqrt[3]{\dfrac{3w}{4\pi d}}$ for d.**

$$r = \sqrt[3]{\frac{3w}{4\pi d}}$$

$$r^3 = \frac{3w}{4\pi d} \qquad \textit{Cube both sides.}$$

$$r^3 \cdot d = \frac{3w}{4\pi d} \cdot d \qquad \textit{Multiply both sides by d.}$$

$$\frac{r^3 d}{r^3} = \frac{3w}{4\pi r^3} \qquad \textit{Divide both sides by } r^3.$$

$$d = \frac{3w}{4\pi r^3}$$

exercises

Exploratory Solve each equation.

1. $\sqrt{x} = 2$
2. $\sqrt{y} = 3$
3. $m + 2\sqrt{5} = 7$
4. $2 + m = {}^-5\sqrt{3}$
5. $\sqrt{2x + 7} = 3$
6. $\sqrt{3x + 7} = 7$
7. $\sqrt[3]{x - 2} = 3$
8. $\sqrt[4]{2x + 7} = 2$
9. $x\sqrt{3} - 5 = 7$
10. $x\sqrt{5} + 6 = 3$
11. $x\sqrt{3} + 4 = 7 + \sqrt{3}$
12. $2z\sqrt{7} + 3 = 5 + 6\sqrt{7}$

Written Solve each equation.

1. $6 + 2x\sqrt{3} = 0$
2. $2 + 5n\sqrt{10} = 0$
3. $x\sqrt{2} + 3x = 4$
4. $x - x\sqrt{5} = 2$
5. $3x + 5 = x\sqrt{3}$
6. $2x + 7 = {}^-x\sqrt{2}$
7. $2x - x\sqrt{11} = 13$
8. $13 - 3x = x\sqrt{5}$
9. $\sqrt{m} - 8 = 0$
10. $\sqrt{t} - 4 = 0$
11. $\sqrt{y - 5} = 7$
12. $\sqrt{x - 4} = 3$
13. $\sqrt[3]{y + 1} = 2$
14. $\sqrt[3]{m - 1} = 3$
15. $\sqrt[3]{y + 2} = 4$
16. $\sqrt[3]{r + 1} = 5$
17. $\sqrt[4]{2a} = 3$
18. $\sqrt[4]{3p} - 2 = 0$
19. $\sqrt{2x + 3} - 7 = 0$
20. $\sqrt{3y - 5} - 3 = 1$
21. $\sqrt{5y + 1} + 6 = 10$
22. $\sqrt{1 + 2r} - 4 = {}^-1$
23. $\sqrt{2x + 3} + 3 = 10$
24. $\sqrt{4a + 8} + 5 = 7$
25. $\sqrt[3]{m + 5} + 6 = 4$
26. $\sqrt[4]{2x + 3} + 5 = 4$
27. $\sqrt{x + 5} = \sqrt{2x - 3}$
28. $\sqrt{x - 4} = \sqrt{2x - 3}$

Solve each equation for the variable indicated.

29. $y = \sqrt{r^2 + s^2}$ for r
30. $t = \sqrt{\dfrac{2s}{g}}$ for s

31. $r = \sqrt[3]{\dfrac{2mM}{c}}$ for c
32. $T = \dfrac{1}{2}\sqrt{\dfrac{u}{g}}$ for g

33. $v = \dfrac{1}{2}\sqrt{1 + \dfrac{T}{\ell}}$ for ℓ
34. $m^2 = \sqrt[3]{\dfrac{rp}{g^2}}$ for p

Challenge Solve each equation.

1. $\sqrt{x + 8} + 3 = \sqrt{x + 35}$
2. $\sqrt{y + 12} + 1 = \sqrt{y + 21}$
3. $\sqrt{z - 4} - 6 = -\sqrt{z + 20}$

Skills Review Solve each system of equations algebraically.

1. $x - 2y = 10$
   $3x + 2y = 14$
2. $y = 5x + 9$
   $3x + y = 25$
3. $3x + 2y = 17$
   $2x + 5y = 4$

4. $x + 2y = 3$
   $5x - 3y = 2$
5. $2x - 3y = 0$
   $6x = 7 - 6y$
6. $\dfrac{1}{3}x + \dfrac{1}{2}y = \dfrac{7}{6}$
   $\dfrac{1}{7}x - \dfrac{1}{3}y = \dfrac{2}{21}$

5–6   Imaginary Numbers

Some equations have irrational solutions.   *Numbers like $\sqrt{2}$ and π are irrational.*

example

1   **Solve each equation.**

a. $5x^3 + 6 = 126$

$$5x^3 = 120$$
$$x^3 = 24$$
$$x = \sqrt[3]{24}$$
$$x = 2\sqrt[3]{3}$$

The solution is $2\sqrt[3]{3}$.

b. $x^2 - 5 = 0$

$$x^2 = 5$$
$$\sqrt{x^2} = \sqrt{5}$$
$$|x| = \sqrt{5}$$
$$x = \pm\sqrt{5}$$

The solutions are $\sqrt{5}$ and $^-\sqrt{5}$.

The equation $x^2 = {}^-1$ has *no* solution among the real numbers. This is because the square of a real number is nonnegative.

The number i is defined to be a solution to $x^2 = {}^-1$. This number is called the **imaginary unit.** The imaginary unit i is *not* a real number.

Using i as you would any constant, you can define square roots of negative numbers.

$$i^2 = {}^-1 \quad \text{so} \quad \sqrt{^-1} = i$$
$$(2i)^2 = 2^2i^2 \text{ or } ^-4 \quad \text{so} \quad \sqrt{^-4} = \sqrt{4}\,\sqrt{^-1} \text{ or } 2i$$
$$(i\sqrt{3})^2 = i^2(\sqrt{3})^2 \text{ or } ^-3 \quad \text{so} \quad \sqrt{^-3} = \sqrt{3}\,\sqrt{^-1} \quad \text{or } i\sqrt{3}$$

> **For any positive real number b,**
> $$\sqrt{^-(b^2)} = \sqrt{b^2}\sqrt{^-1} \text{ or } bi$$
> **where i is a number whose square is $^-1$.**
> **The number i is called the imaginary unit, and bi is called a pure imaginary number.**

Definition of Imaginary Number

Imaginary numbers are simplified by rewriting them as the product of i and a real number. For example, $3i$, $^-i\sqrt{3}$, and $5i\sqrt{10}$ are simplified imaginary numbers.

example

2   **Simplify $\sqrt{^-24}$.**

$$\sqrt{^-24} = \sqrt{24}\,\sqrt{^-1}$$
$$= i\sqrt{24}$$
$$= i\sqrt{4 \cdot 6}$$
$$= 2i\sqrt{6}$$

Imaginary numbers can be added by using the distributive property.

$$3i + 5i = (3 + 5)i$$
$$= 8i$$

Imaginary numbers can be multiplied by using the commutative and associative properties for multiplication.

$$3i \cdot 5i = (3 \cdot 5)(i \cdot i)$$
$$= 15i^2$$
$$= 15(^-1) \qquad i^2 = {}^-1$$
$$= {}^-15$$

> **For imaginary numbers ai and bi where a and b are real numbers,**
> $$ai + bi = (a + b)i \text{ and,}$$
> $$ai \cdot bi = {}^-ab.$$

Addition and Multiplication of Imaginary Numbers

examples

3 Simplify $\sqrt{^-16} + \sqrt{^-25}$.

$$\sqrt{^-16} + \sqrt{^-25} = i\sqrt{16} + i\sqrt{25}$$
$$= 4i + 5i$$
$$= 9i$$

Change $\sqrt{^-16}$ and $\sqrt{^-25}$ to imaginary form before adding.

4 Simplify $\sqrt{^-3} \cdot \sqrt{^-12}$.

$$\sqrt{^-3} \cdot \sqrt{^-12} = i\sqrt{3} \cdot i\sqrt{12}$$
$$= i^2\sqrt{36}$$
$$= {}^-1 \cdot 6$$
$$= {}^-6$$

Change $\sqrt{^-3}$ and $\sqrt{^-12}$ to imaginary form before multiplying.

Simplifying powers of i reveals a curious pattern.

$$i^1 = i$$
$$i^2 = {}^-1$$
$$i^3 = i^2 \cdot i = {}^-1 \cdot i = {}^-i$$
$$i^4 = i^2 \cdot i^2 = {}^-1 \cdot {}^-1 = 1$$
$$i^5 = i^4 \cdot i = 1 \cdot i = i$$
$$i^6 = i^5 \cdot i = i \cdot i = {}^-1$$
$$i^7 = i^6 \cdot i = {}^-1 \cdot i = {}^-i$$
$$i^8 = i^4 \cdot i^4 = 1 \cdot 1 = 1$$

The values i, $^-1$, ^-i, and 1 repeat in cycles of four.

5 **Simplify i^{15}.**

$$i^{15} = i^4 \cdot i^4 \cdot i^4 \cdot i^3$$
$$= 1 \cdot 1 \cdot 1 \cdot {}^-i$$
$$= {}^-i$$

6 **Simplify i^{86}.**

$$i^{86} = (i^2)^{43}$$
$$= ({}^-1)^{43} \qquad i^2 = {}^-1$$
$$= {}^-1 \qquad \quad {}^-1 \text{ raised to an odd power is } {}^-1.$$

7 **Solve $x^2 + 5 = 0$**

$$x^2 + 5 = 0$$
$$x^2 = {}^-5$$
$$x^2 = {}^-1 \cdot 5$$
$$x = {}^\pm i\sqrt{5} \qquad \text{The solutions, both imaginary, are } i\sqrt{5} \text{ and } {}^-i\sqrt{5}.$$

exercises

Exploratory Simplify.

1. $\sqrt{{}^-36}$
2. $\sqrt{{}^-64}$
3. $4\sqrt{{}^-2}$
4. $6\sqrt{{}^-4}$
5. $\sqrt{{}^-3}\sqrt{{}^-3}$
6. $\sqrt{{}^-2}\sqrt{{}^-2}$
7. $\sqrt{{}^-5}\sqrt{5}$
8. $\sqrt{{}^-7}\sqrt{7}$
9. $3 \cdot 2i$
10. $5 \cdot 7i$
11. $4i + 7i$
12. $12i + 3i$
13. $5i - 8i$
14. $10i - 9i$
15. i^6
16. i^{91}

Written Simplify.

1. $\sqrt{{}^-81}$
2. $\sqrt{{}^-121}$
3. $\sqrt{{}^-50}$
4. $\sqrt{{}^-98}$
5. $\sqrt{\dfrac{{}^-4}{9}}$
6. $\sqrt{\dfrac{{}^-9}{16}}$
7. $\sqrt{\dfrac{{}^-1}{3}}$
8. $\sqrt{\dfrac{{}^-1}{2}}$
9. i^5
10. i^{10}
11. i^{11}
12. i^{43}
13. i^{71}
14. i^{112}
15. i^{82}
16. i^{243}
17. $3i + 2i$
18. $2i + 12i$
19. $7i - 5i$
20. $13i - 14i$
21. $\sqrt{{}^-4} + \sqrt{{}^-1}$
22. $\sqrt{{}^-9} + \sqrt{{}^-16}$
23. $\sqrt{{}^-25} + \sqrt{{}^-36}$
24. $\sqrt{{}^-49} + \sqrt{{}^-100}$
25. $\sqrt{{}^-8}\sqrt{{}^-2}$
26. $\sqrt{{}^-15}\sqrt{{}^-5}$
27. $\sqrt{{}^-14}\sqrt{{}^-7}$
28. $\sqrt{{}^-3}\sqrt{{}^-18}$
29. $(\sqrt{{}^-3})^2$
30. $(\sqrt{{}^-12})^2$
31. $(\sqrt{{}^-3})^3$
32. $(\sqrt{{}^-4})^3$
33. $({}^-2\sqrt{{}^-8})(3\sqrt{{}^-2})$
34. $(4\sqrt{{}^-12})({}^-2\sqrt{{}^-3})$
35. $(6\sqrt{{}^-24})({}^-3\sqrt{6})$
36. $(2\sqrt{15})({}^-3\sqrt{{}^-15})$
37. $(2i)(3i)^2$
38. $5i({}^-2i)^2$

Solve each equation.

39. $x^2 + 16 = 0$
40. $a^2 + 49 = 0$
41. $z^2 + 169 = 0$
42. $c^2 + 144 = 0$
43. $n^2 + 3 = 0$
44. $t^2 + 12 = 0$
45. $2y^2 + 8 = 0$
46. $3b^2 + 18 = 0$
47. $5x^2 + 125 = 0$
48. $3z^2 + 24 = 0$
49. $4m^2 + 5 = 0$
50. $9k^2 + 32 = 0$

5-7   Complex Numbers

Numbers such as $3 + 5i$, $6 + i$, and $27 + 2i$ are called **complex numbers.** Notice they each represent the sum of a real number and an imaginary number.

> **A complex number is any number that can be written in the form $a + bi$ where a and b are real numbers and i is the imaginary unit.**

Definition of Complex Number

a is called the real part.   b i is called the imaginary part.

Any real number is also a complex number. For example, $\sqrt{2}$ can be written as $\sqrt{2} + 0i$. Its imaginary part is 0. A complex number is also a real number *only if its imaginary part is 0.*

Any two complex numbers denoted by $a + bi$ and $c + di$, are equal if and only if their real parts are equivalent and their imaginary parts are equivalent. That is,

$$a + bi = c + di \text{ if and only if } a = c \text{ and } b = d.$$

As long as b $\neq$ 0, the complex number a + b i is also called an imaginary number.

example

1   **Find values for x and y such that $2x + 3yi = 6 + 2i$.**

$2x + 3yi = 6 + 2i$
$2x = 6$ and $3y = 2$
$x = 3$ $y = \dfrac{2}{3}$

Check: $2(3) + 3\left(\dfrac{2}{3}\right)i \stackrel{?}{=} 6 + 2i$
$6 + 2i = 6 + 2i$

To add or subtract complex numbers, you combine their real parts and combine their imaginary parts.

examples

2   **Find $(3 + 6i) + (7 - 2i)$.**

$(3 + 6i) + (7 - 2i) = (3 + 7) + (6i - 2i)$
$= 10 + 4i$

3   **Find $(6 - 5i) - (3 - 2i)$.**

$(6 - 5i) - (3 - 2i) = (6 - 3) + (^-5i - ^-2i)$
$= 3 - 3i$

The FOIL method can be used to multiply complex numbers.

4 Find $(6 - 7i)(4 + 3i)$.

$$\qquad\qquad\qquad \text{F} \qquad \text{O} \qquad \text{I} \qquad \text{L}$$

$$
\begin{aligned}
(6 - 7i)(4 + 3i) &= 6 \cdot 4 + 6 \cdot 3i + {}^-7i \cdot 4 + {}^-7i \cdot 3i \\
&= 24 + 18i - 28i - 21i^2 \\
&= (24 + 21) + (18i - 28i) \qquad {}^-21i^2 = 21 \\
&= 45 - 10i
\end{aligned}
$$

5 Find $(3 + 5i)(3 - 5i)$.

$$\qquad\qquad\qquad \text{F} \qquad \text{O} \qquad \text{I} \qquad \text{L}$$

$$
\begin{aligned}
(3 + 5i)(3 - 5i) &= 3 \cdot 3 + 3 \cdot {}^-5i + 5i \cdot 3 + 5i \cdot {}^-5i \\
&= 9 - 15i + 15i - 25i^2 \\
&= (9 + 25) + ({}^-15i + 15i) \qquad {}^-25i^2 = 25 \\
&= 34
\end{aligned}
$$

Complex numbers of the form $a + bi$ and $a - bi$ are called **conjugates** of each other. Notice that the product of complex conjugates is always a real number.

6 Find $(a + bi)(a - bi)$.

$$\qquad\qquad\qquad \text{F} \qquad \text{O} \qquad \text{I} \qquad \text{L}$$

$$
\begin{aligned}
(a + bi)(a - bi) &= a \cdot a + a \cdot {}^-bi + bi \cdot a + bi \cdot {}^-bi \\
&= a^2 - abi + abi - b^2i^2 \\
&= (a^2 + b^2) + ({}^-abi + abi) \qquad {}^-b^2i^2 = b^2 \\
&= a^2 + b^2
\end{aligned}
$$

The following chart summarizes the basic operations with complex numbers.

For any complex numbers $a + bi$ and $c + di$,
$a + bi = c + di$ if and only if $a = c$ and $b = d$
$(a + bi) + (c + di) = (a + c) + (b + d)i$
$(a + bi) - (c + di) = (a - c) + (b - d)i$
$(a + bi)(c + di) = (ac - bd) + (ad + bc)i$

exercises

Exploratory Simplify.

1. $(6 + 3i) + (2 + 8i)$
2. $(4 - i) + (3 + 3i)$
3. $(5 + 2i) - (2 + 2i)$
4. $(7 - 6i) - (5 - 6i)$
5. $(7 + 3i) + (3 - 3i)$
6. $(2 + 4i) + (2 - 4i)$
7. $4(5 + 3i)$
8. $^-6(2 - 3i)$
9. $(4 + \sqrt{-2}) + (3 + \sqrt{-3})$
10. $(13 + \sqrt{-3}) - (20 - \sqrt{-2})$

Find values of x and y for which each equation is true.

11. $x + yi = 5 + 6i$
12. $x + yi = 2 - 3i$
13. $x - yi = 7 - 2i$
14. $x - yi = 4 + 5i$
15. $x + 2yi = 3$
16. $2x + yi = 5i$

Find each product.

17. $(1 + 3i)(2 + 4i)$
18. $(2 - 3i)(1 - 4i)$
19. $(2 - 3i)(1 + 4i)$
20. $(3 + 2i)(4 - i)$
21. $(6 + i)(6 - i)$
22. $(4 - 3i)(4 + 3i)$

Written Simplify.

1. $(3 + 2i) + (4 + 5i)$
2. $(2 + 6i) + (4 + 3i)$
3. $(9 + 6i) - (3 + 2i)$
4. $(11 - 3i) - (^-4 + 5i)$
5. $(5 + 7i) + (^-3 + 2i)$
6. $(8 - 7i) + (^-5 - i)$
7. $(3 - 11i) - (^-5 + 4i)$
8. $(^-6 - 2i) - (^-8 - 3i)$
9. $(4 + 2i\sqrt{3}) + (1 - 5i\sqrt{3})$
10. $(8 - 3i\sqrt{5}) + (^-3 + 2i\sqrt{5})$
11. $2(^-3 + 2i) + 3(^-5 - 2i)$
12. $^-6(2 - i) + 3(4 - 5i)$
13. $(2 - 3i)(5 + i)$
14. $(5 + 3i)(6 - i)$
15. $(6 - 2i)^2$
16. $(2 + i\sqrt{3})^2$
17. $(7 - i\sqrt{2})(5 + i\sqrt{2})$
18. $(4 - 3i)(7 - 2i)$
19. $(3 + 2i)^2$
20. $(3 + 4i)^2$
21. $(\sqrt{2} + i)(\sqrt{2} - i)$
22. $(3 + 2i)(3 - 2i)$
23. $(2 - \sqrt{-3})(2 + \sqrt{-3})$
24. $(3 + \sqrt{-2})(3 - \sqrt{-2})$
25. $(2 + i)(3 - 4i)(1 + 2i)$
26. $(6 - i)(5 + 2i)(3 + 3i)$
27. $(7 - 5i)(2 - 3i)(7 + 5i)$
28. $(9 + 2i)(5 + i)(9 - 2i)$
29. $(4 + 3i)(2 - 7i)(3 + i)$
30. $(7 - i)(4 + 2i)(5 + 2i)$

Find the sum, difference, and product for each pair of complex numbers.

31. $2i, 1 - 3i$
32. $1 + 4i, 3 - i$
33. $7 + 2i, 7 - 2i$
34. $4 + 3i, 4 - 3i$
35. $1 + i, i^3 + i^4$
36. $1 + i, i^2 + i^3$

Find values of x and y for which each sentence is true.

37. $2x + 5yi = 4 + 15i$
38. $3x + 2yi = 18 + 7i$
39. $(x - y) + (x + y)i = 2 - 4i$
40. $(2x + y) + (x - y)i = 7 - i$
41. $(x + 2y) + (2x - y)i = 5 + 5i$
42. $(x + 4y) + (2x - 3y)i = 13 + 7i$

5-8 Dividing Complex Numbers

Since i represents a radical, fractions are usually written without imaginary numbers in the denominator. As with radicals, the denominator should be rationalized.

1 Simplify $\dfrac{3 + 7i}{2i}$.

$$\frac{3 + 7i}{2i} = \frac{3 + 7i}{2i} \cdot \frac{i}{i} \qquad \textit{Why is } \frac{i}{i} \textit{ used?}$$

$$= \frac{3i + 7i^2}{2i^2}$$

$$= \frac{{}^-7 + 3i}{{}^-2}$$

$$= \frac{7 - 3i}{2}$$

2 Simplify $\dfrac{4 + 3i}{1 - 2i}$.

$$\frac{4 + 3i}{1 - 2i} = \frac{4 + 3i}{1 - 2i} \cdot \frac{1 + 2i}{1 + 2i} \qquad \begin{array}{l} \textit{Conjugates can be used in} \\ \textit{rationalizing the denominator.} \end{array}$$

$$= \frac{4 \cdot 1 + 4 \cdot 2i + 3i \cdot 1 + 3i \cdot 2i}{1 \cdot 1 + 1 \cdot 2i + {}^-2i \cdot 1 + {}^-2i \cdot 2i}$$

$$= \frac{4 + 8i + 3i - 6}{1 + 2i - 2i + 4}$$

$$= \frac{{}^-2 + 11i}{5}$$

3 Find the multiplicative inverse of $3 - 5i$.

The multiplicative inverse of $3 - 5i$ is $\dfrac{1}{3 - 5i}$.

Now simplify.

$$\frac{1}{3 - 5i} = \frac{1}{3 - 5i} \cdot \frac{3 + 5i}{3 + 5i}$$

$$= \frac{3 + 5i}{9 - 25i^2}$$

$$= \frac{3 + 5i}{34}$$

Check: $3 - 5i \cdot \dfrac{3 + 5i}{34} = \dfrac{9 + 25}{34}$

$$= 1 \qquad \begin{array}{l} \textit{The product of a number} \\ \textit{and its inverse is 1.} \end{array}$$

The inverse is $\dfrac{3 + 5i}{34}$.

Exploratory Find the conjugate of each complex number.

1. $2 + i$
2. $1 + 3i$
3. $5 - 4i$
4. $3 - 2i$
5. $4i$
6. $7i$
7. ^-5i
8. ^-3i
9. 6
10. 8
11. $5 - 6i$
12. $12 + i$

Find the product of each complex number and its conjugate.

13. $2 + i$
14. $1 + 3i$
15. $5 - 4i$
16. $3 - 2i$
17. $4i$
18. ^-5i
19. $5 - 6i$
20. $12 + i$

Show that each of the following are multiplicative inverses of one another.

21. $3 + 2i; \dfrac{3 - 2i}{13}$
22. $5 - 4i; \dfrac{5 + 4i}{41}$
23. $6 + 8i; \dfrac{3 - 4i}{50}$

Written Find the product of each complex number and its conjugate.

1. $3 - 7i$
2. $6 + 5i$
3. $2 + 9i$
4. $17 - i$
5. $2 - 3i$
6. $7 - 7i$
7. ^-2i
8. ^-10i

Simplify.

9. $\dfrac{3 - 2i}{1 - i}$
10. $\dfrac{4 + 5i}{1 + i}$
11. $\dfrac{1 + i}{3 + 2i}$
12. $\dfrac{1 - i}{4 - 5i}$

13. $\dfrac{3 + 5i}{2i}$
14. $\dfrac{4 - 7i}{-3i}$
15. $\dfrac{5 - 6i}{-3i}$
16. $\dfrac{2 + i}{5i}$

17. $\dfrac{3}{4 - i}$
18. $\dfrac{2}{6 + 5i}$
19. $\dfrac{4}{\sqrt{3} + 2i}$
20. $\dfrac{7}{\sqrt{2} - 3i}$

21. $\dfrac{2 + i\sqrt{3}}{2 - i\sqrt{3}}$
22. $\dfrac{1 + i\sqrt{2}}{1 - i\sqrt{2}}$
23. $\dfrac{3 - i\sqrt{5}}{3 + i\sqrt{5}}$
24. $\dfrac{2 - i\sqrt{7}}{2 + i\sqrt{7}}$

25. $\dfrac{(2 + 3i)^2}{(3 + i)^2}$
26. $\dfrac{(3 + 3i)^2}{(1 + i)^2}$
27. $\dfrac{1 - i}{(1 + i)^2}$
28. $\dfrac{(4 + 3i)^2}{(3 - i)^2}$

Find the multiplicative inverse of each complex number.

29. $3 + i$
30. $2 - 5i$
31. $7 - 3i$
32. $3 + 7i$
33. $\dfrac{4i}{3 + i}$
34. $\dfrac{2i}{5 - i}$
35. $\dfrac{-i}{2 - 3i}$
36. $\dfrac{-3i}{3 + 4i}$

Challenge Show that each of the following is a cube root of 1.

1. $-\frac{1}{2} + \frac{1}{2}i\sqrt{3}$
2. $-\frac{1}{2} - \frac{1}{2}i\sqrt{3}$

Show that each of the following is a cube root of $^-8$.

3. $1 + i\sqrt{3}$
4. $1 - i\sqrt{3}$

Carol Mitchell is an electrical engineer. She often uses complex numbers when working with electrical circuits.

In a simplified electrical circuit there are three basic things to be considered: flow of electric current, I, called amperage, resistance to that flow, Z, called impedance, and electromotive force, E, called voltage. All three are related in the formula $E = I \cdot Z$. This basic formula can be expressed in several ways.

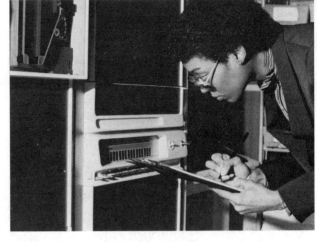

$$E = I \cdot Z \qquad \frac{E}{Z} = I \qquad \frac{E}{I} = Z$$

The amperage, impedance, and voltage are often expressed as complex numbers. Electrical engineers use j instead of i to represent an imaginary number. For electrical engineers, $j = \sqrt{-1}$ and $j^2 = {}^-1$.

Example Compute the voltage, E, when $I = (35 - j40)$ amps and $Z = (10 + j2)$ ohms.

$$\begin{aligned} E &= I \cdot Z \\ &= (35 - j40)(10 + j2) \\ &= 350 + j70 - j400 - j^2 80 \\ &= 350 - j330 + 80 \\ &= 430 - j330 \end{aligned}$$

The voltage is $(430 - j330)$ volts.

Exercises Find E given the following values.

1. $I = (4 + j3)$ amps, $Z = (16 - j28)$ ohms

2. $I = (6 - j8)$ amps, $Z = (14 + j8)$ ohms

Find I given the following values.

3. $E = (70 + j226)$ volts, $Z = (6 + j8)$ ohms

4. $E = (85 + j110)$ volts, $Z = (3 - j4)$ ohms

Find Z given the following values.

5. $E = ({}^-50 + j100)$ volts, $I = ({}^-6 - j2)$ amps

6. $E = (100 + j10)$ volts, $I = ({}^-8 + j3)$ amps

5-9   Properties of Complex Numbers

The following chart summarizes the properties for addition and multiplication of real numbers.

	For any real numbers a, b, and c	
	Addition	Multiplication
commutative	$a + b = b + a$	$a \cdot b = b \cdot a$
associative	$(a + b) + c = a + (b + c)$	$(a \cdot b) \cdot c = a \cdot (b \cdot c)$
identity	$a + 0 = 0 + a$	$a \cdot 1 = 1 \cdot a$
inverse	$a + {}^-a = 0 = {}^-a + a$	$a \cdot \dfrac{1}{a} = 1 = \dfrac{1}{a} \cdot a$ if $a \neq 0$
distributive of multiplication over addition	$a(b + c) = ab + ac$ and $(b + c)a = ba + ca$	

Also, the real numbers are said to be closed under addition and multiplication. This means that the sum or product of any two real numbers is also a real number.

A mathematical system that has the properties stated above is called a **field.** The real number system forms a field. The rational number system forms a field. The complex number system also forms a field.

The real number system consists of the real numbers along with the operations of addition and multiplication.

examples

1   Show that addition of complex numbers is commutative.

Let $a + bi$ and $c + di$ be two complex numbers.

$$(a + bi) + (c + di) = (a + c) + (b + d)i \quad \text{Definition of Complex Addition}$$
$$= (c + a) + (d + b)i \quad \text{Commutativity of Addition for Reals}$$
$$= (c + di) + (a + bi) \quad \text{Definition of Complex Addition}$$

2   Show that multiplication of complex numbers is commutative.

Let $a + bi$ and $c + di$ be two complex numbers.

$$(a + bi)(c + di) = (ac - bd) + (ad + bc)i \quad \text{Definition of Complex Multiplication}$$
$$= (ca - db) + (da + cb)i \quad \text{Commutativity of Multiplication for Reals}$$
$$= (ca - db) + (cb + da)i \quad \text{Commutativity of Addition for Reals}$$
$$= (c + di)(a + bi) \quad \text{Definition of Complex Multiplication}$$

3 **Show that 0 is the additive identity for complex numbers.**

Let $a + bi$ be a complex number.
$$(a + bi) + 0 = (a + bi) + (0 + 0i)$$
$$= (a + 0) + (b + 0)i$$
$$= a + bi$$

4 **Show that 1 is the multiplicative identity for complex numbers.**

Let $a + bi$ be a complex number.
$$(a + bi)(1) = (a + bi)(1 + 0i)$$
$$= (a \cdot 1 - b \cdot 0) + (a \cdot 0 + b \cdot 1)i$$
$$= a + bi$$

If $a + bi$ is a complex number, then $^-a - bi$ is its additive inverse.
$$(a + bi) + (^-a - bi) = (a - a) + (b - b)i$$
$$= 0 + 0i$$
$$= 0$$

The multiplicative inverse of $a + bi$ is $\dfrac{a - bi}{a^2 + b^2}$.
$$(a + bi)\left(\frac{a - bi}{a^2 + b^2}\right) = \frac{(a + bi)(a - bi)}{a^2 + b^2}$$
$$= \frac{a^2 + b^2}{a^2 + b^2}$$
$$= 1$$

exercises

Exploratory Which field properties are *not* satisfied by each set of numbers?

1. natural numbers
2. integers
3. pure imaginary numbers
4. irrational numbers
5. imaginary numbers

Written Choose several complex numbers and perform the necessary operation to show each of the following properties.

1. commutative property of addition
2. commutative property of multiplication
3. associative property of addition
4. associative property of multiplication
5. distributive property of multiplication over addition

Find both the additive and multiplicative inverses for each complex number.

6. $1 + 4i$
7. $5 + 4i$
8. $3 - 2i$
9. $11 - i$
10. $^-2 - 8i$
11. $^-3 - 2i$

12. Show that addition of complex numbers is associative.
13. Show that multiplication of complex numbers is associative.
14. Show that multiplication is distributive over addition for complex numbers.

square root   (139)
nth root   (139)
radical sign   (139)
index   (139)
radicand   (139)
conjugates   (146)
radical equations   (153)

imaginary unit   (156)
pure imaginary number   (156)
complex number   (159)
real part   (159)
imaginary part   (159)
complex conjugates   (160)
field   (165)

Chapter Summary

1. **Definition of Square Root:**   For any numbers a and b, if $a^2 = b$, then a is a square root of b.   (139)
2. **Definition of nth Root:**   For any numbers a and b, and any positive integer n, if $a^n = b$, then a is an nth root of b.   (139)
3. **The Real nth Roots of b, $\sqrt[n]{b}$**   (140)

	$b > 0$	$b < 0$	$b = 0$
n even	one positive root one negative root	no real roots	one real root, 0
n odd	one positive root no negative roots	no positive roots one negative root	one real root, 0

4. **Property of nth Roots:**   For any number a, and any integer n greater than one: **1.** If n is even, then $\sqrt[n]{a^n} = |a|$. **2.** If n is odd, then $\sqrt[n]{a^n} = a$. (140)
5. **Product and Quotient Properties of Radicals:**   For any numbers a and b, and any integer n greater than one:

   1. If n is even, then $\sqrt[n]{ab} = \sqrt[n]{a} \cdot \sqrt[n]{b}$ and $\sqrt[n]{\dfrac{a}{b}} = \dfrac{\sqrt[n]{a}}{\sqrt[n]{b}}$ as long as $a \geq 0$

      and $b > 0$.   (143 and 148)

   2. If n is odd, then $\sqrt[n]{ab} = \sqrt[n]{a} \cdot \sqrt[n]{b}$ and $\sqrt[n]{\dfrac{a}{b}} = \dfrac{\sqrt[n]{a}}{\sqrt[n]{b}}$ as long as $b \neq 0$.

      (143 and 148)
6. **Conditions for Simplifed Radicals:**   **1.** The index n is as small as possible.   **2.** The radicand contains no factor (other than one) which is the nth power of an integer or polynomial.   **3.** The radicand contains no fractions.   **4.** No radicals appear in the denominator.   (149)
7. **Definition of Imaginary Number:**   For any positive real number, b, $\sqrt{-(b^2)} = bi$ where i is a number whose square is $^-1$.   (156)
8. **Definition of a Complex Number:**   A complex number is any number that can be written in the form $a + bi$ where a and b are real numbers and i is the imaginary unit.   (159)

9. For any complex numbers $a + bi$ and $c + di$,

   1. $a + bi = c + di$ if and only if $a = c$ and $b = d$.

   2. $(a + bi) + (c + di) = (a + c) + (b + d)i$.

   3. $(a + bi) - (c + di) = (a - c) + (b - d)i$.

   4. $(a + bi)(c + di) = (ac - bd) + (ad + bc)i$.   (160)

Chapter Review

5–1 **Find the principal roots of each expression.**

  1. $\sqrt{49a^2}$ **2.** $\sqrt[3]{-27}$ **3.** $\sqrt[3]{8x^3y^6}$ **4.** $\sqrt[4]{16}$

  Use the table of powers and roots to find each value.

  5. $\sqrt[3]{39}$ **6.** $\sqrt[3]{290}$ **7.** $(9.8)^3$ **8.** $(1.5)^3$

5–2 **Simplify.**

  9. $\sqrt[3]{48a^2}$ **10.** $\sqrt[4]{32m^5}$ **11.** $^-3\sqrt{18} \cdot 5\sqrt{15}$

  12. $2\sqrt[3]{54} \cdot 4\sqrt[3]{16}$ **13.** $\sqrt{5}(\sqrt{10} + 2)$ **14.** $\sqrt{3}(\sqrt{6} + \sqrt{12})$

  15. $\sqrt[3]{3}(\sqrt[3]{16} + \sqrt[3]{9})$ **16.** $\sqrt{3m^3n^4} \cdot \sqrt{24m^6n}$ **17.** $\sqrt[3]{2xy^4} \cdot \sqrt[3]{36x^2y^2}$

5–3 **Simplify.**

  18. $3\sqrt{12} - 4\sqrt{75} + 4$ **19.** $\sqrt[3]{40} + \sqrt[3]{135} - \sqrt[3]{5}$

  20. $(6 + \sqrt{2})(10 + \sqrt{5})$ **21.** $(3 + \sqrt{5})(3 - \sqrt{5})$

5–4 **Simplify.**

  22. $\sqrt{\dfrac{10}{2}}$ **23.** $\dfrac{\sqrt[3]{80}}{\sqrt[3]{2}}$ **24.** $\dfrac{4}{\sqrt[3]{16}}$ **25.** $\dfrac{\sqrt{3} + \sqrt{2}}{4 + \sqrt{3}}$

5–5 **Solve each equation.**

  26. $\sqrt{2x + 7} = 3$ **27.** $\sqrt[3]{y + 2} = 4$ **28.** $\sqrt{5y + 1} + 6 = 10$

5–6 **Simplify.**

  29. $\sqrt{-8}$ **30.** $\sqrt{-24}$ **31.** i^7

  32. $3i + 2i$ **33.** $\sqrt{-3} \cdot \sqrt{-3}$ **34.** $(2\sqrt{5})(-3\sqrt{-5})$

5–7 **Find the sum, difference, and product for each pair of complex numbers.**

  35. $7 + 2i, 5 - 3i$ **36.** $3 + 8i, 3 - 8i$

  37. Find values of x and y for which $2x + 5yi = 4 + 15i$ is true.

5–8 **Simplify.**

  38. $\dfrac{4 + 3i}{1 - 2i}$ **39.** $\dfrac{7 - 3i}{2i}$ **40.** $\dfrac{(4 - 3i)^2}{(3 + i)^2}$

5–9 **41.** Which property of the complex number field is shown by
$(2 + 7i) + (3 - 5i) = (3 - 5i) + (2 + 7i)$?

Find the principal root of each expression.

1. $\sqrt{81x^2}$ **2.** $\sqrt[3]{-27y^3}$ **3.** $\sqrt{x^2 - 8xy + 16y^2}$

Simplify.

4. $\sqrt[3]{108m^4}$

5. $7\sqrt[3]{16} \cdot 5\sqrt[3]{20}$

6. $\sqrt{125x^2y} \cdot 3\sqrt{81x^2y^2}$

7. $2\sqrt{27} + 2\sqrt{3} - 7\sqrt{48}$

8. $(4 - \sqrt{3})(4 + \sqrt{3})$

9. $(\sqrt{3} - \sqrt{5})(\sqrt{15} + 3)$

10. $\dfrac{3}{\sqrt[3]{4}}$

11. $\dfrac{3}{\sqrt[4]{8}}$

12. $\dfrac{2 + \sqrt{2}}{1 - \sqrt{2}}$

13. $\sqrt[3]{2}(\sqrt[3]{24} - \sqrt[3]{4})$

14. $\sqrt[3]{16x^3} + 5\sqrt[3]{54x^3} - 3\sqrt[3]{128x^3}$

15. $\sqrt{\dfrac{5}{32}} + \sqrt{90} + \dfrac{\sqrt{30}}{\sqrt{3}} - \sqrt{\dfrac{2}{5}}$

Solve each equation.

16. $\sqrt{2x - 5} = 9$

17. $\sqrt[3]{a + 3} - 1 = 2$

Find the sum, difference, and product for each pair of complex numbers.

18. $7 - 3i, 4 + 5i$

19. $4 - 6i, 4 + 6i$

Simplify.

20. $\sqrt{-50}$

21. $3i + \sqrt{-4}$

22. $\sqrt{-3} \cdot \sqrt{-24}$

23. $\dfrac{4 - 5i}{3 + 7i}$

24. $\dfrac{4 - 7i}{2i}$

25. $\dfrac{(2 + 3i)^2}{(1 - i)^2}$

26. Which property of the complex number field is shown by
$[(3 + 4i) + (4 + 2i)] + (6 - 5i) = (3 + 4i) + [(4 + 2i) + (6 - 5i)]$?

chapter
6
Quadratic Equations

Quadratic equations can be used in many situations. For example, Joel Bellman wants to build a swimming pool with a sidewalk of uniform width surrounding it. Joel wants the dimensions of the pool and sidewalk to be 15 meters by 20 meters. The pool must have an area of 150 square meters. To find out how wide the sidewalk must be, Joel uses a quadratic equation.

6–1 Quadratic Equations

Any equation that can be written in the form $ax^2 + bx + c = 0$, $a \neq 0$, is called a **quadratic equation.** Equations such as $z^2 - 8 = 0$ and $x^2 - 2x - 15 = 0$ are quadratic equations. You have learned how to solve some types of quadratic equations.

example

1 **Solve $x^2 - 8 = 0$.**

$x^2 - 8 = 0$ *In this quadratic equation, $b = 0$.*

$x^2 = 8$

$x = \pm\sqrt{8}$ or $\pm 2\sqrt{2}$ The solutions are $2\sqrt{2}$ and $^-2\sqrt{2}$.

Other quadratic equations can be solved using factoring. This method depends on the following property.

> **For any numbers a and b,**
> **if $ab = 0$, then $a = 0$ or $b = 0$.**

Zero Product Property

Both a and b can be zero.

examples

2 **Solve $x^2 - 2x - 15 = 0$.**

$x^2 - 2x - 15 = 0$

$(x - 5)(x + 3) = 0$ *Factor.*

$x - 5 = 0$ or $x + 3 = 0$ *Zero Product Property*

$x = 5$ or $x = ^-3$

Check: $x^2 - 2x - 15 = 0$

$(5)^2 - 2(5) - 15 \overset{?}{=} 0$ or $(^-3)^2 - 2(^-3) - 15 \overset{?}{=} 0$

$0 = 0$ $0 = 0$

The solutions are 5 and $^-3$.

3 **Solve $9x^2 - 24x = ^-16$.**

$9x^2 - 24x = ^-16$

$9x^2 - 24x + 16 = 0$

$(3x - 4)(3x - 4) = 0$

$3x - 4 = 0$ or $3x - 4 = 0$

$3x = 4$ $3x = 4$

$x = \dfrac{4}{3}$ $x = \dfrac{4}{3}$

Check: $9x^2 - 24x = ^-16$

$9\left(\dfrac{4}{3}\right)^2 - 24\left(\dfrac{4}{3}\right) \overset{?}{=} ^-16$

$16 - 32 \overset{?}{=} ^-16$

$^-16 = ^-16$

The solution is $\dfrac{4}{3}$.

exercises

Exploratory Identify which of the following are quadratic equations.

1. $4x^2 + 7x - 3 = 0$
2. $5y^4 - 7y^2 = 0$
3. $2a^2 + 7a = 0$
4. $4x^2 - 2x + 11 = 0$
5. $3z^3 + 4 = 0$
6. $9m^2 - m + 4 = 0$
7. $\frac{1}{2}y^2 + \frac{3}{4} = 0$
8. $\frac{2}{3}c^3 - 3c^2 + 2c = 0$
9. $z^2 + 7z - 3 = z^3$
10. $3d^2 - 9 = d$

Solve each equation.

11. $(x - 4)(x + 5) = 0$
12. $(y - 3)(y + 7) = 0$
13. $(a + 6)(a + 2) = 0$
14. $(m - 8)(m - 1) = 0$
15. $z(z - 1)^2 = 0$
16. $s(s + 4) = 0$
17. $(3y + 7)(y + 5) = 0$
18. $(2b + 5)(b - 1) = 0$
19. $(2x + 3)(3x - 1) = 0$
20. $(3c + 4)(5c - 1) = 0$

Written Solve each equation. Factor

1. $x^2 + 6x + 8 = 0$
2. $z^2 + 4z + 3 = 0$
3. $a^2 - 9a + 20 = 0$
4. $m^2 - 8m + 12 = 0$
5. $b^2 + 3b - 10 = 0$
6. $y^2 - 4y - 21 = 0$
7. $x^2 + 4x + 4 = 0$
8. $c^2 - 12c + 36 = 0$
9. $n^2 + 3n = 0$
10. $z^2 - 5z = 0$
11. $d^2 - 3d = 4$
12. $m^2 + 6m = 27$
13. $z^2 + z = 30$
14. $y^2 - y = 12$
15. $2x^2 + 5x + 3 = 0$
16. $2a^2 + 9a + 4 = 0$
17. $2z^2 - 3z - 9 = 0$
18. $3b^2 + 13b - 10 = 0$
19. $3c^2 = 5c$
20. $10y^2 = y$
21. $6d^2 + 13d + 6 = 0$
22. $12m^2 + 25m + 12 = 0$
23. $10x^2 + 33x - 7 = 0$
24. $6n^2 - 5n - 25 = 0$
25. $24y^2 - 22y + 3 = 0$
26. $16b^2 - 12b + 2 = 0$
27. $4s^2 - 11s - 3 = 0$
28. $4a^2 - 17a + 4 = 0$
29. $z^2 + 3z - 40 = 0$
30. $6m^2 + 7m - 3 = 0$
31. $3r^2 - 14r + 8 = 0$
32. $2y^2 + 11y - 21 = 0$
33. $12c^2 - 17c - 5 = 0$
34. $3t^2 + 4t - 15 = 0$
35. $12p^2 + 8p = 15$
36. $18n^2 - 3n = 1$
37. $4b^2 - 13b = 12$
38. $18m^2 - 3m = 15$
39. $4x^2 + 9 = 12x$
40. $9y^2 + 16 = {}^-24y$
41. $121 = 16b^2$
42. $4t^2 = 25$
43. $n^3 = 9n$
44. $a^3 = 81a$
45. $35z^3 + 16z^2 = 12z$
46. $18r^3 + 16r = 34r^2$
47. $25d^3 + 9d = 30d^2$
48. $16t^3 = 40t^2 - 25t$

Some problems may be solved by using a guess-and-check strategy. This procedure involves first making an educated guess for the solution to a problem. The next step is to check your guess in terms of the problem. Even though it may not be correct, it may give you an indication of how to improve your next guess. This procedure is repeated until you arrive at the correct answer.

Example **Find the least prime number greater than 720.**

One way to solve this problem is to check each integer beginning with 721 for prime divisors until you find a prime number.

However, if known information is used, time and effort in this guess-and-check method can be saved. Obviously, any even integer greater than 720 is not prime. Since 720 is divisible by 3, every third integer greater than 720 will not be prime. Any integer greater than 720 whose last digit is 5 or 0 is not prime. Thus, many possibilities are eliminated.

Try 721.   *Using a calculator is helpful.*

$721 \div 7 = 103$ *not prime*

Try 727.

$727 \div 7 = 103.9$	$727 \div 11 = 66.1$
$727 \div 13 = 55.9$	$727 \div 17 = 42.8$
$727 \div 19 = 38.3$	$727 \div 23 = 31.6$
$727 \div 29 = 25.1$	*Why can you stop after this division?*

Thus, 727 is the least prime number greater than 720

Exercises   Solve each problem.

1. Find the least prime number greater than 840.

2. Rich and Peg raise cows and chickens. They counted all the heads and got 12. They counted all the feet and got 40. How many cows and chickens do they have?

3. Supply a digit for each letter so the multiplication problem is correct. Each letter represents a different digit.

    ABCDE
    × 4
    ———
    EDCBA

4. Write an eight-digit number using the digits 1, 2, 3, and 4 each twice so that the 1's are separated by 1 digit, the 2's are separated by 2 digits, the 3's are separated by 3 digits, and the 4's are separated by 4 digits.

5. Copy the diagram below. In each block write a digit such that the digit in the first block indicates the total number of zeros in the entire ten-digit number, the digit in the block marked "1" indicates the total number of 1's in the number, and so on to the last block whose digit indicates the total number of 9's in the number.

0	1	2	3	4	5	6	7	8	9

6–2   Completing the Square

An equation like $(x - 4)^2 = 3$ can be solved by taking the square root of both sides.

$$(x - 4)^2 = 3$$
$$\sqrt{(x - 4)^2} = \sqrt{3}$$
$$|x - 4| = \sqrt{3}$$
$$x - 4 = \pm\sqrt{3}$$
$$x = 4 \pm \sqrt{3} \qquad \text{The solutions are } 4 + \sqrt{3} \text{ and } 4 - \sqrt{3}.$$

The equation $x^2 - 6x + 9 = 2$ can be solved in a similar way.

$$x^2 - 6x + 9 = 2$$
$$(x - 3)^2 = 2$$
$$x - 3 = \pm\sqrt{2}$$
$$x = 3 \pm \sqrt{2} \qquad \text{The solutions are } 3 + \sqrt{2} \text{ and } 3 - \sqrt{2}.$$

To solve a quadratic equation by taking square roots you must have a perfect square equal to a constant. A method called **completing the square** is based on this concept.

Consider the following perfect squares.

$$(x + 7)^2 = x^2 + 14x + 49 \qquad\qquad (x + b)^2 = x^2 + 2bx + b^2$$
$$(14 \div 2)^2 = 7^2 \text{ or } 49 \qquad\qquad (2b \div 2)^2 = b^2$$

The pattern shown above can be used to complete the square when two terms are known. Complete the square for $x^2 - 8x$.

$$x^2 - 8x + \underline{\boxed{}}$$
$$(^-8 \div 2)^2 = (^-4)^2 \text{ or } 16 \qquad \text{The answer is } x^2 - 8x + 16.$$

This example shows how to solve a quadratic equation by completing the square.

---

example

1 **Solve $x^2 - 8x + 11 = 0$.**

$x^2 - 8x + 11 = 0$	*Not a perfect square*
$x^2 - 8x = ^-11$	*Subtract 11 from each side.*
$x^2 - 8x + 16 = ^-11 + 16$	*Add $\left(\frac{^-8}{2}\right)^2$ or 16 to each side.*
$(x - 4)^2 = 5$	*Factor.*
$x - 4 = \pm\sqrt{5}$	*Take the square root of each side.*
$x = 4 \pm \sqrt{5}$	*Solve for x.*

The solutions are $4 + \sqrt{5}$ and $4 - \sqrt{5}$.

When the coefficient of the squared term is *not* 1, another step is required.

2 **Solve $2m^2 - 8m + 3 = 0$.**

$$2m^2 - 8m + 3 = 0$$

$$m^2 - 4m + \frac{3}{2} = 0 \qquad \text{\textit{Divide each side by 2.}}$$

$$m^2 - 4m = -\frac{3}{2}$$

$$m^2 - 4m + 4 = -\frac{3}{2} + 4 \qquad \text{\textit{Add ($^-4 \div 2$)}}^2 \text{ \textit{or 4 to each side.}}$$

$$(m - 2)^2 = \frac{5}{2} \qquad \text{\textit{Factor.}}$$

$$m - 2 = \pm\sqrt{\frac{5}{2}} \qquad \text{\textit{Take the square root of each side.}}$$

$$m - 2 = \pm\frac{\sqrt{10}}{2} \qquad \text{\textit{Rationalize the denominator.}}$$

$$m = 2 \pm\frac{\sqrt{10}}{2} \qquad \text{\textit{Solve for m.}}$$

The solutions are $2 + \dfrac{\sqrt{10}}{2}$ and $2 - \dfrac{\sqrt{10}}{2}$.

3 **Solve $3x^2 - 11x - 4 = 0$.**

$$3x^2 - 11x - 4 = 0$$

$$x^2 - \frac{11}{3}x - \frac{4}{3} = 0 \qquad \text{\textit{Divide each side by 3.}}$$

$$x^2 - \frac{11}{3}x = \frac{4}{3}$$

$$x^2 - \frac{11}{3}x + \frac{121}{36} = \frac{4}{3} + \frac{121}{36} \qquad \text{\textit{Add}} \left(-\frac{11}{3} \div 2\right)^2 \text{\textit{or}} \frac{121}{36} \text{\textit{to each side.}}$$

$$\left(x - \frac{11}{6}\right)^2 = \frac{169}{36} \qquad \text{\textit{Factor.}}$$

$$x - \frac{11}{6} = \pm\frac{13}{6} \qquad \text{\textit{Take square root of each side.}}$$

$$x = 4 \text{ or } x = -\frac{1}{3}$$

The solutions are 4 and $-\dfrac{1}{3}$.

exercises

Exploratory State whether or not each trinomial is a perfect square.

1. $x^2 + 4x + 4$

2. $a^2 + 14a + 28$

3. $b^2 - 6b - 9$

4. $x^2 - x + \dfrac{1}{4}$

5. $m^2 - 10m + 25$

6. $a^2 - 3a + \dfrac{9}{2}$

7. $x^2 + 5x + \dfrac{25}{4}$

8. $t^2 - 12t - 36$

9. $c^2 + 14c + 49$

Find the value of c that makes each trinomial a perfect square.

10. $y^2 - 6y + c$

11. $x^2 + 2x + c$

12. $m^2 - 20m + c$

13. $t^2 + 40t + c$

14. $n^2 + 12n + c$

15. $x^2 + 18x + c$

16. $y^2 + 3y + c$

17. $r^2 - 9r + c$

18. $s^2 + 11s + c$

19. $a^2 - 100a + c$

20. $n^2 - n + c$

21. $x^2 + 15x + c$

Written Find the value of c that makes each trinomial a perfect square.

1. $x^2 + 6x + c$

2. $x^2 - 10x + c$

3. $y^2 + \frac{1}{2}y + c$

4. $a^2 + 9a + c$

5. $r^2 + r + c$

6. $x^2 - 16x + c$

7. $y^2 - 3y + c$

8. $m^2 - \frac{2}{3}m + c$

9. $b^2 + 7b + c$

10. $a^2 - \frac{4}{5}a + c$

11. $r^2 + 50r + c$

12. $n^2 - 30n + c$

Solve each equation by completing the square.

13. $y^2 - 2y = 24$

14. $t^2 + 4t = 96$

15. $z^2 + 3z = 88$

16. $x^2 - 3x = 10$

17. $x^2 - 8x + 15 = 0$

18. $r^2 - 6r + 8 = 0$

19. $c^2 + 8c - 20 = 0$

20. $b^2 + 2b - 48 = 0$

21. $x^2 - 7x + 12 = 0$

22. $s^2 - 10s + 21 = 0$

23. $x^2 + 8x - 84 = 0$

24. $m^2 + 3m - 180 = 0$

25. $x^2 + 3x - 40 = 0$

26. $y^2 + 12y + 4 = 0$

27. $n^2 - 8n + 14 = 0$

28. $r^2 + 5r - 8 = 0$

29. $x^2 - 7x + 5 = 0$

30. $t^2 + 3t - 8 = 0$

31. $a^2 - 5a - 10 = 0$

32. $b^2 - \frac{3}{4}b + \frac{1}{8} = 0$

33. $y^2 + \frac{7}{3}y + \frac{2}{3} = 0$

34. $4x^2 + 19x - 5 = 0$

35. $6m^2 + 7m - 3 = 0$

36. $3c^2 - 14c + 8 = 0$

37. $2y^2 + 11y - 21 = 0$

38. $12r^2 - 17r - 5 = 0$

39. $3t^2 + 4t - 15 = 0$

40. $6s^2 + 2s + 3 = 0$

41. $3z^2 - 12z + 4 = 0$

42. $2x^2 - 3x + 4 = 0$

43. $4a^2 - a + 3 = 0$

44. $6b^2 + 14b + 10 = 0$

Skills Review Factor.

1. $x^3 - 7x^2 + 12x$

2. $6m^4 - 34m^3 + 20m^2$

3. $7x^3 - 28x$

4. $16a^2 - a^2b^4$

5. $4ax + 14ay - 10bx - 35by$

6. $7mx^2 + 2nx^2 - 7my^2 - 2ny^2$

7. $b^3 - 27$

8. $8x^3 - 27y^3$

9. $32m^5 + 108m^2$

10. $5r^4s + 625rs^4$

6–3   The Quadratic Formula

Completing the square can be used to develop a general formula for solving quadratic equations.

$$ax^2 + bx + c = 0 \quad (a \neq 0)$$ *Start with the general form of a quadratic equation.*

$$x^2 + \frac{b}{a}x + \frac{c}{a} = 0$$ *Divide by a so the coefficient of x^2 is 1.*

$$x^2 + \frac{b}{a}x = -\frac{c}{a}$$ *Subtract $\frac{c}{a}$ from each side.*

$$x^2 + \frac{b}{a}x + \left(\frac{b}{2a}\right)^2 = -\frac{c}{a} + \left(\frac{b}{2a}\right)^2$$ *Complete the square.*

$$\left(x + \frac{b}{2a}\right)^2 = -\frac{c}{a} + \frac{b^2}{4a^2}$$ *Factor.*

$$\left(x + \frac{b}{2a}\right)^2 = \frac{b^2 - 4ac}{4a^2}$$ *Add.*

$$\left|x + \frac{b}{2a}\right| = \sqrt{\frac{b^2 - 4ac}{4a^2}}$$ *Take the square root of each side.*

$$x + \frac{b}{2a} = \pm\frac{\sqrt{b^2 - 4ac}}{2a}$$ *Simplify.*

$$x = \frac{^-b \pm \sqrt{b^2 - 4ac}}{2a}$$ *Solve for x.*

This formula is called the **quadratic formula** and can be used to solve *any* quadratic equation.

The solutions of a quadratic equation of the form $ax^2 + bx + c = 0$ with $a \neq 0$ are given by this formula.

Quadratic Formula

$$x = \frac{^-b \pm \sqrt{b^2 - 4ac}}{2a}$$

---

example

1 **Solve $x^2 - 3x - 28 = 0$ using the quadratic formula.**

$$x = \frac{^-b \pm \sqrt{b^2 - 4ac}}{2a}$$

$$= \frac{^-(^-3) \pm \sqrt{(^-3)^2 - 4(1)(^-28)}}{2(1)}$$ *Substitute the following values into the formula.*
                                        $a = 1, b = ^-3, c = ^-28$

$$= \frac{3 \pm \sqrt{121}}{2}$$

$$= \frac{3 \pm 11}{2}$$

The solutions are $\frac{3 + 11}{2}$ and $\frac{3 - 11}{2}$ or 7 and $^-4$.

The quadratic formula yields *both* solutions to a quadratic equation, even if those solutions are imaginary.

examples

2 **Solve $2x^2 + 3x - 7 = 0$**

$$x = \frac{-b \pm \sqrt{b^2 - 4ac}}{2a}$$

$$= \frac{-3 \pm \sqrt{3^2 - 4(2)(-7)}}{2(2)} \qquad a = 2, b = 3, c = -7$$

$$= \frac{-3 \pm \sqrt{9 + 56}}{4}$$

$$= \frac{-3 \pm \sqrt{65}}{4}$$

The solutions are $\dfrac{-3 + \sqrt{65}}{4}$ and $\dfrac{-3 - \sqrt{65}}{4}$.

3 **Solve $3x^2 - 5x + 9 = 0$.**

$$x = \frac{-b \pm \sqrt{b^2 - 4ac}}{2a}$$

$$= \frac{-(-5) \pm \sqrt{(-5)^2 - 4(3)(9)}}{2(3)} \qquad a = 3, b = -5, c = 9$$

$$= \frac{5 \pm \sqrt{25 - 108}}{6}$$

$$= \frac{5 \pm \sqrt{-83}}{6}$$

The solutions are $\dfrac{5 + i\sqrt{83}}{6}$ and $\dfrac{5 - i\sqrt{83}}{6}$.

Some cubic equations can be solved using the quadratic formula.

example

4 **Solve $x^3 - 27 = 0$.**

$$x^3 - 27 = 0 \qquad \textit{The left side is the difference of two cubes.}$$
$$(x - 3)(x^2 + 3x + 9) = 0 \qquad \textit{Factor.}$$
$$x - 3 = 0 \quad \text{or} \quad x^2 + 3x + 9 = 0 \qquad \textit{Zero Product Property}$$

$$x = 3 \quad \text{or} \qquad\qquad x = \frac{-3 \pm \sqrt{(3)^2 - 4(1)(9)}}{2(1)}$$

$$= \frac{-3 \pm \sqrt{-27}}{2}$$

$$= \frac{-3 \pm 3i\sqrt{3}}{2}$$

The solutions are 3, $\dfrac{-3 + 3i\sqrt{3}}{2}$ and $\dfrac{-3 - 3i\sqrt{3}}{2}$.

exercises

Exploratory State the values of a, b, and c for each quadratic equation.

1. $5x^2 - 3x + 7 = 0$
2. $2y^2 + y - 3 = 0$
3. $z^2 + 2z - 1 = 0$
4. $c^2 - 6c - 1 = 0$
5. $m^2 + m = 0$
6. $5x^2 - 3 = 0$
7. $4x^2 + 2x = 7$
8. $7y^2 + 4 = 2y$
9. $5t^2 - 6 = t$
10. $3r^2 - 4r = {}^-1$
11. $3z^2 = 2z - 7$
12. $x^2 = 1 - x$

Written Solve each equation using the quadratic formula.

1. $x^2 - x - 30 = 0$
2. $x^2 + 10x + 16 = 0$
3. $y^2 + 2y - 15 = 0$
4. $r^2 + 13r + 42 = 0$
5. $t^2 - 10t + 24 = 0$
6. $s^2 + 5s - 24 = 0$
7. $x^2 - 5x + 4 = 0$
8. $5x^2 - x - 4 = 0$
9. $3x^2 - 7x - 20 = 0$
10. $4x^2 - 11x - 3 = 0$
11. $6m^2 - m - 15 = 0$
12. $24x^2 - 14x - 5 = 0$
13. $14r^2 + 33r - 5 = 0$
14. $6y^2 + 19y + 15 = 0$
15. $20a^2 + 3a - 2 = 0$
16. $15x^2 + 34x + 15 = 0$
17. $24y^2 - 2y = 15$
18. $3x^2 + 5x = 28$
19. $2x^2 - x - 15 = 0$
20. $4x^2 - 9x + 5 = 0$
21. $14r^2 - 45r - 14 = 0$
22. $2x^2 - 5x + 3 = 0$
23. $t^2 - 13t = 0$
24. $3t^2 - 12t = 0$
25. $12x^2 - 7x - 12 = 0$
26. $21x^2 + 20x - 1 = 0$
27. $7n^2 + 20n - 32 = 0$
28. $6y^2 - 5y - 6 = 0$
29. $8r^2 = 60$
30. $12x^2 - 11x = 3$
31. $2x^2 + 3x + 3 = 0$
32. $6y^2 + 8y + 5 = 0$
33. $5m^2 + 7m + 3 = 0$
34. $2x^2 - 5x + 4 = 0$
35. $x^2 - 9x + 21 = 0$
36. $2z^2 + 2z + 3 = 0$
37. $6t^2 = 2t - 1$
38. $7y^2 = y + 2$
39. $8a^2 = {}^-2a$
40. $24t = 7t^2$
41. $8r^2 + 6r + 1 = 0$
42. $3x^2 - 6x + 8 = 0$
43. $x^3 - 8 = 0$
44. $x^3 + 8 = 0$
45. $x^3 + 64 = 0$
46. $x^3 - 64 = 0$
47. $a^3 = 125$
48. $a^3 = 1$

49. Write a computer program to find only the *real* roots of quadratic equations.

Perfect Numbers

excursions in algebra

Hrotsvitha (932–1002) was a nun who lived in a Benedictine Abbey in Saxony. She was one of the first persons to write about **perfect numbers**. A perfect number is one that is equal to the sum of its *aliquot* parts. That is, it is equal to the sum of all its factors including 1, but *not* including itself. Consider this example.

$$6 = \underbrace{1 + 2 + 3}$$

factors of 6, but <u>not</u> including 6

Hrotsvitha wrote about three perfect numbers other than 6, namely 28, 496, and 8128.

Exercises Show that each of the following are perfect numbers.

1. 28
2. 496
3. 8128

6-4   The Discriminant

In the quadratic formula the expression under the radical sign, $b^2 - 4ac$, is called the **discriminant.** For example, the discriminant of the equation $2x^2 + 6x - 7$ is $6^2 - 4(2)(^-7)$, or 92.

The discriminant can give information about the solutions of a quadratic equation.

Equation	Value of the Discriminant	Solutions
$x^2 - 14x + 49 = 0$	0	7
$4x^2 + 20x + 25 = 0$	0	$-\dfrac{5}{2}$
$2y^2 - 5y + 3 = 0$	1	$1, \dfrac{3}{2}$
$a^2 + a - 12 = 0$	49	$^-4, 3$
$x^2 + 5x - 3 = 0$	37	$\dfrac{^-5 + \sqrt{37}}{2}, \dfrac{^-5 - \sqrt{37}}{2}$
$2z^2 - 7z + 1 = 0$	41	$\dfrac{7 + \sqrt{41}}{4}, \dfrac{7 - \sqrt{41}}{4}$
$3y^2 + 4y + 5 = 0$	$^-44$	$\dfrac{^-2 + i\sqrt{11}}{3}, \dfrac{^-2 - i\sqrt{11}}{3}$
$m^2 - 4m + 6 = 0$	$^-8$	$2 + i\sqrt{2}, 2 - i\sqrt{2}$

The chart below summarizes the information the discriminant of a quadratic equation gives about its solutions. The coefficients of the variables in the equation must be real numbers.

Discriminant	Nature of the Solutions
zero	one real solution
positive	two real solutions
negative	two imaginary solutions

A quadratic equation with integral coefficients has two rational solutions if and only if its discriminant is a perfect square.

1   **Describe the nature of the solutions to $x^2 + 6x + 10 = 0$.**

$b^2 - 4ac = (6)^2 - 4(1)(10)$ *a = 1, b = 6, c = 10*
$= 36 - 40$
$= ^-4$

The value of the discriminant is negative, so $x^2 + 6x + 10 = 0$ has two imaginary solutions.

exercises

Exploratory Find the value of the discriminant for each quadratic equation.

1. $x^2 + 5x - 2 = 0$
2. $y^2 + 6y + 9 = 0$
3. $2x^2 - 5x + 3 = 0$
4. $a^2 = 16$
5. $t^2 - 8t + 16 = 0$
6. $5x^2 + 16x + 3 = 0$
7. $2y^2 + y - 10 = 0$
8. $6a^2 + 2a + 1 = 0$
9. $12a^2 - 7a + 1 = 0$
10. $^-3x^2 + x - 2 = 0$
11. $x^2 + 4 = 0$
12. $3a^2 - a + 3 = 0$

Written Find the value of the discriminant for each quadratic equation. Describe the nature of the solutions. Then solve each equation.

1. $x^2 - 2x - 35 = 0$
2. $a^2 + 12a + 32 = 0$
3. $y^2 - 4y + 4 = 0$
4. $x^2 - 10x + 25 = 0$
5. $x^2 - 4x + 1 = 0$
6. $m^2 - 6m + 4 = 0$
7. $4x^2 + 8x + 3 = 0$
8. $4y^2 + 16y + 15 = 0$
9. $3x^2 + 11x + 4 = 0$
10. $z^2 + 4z + 2 = 0$
11. $m^2 - 2m + 5 = 0$
12. $y^2 - 6y + 13 = 0$
13. $a^2 + 9a - 2 = 0$
14. $c^2 - 12c + 42 = 0$
15. $a^2 = 6a$
16. $3m^2 = 108m$
17. $4x^2 - 8x + 13 = 0$
18. $x^2 + 4x + 53 = 0$
19. $3n^2 - 19n = ^-6$
20. $2a^2 - 13a = 7$
21. $x^2 - x + 1 = 0$
22. $n^2 + 4n + 29 = 0$
23. $a^2 + a - 5 = 0$
24. $3b^2 + 7b + 3 = 0$

Quadratic Equations

The calculator can be used to solve a quadratic equation.

Example Solve $5x^2 - 2x - 3 = 0$ using the quadratic formula.

$$x = \frac{^-b \pm \sqrt{b^2 - 4ac}}{2a}$$
$$= \frac{^-(^-2) + \sqrt{(^-2)^2 - 4(5)(^-3)}}{2(5)}$$

First evaluate the discriminant and store the result in memory.

ENTER: 2 [+/-] [x²] [−] 4 [×] 5 [×] 3 [+/-] [=] [STO]

DISPLAY: 64   *There are 2 rational solutions since the discriminant is positive and a perfect square.*

Then find the solutions.

ENTER: 2 [+/-] [+/-] [+] [RCL] [√x] [=] [÷] [(] 2 [×] 5 [)] [=]

DISPLAY: 1

ENTER: 2 [+/-] [+/-] [−] [RCL] [√x] [=] [÷] [(] 2 [×] 5 [)] [=]

DISPLAY: −0.6

The solutions are 1 and $^-0.6$.

Exercises Solve each equation using the quadratic formula.

1. $3y^2 - 4y - 10 = 0$
2. $z^2 + 9z + 2 = 0$
3. $2x^2 + 5x - 9 = 0$
4. $11m^2 - 12m - 10 = 0$
5. $4a^2 + 3a - 2 = 0$
6. $t^2 - 16t + 4 = 0$

6–5   Sum and Product of Solutions

Sometimes an equation must be found to fit certain conditions. For example, suppose you know that the solutions of a quadratic equation are 5 and $^-7$. Find the quadratic equation.

Let x stand for a solution to the equation.

Then $x = 5$ or $x = {}^-7$.

If $x = 5$, then $x - 5 = 0$. If $x = {}^-7$, then $x + 7 = 0$.

$$(x - 5)(x + 7) = 0 \qquad \text{Why?}$$
$$x^2 + 2x - 35 = 0$$

The quadratic equation $x^2 + 2x - 35 = 0$ has solutions 5 and $^-7$. Solve that equation as a check.

Consider the sum and product of 5 and $^-7$.

$$\text{sum} = 5 + {}^-7 = {}^-2 \qquad \text{product} = 5 \cdot {}^-7 = {}^-35$$

How are the sum and product related to $x^2 + 2x - 35 = 0$?

In general, the solutions of $ax^2 + bx + c = 0$ are $\dfrac{{}^-b + \sqrt{b^2 - 4ac}}{2a}$ and $\dfrac{{}^-b - \sqrt{b^2 - 4ac}}{2a}$. If these solutions are called s_1 and s_2 where $s_1 = \dfrac{{}^-b + \sqrt{b^2 - 4ac}}{2a}$ and $s_2 = \dfrac{{}^-b - \sqrt{b^2 - 4ac}}{2a}$, then the sum and product can be found.

$$
\begin{aligned}
s_1 + s_2 &= \frac{{}^-b + \sqrt{b^2 - 4ac}}{2a} + \frac{{}^-b - \sqrt{b^2 - 4ac}}{2a} \\
&= \frac{{}^-2b}{2a} \\
&= -\frac{b}{a}
\end{aligned}
$$

$$
\begin{aligned}
s_1 s_2 &= \frac{{}^-b + \sqrt{b^2 - 4ac}}{2a} \cdot \frac{{}^-b - \sqrt{b^2 - 4ac}}{2a} \\
&= \frac{b^2 - (b^2 - 4ac)}{4a^2} \\
&= \frac{c}{a}
\end{aligned}
$$

The following conclusions can now be stated.

> The solutions to $ax^2 + bx + c = 0$ with $a \neq 0$ are s_1 and s_2 if and only if the following is true.
> $$s_1 + s_2 = -\frac{b}{a} \text{ and } s_1 s_2 = \frac{c}{a}$$

Sum and Product of Solutions

1 **Find the sum and product of the solutions of $3x^2 - 16x - 12 = 0$. Then solve the equation.**

$$s_1 + s_2 = -\frac{b}{a} \qquad\qquad s_1 s_2 = \frac{c}{a}$$

$$= -\frac{-16}{3} \qquad\qquad\qquad = \frac{-12}{3}$$

$$= \frac{16}{3} \qquad\qquad\qquad = {}^-4$$

$$x = \frac{-b \pm \sqrt{b^2 - 4ac}}{2a}$$

$$= \frac{-({}^-16) \pm \sqrt{({}^-16)^2 - 4(3)({}^-12)}}{2(3)}$$

$$= \frac{16 \pm \sqrt{256 + 144}}{6}$$

$$= \frac{16 \pm \sqrt{400}}{6}$$

$$= \frac{16 \pm 20}{6} \qquad \text{The solutions are } \frac{16 + 20}{6} \text{ and } \frac{16 - 20}{6} \text{ or 6 and } -\frac{2}{3}.$$

2 **Find a quadratic equation that has solutions $-\frac{5}{4}$ and $\frac{16}{5}$.**

$$s_1 + s_2 = -\frac{5}{4} + \frac{16}{5}$$

$$= \frac{39}{20} \qquad\qquad -\frac{b}{a} = \frac{39}{20}$$

$$s_1 s_2 = \left(-\frac{5}{4}\right)\left(\frac{16}{5}\right)$$

$$= {}^-4 \qquad\qquad \frac{c}{a} = {}^-4 \text{ or } \frac{-80}{20} \qquad \text{If } \frac{c}{a} = {}^-4 \text{ and } a = 20, \text{ then } c = {}^-80.$$

Therefore, $a = 20$, $b = {}^-39$, and $c = {}^-80$.

The equation is $20x^2 - 39x - 80 = 0$.

3 **Find a quadratic equation that has solutions $5 + 2i$ and $5 - 2i$.**

$$s_1 + s_2 = (5 + 2i) + (5 - 2i)$$

$$= 10 \qquad\qquad -\frac{b}{a} = 10 \text{ or } \frac{10}{1}$$

$$s_1 s_2 = (5 + 2i)(5 - 2i)$$

$$= 25 + 4$$

$$= 29 \qquad\qquad \frac{c}{a} = 29 \text{ or } \frac{29}{1}$$

Therefore, $a = 1$, $b = {}^-10$, and $c = 29$.

The equation is $x^2 - 10x + 29 = 0$.

4 **Find k such that $^-3$ is a solution of $x^2 + kx - 24 = 0$.**

Let $s_1 = {}^-3$.
Solve for s_2. 　　　　　　　　　Now solve for k.

$$s_1 s_2 = \frac{c}{a} \qquad\qquad\qquad s_1 + s_2 = -\frac{b}{a}$$

$$^-3(s_2) = \frac{-24}{1} \qquad\qquad {}^-3 + 8 = -\frac{k}{1} \qquad \textit{Substitute 8 for } s_2.$$

$$s_2 = 8 \qquad\qquad\qquad\qquad {}^-5 = k$$

exercises

Exploratory State the sum and the product of the solutions of each quadratic equation.

1. $x^2 + 7x - 4 = 0$
2. $x^2 + 8x + 7 = 0$
3. $x^2 - 3x + 5 = 0$
4. $2x^2 + 8x - 3 = 0$
5. $3x^2 + 7x - 9 = 0$
6. $2x^2 + 7 = 0$
7. $5x^2 - 3x = 0$
8. $4x^2 + 3x - 12 = 0$
9. $5x^2 = 3$
10. $2x^2 + 9x = 0$
11. $3x^2 - 2x + 11 = 0$
12. $7x^2 = 0$
13. $2x^2 - \frac{1}{2}x + \frac{2}{3} = 0$
14. $x^2 + 4x - \frac{5}{3} = 0$
15. $3x^2 - \frac{x}{5} - \frac{4}{5} = 0$

16. In $ax^2 + bx + c = 0$, if $b = 0$, what do you know about the solutions? If $c = 0$, what do you know about the solutions?

Written Find the sum and the product of the solutions of each quadratic equation. Then solve each equation.

1. $x^2 + 6x - 7 = 0$
2. $y^2 + 5y + 6 = 0$
3. $2z^2 - 5z - 3 = 0$
4. $6t^2 + 28t - 10 = 0$
5. $x^2 - 3x + 1 = 0$
6. $2c^2 - 5c + 1 = 0$
7. $4a^2 + 21a = 18$
8. $3b^2 - 8b = 35$
9. $2x^2 - 6x + 5 = 0$
10. $y^2 + 9y + 25 = 0$
11. $9n^2 - 1 = 0$
12. $s^2 - 16 = 0$
13. $2x^2 - 7x = 15$
14. $8m^2 + 6m = {}^-1$
15. $15c^2 - 2c - 8 = 0$
16. $4k^2 + 27k - 7 = 0$
17. $a^2 + 25a + 156 = 0$
18. $x^2 + 4x - 77 = 0$
19. $3z^2 - 7z + 3 = 0$
20. $7s^2 + 5s - 1 = 0$
21. $12x^2 + 19x + 4 = 0$

Find a quadratic equation having the given solutions.

22. $8, {}^-2$
23. $5, {}^-2$
24. $6, 4$
25. ${}^-2, 3$
26. $6, {}^-6$
27. ${}^-9, {}^-4$
28. $3, \frac{1}{2}$
29. $5, \frac{2}{3}$
30. $-\frac{3}{4}, 12$
31. $\frac{3}{4}, {}^-4$
32. $-\frac{1}{2}, \frac{1}{2}$
33. $-\frac{2}{5}, \frac{2}{5}$
34. $\frac{5}{8}, \frac{1}{4}$
35. $\frac{1}{3}, \frac{1}{2}$
36. $\sqrt{3}, 2\sqrt{3}$
37. $\sqrt{2}, {}^-5\sqrt{2}$
38. $2 + \sqrt{3}, 2 - \sqrt{3}$
39. $5 - \sqrt{2}, 5 + \sqrt{2}$
40. $3i, {}^-3i$
41. ${}^-6i, 6i$
42. $3 + 7i, 3 - 7i$
43. $5 + i\sqrt{3}, 5 - i\sqrt{3}$
44. $\frac{1 + \sqrt{7}}{2}, \frac{1 - \sqrt{7}}{2}$
45. $\frac{5 - 3i}{4}, \frac{5 + 3i}{4}$

Find k such that the number given is a solution of the equation given.

46. $3; x^2 + kx - 21 = 0$
47. $1; x^2 + kx - 5 = 0$
48. $-\frac{3}{2}; 2x^2 + kx - 12 = 0$
49. $3; 6x^2 + kx - 5 = 0$

Contest Problem   excursions in algebra

The following problem appeared in a high school contest of the Mathematical Association of America.

Suppose s_1 and s_2 are solutions to the equation $ax^2 + bx + c = 0$. Find the value of $\frac{s_1^2 + s_2^2}{s_1^2 s_2^2}$ in terms of a, b, and c. (Hint: $s_1^2 + s_2^2 = (s_1 + s_2)^2 - 2s_1 s_2$)

Some banks offer free checking accounts if you maintain a minimum balance. Dick Gallegez wondered if this is really a "gimmick." He might do better to use a regular account, put the minimum amount in savings, and collect interest.

Example   Dick's bank offers free checking if a minimum of $500 is kept on deposit. If not, the bank charges $2.00 plus a service charge of 10¢ per check. Would he do better with free checking or with savings at 5% interest?

First, he finds the bank charges on a regular checking account. Dick writes about 20 checks a month.

20	*number of checks*	$2.00	*charge for checks*
× $0.10		+ $2.00	*fixed charge*
$2.00		$4.00	*total charges*

The free checking would save about $4.00 each month.

Now, compare this with what the minimum balance of $500 would earn at 5% interest.

$$i = p \cdot r \cdot t$$
$$= 500 \cdot 0.05 \cdot \frac{1}{12} \qquad one\ month = \frac{1}{12}\ year$$
$$\approx 2.08$$

He could earn about $2.08 a month interest. In this example, free checking would be better.

Exercises   Find out if free checking would be better in each situation.

1. The bank charges a flat rate of $2.00 on all accounts with minimum balances less than $300. You could earn 6% interest if the minimum balance were in savings.

2. The bank charges a minimum of $2.50 or 5¢ a check, whichever is greater. The minimum for free checking is $1000. You write about 30 checks a month and could earn $5\frac{1}{2}$% interest on money in savings.

3. The bank charges $1.00 per month or 10¢ a check, whichever is greater, if the minimum balance is less than $600. You could earn 6% interest if the minimum balance were in savings and you write about 15 checks per month.

4. The bank charges $3.00 per month on all accounts in which the minimum balance is less than $750. You could earn 7% interest on a long-term savings deposit.

6–6 Using Quadratic Equations

Sometimes a drawing will help you write an equation to solve a problem. Consider the following problem.

The Pinetown Recreation Bureau planned to build an ice-skating rink with dimensions 30 meters by 60 meters. Their budget has been cut, so they must reduce the area of the rink to 1000 square meters. A strip will be removed from one end, and a strip of the same width will be removed from one side. Find the width of the strips.

Define a variable.   The problem asks for the width of the strips. Let w stand for the width of the strips.

Make a drawing.

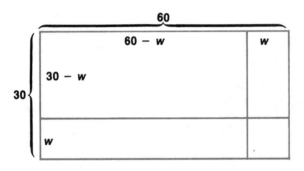

Write an equation.

$$\text{length} \times \text{width} = \text{area}$$
$$(30 - w)(60 - w) = 1000$$

Solve the equation.

$$(30 - w)(60 - w) = 1000$$
$$1800 - 30w - 60w + w^2 = 1000$$
$$1800 - 90w + w^2 = 1000$$
$$800 - 90w + w^2 = 0$$
$$(10 - w)(80 - w) = 0$$

$$10 - w = 0 \quad \text{or} \quad 80 - w = 0$$
$$10 = w \quad \text{or} \quad 80 = w$$

There are two solutions to the equation, 10 and 80. But only one, 10, can be used in answering the problem. The other solution, 80, is not a reasonable answer. Why?

Always check all solutions to a problem!

Answer the problem.   Each strip will be 10 meters wide.

exercises

Written Solve each problem.

1. Find two consecutive integers whose product is 702.

2. Find two consecutive even integers whose product is 288.

3. Find two consecutive odd integers whose product is 1443.

4. Find two consecutive integers whose product is 552.

5. If the product of two consecutive odd integers is decreased by one-third the lesser integer, the result is 250. Find the integers.

6. If the product of two consecutive integers is decreased by 20 times the greater integer, the result is 442. Find the integers.

7. The sum of the squares of two consecutive integers is 265. Find the integers.

8. The sum of the squares of two consecutive even integers is 244. Find the integers.

9. A local park is 30 meters long by 20 meters wide. Plans are being made to double the area by adding a strip at one end and another of the same width on one side. Find the width of the strips.

10. Jackie Ruben is building a children's playhouse. She wants each window to have an area of 315 square inches for adequate air. For eye appeal, she wants each window to be six inches higher than wide. What are the dimensions of each window?

11. The length of Hillcrest Garden is 6 feet more than its width. A walkway 3 feet wide surrounds the outside of the garden. The total area of the walkway is 288 square feet. Find the dimensions of the garden.

12. A rectangular picture is 12 by 16 inches. If a frame of uniform width contains an area of 165 square inches, what is the width of the frame?

13. The difference of the squares of two consecutive integers is 21. Find the integers.

14. The difference of the squares of two consecutive odd integers is 48. Find the integers.

15. If a number is increased by its square, the result is 72. Find the number.

16. The square of a number exceeds 11 times the number by 312. Find the number.

17. If a number is decreased by its square, the result is $\frac{2}{9}$. Find the number.

18. The square of a number decreased by the square of one-half the number is 108. Find the number.

19. The sum of a number and its reciprocal is $\frac{10}{3}$. Find the number.

20. A number increased by 4 times its reciprocal is $\frac{20}{3}$. Find the number.

21. The Hillside Garden Club wants to double the area of its rectangular display of roses. If it is now 6 meters by 4 meters, by what equal amount must each dimension be increased?

22. A rectangular garden 25 feet by 50 feet is increased on all sides by the same amount. Its area increases 400 square feet. By how much is each dimension increased?

23. If a number is decreased by its reciprocal, the result is $\frac{11}{30}$. Find the number.

24. The difference between a number and its reciprocal is $\frac{16}{15}$. Find the number.

25. Jim Finley is a professional photographer. He has a photo 8 centimeters long and 6 centimeters wide. A customer wants a print of the photo. The print is to have half the area of the original. Jim plans to reduce the length and width of the photo by the same amount. What are the dimensions of the print?

26. Gary and Jan's family room has a rug that is 9 feet by 12 feet. A strip of floor of equal width is uncovered along all edges of the rug. If the area of the uncovered floor is 270 square feet, how wide is the strip?

27. The square of a number increased by 21 is 10 times the number. Find the number.

28. Two numbers differ by 9. The sum of their squares is 653. Find the numbers.

29. Three times the square of a number equals 21 times the number. Find the number.

30. Thirty decreased by one-half of a number is one-sixth of the square of the number. Find the number.

31. A rectangular flower bed in Lake Park is 20 by 28 meters. A walk of uniform width surrounds the flower bed. If the area of the flower bed and walk is 1008 square meters, what is the width of the walk?

32. Three boys are to mow a rectangular lawn with dimensions 100 by 120 feet. Bill is going to mow one-third of the lawn by mowing a strip of uniform width around the outer edge of the lawn. What is the width of the strip?

Handshakes   excursions in algebra

At the conclusion of a committee meeting, a total of 28 handshakes were exchanged. Assuming each person was equally polite toward all the others, how many people were present? (Hint: Assume n persons were at the meeting. With how many persons did each person shake hands? Use a quadratic equation.)

6–7   Quadratic Form

The equation $x^4 - 20x^2 + 64 = 0$ is *not* a quadratic equation. But it looks very much like a quadratic equation. It is in **quadratic form.** It can be written as $(x^2)^2 - 20(x^2) + 64 = 0$.

For any numbers a, b, and c, except $a = 0$, an equation that may be written as $a[f(x)]^2 + b[f(x)] + c = 0$, where $f(x)$ is some expression in x, is in quadratic form.

Definition of Quadratic Form

An equation in quadratic form can be solved by the same methods used for solving quadratic equations.

In an equation such as $x^2 + 2x + 1 = 0$, $f(x)$ is just x.

examples

1   **Solve $x^4 - 13x^2 + 36 = 0$.**

$$x^4 - 13x^2 + 36 = 0$$
$$(x^2)^2 - 13x^2 + 36 = 0 \qquad \textit{The equation is in quadratic form.}$$
$$(x^2 - 9)(x^2 - 4) = 0$$
$$(x + 3)(x - 3)(x + 2)(x - 2) = 0$$
$$x + 3 = 0 \quad \text{or} \quad x - 3 = 0 \quad \text{or} \quad x + 2 = 0 \quad \text{or} \quad x - 2 = 0$$
$$x = {}^-3 \quad \text{or} \qquad x = 3 \quad \text{or} \qquad x = {}^-2 \quad \text{or} \qquad x = 2$$

The solutions are $^-3$, 3, $^-2$, and 2.

2   **Solve $x^4 - 20x^2 + 64 = 0$.**

$$x^4 - 20x^2 + 64 = 0$$
$$(x^2)^2 - 20x^2 + 64 = 0 \qquad \textit{The equation is in quadratic form.}$$
$$x^2 = \frac{^-b \pm \sqrt{b^2 - 4ac}}{2a} \qquad \textit{The equation is quadratic in } x^2.$$
$$= \frac{^-(^-20) \pm \sqrt{(^-20)^2 - 4(1)(64)}}{2(1)} \qquad a = 1,\ b = {}^-20,\ c = 64$$
$$= \frac{20 \pm \sqrt{400 - 256}}{2}$$
$$= \frac{20 \pm \sqrt{144}}{2}$$
$$= \frac{20 \pm 12}{2}$$
$$x^2 = 16 \quad \text{or} \quad x^2 = 4$$
$$x = {}^\pm 4 \quad \text{or} \quad x = {}^\pm 2$$

The solutions are 4, $^-4$, 2 and $^-2$.

3 Solve $x - 7\sqrt{x} - 8 = 0$.

$$x - 7\sqrt{x} - 8 = 0$$
$$(\sqrt{x})^2 - 7(\sqrt{x}) - 8 = 0 \qquad f(x) = \sqrt{x}$$
$$\sqrt{x} = \frac{-b \pm \sqrt{b^2 - 4ac}}{2a}$$
$$= \frac{-(-7) \pm \sqrt{(-7)^2 - 4(1)(-8)}}{2(1)} \qquad a = 1, b = -7, c = -8$$
$$= \frac{7 \pm \sqrt{81}}{2}$$
$$= \frac{7 \pm 9}{2}$$
$$\sqrt{x} = 8 \quad \text{or} \quad \sqrt{x} = -1$$
$$x = 64 \quad \text{or} \quad x = 1$$

Check:

$x - 7\sqrt{x} - 8 = 0$	$x - 7\sqrt{x} - 8 = 0$
$64 - 7\sqrt{64} - 8 \overset{?}{=} 0$	$1 - 7\sqrt{1} - 8 \overset{?}{=} 0$
$64 - 7 \cdot 8 - 8 \overset{?}{=} 0$	$1 - 7 - 8 \overset{?}{=} 0$
$0 = 0$	$-14 \neq 0$

The solution is 64.

exercises

Exploratory State whether each equation is in quadratic form.

1. $x^4 + 5x^2 + 3 = 0$
2. $4y^4 - 3y^2 + 2 = 0$
3. $6x^4 + 7x - 8 = 0$
4. $6x^4 + 8x^2 = 0$
5. $6x + 5\sqrt{x} - 2 = 0$
6. $2p + 5\sqrt{p} = 9$
7. $5r^4 - 3r^3 + 2r = 0$
8. $x^4 + 5x - 4 = 0$
9. $x\sqrt{x} + 6x = 7\sqrt{x}$
10. $5x^4 = 2x^2 + 1$
11. $9q^4 = 4$
12. $3p = \sqrt{p}$
13. $m^4 + 9m^2 + 18 = 0$
14. $t^5 - 2t^3 - t = 0$
15. $3x^4 = x^2$
16. $x^4 - 11x^2 + 24 = 0$

Written Solve each equation.

1. $x^4 - 5x^2 + 4 = 0$
2. $y^4 - 3y^2 + 2 = 0$
3. $z^4 - 25z^2 + 144 = 0$
4. $m^4 - 40m^2 + 144 = 0$
5. $s^4 - 25 = 0$
6. $x^4 - 16 = 0$
7. $y^4 - 9 = 0$
8. $a^4 - 36 = 0$
9. $x^4 - 25x^2 = 0$
10. $z^4 - 9z^2 = 0$
11. $b^4 + 9b^2 + 18 = 0$
12. $c^4 - 2c^2 - 8 = 0$
13. $x^4 - 6x^2 + 8 = 0$
14. $y^4 - 11y^2 + 24 = 0$
15. $m - 9\sqrt{m} + 8 = 0$
16. $s - 13\sqrt{s} + 36 = 0$
17. $x - 2\sqrt{x} + 1 = 0$
18. $z - 16\sqrt{z} + 64 = 0$
19. $a^6 - 64a^3 = 0$
20. $m^6 - 64 = 0$
21. $z^6 - 7z^3 - 8 = 0$
22. $a^6 + 26a^3 - 27 = 0$
23. $y^6 - 10y^3 + 16 = 0$
24. $m^6 - 2m^3 + 1 = 0$

190 *Quadratic Equations*

quadratic equation (171)
zero product property (171)
completing the square (174)

quadratic formula (177)
discriminant (180)
quadratic form (189)

Chapter Summary

1. **Zero Product Property:** For any numbers a and b, if $ab = 0$, then $a = 0$ or $b = 0$. (171)

2. Completing the square can be used to solve quadratic equations. (174)

3. **Quadratic Formula:** The solutions of a quadratic equation of the form $ax^2 + bx + c = 0$ with $a \neq 0$ are given by the following formula.

$$x = \frac{-b \pm \sqrt{b^2 - 4ac}}{2a} \quad (177)$$

4. The discriminant, $b^2 - 4ac$, gives information about the solutions of a quadratic equation whose coefficients are real numbers. (180)

Discriminant	Nature of the Solutions
zero	one real solution
positive	two real solutions
negative	two imaginary solutions

5. The solutions to $ax^2 + bx + c = 0$, with $a \neq 0$, are s_1 and s_2 if and only if the following is true.

$$s_1 + s_2 = -\frac{b}{a} \text{ and } s_1 s_2 = \frac{c}{a} \quad (182)$$

6. **Definition of Quadratic Form:** For any numbers a, b, and c, except $a = 0$, an equation that may be written as $a[f(x)]^2 + b[f(x)] + c = 0$, where $f(x)$ is some expression in x, is in quadratic form. (189)

7. An equation in quadratic form can be solved by the same methods used for solving quadratic equations. (189)

6-1 Solve each equation.

   1. $(2x + 3)(3x - 1) = 0$ **2.** $(x + 7)(4x - 5) = 0$

   3. $2x^2 + 5x + 3 = 0$ **4.** $2x^2 + 9x + 4 = 0$

   5. $15a^2 + 13a = 6$ **6.** $8b^2 + 10b = 3$

6-2 Find the value of c that makes each trinomial a perfect square.

   7. $x^2 + 14x + c$ **8.** $a^2 - 7a + c$

Solve each equation by completing the square.

   9. $x^2 - 20x + 75 = 0$ **10.** $x^2 - 5x - 24 = 0$

  11. $2t^2 + t - 21 = 0$ **12.** $r^2 + 4r = 96$

6-3 Solve each equation using the quadratic formula.

  13. $3x^2 - 11x + 10 = 0$ **14.** $2x^2 - 8x = 0$

  15. $2p^2 - 9 = 0$ **16.** $2q^2 - 5q + 4 = 0$

6-4 Find the value of the discriminant for each quadratic equation. Describe the nature of the solutions. Then solve each equation.

  17. $4x^2 - 40x + 25 = 0$ **18.** $2y^2 + 6y + 5 = 0$

  19. $n^2 = 8n - 16$ **20.** $7b^2 = 4b$

6-5 Find the sum and the product of the solutions for each quadratic equation. Then solve each equation.

  21. $x^2 - 12x - 45 = 0$ **22.** $2m^2 - 10m + 9 = 0$

  23. $3s^2 - 11 = 0$ **24.** $2x^2 = 3 - 5x$

Find a quadratic equation having the given solutions.

  25. $4, \,^-6$ **26.** $\dfrac{3}{4}, \dfrac{1}{3}$

  27. $5 - 3i, 5 + 3i$ **28.** $2 - \sqrt{3}, 2 + \sqrt{3}$

6-6 Solve each problem.

  29. The square of a number decreased by twenty times that number is 384. Find the number.

  30. Find five consecutive integers such that the sum of the squares of the smallest and largest is 208.

  31. A rectangular lawn has dimensions 24 feet by 32 feet. A sidewalk will be constructed along the inside edges of all four sides. The remaining lawn will have an area of 425 square feet. The walk will be how wide?

6-7 Solve each equation.

  32. $x^4 - 8x^2 + 16 = 0$ **33.** $x^4 - 12x^2 + 27 = 0$

  34. $p - 4\sqrt{p} - 45 = 0$ **35.** $r + 9\sqrt{r} = \,^-8$

Solve each equation.

1. $x^2 + 8x - 33 = 0$

2. $6y^2 - y - 15 = 0$

3. $x^2 - 6x + 8 = 0$

4. $y^2 + 7y - 18 = 0$

5. $3x^2 + x - 14 = 0$

6. $12x^2 - 5x = 3$

7. $5x^2 - 125 = 0$

8. $4x^2 = 324$

9. $x^2 + 6x - 216 = 0$

10. $3x^2 + 4x + 2 = 0$

11. $x^4 - 9x^2 + 20 = 0$

12. $x - 9\sqrt{x} + 8 = 0$

13. $2x + 3\sqrt{x} = 9$

14. $x^4 - 11x^2 - 80 = 0$

Find the value of c that makes each trinomial a perfect square.

15. $n^2 + 6n + c$

16. $x^2 - 5x + c$

State the value of the discriminant for each quadratic equation. Describe the nature of the solutions.

17. $6x^2 + 7x - 5 = 0$

18. $2y^2 - 9y + 11 = 0$

19. $9a^2 - 30a + 25 = 0$

20. $7m^2 = 4m$

Find the sum and the product of the solutions for each quadratic equation.

21. $x^2 - 15x + 56 = 0$

22. $2x^2 - 3x - 12 = 0$

23. $x + 7 = 4x^2$

24. $2x^2 = 3 - 5x$

Find a quadratic equation having the given solutions.

25. $0, ^-3$

26. $8, ^-3$

27. $\dfrac{4}{3}, \dfrac{2}{3}$

28. $5 + 2i, 5 - 2i$

Solve each problem.

29. The sum of the squares of two consecutive odd integers is 1154. Find the integers.

30. The Dolphin Pool Company will build a pool for Sally Wadman having 600 square feet of surface. Ms. Wadman's pool, with a deck of uniform width, has dimensions 30 feet by 40 feet. What will be the width of the decking around the pool?

cumulative review

Simplify.

1. $(2m + 3n) + (8m - 2n)$

2. $(3z^2 + 5z - 4) - (3z^2 + 5z + 2)$

3. $2(5x + 3y) + 2(6y - 2x)$

4. $(a^7b^3)(^-2ab^5)$

5. $(3w^4z^6)^2(5w^3z^4)$

6. $\dfrac{10xy^5}{^-2x^4y^3}$

7. $(4k^2 - 3k + 10) - (3k^2 - 20k + 2)$

8. $(a + 2)(a^2 + 2a + 4)$

9. $(r + s)^3$

10. $(2x - y)^2$

Solve each open sentence.

11. $6a - 7 = 11$

12. $18 = 3 - 5y$

13. $4x - 3 = 7x + 18$

14. $\dfrac{1}{6} - \dfrac{3}{10}x = \dfrac{2}{15}$

15. $3(6 - 7m) + 12m = ^-2(m + 5)$

16. $\left|5 - 4c\right| = c - 10$

17. $2(2x - 3) \le ^-10$

18. $\left|z - 3\right| > 5$

19. $^-3 - x < 2x < 3 + x$

20. $\dfrac{2}{3}x - 2 \ge \dfrac{5}{6}x + 2$

Graph each equation or inequality.

21. $y = ^-x + 3$

22. $6x - 3y = 12$

23. $y = ^-2$

24. $^-7x < 14y$

Find the standard form of the equation of a line satisfying each of the following conditions.

25. slope $= \dfrac{5}{6}$ and passes through $(2, 10)$

26. passes through $(^-4, 7)$ and $(^-8, ^-1)$

Solve each system of equations.

27. $x + y = 10$
    $x - y = 6$

28. $2a - 4b = 2$
    $4a + 2b = 9$

29. $r + 5s = 6$
    $3r - 2s = 1$

30. $4y = 2x - 12$
    $\dfrac{5x + 3y}{4} = 1$

Factor.

31. $9a^3b^2 + 12ab^3$

32. $12x^2y^2 - 20x^2y^5 + 8xy^4$

33. $a^2 - 144$

34. $14x^2 - 56y^2$

35. $b^2 + 14b + 49$

36. $8y^3 - 27$

37. $z^2 + 10z + 16$

38. $2c^2 + 7c - 15$

39. $2r + 2s + rt + st$

40. $9a^2 + 3a - c - c^2$

Divide.

41. $(6a^2 + 11a - 10) \div (3a - 2)$

42. $(x^3 - 3x + 10) \div (x - 1)$

Find the principal root of each expression.

43. $^-\sqrt{121}$

44. $\sqrt{100a^4}$

45. $\sqrt[3]{27x^6y^3}$

46. $\sqrt[4]{81m^8n^4}$

Simplify.

47. $(\sqrt{3})(\sqrt{8})$

48. $(2\sqrt{6})(5\sqrt{3})$

49. $2\sqrt{7} + 8\sqrt{7}$

50. $3\sqrt{54} + 4\sqrt{6} + 8\sqrt{18}$

51. $\dfrac{5}{\sqrt{7}}$

52. $\sqrt{\dfrac{4}{7}}$

53. $\dfrac{4\sqrt{2} - 8}{\sqrt{2}}$

54. $\sqrt{\dfrac{3}{8}} + \sqrt{72} - \sqrt{\dfrac{8}{3}}$

55. $\sqrt[3]{135r^7s^5}$

56. $5\sqrt[3]{16}$

57. $(6 + \sqrt{3})(6 - \sqrt{3})$

58. $(7 + \sqrt{3})(8 - \sqrt{6})$

59. $\dfrac{1 + \sqrt{3}}{2 - \sqrt{3}}$

60. $\sqrt{^-49}$

61. $\sqrt{^-2} \cdot \sqrt{^-24}$

62. $^-\sqrt{3} \cdot \sqrt{^-18}$

63. $(4 + 7i) - (2 - 8i)$

64. $(2 + 5i)(3 - i)$

65. $\dfrac{5 + 6i}{2i}$

66. $\dfrac{2 + i\sqrt{3}}{2 - i\sqrt{3}}$

Solve each equation.

67. $3 + 2x\sqrt{3} = 5$

68. $\sqrt{2y + 12} = 10$

69. $x^2 + 5x + 6 = 0$

70. $3y^2 - 15y - 18 = 0$

71. $r^2 + 4r + 10 = 0$

72. $2z^2 + 5z + 3 = 0$

73. $4m^2 + 2m = 2$

74. $2a^2 - 3 = ^-2a$

75. $6x^2 - 3x + 1 = 0$

76. $t^4 - 5t^2 + 2 = 0$

Solve each problem.

77. Tony wants to buy a television set that is on sale for 30% off its original price. If the set will cost Tony $420 on sale, what was the original cost of the set?

78. How many pounds of cashews costing $5.75 a pound should be mixed with 4 pounds of walnuts costing $3.50 a pound to obtain a mixture costing $5.00 a pound?

79. Find two consecutive odd integers whose product is 195.

80. A rectangular picture and the frame measure 29 by 34 centimeters. The area of the frame alone is 236 square centimeters. What is the width of the frame?

81. A certain number decreased by 3 is multiplied by the same number increased by 3. The product is 27. What is the number?

82. The length of the top of Ron's bookcase is 30 cm more than the width. The area of the top is 1800 cm². What are its dimensions?

chapter
7 Quadratic Relations and Functions

George Ri

Many architectural designs have the shape of mathematical curves. In this chapter, you will study the equations and graphs for some of these curves.

7-1 Quadratic Functions

A rocket is launched with an initial velocity of 50 meters per second. The height of the rocket is a function of the time after blast off. The height, $h(t)$, of the rocket t seconds after blast off is given by the equation $h(t) = 50t - 5t^2$. This equation is an example of a quadratic equation. Quadratic equations are used to describe **quadratic functions.**

A quadratic function is a function described by an equation of the form $f(x) = ax^2 + bx + c$ where $a \neq 0$.

Definition of
Quadratic Function

The term ax^2 is called the *quadratic term*. The term bx is the *linear term*. The term c is the *constant term*.

$f(x) = bx + c$ describes a linear function. $f(x) = c$ describes a constant function.

examples

1 Write $f(x) = (x + 3)^2 + 5$ in quadratic form. Identify the quadratic term, the linear term, and the constant term.

$$f(x) = (x + 3)^2 + 5$$
$$= x^2 + 6x + 9 + 5$$
$$= x^2 + 6x + 14$$

The quadratic term is x^2.
The linear term is $6x$.
The constant term is 14.

2 A theater has seats for 500 people. It is filled to capacity for each show and tickets cost $3.00 per show. The owner wants to increase ticket prices. She estimates that for each $0.20 increase in price, 25 fewer people will attend. Write a quadratic equation to describe the owner's income after she increases her prices.

Let p = number of $0.20 price increases.
Then $3.00 + 0.20p$ = ticket price.
And $500 - 25p$ = number tickets sold.

Income = (number of tickets sold) × (ticket price)
$$I = (500 - 25p) \cdot (3.00 + 0.20p)$$
$$= 1500 + 100p - 75p - 5p^2$$
$$= 1500 + 25p - 5p^2$$

exercises

Exploratory State whether each of the following is a quadratic equation.

1. $f(x) = x^2 + 3x + 5$
2. $f(x) = {}^-3x^2 - 8x - 7$
3. $f(x) = 2x - 6$
4. $f(x) = (x - 4)^2$
5. $g(x) = {}^-3(x - 4)^2 - 6$
6. $p(x) = x + 1$
7. $m(x) = 3x^2$
8. $r(s) = s^2 + 2s$
9. $f(x) = \dfrac{1}{x^2} + \dfrac{1}{x} + 1$
10. $g(x) = -\dfrac{1}{3}x + \dfrac{4}{5}$

For each equation identify the quadratic term, the linear term, and the constant term.

11. $f(x) = x^2 + 3x - \dfrac{1}{4}$
12. $f(x) = 4x^2 - 8x - 2$
13. $m(x) = x^2 - 3x - \dfrac{1}{4}$
14. $g(p) = \dfrac{1}{3}p + 4$
15. $g(a) = 3a^2 - 2$
16. $n(x) = {}^-4x^2 - 8x - 9$
17. $z = x^2 + 3x$
18. $q = {}^-4x^2 - 2x$
19. $h(x) = (x + 3)^2$
20. $h(x) = (2x - 5)^2$

Written Write each equation in quadratic form.

1. $f(x) = (x - 2)^2$
2. $f(x) = (x + 4)^2$
3. $f(x) = (3x + 2)^2$
4. $f(x) = (2x - 5)^2$
5. $f(x) = 2(4x + 1)^2$
6. $f(x) = {}^-4(2x - 4)^2$
7. $f(x) = 3(x - 4)^2 - 6$
8. $f(x) = 4(x + 1)^2 + 10$
9. $f(x) = 5(3x - 2)^2 + 4$
10. $f(x) = {}^-3(2x + 2)^2 + 6$
11. $f(x) = \dfrac{1}{5}(10x - 5)^2 + 8$
12. $f(x) = \dfrac{1}{6}(6x + 12)^2 + 5$

13. Write a quadratic equation to describe the area of a circle in terms of its radius.

14. Write a quadratic equation to describe the area of an isosceles right triangle in terms of its legs.

Define a variable and write a quadratic equation to describe each of the following. Do *not* solve the equation.

15. The product of two numbers whose sum is 40

16. The product of two numbers whose sum is 36

17. The product of two numbers whose difference is 64

18. The product of two numbers whose difference is 25

19. The area of a rectangle whose perimeter is 20 centimeters

20. The area of a rectangle whose perimeter is 64 millimeters

21. The product of two consecutive integers is 9 less than the square of the second integer.

22. The square of an integer is 97 less than the square of the next consecutive integer.

23. A taxi service transports 300 passengers a day between two airports. The charge is $8.00. The owner estimates that for each $1 increase in fare, he will lose 20 passengers. Write a quadratic equation to describe the owner's income after he increases his prices.

24. Last year 200 people came to see the fall play at Jones High School. The cost per ticket was $2.00. This year the drama teacher wants to increase the ticket price. He estimates that for each $0.25 increase, 10 fewer people will come to the play. Write a quadratic equation to describe the income after the price is increased.

25. Ms. Morrison has 120 meters of fence to make a rectangular pen for her ducks. She will use the side of a shed for one side of the pen. Write a quadratic equation to describe the area of the pen.

26. Bill Taylor's garden has a fence along one side. He wishes to fence in the other three sides with 200 feet of fencing. Write a quadratic equation to describe the area of the garden.

Skills Review   Simplify.

1. $\dfrac{3}{2 - 2i}$

2. $\dfrac{2}{4 + i}$

3. $\dfrac{3 + 6i}{^-2i}$

4. $\dfrac{7 - 5i}{3i}$

5. $\dfrac{3 + i}{2 + 3i}$

6. $\dfrac{2 - 4i}{1 - 5i}$

7. $\dfrac{6 - 3i}{2 - i}$

8. $\dfrac{5 - 3i}{6 + 4i}$

9. $\dfrac{2 - 2i}{4 + i}$

10. $\dfrac{3 + 7i}{3 - 7i}$

11. $\dfrac{3 - i\sqrt{6}}{3 + i\sqrt{6}}$

12. $\dfrac{3 + i\sqrt{3}}{3 - i\sqrt{3}}$

Groups   excursions in algebra

A **group** is a mathematical system that has one operation. This operation must be associative. In addition, there is an identity and all elements of a group have inverses.

The real numbers form a group under addition.

1. For any real numbers a, b, and c, $(a + b) + c = a + (b + c)$.   *Addition is associative.*

2. For any real number a, $a + 0 = a = 0 + a$.   *0 is the additive identity.*

3. For any real number a, $a + {}^-a = 0 = {}^-a + a$.   *$^-a$ is the additive inverse of a.*

Exercises   Are the following systems groups? Write *yes* or *no*.

1. rationals, under addition

2. integers, under multiplication

3. whole numbers, under addition

4. integers, under addition

5. 0 and 1, under addition

6. rationals, under multiplication

A group is not necessarily commutative. A commutative group is Abelian, named after Niels Abel (1802 – 1829), a Norwegian mathematician.

7–2   Parabolas

Consider the following situation.

> A rocket is launched with an initial velocity of 50 meters per second. The height, $h(t)$, of the rocket t seconds after blast-off is given by the equation $h(t) = 50t - 5t^2$.

A graph of this equation can be drawn by making a table of values, plotting points, and connecting the points with a smooth curve. The resulting graph is called a **parabola.**

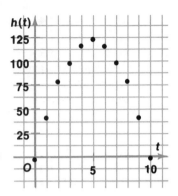

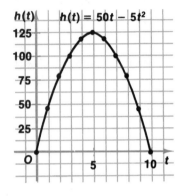

t	$50t - 5t^2$	$h(t)$
0	$50(0)-5(0)^2$	0
1	$50(1)-5(1)^2$	45
2	$50(2)-5(2)^2$	80
3	$50(3)-5(3)^2$	105
4	$50(4)-5(4)^2$	120
5	$50(5)-5(5)^2$	125
6	$50(6)-5(6)^2$	120
7	$50(7)-5(7)^2$	105
8	$50(8)-5(8)^2$	80
9	$50(9)-5(9)^2$	45
10	$50(10)-5(10)^2$	0

Notice that 10 seconds after blast-off, the height of the rocket is zero. This means that it has returned to earth. It appears to have reached its maximum height of 125 meters at 5 seconds after blast-off. Test some other values of t between 4 and 6 to check.

Test values of t like 4.9 and 5.1 to determine if the maximum height is reached at 5 seconds.

The graph of any quadratic function is a parabola. Parabolas have certain common characteristics. They all have an **axis of symmetry** and a **vertex.** The axis of symmetry is the line about which the parabola is symmetric. The vertex is the point of intersection of the parabola and the line of symmetry.

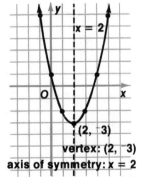

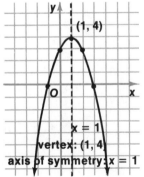

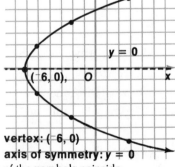

If the sketches are folded along the axis of symmetry, the two halves of the parabola coincide.

The graphs of $y = x^2$, $y = 2x^2$, $y = 3x^2$, and $y = \frac{1}{2}x^2$ are drawn on the same set of axes.

Each graph has vertex $(0, 0)$.

Each graph has axis of
symmetry $x = 0$.

Each graph opens upward.

The greater the coefficient of x^2,
the narrower the graph.

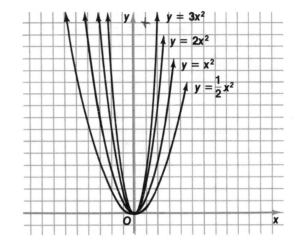

The graphs of $y = {}^{-}x^2$, $y = {}^{-}2x^2$, $y = {}^{-}3x^2$, and $y = -\frac{1}{2}x^2$ are drawn
on the same set of axes.

Each graph has vertex $(0, 0)$.

Each graph has axis of
symmetry $x = 0$.

Each graph opens downward.

The greater the absolute value
of the coefficient of x^2, the
narrower the graph.

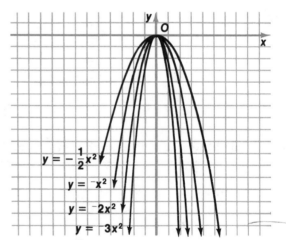

By studying these graphs, and many like them, the following conclusions can be made about the graph of $y = ax^2$.

$y = ax^2$	a is positive	a is negative
Vertex	$(0, 0)$	$(0, 0)$
Axis of symmetry	$x = 0$	$x = 0$
Direction of opening	upward	downward
As the value of $\lvert a \rvert$ increases, the graphs of $y = ax^2$ narrow.		

Exploratory Complete each table of values.

1.
x	$^-6$	6	$^-4$	4	$-\frac{1}{2}$	$\frac{1}{2}$
$^-2x^2$						

2.
x	$^-9$	9	$^-3$	3	$-\frac{1}{3}$	$\frac{1}{3}$
$\frac{1}{3}x^2$						

3. Plot each set of points in Exercise 1 and connect the points with a smooth curve.

4. Plot each set of points in Exercise 2 and connect the points with a smooth curve.

Written For each problem, sketch the graphs of the equations on the same set of axes.

1. $y = x^2, y = 3x^2, y = \frac{1}{3}x^2$

2. $y = {}^-x^2, y = {}^-3x^2, y = -\frac{1}{3}x^2$

3. $y = x^2, y = {}^-x^2$

4. $y = 4x^2, y = {}^-4x^2$

5. $f(x) = 3x^2, f(x) = {}^-2x^2, f(x) = \frac{1}{4}x^2$

6. $f(x) = -\frac{1}{4}x^2, f(x) = -\frac{1}{3}x^2, f(x) = {}^-x^2$

For each equation, state the vertex, axis of symmetry, and direction of opening.

7. $f(x) = 2x^2$

8. $f(x) = -\frac{1}{3}x^2$

9. $y = {}^-x^2$

10. $y = {}^-3x^2$

11. $f(x) = \frac{1}{3}x^2$

12. $f(x) = 4x^2$

13. $y = \frac{3}{4}x^2$

14. $y = \frac{7}{9}x^2$

15. $f(x) = -\frac{4}{3}x^2$

16. $f(x) = {}^-5x^2$

Determine a value of a so that each point named is on the graph of $f(x) = ax^2$.

> **Sample:** $(5, {}^-4)$
> $$f(x) = ax^2$$
> $${}^-4 = a(5)^2 \quad \textit{Substitute 5 for x and } {}^-4 \textit{ for f(x).}$$
> $${}^-4 = a \cdot 25$$
> $$a = -\frac{4}{25}$$

17. $(2, 2)$

18. $(4, {}^-4)$

19. $(1, 1)$

20. $(6, 6)$

21. $(3, {}^-18)$

22. $({}^-2, 5)$

23. $\left(\frac{1}{2}, {}^-1\right)$

24. $({}^-3, 3)$

25. $({}^-1, 3)$

26. $({}^-1, 1)$

27. $({}^-3, 6)$

28. (x, y)

29. If the coordinates $(4, 4)$ satisfy the equation $f(x) = \frac{1}{4}x^2$, then what equation does $(4, {}^-4)$ satisfy?

30. How does the graph of $f(x) = 4x^2$ compare to the graph of $f(x) = {}^-3x^2$?

Communication in everyday life depends on a knowledge of English grammar. In the same manner, communication in algebra depends on a knowledge of mathematical grammar.

Arrangement of symbols is an important part of grammar and music. Examples in music, English, and mathematics are given below. In each case, the statement on the left communicates a thought. The statement on the right is nonsense.

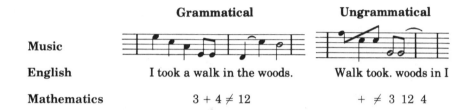

	Grammatical	**Ungrammatical**
Music		
English	I took a walk in the woods.	Walk took. woods in I
Mathematics	$3 + 4 \neq 12$	$+ \neq 3\ 12\ 4$

Punctuation also plays an important role in grammar. Study the two sentences.

My mother, my sister Carol, Andrew, and I went to the theater.

My mother, my sister, Carol, Andrew, and I went to the theater.

In the first sentence, four people, namely my mother, my sister Carol, Andrew, and I, went to the theater. In the second sentence, five people, namely my mother, my sister, Carol, Andrew, and I, went to the theater.

Now study the following mathematical sentences.

$$g(a) = 3a^2 - 2 \qquad G(a) = (3a)^2 - 2$$

In the first sentence, g of a equals three times a squared, minus two. In the second sentence, G of a equals three times a, quantity squared, minus two. In other words, in the first sentence, square a and then multiply by three. In the second sentence, multiply three times a and then square the product.

Exercises For each pair of equations, explain how the first and second equation differ.

1. $f(x) = (x - 2)^2 \qquad F(x) = x^2 - 2$ **2.** $f(x) = 3(x + 4)^2 \qquad F(x) = (3x + 4)^2$

3. $f(x) = x^2 + 3x + 5 \qquad F(x) = x^2 + 3(x + 5)$ **4.** $f(x) = (x - 4)^2 \qquad F(x) = (4 - x)^2$

5. $h(x) = (2x - 5)^2 \qquad H(x) = (2x)^2 - 5^2$ **6.** $m(x) = (^-2x)^2 + 3 \qquad M(x) = ^-(2x)^2 + 3$

7. $g(x) = 4x^2 - 2 \qquad G(x) = 4(x^2 - 2)$ **8.** $n(x) = (x + 2)^2 + 8 \qquad N(x) = x^2 + 4 + 8$

7–3   Graphing $y = a(x - h)^2$

You have studied parabolas with equations of the form $y = ax^2$. No matter what the value of a, each parabola has axis of symmetry $x = 0$ and vertex $(0, 0)$.

Below, the graphs of $y = x^2$, $y = (x - 3)^2$, and $y = (x + 3)^2$ are drawn on the same set of axes.

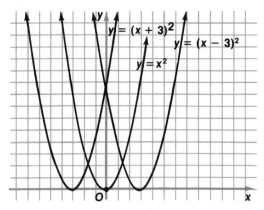

Notice that each graph has the same shape. The only difference is their horizontal position.

Below, the graphs of $y = (x - 3)^2$, $y = 2(x - 3)^2$, and $y = \frac{1}{2}(x - 3)^2$ are drawn on the same set of axes.

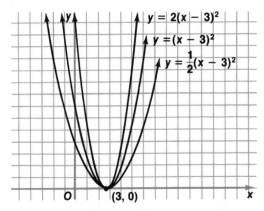

Notice that each graph has the same vertex and axis of symmetry. The only difference is their shape. Their widths vary.

In general, the graph of $f(x) = a(x - h)^2$ has the same shape and direction of opening as the graph of $f(x) = ax^2$. But its position is translated $|h|$ units to the left or right.

$y = a(x - h)^2$	a is positive	a is negative
Vertex	$(h, 0)$	$(h, 0)$
Axis of symmetry	$x = h$	$x = h$
Direction of opening	upward	downward
As the value of $|a|$ increases, the graphs of $y = a(x - h)^2$ narrow.		

1 **Graph $f(x) = {}^-3(x - 5)^2$.**

Since h is 5, the vertex is (5, 0) and the axis of symmetry is $x = 5$.

Since a is $^-3$, the graph opens downward and is narrower than the graph of $f(x) = x^2$.

It is helpful to find several points on the graph other than the vertex.

$$f(4) = {}^-3(4 - 5)^2 \text{ or } {}^-3$$
$$f(6) = {}^-3(6 - 5)^2 \text{ or } {}^-3$$
$$f(3) = {}^-3(3 - 5)^2 \text{ or } {}^-12$$
$$f(7) = {}^-3(7 - 5)^2 \text{ or } {}^-12$$

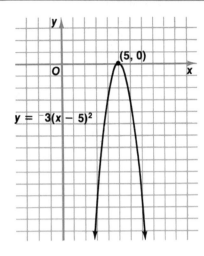

2 **Graph $f(x) = 3x^2 + 12x + 12$.**

First, write the equation in the form $f(x) = a(x - h)^2$, if possible.

$$f(x) = 3x^2 + 12x + 12$$
$$= 3(x^2 + 4x + 4)$$
$$= 3(x + 2)^2$$
$$= 3(x - {}^-2)^2$$

Therefore, a is 3 and h is $^-2$.
The vertex is $(^-2, 0)$.
The axis of symmetry is $x = {}^-2$.
The graph opens upward and is narrower than the graph of $f(x) = x^2$.

$$f(^-1) = 3(^-1 - {}^-2)^2 \text{ or } 3$$
$$f(^-3) = 3(^-3 - {}^-2)^2 \text{ or } 3$$
$$f(0) = 3(0 - {}^-2)^2 \text{ or } 12$$
$$f(^-4) = 3(^-4 - {}^-2)^2 \text{ or } 12$$

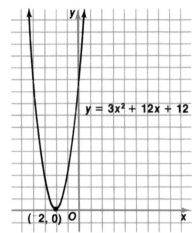

exercises

Exploratory Name the vertex, axis of symmetry, and direction of opening for the graph of each of the following.

1. $y = x^2$

2. $y = {}^-2x^2$

3. $f(x) = (x - 3)^2$

4. $f(x) = (x + 7)^2$

5. $f(x) = {}^-2(x + 4)^2$

6. $f(x) = 4(x - 2)^2$

7. $y = 6(x + 3)^2$

8. $y = {}^-5(x - 1)^2$

9. $y = -\frac{1}{3}(x + 2)^2$

10. $y = \frac{1}{6}(x - 4)^2$

11. $f(x) = \frac{1}{4}(x - 2)^2$

12. $f(x) = \frac{2}{3}\left(x - \frac{3}{4}\right)^2$

Written Write each equation in the form $f(x) = a(x - h)^2$. Then name the vertex, axis of symmetry, and direction of opening for the graph of each equation.

1. $f(x) = x^2 - 2x + 1$

2. $f(x) = x^2 + 8x + 16$

3. $f(x) = \frac{2}{5}x^2 + \frac{8}{5}x + \frac{8}{5}$

4. $f(x) = {}^-3x^2 - 18x - 27$

5. $f(x) = 6x^2 + 60x + 150$

6. $f(x) = 4x^2 - 8x + 4$

7. $f(x) = {}^-9x^2 + 18x - 9$

8. $f(x) = \frac{3}{4}x^2 - 6x + 12$

9. $f(x) = 4x^2 - 44x + 121$

10. $f(x) = 4x^2 + 60x + 225$

11. $f(x) = 5x^2 - 30x + 45$

12. $f(x) = {}^-3x^2 - 6x - 3$

13. $f(x) = 8x^2 + 24x + 18$

14. $f(x) = \frac{9}{2}x^2 - 3x + \frac{1}{2}$

15. $f(x) = 9x^2 - 60x + 100$

16. $f(x) = 9x^2 + 30x + 25$

Draw the graphs for each pair of equations on the same set of axes.

17. $y = 2x^2$ and $y = 2(x - 3)^2$

18. $y = {}^-3x^2$ and $y = {}^-3(x + 2)^2$

19. $f(x) = {}^-3x^2$ and $g(x) = {}^-3\left(x + \frac{1}{4}\right)^2$

20. $f(x) = 4x^2$ and $h(x) = 4(x - 6)^2$

21. $f(x) = -\frac{1}{4}x^2$ and $f(x) = -\frac{1}{4}(x + 2)^2$

22. $f(x) = {}^-5x^2$ and $g(x) = {}^-5(x - 10)^2$

23. Write the equation of a parabola with position 3 units to the right of the parabola with equation $f(x) = x^2$.

24. Write the equation of a parabola with position 4 units to the left of the parabola with equation $f(x) = {}^-2x^2$.

25. Write the equation of a parabola with position $\frac{3}{4}$ unit to the left of the parabola with equation $f(x) = -\frac{1}{4}x^2$.

26. Write the equation of a parabola with position 6 units to the right of the parabola with equation $f(x) = 5x^2$.

Draw the graph for each of the following.

27. $f(x) = 3x^2 + 18x + 27$

28. $f(x) = 4x^2 - 16x + 16$

29. $f(x) = {}^-2x^2 + 20x - 50$

30. $f(x) = {}^-5x^2 - 40x - 80$

Challenge Complete the following table.

	vertex	direction of opening	contains the point	axis of symmetry	equation of the parabola
1.	(0, 0)	up	(4, 2)		
2.	(3, 0)	down	(${}^-2$, ${}^-4$)		
3.	(${}^-2$, 0)	up	(0, 4)		
4.	(5, 0)	down	(6, ${}^-3$)		
5.	(${}^-4$, 0)	up	(${}^-6$, 12)		
6.	(${}^-1$, 0)	up	(0, 7)		

7-4 Graphing $y = a(x - h)^2 + k$

Below, the graphs of $y = x^2$, $y = x^2 + 3$, and $y = x^2 - 3$ are drawn on the same set of axes.

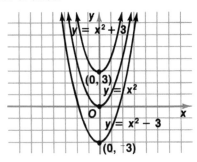

Notice that each graph has the same shape. The only difference is their vertical position.

Study the graphs of $y = x^2 - 3$, $y = (x - 2)^2 - 3$, and $y = (x + 2)^2 - 3$.

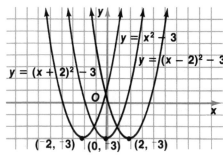

How do these graphs compare?

How do you think the graphs of $y = (x + 2)^2 - 3$, $y = 4(x + 2)^2 - 3$, and $y = \frac{1}{4}(x + 2)^2 - 3$ compare?

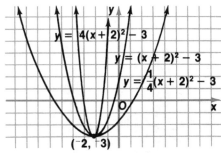

In general, as the value of k changes, the graph of $f(x) = a(x - h)^2 + k$ is translated $|k|$ units up or down.

$y = a(x - h)^2 + k$	a is positive	a is negative
Vertex	(h, k)	(h, k)
Axis of symmetry	$x = h$	$x = h$
Direction of opening	upward	downward
As the value of $|a|$ increases, the graphs of $y = a(x - h)^2 + k$ narrow.		

1 **Graph $f(x) = \frac{1}{2}(x - 2)^2 - 5$.**

The value of a is $\frac{1}{2}$, h is 2, and k is $^-5$.

The vertex is $(2, ^-5)$.

The axis of symmetry is $x = 2$.

The graph opens upward and is wider than the graph of $f(x) = x^2$.

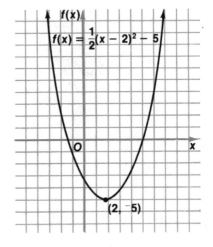

x	$\frac{1}{2}(x - 2)^2 - 5$	$f(x)$
4	$\frac{1}{2}(4 - 2)^2 - 5$	$^-3$
0	$\frac{1}{2}(0 - 2)^2 - 5$	$^-3$
6	$\frac{1}{2}(6 - 2)^2 - 5$	3
$^-2$	$\frac{1}{2}(^-2 - 2)^2 - 5$	3

2 **Graph $f(x) = 2x^2 - 12x + 19$.**

First, write the equation in the form $f(x) = a(x - h)^2 + k$. To do this, you must complete the square.

$$f(x) = 2x^2 - 12x + 19$$
$$= 2(x^2 - 6x) + 19$$
$$= 2(x^2 - 6x + 9) + 19 - 2(9)$$
$$= 2(x - 3)^2 + 1$$

Therefore, a is 2, h is 3, and k is 1.

The vertex is $(3, 1)$.

The axis of symmetry is $x = 3$.

The graph opens upward and is narrower than the graph of $f(x) = x^2$.

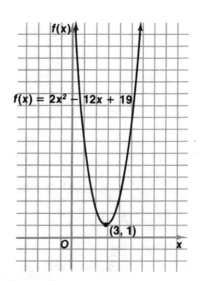

x	$2(x - 3)^2 + 1$	$f(x)$
2	$2(2 - 3)^2 + 1$	3
4	$2(4 - 3)^2 + 1$	3
1	$2(1 - 3)^2 + 1$	9
5	$2(5 - 3)^2 + 1$	9

3 Graph $f(x) = {}^-2x^2 - 12x - 22$.

First, write the equation in the form $f(x) = a(x - h)^2 + k$.
To do this, you must complete the square.

$$f(x) = {}^-2x^2 - 12x - 22$$
$$= {}^-2(x^2 + 6x) - 22$$
$$= {}^-2(x^2 + 6x + 9) - 22 + 2(9)$$
$$= {}^-2(x + 3)^2 - 4$$

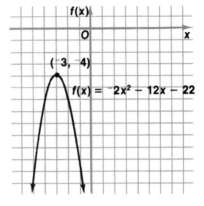

Therefore, a is $^-2$, h is $^-3$, and k is $^-4$.
The vertex is $(^-3, {}^-4)$.
The axis of symmetry is $x = {}^-3$.
The graph opens downward and is
narrower than the graph of $f(x) = x^2$.

exercises

Exploratory Name the vertex, axis of symmetry, and direction of opening for the graph of each of the following.

1. $y = 2x^2$
2. $y = -\dfrac{1}{5}x^2$
3. $f(x) = 4(x - 8)^2$
4. $f(x) = {}^-1(x + 2)^2$
5. $f(x) = {}^-3x^2 + 6$
6. $g(x) = 5x^2 - 6$
7. $y = 5(x + 3)^2 - 1$
8. $y = {}^-2(x - 2)^2 - 2$
9. $f(x) = 2(x - 1)^2 + \dfrac{1}{3}$
10. $f(x) = 4(x + 2)^2 - \dfrac{3}{2}$
11. $f(x) = -\dfrac{1}{3}(x + 2)^2 - \dfrac{4}{3}$
12. $g(x) = 3\left(x - \dfrac{1}{2}\right)^2 + \dfrac{1}{4}$

Written Draw the graph for each of the following.

1. $f(x) = (x + 2)^2 - 3$
2. $f(x) = (x - 3)^2 + 4$
3. $f(x) = x^2 - 4$
4. $f(x) = 2x^2 + 3$
5. $f(x) = 2(x + 3)^2 - 5$
6. $f(x) = 3(x - 1)^2 + 2$
7. $f(x) = \dfrac{1}{2}(x + 3)^2 - 5$
8. $f(x) = \dfrac{1}{3}(x - 1)^2 + 2$
9. $f(x) = x^2 + 6x + 2$
10. $f(x) = x^2 - 2x + 7$
11. $f(x) = {}^-2x^2 + 16x - 31$
12. $f(x) = {}^-x^2 - 4x - 10$
13. $f(x) = 2x^2 + 8x + 10$
14. $f(x) = 3x^2 + 18x + 6$
15. $f(x) = {}^-9x^2 - 18x - 6$
16. $f(x) = {}^-4x^2 - 16x + 2$
17. $f(x) = {}^-0.25x^2 - 2.5x - 0.25$
18. $f(x) = -\dfrac{2}{3}x^2 + 4x - 9$

Challenge Given $f(x) = ax^2 + bx + c$ with $a \neq 0$, complete the square to rewrite the equation in the form $f(x) = a(x - h)^2 + k$. State an expression for h and k in terms of a, b, and c.

7–5 Using Parabolas

A ball is thrown vertically upward at a starting speed of 80 feet per second. The height it will reach after t seconds is given by the following equation.

$$h(t) = {}^-16t^2 + 80t$$

This equation represents height in feet.

At what time does the ball reach its maximum height?

Compare the time-lapse photograph to the graph of $h(t) = {}^-16t^2 + 80t$. They both give a visual description of the height of the ball at a certain time.

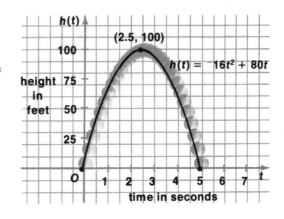

The graph is a parabola. Its highest point is the vertex (2.5, 100). This shows that the ball reaches a maximum height of 100 feet in 2.5 seconds.

Many problem situations involve finding **maximum** or **minimum** **values.** If such a problem can be described by a quadratic equation, it often can be solved by finding the vertex of its graph.

---

example

1 Find two numbers whose difference is 64 and whose product is a minimum.

Define a variable.

Let x stand for the lesser number.
Then $64 + x$ stands for the other number.

Write an equation.

$$\text{product} = (x) \cdot (64 + x)$$
$$= 64x + x^2$$

Solve the problem.

The equation above is quadratic. So find the vertex by writing the equation in the form $y = a(x - h)^2 + k$. Then the vertex is (h, k). Let y stand for the product.

$$y = 64x + x^2$$
$$= x^2 + 64x + \left(\frac{64}{2}\right)^2 - \left(\frac{64}{2}\right)^2$$
$$= (x + 32)^2 - 1024$$

The vertex is $({}^-32, {}^-1024)$.
The product is minimized when x is $^-32$.
So $64 + x$ is $64 + {}^-32$ or 32.

Answer the problem.

The two numbers are $^-32$ and 32.

2 A theater has seats for 500 people. It is filled to capacity for each show and tickets cost $3.00 per show. The owner wants to increase ticket prices. She estimates that for each $0.20 increase in price, 25 fewer people will attend. What ticket price will maximize her income?

Let p = number of $0.20 price increases. Then $3.00 + 0.20p$ stands for the ticket price and $500 - 25p$ stands for the number of tickets sold.

$$
\begin{aligned}
\textit{Income} &= \textit{(number of tickets sold)} \times \quad \textit{(ticket price)} \\
&= \quad (500 - 25p) \qquad \cdot (3.00 + 0.20p) \\
&= 1500 + 100p - 75p - 5p^2 \\
&= 1500 + 25p - 5p^2
\end{aligned}
$$

The equation is quadratic. So find the vertex by writing the equation in the form $y = a(x - h)^2 + k$. Let y stand for income.

$$
\begin{aligned}
y &= 1500 + 25p - 5p^2 \\
&= {}^-5(p^2 - 5p) + 1500 \\
&= {}^-5\left[p^2 - 5p + \left(-\frac{5}{2}\right)^2\right] + 1500 + 5\left(-\frac{5}{2}\right)^2 \\
&= {}^-5\left(p - \frac{5}{2}\right) + \frac{6125}{4}
\end{aligned}
$$

The vertex is $\left(\frac{5}{2}, \frac{6125}{4}\right)$.

The income is maximized when the owner makes $\frac{5}{2}$ or $2\frac{1}{2}$ price increases. Since each increase is to be $0.20, the total increase is $2\frac{1}{2}(0.20)$ or $0.50. A ticket price of $3.50 will maximize the owner's income.

exercises

Exploratory A newsletter has a circulation of 50,000 and sells for 40¢ a copy. Due to increased labor and production costs the publisher will raise the price of the newsletter. A publisher's survey indicates that for each 10¢ increase in price, the circulation decreases by 5000.

1. Let x stand for the number of 10¢ price increases. Write an algebraic expression to describe the increased price per copy.

2. Write an algebraic expression to describe the reduced circulation after the price increase.

3. The publisher's income on the newsletter is the product of the price per copy and the circulation. It is also a function of the number of price increases. Write an equation to describe this function.

4. Draw a graph relating the publisher's income to the number of price increases. Use number of price increases for the x-axis and income in dollars for the y-axis.

5. What price per copy will maximize the publisher's income on the newsletter?

A manufacturer can sell x items per month at a price of $(300 - 2x)$ dollars per item. It costs the manufacturer $(20x + 1000)$ dollars to produce x items.

6. One item sells for $(300 - 2x)$ dollars. Write an algebraic expression to describe the price of x items.

7. The manufacturer's profit is the selling price minus the cost of producing the items. Write an algebraic expression to describe the manufacturer's profit on x items in one month.

8. The manufacturer's profit is a function of the number of items sold. Write an equation to describe this function.

9. Draw a graph relating the manufacturer's profit to the number of items produced. Use number of items for the x-axis and profit in dollars for the y-axis.

10. How many items should the manufacturer produce in one month to maximize profit?

Written   Solve each problem.

1. Find two numbers whose sum is 36 and whose product is a maximum.

2. Find two numbers whose sum is 40 and whose product is a maximum.

3. Find two numbers whose difference is 48 and whose product is a minimum.

4. Find two numbers whose difference is 25 and whose product is a minimum.

5. Find two numbers whose difference is $^-16$ and whose product is a minimum.

6. Find two numbers whose difference is $^-20$ and whose product is a minimum.

7. Find two numbers whose sum is 56 and whose product is a maximum.

8. Find two numbers whose difference is 64 and whose product is a minimum.

9. Find the dimensions and maximum area of a rectangle if its perimeter is 40 centimeters.

10. Find the dimensions and maximum area of a rectangle if its perimeter is 24 inches.

11. George Polo has 120 meters of fence to make a rectangular pen for rabbits. If a shed is used as one side of the pen, what would be the length and width for maximum area?

12. Sara Meyer has 150 feet of fence to put around a rectangular garden. If a 10 foot opening is left on one side for a gate, what would be the length and width for maximum area?

13. A taxi service operates between two airports transporting 300 passengers a day. The charge is $8.00. The owner estimates that 20 passengers will be lost for each $1 increase in the fare. What charge would be most profitable for the service?

14. An airline transports 800 people a week between two cities. A round trip ticket costs $300. The company wants to increase the price. They estimate that for each $5 increase 10 passengers will be lost. What ticket price will maximize their income?

15. An object is fired vertically from the top of a tower at a velocity of 80 feet per second. The tower is 200 feet high. The height of the object above the ground t seconds after firing is given by the formula $h(t) = {}^-16t^2 + 80t + 200$. What is the maximum height reached by the object? How long after firing does it reach maximum height?

16. A ball is thrown vertically into the air with an initial velocity of 64 feet per second. The formula $h(t) = 64t - 16t^2$ gives its height above the ground after t seconds. What is its height after 1.5 seconds? What is its maximum height? How many seconds will pass before it returns to the ground?

17. Ken Graham has 1200 meters of fence to put around two rectangular yards. If the yards are to be separated by part of the fence, what would be the length and width for maximum area?

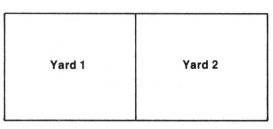

18. A square, which is 5 centimeters by 5 centimeters, is cut from each corner of a rectangular piece of cardboard and the sides are folded up to make a box. If the bottom of the box must have a perimeter of 50 centimeters, what would be the length, width, and height for maximum volume?

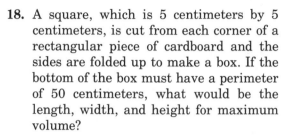

19. A wire 36 cm long is cut into 2 pieces and each piece is bent to form a square. How long should each piece be to minimize the sum of the areas of the two squares?

20. A wire 32 in. long is cut into 2 pieces. One piece is bent to form a square. The other piece is bent to form a rectangle which is 2 in. longer than it is wide. How long should each piece be to minimize the sum of the areas of the square and the rectangle?

21. Last year 200 people came to see the fall play at Jones High School. The cost per ticket was $2.00. This year the drama teacher wants to increase the ticket price. He estimates that for each $0.25 increase, 10 fewer people will come to the play. What ticket price will maximize the income?

22. The steamship, *The Golden Conifer,* is rented to take 100 campers to Pine Mountain. The fare is $5 per camper. The steamship company has agreed to reduce the fare by two cents per passenger for every camper over 100. How many passengers will produce a maximum rental for the company?

Age of Diophantus   excursions in algebra

The solution to this riddle is the age of the ancient Greek mathematician, Diophantus.

His youth lasted one-sixth of his life. He grew a beard after one-twelfth more. He married after one-seventh more. He had a son 5 years later. His son lived half as long as his father. Diophantus died 4 years after his son died.

7–6 Graphing Quadratic Inequalities

The graph of $y = x^2 - 6x + 5$ is a parabola that separates the coordinate plane into two regions. The graph of $y > x^2 - 6x + 5$ is the region *inside* the parabola. The graph of $y < x^2 - 6x + 5$ is the region *outside* the parabola.

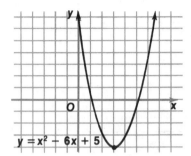

$y = x^2 - 6x + 5$

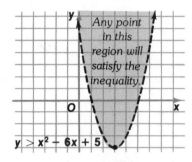

Any point in this region will satisfy the inequality.

$y > x^2 - 6x + 5$

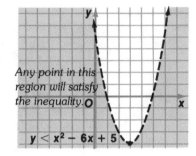

Any point in this region will satisfy the inequality.

$y < x^2 - 6x + 5$

The parabola described by $y = x^2 - 6x + 5$ is called the **boundary** of each region. If it is broken, it is not part of the graph. If it is solid, it is part of the graph.

Note that > tells you the boundary is not included

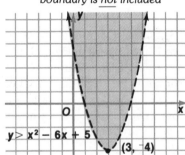

$y > x^2 - 6x + 5$

$(3, {}^-4)$

Note that ≥ tells you the boundary is included.

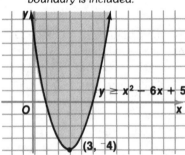

$y \geq x^2 - 6x + 5$

$(3, {}^-4)$

examples

1 Graph $y \leq {}^-2x^2 + 8x - 4$.

$y \leq {}^-2x^2 + 8x - 4$

$y \leq {}^-2(x^2 - 4x) - 4$

$y \leq {}^-2\left[x^2 - 4x + \left(-\frac{4}{2} \right)^2 \right] - 4 + 2\left(-\frac{4}{2} \right)^2$

$y \leq {}^-2(x - 2)^2 + 4$

The boundary is a parabola with vertex (2, 4), axis of symmetry $x = 2$, and it opens downward.

Test several ordered pairs to determine if the region inside the parabola or the region outside the parabola belongs to the graph.

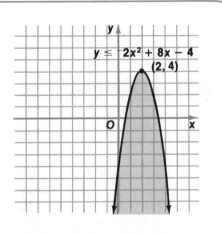

$y \leq {}^-2x^2 + 8x - 4$

$(2, 4)$

region	(x, y)	$^{-}2x^2 + 8x - 4$	belongs?
inside	$(2, 0)$	$^{-}2(2)^2 + 8(2) - 4$ or 4	yes
inside	$(2, ^{-}3)$	$^{-}2(2)^2 + 8(2) - 4$ or 4	yes
outside	$(0, 3)$	$^{-}2(0)^2 + 8(0) - 4$ or $^{-}4$	no
outside	$(^{-}1, 0)$	$^{-}2(^{-}1)^2 + 8(^{-}1) - 4$ or $^{-}14$	no

2 Graph $y > x^2 - 7x + 10$.

$y > x^2 - 7x + 10$

$y > \left(x - \dfrac{7}{2}\right)^2 - \dfrac{9}{4}$

The boundary is a parabola with vertex $\left(\dfrac{7}{2}, -\dfrac{9}{4}\right)$, axis of symmetry $x = \dfrac{7}{2}$, and it opens upward.

Test several ordered pairs to determine if the region inside the parabola or the region outside the parabola belongs to the graph.

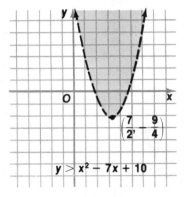

region	(x, y)	$x^2 - 7x + 10$	belongs?
inside	$(3, 0)$	$(3)^2 - 7(3) + 10$ or $^{-}2$	yes
inside	$(4, 3)$	$(4)^2 - 7(4) + 10$ or $^{-}2$	yes
outside	$(0, 0)$	$(0)^2 - 7(0) + 10$ or 10	no
outside	$(^{-}1, 2)$	$(^{-}1)^2 - 7(^{-}1) + 10$ or 18	no

exercises

Exploratory Express each equation in the form $y = a(x - h)^2 + k$.

1. $y = x^2 + 4x + 4$
2. $y = x^2 - 6x + 9$
3. $y = x^2 + 8x + 17$
4. $y = x^2 + 10x + 40$
5. $y = 3x^2 - 24x + 4$
6. $y = ^{-}2x^2 - 8x + 4$
7. $y = x^2 + 3x - 1$
8. $y = x^2 - 5x + 10$
9. $y = 2x^2 + 6x - 5$
10. $y = ^{-}3x^2 + 7x - 8$

Written Draw the graph of each inequality.

1. $y > x^2 + 2x + 1$
2. $y \leq x^2 + 6x + 9$
3. $y \geq x^2 + 8x + 16$
4. $y > x^2 - 10x + 25$
5. $y \leq x^2 - 16$
6. $y \geq x^2 - 49$
7. $y \leq x^2 - 13x + 36$
8. $y > x^2 + x - 30$
9. $y \geq x^2 + 3x - 18$
10. $y < x^2 - x - 20$
11. $y > x^2 + 3x - 4$
12. $y < x^2 + 4x + 3$
13. $y > 4x^2 - 8x + 3$
14. $y \leq 2x^2 + x - 3$
15. $y \geq ^{-}x^2 + 6x + 8$
16. $y \leq ^{-}x^2 - 7x + 10$
17. $y < ^{-}3x^2 + 5x + 2$
18. $y > ^{-}4x^2 - 3x - 6$

Ralph and June Myers have saved $1000. They want to invest the money so that it is relatively safe and will earn some additional money. They are considering two possibilities.

They can buy a certificate of deposit at the bank and earn $9\frac{3}{4}\%$ interest if they hold the certificate of deposit for two years. How much interest will they earn?

$$I = \ p \ \cdot \ r \ \cdot t$$
$$= 1000 \cdot 0.0975 \cdot 2$$
$$= \ 195$$

They will earn $195 interest. They will have to pay about 20% income tax on the interest.

20% of $195 is $39

$195 − $39 is $156

They will have $1000 + $156 or $1156 after two years.

They can purchase some preferred stock which pays $10\frac{1}{2}\%$ annual dividends. How much is the dividend for two years?

$$I = \ p \ \cdot \ r \ \cdot t$$
$$= 1000 \cdot 0.105 \cdot 2$$
$$= \$210$$

Since there is a $200 tax exclusion per person per year, they will not be taxed on the dividends. However, they must pay a brokerage fee of about $30 for buying the stock and about the same for selling it.

$210 − $30 · 2 is $150

Assuming the value of the stock does not go up or down, they will have $1150 after two years. The certificate of deposit is the better investment.

Exercises   **Determine whether stocks or a certificate of deposit would be the better investment if the stock value ($1000) varies as follows.**

1. The stock value ($1000) goes down 5% over the 2 years.

2. The stock value goes up 5% over the 2 years.

3. The stock does not pay a dividend but goes up 10% over a 2-year period. The year the stock is sold, income tax of 20% is charged on one-half the amount the stock went up.

4. The dividends are 7% per year. The stock goes up 10% in 2 years. The year the stock is sold, income tax of 20% is charged on one-half the amount the stock went up.

7-7 Solving Quadratic Inequalities

Use the graph of $y = x^2 + 5x - 6$ to help solve $0 \geq x^2 + 5x - 6$.

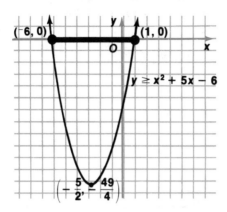

Each point on the x-axis has a y-coordinate of 0. The graph shows that each x-coordinate between ⁻6 and 1 has a corresponding y-coordinate less than 0. Thus, these values of x satisfy the inequality.

The inequality can also be solved algebraically.

$$x^2 + 5x - 6 \leq 0$$
$$(x - 1)(x + 6) \leq 0 \qquad \textit{Factor.}$$

Recall that the product of two factors is negative only if one factor is positive and one factor is negative.

$x - 1 \leq 0$ and $x + 6 \geq 0$	or	$x - 1 \geq 0$ and $x + 6 \leq 0$
$x \leq 1$ and $x \geq ⁻6$	or	$x \geq 1$ and $x \leq ⁻6$
$⁻6 \leq x \leq 1$		**never true**

Using either the graphic or the algebraic method produces the same solution, $\{x \mid ⁻6 \leq x \leq 1\}$.

1 **Use the graphic method to solve $x^2 + 8x > ⁻15$.**

$x^2 + 8x + 15 > 0$

Graph $y = x^2 + 8x + 15$.

The solution set is
$\{x \mid x < ⁻5 \text{ or } x > ⁻3\}$.

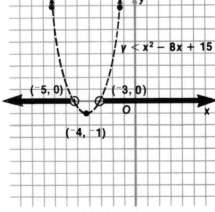

2 Use the algebraic method to solve $x^2 > 2x + 8$.

$x^2 - 2x - 8 > 0$ *The product of two factors is positive only if both*
$(x - 4)(x + 2) > 0$ *factors are positive or both factors are negative.*

$x - 4 > 0$ and $x + 2 > 0$ or $x - 4 < 0$ and $x + 2 < 0$
$x > 4$ and $x > {}^-2$ or $x < 4$ and $x < {}^-2$

$x > 4$ or $x < {}^-2$

The solution set is $\{x \mid x > 4 \text{ or } x < {}^-2\}$.

exercises

Exploratory Indicate if the factors must be positive or negative in each quadratic inequality.

1. $(x - 8)(x + 2) < 0$
2. $(x + 4)(x - 3) > 0$
3. $(x + 6)(x + 2) > 0$
4. $(x - 8)(x - 7) < 0$
5. $(x + 2)(x - 3) \geq 0$
6. $(x + 7)(x - 11) \leq 0$
7. $x^2 + 10x + 25 \leq 0$
8. $x^2 - 11x - 26 > 0$
9. $x^2 - 8x + 16 \leq 0$
10. $x^2 + 3x - 18 > 0$

Written Solve each inequality.

1. $x^2 + x - 6 > 0$
2. $y^2 + 4y - 21 < 0$
3. $p^2 + 2p \geq 24$
4. $m^2 - 4m \leq 5$
5. $2b^2 - b < 6$
6. $6r^2 + 5r > 4$
7. $x^2 - 4x \leq 0$
8. $z^2 \geq 2z$
9. $t^2 \leq 36$
10. $b^2 \geq 3b + 28$
11. $r^2 + 12r \leq {}^-27$
12. $a^2 - 10a + 25 \geq 0$
13. $5c - 2c^2 > {}^-3$
14. ${}^-5y - 3y^2 < {}^-2$
15. $b^2 + 8b \geq {}^-16$
16. $m^2 \leq 3$
17. $4t^2 - 9 < {}^-4t$
18. $9s^2 - 2 > {}^-6s$

Challenge Solve each inequality.

1. $(x - 3)(x + 4)(x - 1) > 0$
2. $(x + 2)(x - 3)(x + 6) < 0$
3. $(x - 8)(x + 4)(x + 2) \leq 0$
4. $(x + 5)(x + 6)(x + 7) \geq 0$
5. $(x + 2)(x + 3)(x - 1)(x - 2) > 0$
6. $(x - 6)(x + 5)(x - 4)(x + 1) > 0$

quadratic function (197)   vertex (200)
quadratic term (197)   axis of symmetry (200)
linear term (197)   maximum value (210)
constant term (197)   minimum value (210)
parabola (200)   boundary (214)

Chapter Summary

1. A quadratic function is a function described by an equation of the form $f(x) = ax^2 + bx + c$ where $a \neq 0$.

   The term ax^2 is called the quadratic term.
   The term bx is called the linear term.
   The term c is called the constant term. (197)

2. The graph of a quadratic function is called a parabola. (200)

3. If the sketches of parabolas are folded along their axes of symmetry, the two halves of the parabolas coincide. (200)

4. In general, the graph of $f(x) = a(x - h)^2$ has the same shape and direction of opening as the graph of $f(x) = ax^2$. But its position is translated $|h|$ units to the right or left. (204)

5. In general, as the value of k changes, the graph of $f(x) = a(x - h)^2 + k$ is translated $|k|$ units up or down. (207)

6.

$y = a(x - h)^2 + k$	a is a positive	a is negative
Vertex	(h, k)	(h, k)
Axis of symmetry	$x = h$	$x = h$
Direction of opening	upward	downward
As the value of $|a|$ increases, the graphs of $y = a(x - h)^2 + k$ narrow.		

(207)

7. If a maximum or minimum problem can be described by a quadratic equation, it often can be solved by finding the vertex of the corresponding graph. (210)

8. The graph of a quadratic inequality will include either the region inside the boundary or outside the boundary. The boundary itself may or may not be included. (214)

9. Quadratic inequalities can be solved using either graphic or algebraic methods. (217)

7-1 For each equation, identify the quadratic term, the linear term, and the constant term.

1. $y = x^2 + 2x + 5$
2. $y = x - 7$
3. $y = 16$
4. $y = {}^-3x^2 + 2$

Write each equation in quadratic form.

5. $f(x) = 3(x + 2)^2 - 7$
6. $f(x) = {}^-3(x - 7)^2 + 6$
7. $f(x) = {}^-2(x - 3)^2 + 9$
8. $f(x) = 4(x + 6)^2 - 21$

7-2 Draw the graph of each equation.

9. $y = 2x^2$
10. $y = -\frac{1}{3}x^2$
11. $f(x) = {}^-3x^2$
12. $f(x) = \frac{2}{3}x^2$

Determine the value of a so that each point is on the graph of $y = ax^2$.

13. $(6, 3)$
14. $(2, 2)$
15. $(2, 1)$
16. $({}^-3, {}^-3)$

7-3 Draw the graph of each equation. Then name the vertex, axis of symmetry, and direction of opening.

17. $y = (x - 3)^2$
18. $y = (x + 2)^2$
19. $y = \frac{1}{2}(x - 4)^2$
20. $y = {}^-3(x + 2)^2$
21. $f(x) = x^2 + 16x + 64$
22. $f(x) = 3x^2 + 30x + 75$

7-4 Draw the graph of each quadratic equation. Then name the vertex, axis of symmetry, and direction of opening.

23. $y = (x - 2)^2 - 3$
24. $y = {}^-2x^2 - 4$
25. $y = {}^-2(x + 1)^2 - 2$
26. $y = \frac{1}{2}(x + 2)^2 - 1$
27. $f(x) = 3x^2 - 6x + 10$
28. $f(x) = {}^-5x^2 - 20x + 2$

7-5 29. Find two numbers whose sum is 64 and whose product is a maximum.

30. Find two numbers whose difference is 5 and whose product is a minimum.

7-6 Draw the graph of each inequality.

31. $y > x^2 + 3x - 4$
32. $y < x^2 + 4x + 3$

7-7 Solve each inequality.

33. $(x - 4)(x + 2) < 0$
34. $x^2 + 8x - 9 > 0$

Write each equation in quadratic form.

1. $y = (x + 2)^2 + 8$

2. $y = 2(x - 3)^2 + 5$

3. $y = \frac{1}{2}(x + 4)^2 - 7$

4. $y = {}^-(x + 2)^2$

Draw the graph of each equation. Then name the vertex, axis of symmetry, and direction of opening.

5. $y = (x + 2)^2 + 1$

6. $y = (x - 3)^2$

7. $y = \frac{1}{2}(x + 8)^2 - 3$

8. $y = {}^-2(x + 4)^2 - 6$

9. $y = x^2 + 3x + 6$

10. $y = x^2 - 8x - 9$

11. $f(x) = 2x^2 + 8x + 9$

12. $f(x) = {}^-x^2 - 10x + 10$

Solve each problem

13. Find two numbers whose sum is 18 and whose product is a maximum.

14. A rocket is shot vertically with an initial velocity of 40 feet per second. Its height above the ground after t seconds is given by $h(t) = 40t - 16t^2$. What is its maximum height? When will it return to earth?

Graph each inequality.

15. $y \leq x^2 + 6x - 7$

16. $y < {}^-x^2 + 4x - 4$

Solve each inequality.

17. $(x + 5)(x + 3) < 0$

18. $2x^2 + 3x - 2 > 0$

chapter
8 Conics

The cables on this bridge approximate the shape of a parabola. The parabola is one of the four mathematical curves formed by the intersection of a plane with the surface of a cone. Circles, ellipses, and hyperbolas are also conic sections.

8–1　Distance

The distance between two points on a number line can be found using absolute value.

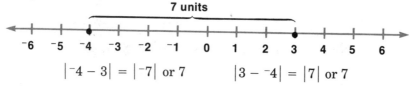

7 units

$$|^-4 - 3| = |^-7| \text{ or } 7 \qquad |3 - {}^-4| = |7| \text{ or } 7$$

On a number line, the distance between two points whose coordinates are a and b is $|a - b|$ or $|b - a|$.

Distance Between Points on a Number line

Consider two points in a plane with coordinates $(^-2, {}^-6)$ and $(3, {}^-6)$. These points lie on a horizontal line. You can use absolute value to find the distance between the points.

$$|^-2 - 3| = |^-5| \text{ or } 5 \qquad \textit{Find the difference between the x-coordinates.}$$

The points with coordinates $(^-2, 3)$ and $(^-2, {}^-6)$ lie on a vertical line. The distance between these two points is 9 units.

$$|3 - {}^-6| = |9| \text{ or } 9 \qquad \textit{Find the difference between the y-coordinates.}$$

To find the distance between points in the coordinate plane, use the Pythagorean Theorem.

example

1　**Find the distance between two points with coordinates $(^-2, 3)$ and $(2, {}^-4)$.**

Form a right triangle by extending vertical and horizontal segments from each point.

The square of the hypotenuse of a right triangle equals the sum of the squares of the other two sides.

$$d^2 = |3 - {}^-4|^2 + |^-2 - 2|^2$$
$$d^2 = \quad 7^2 \quad + \quad 4^2$$
$$d^2 = 65$$
$$d = \sqrt{65} \qquad \textit{Distance is positive.} \qquad d \approx 8.062$$

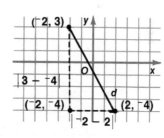

The Pythagorean Theorem can be used to develop a general formula for finding the distance between two points in the plane.

Suppose (x_1, y_1) and (x_2, y_2) name two points in the plane. Form a triangle by drawing a vertical line through (x_1, y_1) and drawing a horizontal line through (x_2, y_2). These lines intersect at the point (x_1, y_2).　*Why?*

$$d^2 = |x_2 - x_1|^2 + |y_2 - y_1|^2$$
$$d^2 = (x_2 - x_1)^2 + (y_2 - y_1)^2 \qquad \textit{Why can } (x_2 - x_1)^2$$
$$d = \sqrt{(x_2 - x_1)^2 + (y_2 - y_1)^2} \qquad \textit{be substituted for } |x_2 - x_1|^2?$$

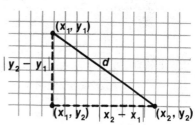

The distance between two points with coordinates (x_1, y_1) and (x_2, y_2) is given by the following formula.

$$d = \sqrt{(x_2 - x_1)^2 + (y_2 - y_1)^2}$$

Distance Formula for Two Points in the Plane

---

example 2

Use the distance formula to find the distance between $(^-1, 6)$ and $(5, ^-4)$.

$$
\begin{aligned}
d &= \sqrt{(x_2 - x_1)^2 + (y_2 - y_1)^2} \\
&= \sqrt{(5 - {}^-1)^2 + ({}^-4 - 6)^2} \\
&= \sqrt{(6)^2 + ({}^-10)^2} \\
&= \sqrt{36 + 100} \\
&= \sqrt{136} \\
&= 2\sqrt{34} \qquad \text{The distance is } 2\sqrt{34} \text{ units.}
\end{aligned}
$$

The distance formula can be used to show that a given point on a line segment is the midpoint of that line segment.

---

example 3

The point $(3, 1)$ lies on the line segment having endpoints whose coordinates are $(6, ^-1)$ and $(0, 3)$. Show that $(3, 1)$ is the midpoint of the line segment.

distance between (3, 1) and (6, $^-$1)

$$
\begin{aligned}
d &= \sqrt{(6 - 3)^2 + ({}^-1 - 1)^2} \\
&= \sqrt{(3)^2 + ({}^-2)^2} \\
&= \sqrt{9 + 4} \\
&= \sqrt{13}
\end{aligned}
$$

distance between (3, 1) and (0, 3)

$$
\begin{aligned}
d &= \sqrt{(0 - 3)^2 + (3 - 1)^2} \\
&= \sqrt{({}^-3)^2 + (2)^2} \\
&= \sqrt{9 + 4} \\
&= \sqrt{13}
\end{aligned}
$$

The distance formula also can be used to find the coordinates of the midpoint of a line segment.

If a line segment has endpoints with coordinates (x_1, y_1) and (x_2, y_2), then the midpoint of the line segment has coordinates $\left(\dfrac{x_1 + x_2}{2}, \dfrac{y_1 + y_2}{2}\right)$.

Midpoint Formula

---

example 4

Find the coordinates of the midpoint of a line segment having endpoints whose coordinates are $(1, ^-5)$ and $(^-4, ^-7)$.

The coordinates of the midpoint are $\left(\dfrac{1 + {}^-4}{2}, \dfrac{{}^-5 + {}^-7}{2}\right)$ or $\left(-\dfrac{3}{2}, {}^-6\right)$.

---

exercises

Exploratory In each of the following, the coordinates of two points on the number line are given. Find the distance between these points.

1. $3, 5$
2. $^-4, ^-8$
3. $^-3, 6$
4. $^-6, 9$
5. $^-11, 0$
6. $^-16, 0$
7. $^-32, ^-16$
8. $^-19, 14$
9. $16.2, ^-14.9$
10. $7.5, ^-7.5$
11. $14\frac{2}{5}, ^-8\frac{3}{10}$
12. $3\frac{1}{2}, ^-6\frac{1}{3}$

Written Use the distance formula to find the distance between each pair of points whose coordinates are given. — *plug into formula*

1. $(3, 6), (7, ^-8)$
2. $(4, 2), (^-3, ^-6)$
3. $(^-3, 1), (4, ^-2)$
4. $(^-8, ^-7), (^-2, ^-1)$
5. $(6, 7), (8, 0)$
6. $(9, 3), (^-6, ^-8)$
7. $\left(\frac{1}{3}, \frac{1}{5}\right), (2, ^-4)$
8. $\left(1, \frac{1}{2}\right), \left(\frac{1}{3}, ^-2\right)$
9. $(0.2, 0.6), (0.3, 0.4)$
10. $(^-0.2, 0.4), (^-0.5, ^-0.6)$
11. $(^-2.4, 0.6), (1.7, 0.8)$
12. $(3, 3), (\sqrt{3}, \sqrt{3})$
13. $(3, \sqrt{3}), (4, \sqrt{3})$
14. $(^-2\sqrt{7}, 10), (4\sqrt{7}, 8)$
15. $(2\sqrt{3}, 4\sqrt{3}), (2\sqrt{3}, ^-\sqrt{3})$

Each pair of points represented by the following coordinates is 5 units apart. Find c in each case.

16. $(3, 5), (c, 2)$
17. $(^-4, c), (^-7, 7)$
18. $(c, 1.9), (1.2, 5.9)$
19. $(13, 10.1), (9, c)$

Find the midpoints of line segments having endpoints with the following coordinates.

20. $(6, 7), (8, 0)$
21. $(9, 3), (^-6, ^-8)$
22. $\left(\frac{1}{3}, \frac{1}{5}\right), (2, ^-4)$
23. $\left(1, \frac{1}{2}\right), \left(\frac{1}{3}, ^-2\right)$
24. $(^-2.4, 0.6), (1.7, 0.8)$
25. $(3, 3), (\sqrt{2}, ^-\sqrt{2})$

26. Find the perimeter of a quadrilateral with vertices at $(6, 3), (4, 5), (^-4, 6)$, and $(^-5, ^-8)$.
27. Find the lengths of the diagonals of a parallelogram with vertices at $(6, 8)$, $(^-14, 8), (8, ^-2)$, and $(^-12, ^-2)$.
28. Parallelogram $ABCD$ has vertices $A(^-5, 1)$, $B(0, 2)$, $C(^-3, 6)$, and $D(^-8, 5)$. Show that the diagonals of $ABCD$ bisect each other.
29. Show that triangle ABC with vertices $A(^-3, 0)$, $B(^-1, 4)$, and $C(1, ^-2)$ is an isosceles triangle.
30. Triangle ABC has vertices $A(^-2, 8)$, $B(3, 5)$, and $C(7, ^-4)$. Find the coordinates of the midpoint of each side.
31. Right triangle DEF has vertices $D(0, 1)$, $E(4, 1)$, and $F(0, 7)$. Show that the midpoint of the hypotenuse is the same distance from each vertex.
32. Show that $\left(\frac{x_1 + x_2}{2}, \frac{y_1 + y_2}{2}\right)$ is the midpoint of a line segment having endpoints with coordinates (x_1, y_1) and (x_2, y_2).
33. Write a computer program to find the distance between any two points in the coordinate plane. Use the points in Written Exercises 1–6 as data.

Challenge Solve each problem.

1. Find the coordinates of a point one-fourth of the distance from $A(3, ^-2)$ to $B(11, 2)$.
2. Find the coordinates of a point three-fourths of the distance from $X(5, 8)$ to $Y(^-7, 16)$.

8-2   Parabolas

The shape of the reflectors in automobile head-
lights is based on the **parabola.** The diagram at the
right shows a cross section of a reflector. The light
source is placed at a special point so the light is reflected in parallel rays. In this way, a straight beam
of light is formed.

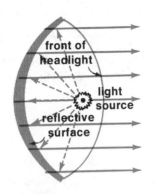

The point where the light source is placed is called
the **focus** of the parabola. Parabolas can be defined
in terms of the focus.

> **A parabola is the set of all points in a plane that are the
> same distance from a given point and a given line. The
> point is called the *focus*. The line is called the *directrix*.**

*Definition
of Parabola*

The parabola at the right has focus (3, 4) and directrix $y = {}^-2$.
You can use the distance formula and the definition of a parabola
to find the equation of this parabola. Let (x, y) be a point on the
parabola. This point must be the same distance from the focus,
(3, 4), as it is from the directrix, $y = {}^-2$.

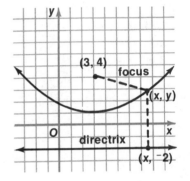

distance between (x, y) and $(3, 4)$ = distance between (x, y) and $(x, {}^-2)$

$$\sqrt{(x - 3)^2 + (y - 4)^2} = \sqrt{(x - x)^2 + (y - {}^-2)^2}$$
$$(x - 3)^2 + (y - 4)^2 = (x - x)^2 + (y + 2)^2$$
$$(x - 3)^2 + y^2 - 8y + 16 = y^2 + 4y + 4$$
$$(x - 3)^2 = 12y - 12$$
$$\frac{1}{12}(x - 3)^2 + 1 = y$$

The equation of a parabola with focus (3, 4) and directrix $y = {}^-2$
is $y = \frac{1}{12}(x - 3)^2 + 1$. The vertex is (3, 1) and the axis of symmetry
is $x = 3$.

The equation for a parabola can be written in the form $y = a(x - h)^2 + k$ or in the form $x = a(y - k)^2 + h$. Either form provides valuable information about the graph.

Information About Parabolas		
form of equation	$y = a(x - h)^2 + k$	$x = a(y - k)^2 + h$
axis of symmetry	$x = h$	$y = k$
vertex	(h, k)	(h, k)
focus	$\left(h, k + \dfrac{1}{4a}\right)$	$\left(h + \dfrac{1}{4a}, k\right)$
directrix	$y = k - \dfrac{1}{4a}$	$x = h - \dfrac{1}{4a}$
direction of opening	upward if $a > 0$, downward if $a < 0$	right if $a > 0$, left if $a < 0$

1 **Draw the graph of a parabola with equation $y = \frac{1}{4}(x - 2)^2 - 3$.**

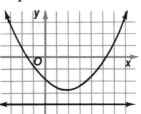

vertex:	$(2, {}^-3)$
axis of symmetry:	$x = 2$
focus:	$\left(2, {}^-3 + \frac{1}{1}\right)$ or $(2, {}^-2)$
directrix:	$y = {}^-3 - \frac{1}{1}$ or ${}^-4$
direction of opening:	upward since $a = \frac{1}{4}$

The graph of $y = x^2 - 6x + 6$ is a parabola. This equation can be written in the form $y = a(x - h)^2 + k$ by completing the square.

$$y = x^2 - 6x + 6$$
$$y = x^2 - 6x + \square - \square + 6$$
$$y = x^2 - 6x + \left(\frac{-6}{2}\right)^2 - \left(\frac{-6}{2}\right)^2 + 6$$
$$y = (x - 3)^2 - 3$$

Consider the line segment through the focus of a parabola perpendicular to its axis of symmetry with endpoints on the parabola. This segment is called the **latus rectum.** In the figure at the right, the latus rectum is $\overline{AB}$. The length of the latus rectum of the parabola given by the equation $y = a(x - h)^2 + k$ is $\left|\frac{1}{a}\right|$. Points A and B are $\left(\frac{1}{2}\right)\left(\frac{1}{a}\right)$ units each from the focus. This information can also be used in graphing.

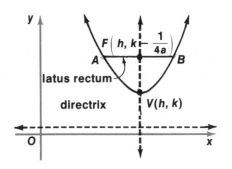

2 **Draw the graph of a parabola with equation $8x = y^2 + 4y + 28$.**

First write the equation in the form $x = a(y - k)^2 + h$.

$$8x = y^2 + 4y + 28$$
$$8x = y^2 + 4y + \left(\frac{4}{2}\right)^2 - \left(\frac{4}{2}\right)^2 + 28 \quad \textit{Complete the square.}$$
$$8x = (y + 2)^2 + 24$$
$$x = \frac{1}{8}(y + 2)^2 + 3$$

vertex:	$(3, {}^-2)$
axis of symmetry:	$y = {}^-2$
focus:	$(3 + 2, {}^-2)$ or $(5, {}^-2)$
directrix:	$x = 3 - 2$ or 1
direction of opening:	right since $a = \frac{1}{8}$
length of latus rectum:	$\frac{1}{\frac{1}{8}}$ or 8 units; ± 4 units from focus

exercises

Exploratory Complete the square to find the value of c for each expression.

1. $x^2 + 4x + c$
2. $x^2 + 6x + c$
3. $y^2 - 8y + c$
4. $p^2 - 10p + c$
5. $r^2 + 3r + c$
6. $m^2 - 3m + c$
7. $x^2 - 7x + c$
8. $t^2 + 15t + c$
9. $m^2 - 4.1m + c$
10. $n^2 + 0.3n + c$

Change each equation to the form $y = a(x - h)^2 + k$.

11. $x^2 = 10y$
12. $x^2 = {}^-2y$
13. $y = x^2 - 6x + 33$
14. $y = x^2 + 4x + 1$
15. $y = 3x^2 - 24x + 50$
16. $y = \frac{1}{2}x^2 - 3x + \frac{19}{2}$

Change each equation to the form $x = a(y - k)^2 + h$.

17. $6x = y^2$
18. $y^2 = {}^-12x$
19. $x = y^2 + 8y + 20$
20. $x = y^2 - 14y + 25$
21. $x = \frac{1}{4}y^2 - \frac{1}{2}y - 3$
22. $x = 5y^2 - 25y + 60$

Written Name the vertex, axis of symmetry, focus, directrix, and direction of opening of the parabola whose equation is given. Then, find the length of the latus rectum and draw the graph.

1. $x^2 = 6y$
2. $y^2 = {}^-8x$
3. $(x + 2)^2 = y - 3$
4. $(x - 4)^2 = 4(y + 2)$
5. $(x - 8)^2 = \frac{1}{2}(y + 1)$
6. $(x + 3)^2 = \frac{1}{4}(y - 2)$
7. $x^2 = (y - 1)$
8. $(x + 2)^2 = 6y$
9. $(y + 3)^2 = 4(x - 2)$
10. $(y - 8)^2 = {}^-4(x - 4)$
11. $y = x^2 - 6x + 33$
12. $x = y^2 + 8y + 20$
13. $x = y^2 - 14y + 25$
14. $y = \frac{1}{2}x^2 - 3x + \frac{19}{2}$
15. $x = \frac{1}{4}y^2 - \frac{1}{2}y - 3$
16. $y = x^2 + 4x + 1$
17. $y = 3x^2 - 24x + 50$
18. $x = 5y^2 - 25y + 60$

The focus and directrix of a parabola are given. Write an equation for each parabola. Then, draw the graph of the equation.

19. $(2, 4), y = 6$
20. $(3, 5), y = 1$
21. $(8, 0), y = 4$
22. $(0, 3), y = {}^-1$
23. $(5, 5), y = {}^-3$
24. $(6, 2), x = 4$
25. $(3, {}^-1), x = {}^-2$
26. $(4, {}^-3), y = 6$
27. $(0, 4), x = 1$

Write the equation of each parabola described below. Then, draw the graph.

28. Vertex $(0, 0)$, focus $(0, {}^-4)$
29. Vertex $(5, {}^-1)$, focus $(3, {}^-1)$
30. Vertex $(4, 3)$, axis $y = 3$, length of latus rectum 4, $a > 0$
31. Vertex $({}^-7, 4)$, axis $x = {}^-7$, length of latus rectum 6, $a < 0$

Challenge If the equation of a parabola is $y = a(x - h)^2 + k$, show that the length of the latus rectum is $\frac{1}{a}$.

The parabola is a very practical curve. Recall that if a light source is placed at the focus of a parabolic reflector, the light emitted is reflected off the parabola and straight ahead.

Conversely, with sunlight directed at a reflector, temperatures at the focal point can reach over one thousand degrees Fahrenheit, hot enough to melt steel.

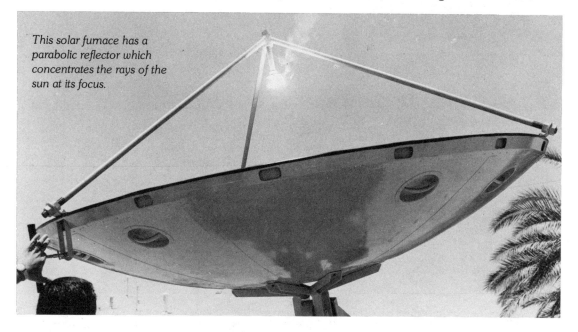

This solar furnace has a parabolic reflector which concentrates the rays of the sun at its focus.

Sound can be reflected in a similar way. If a microphone is placed at the focus of a parabolic reflector, it can pick up very faint noises. You may have seen such a reflector being used at a televised football game. It will pick up the signal calls all the way from the sidelines.

Radar antennas also use parabolic reflectors. Radio signals are focused on a receiver placed at the focus.

The focus for a parabola with equation $y = ax^2 + bx + c$ has the following coordinates.

$$\left(-\frac{b}{2a}, \frac{4ac - b^2 + 1}{4a}\right)$$

Exercises   Find a focus for each parabola with the given equation.

1. $y = x^2 + 6x + 9$

2. $y = 2x^2 + 4x + 7$

3. $y = \frac{1}{2}x^2 - 2x - \frac{5}{2}$

4. $y = \frac{1}{4}x^2 - 2x + 3$

The shape of a record turntable is a **circle.** All points along the edge of the turntable are the same distance from the spindle.

> A circle is the set of points in the plane each of which is the same distance from a given point. The given distance is the *radius* of the circle, and the given point is the *center* of the circle.

Definition of Circle

The circle at the right has center (2, ⁻3) and radius 6 units. You can use the distance formula and the definition of a circle to find the equation of this circle.

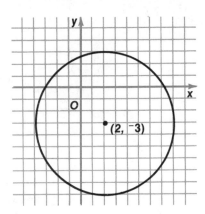

Let (x, y) be a point of the circle. This point must be 6 units from the center of the circle, (2, ⁻3).

$$\text{distance between } (x, y) \text{ and } (2, {}^-3) = 6$$
$$\sqrt{(x - 2)^2 + (y - {}^-3)^2} = 6$$
$$(x - 2)^2 + (y - {}^-3)^2 = 6^2$$
$$(x - 2)^2 + (y + 3)^2 = 36$$

The equation of a circle with center (2, ⁻3) and radius 6 units is $(x - 2)^2 + (y + 3)^2 = 36$.

> The equation of a circle with center (h, k) and radius r units is $(x - h)^2 + (y - k)^2 = r^2$.

Equation of Circle

1 **Draw the graph of a circle with equation $(x - 10)^2 + (y - 10)^2 = 100$.**

Center: (10, 10)
Radius: 10 units

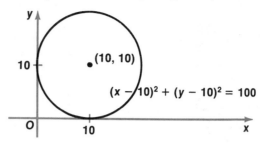

The graph of $x^2 + y^2 - 4x + 10y = 9$ is a circle. To write the equation in the form $(x - h)^2 + (y - k)^2 = r^2$, complete the square for each variable.

$$x^2 + y^2 - 4x + 10y = 9$$
$$x^2 - 4x + \blacksquare + y^2 + 10y + \square = 9 + \blacksquare + \square$$
$$x^2 - 4x + \left(\frac{-4}{2}\right)^2 + y^2 + 10y + \left(\frac{10}{2}\right)^2 = 9 + \left(\frac{-4}{2}\right)^2 + \left(\frac{10}{2}\right)^2$$
$$(x - 2)^2 + (y + 5)^2 = 38$$

The circle has center $(2, {}^-5)$ and radius $\sqrt{38}$ units.

2 **A circle has equation $x^2 + 3 + y^2 + 9y - 10x = 2$. Find the center and radius of the circle. Then draw the graph.**

$$x^2 + 3 + y^2 + 9y - 10x = 2$$
$$x^2 - 10x + \blacksquare + y^2 + 9y + \square = 2 - 3 + \blacksquare + \square$$
$$x^2 - 10x + \left(\frac{-10}{2}\right)^2 + y^2 + 9y + \left(\frac{9}{2}\right)^2 = {}^-1 + \left(\frac{-10}{2}\right)^2 + \left(\frac{9}{2}\right)^2$$
$$(x - 5)^2 + \left(y + \frac{9}{2}\right)^2 = \frac{177}{4}$$

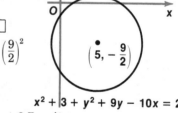

The circle has center $\left(5, -\frac{9}{2}\right)$ and radius $\frac{\sqrt{177}}{2}$ or about 6.7 units.

exercises

Exploratory   State whether the graph for each of the following equations is a circle or a parabola.

1. $x^2 + y^2 + 7x - 5 = 0$
2. $x^2 + 4x + 4 = 9y + 27$
3. $y^2 = 6x - 4$
4. $y = x^2 + 8x + y^2$
5. $x^2 + y + y^2 = 12 - 3x$
6. $x^2 = 5y$
7. $x^2 + 14x + y^2 + 6y = 23$
8. $y^2 + 8y = 14x$
9. $y^2 + 6y + 9 = x$
10. $x^2 = 6y - y^2$

State the center and radius of each circle whose equation is given.

11. $x^2 + y^2 = 16$

12. $x^2 + (y - 2)^2 = 25$

13. $(x - 2)^2 + y^2 = 9$

14. $x^2 + y^2 = 40$

15. $(x - 10)^2 + (y + 10)^2 = 100$

16. $(x + 2)^2 + (y - 3)^2 = 81$

17. $(x + 4)^2 + \left(y - \frac{1}{2}\right)^2 = 6$

18. $(x - 4)^2 + y^2 = \frac{16}{25}$

19. $(x + 5)^2 + (y - 2)^2 = \frac{3}{4}$

20. $x^2 + (y + 5)^2 = \frac{81}{64}$

Written Find the center and radius of each circle whose equation is given. Then draw the graph.

1. $(x - 2)^2 + y^2 = 9$

2. $(x + 4)^2 + y^2 = 49$

3. $x^2 + (y - 8)^2 = 64$

4. $x^2 + (y + 2)^2 = 4$

5. $x^2 + y^2 = 64$

6. $x^2 + y^2 = 121$

7. $(x - 2)^2 + (y - 5)^2 = 16$

8. $(x + 2)^2 + (y - 1)^2 = 81$

9. $(x + 8)^2 + (y - 3)^2 = 25$

10. $(x - 3)^2 + (y + 2)^2 = 169$

11. $(x + 1)^2 + (y + 9)^2 = 36$

12. $(x - 5)^2 + (y - 7)^2 = 49$

13. $x^2 + y^2 - 12x - 16y + 84 = 0$

14. $x^2 + y^2 - 18x - 18y + 53 = 0$

15. $x^2 + y^2 + 8x - 6y = 0$

16. $x^2 + y^2 + 14x + 6y = 23$

17. $x^2 + y^2 - 4x = 9$

18. $x^2 + y^2 - 6y = 16$

19. $3x^2 + 3y^2 + 6y + 9x = 2$

20. $x^2 + y^2 + 9x - 8y = {}^-4$

21. $y^2 + 3 + x^2 + 9x - 10y = 6.75$

22. $4x^2 + 4y^2 + 36y = {}^-5$

23. $x^2 + 2x + y^2 + 4y = 9$

24. $x^2 + y^2 + 4x = 8$

25. $x^2 + 2x + y^2 = 10$

26. $x^2 + y^2 + 14x + 6y = {}^-50$

Write an equation for each circle whose center and radius is given.

27. $(6, 2), 5$

28. $(6, 0), 6$

29. $(0, 3), 2$

30. $({}^-3, {}^-5), 5$

31. $({}^-6, 2), \frac{1}{4}$

32. $({}^-1, {}^-3), \frac{2}{3}$

Write the equation of each circle described below.

33. The circle has center $(1, 5)$ and passes through the origin.

34. The circle has center $(4, {}^-2)$ and passes through $(9, {}^-3)$.

35. The endpoints of a diameter of the circle are $(5, 2)$ and $({}^-1, 2)$.

36. The endpoints of a diameter of the circle are $(4, {}^-3)$ and $(8, 5)$.

Contest Problem   excursions in algebra

The following problem appeared in a high school mathematics contest sponsored by the Mathematical Association of America.

In a group of cows and chickens, the number of legs was 14 more than twice the number of heads. How many cows are in the group?

8–4 Ellipses

A circle can be considered as a special case of a more general curve called an **ellipse.** A circle is defined in terms of a given point and a given distance. An ellipse is defined in terms of *two* given points and *two* distances. The instructions below show one way to draw an ellipse.

Use a piece of string about 25 cm long. Put two thumbtacks through a piece of paper from the back, about 10 cm apart. Loop the string around the tacks. Place the pencil in the loop. Keep the string tight and draw around the tacks.

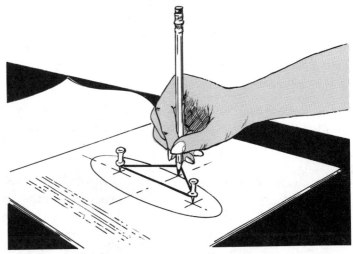

The points where the tacks are placed are called the **foci** of the ellipse. Ellipses can be defined in terms of their foci.

> **An ellipse is the set of all points in the plane such that the sum of the distances from two given points, called the foci, is constant.**

Definition of Ellipse

The ellipse at the right has foci $(^-3, 0)$ and $(3, 0)$. The sum of the distances from the two foci is 8 units. You can use the distance formula and the definition of an ellipse to find the equation of this ellipse.

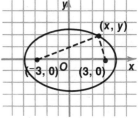

Let (x, y) be a point on the ellipse. The distance between this point and $(^-3, 0)$ *plus* the distance between the point and $(3, 0)$ is 8 units.

$$\underset{\substack{\text{distance between}\\(x, y)\text{ and }(^-3, 0)}}{} + \underset{\substack{\text{distance between}\\(x, y)\text{ and }(3, 0)}}{} = 8$$

$$\sqrt{(x - {}^-3)^2 + (y - 0)^2} + \sqrt{(x - 3)^2 + (y - 0)^2} = 8$$

$$\sqrt{(x + 3)^2 + y^2} = 8 - \sqrt{(x - 3)^2 + y^2}$$

$$(x + 3)^2 + y^2 = 64 - 16\sqrt{(x - 3)^2 + y^2} + (x - 3)^2 + y^2$$

$$3x - 16 = {}^-4\sqrt{(x - 3)^2 + y^2} \quad \text{\textit{Simplify.}}$$

$$9x^2 - 96x + 256 = 16[(x - 3)^2 + y^2] \quad \text{\textit{Square both sides.}}$$

$$112 = 7x^2 + 16y^2 \quad \text{\textit{Simplify.}}$$

$$1 = \frac{x^2}{16} + \frac{y^2}{7}$$

The equation of an ellipse with foci ($^-3$, 0) and (3, 0), and with 8 units as the sum of the distances from the two foci is $\frac{x^2}{16} + \frac{y^2}{7} = 1$.

An ellipse has two axes of symmetry. The longer axis of symmetry is called the **major axis.** The shorter axis of symmetry is called the **minor axis.** The intersection of the two axes is the center of the ellipse.

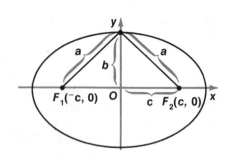

In the figure at the right, the sum of the distances from the foci to any point on the ellipse is $2a$ units. The distance from the center to a focus is c units. Using the Pythagorean Theorem, it can be shown that $b^2 = a^2 - c^2$.

What are the lengths of the major axis and the minor axis?

The method used to find the equation of the ellipse on the previous page can be used to find the general equation of an ellipse.

The general equation of an ellipse whose foci are (^-c, 0) and (c, 0), and the sum of the distances from the two foci is $2a$ units, is the following.

$$\frac{x^2}{a^2} + \frac{y^2}{b^2} = 1 \text{ where } b^2 = a^2 - c^2$$

Equation of Ellipse

The general equation of an ellipse whose foci are (0, ^-c) and (0, c) and the sum of the distances from the two foci is $2a$ units, is the following.

$$\frac{x^2}{b^2} + \frac{y^2}{a^2} = 1 \text{ where } b^2 = a^2 - c^2$$

---

example

1 **Write the equation of the ellipse shown below.**

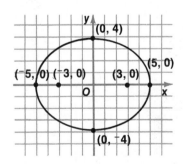

To write the equation for this ellipse, you must know the sum of the distances from the two foci. The distance between ($^-5$, 0) and ($^-3$, 0) is 2 units. The distance between ($^-5$, 0) and (3, 0) is 8 units.

$$2a = 2 + 8$$
$$2a = 10$$
$$a = 5$$

Since the foci are ($^-3$, 0) and (3, 0), $c = 3$.

$$b^2 = a^2 - c^2$$
$$b^2 = 5^2 - 3^2$$
$$b^2 = 16$$

$b = 4$ The equation is $\frac{x^2}{5^2} + \frac{y^2}{4^2} = 1$ or $\frac{x^2}{25} + \frac{y^2}{16} = 1$.

Note that in the equation of an ellipse, $a^2 > b^2$. This makes it easy to decide in a given equation whether the foci are on the x-axis or the y-axis. For example in the ellipse given by the equation $\frac{x^2}{16} + \frac{y^2}{25} = 1$, $25 > 16$. Therefore, 25 must be a^2 and 16 must be b^2, so the foci of the ellipse are on the y-axis.

example

2 **An ellipse has equation $9x^2 + y^2 = 36$. Find its foci, the lengths of major axis and minor axis, and draw the graph.**

First, write the equation in the general form.

$\frac{x^2}{4} + \frac{y^2}{36} = 1$ *Divide both sides by 36.*

a^2 must be 36 since $36 > 4$.

$a = 6$ and $b = 2$

$b^2 = a^2 - c^2 \rightarrow c^2 = a^2 - b^2$

$c^2 = 36 - 4$

$c = \sqrt{32}$ or $4\sqrt{2}$

The foci are $(0, 4\sqrt{2}\,)$ and $(0, {}^-4\sqrt{2})$ and are on the vertical axis.

The length of the major axis is $2a$ or 12.

The length of the minor axis is $2b$ or 4.

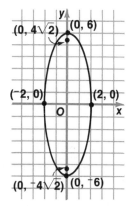

An equation of the form $\frac{x^2}{a^2} + \frac{y^2}{b^2} = 1$ represents an ellipse with center $(0, 0)$. Suppose an ellipse has the same shape but its center is at (h, k). This ellipse has an equation of the following form.

$$\frac{(x - h)^2}{a^2} + \frac{(y - k)^2}{b^2} = 1$$

example

3 **Draw the graph of $\frac{(x + 2)^2}{36} + \frac{(y - 3)^2}{9} = 1$.**

The graph has the same shape as the graph of $\frac{x^2}{36} + \frac{y^2}{9} = 1$, but has center at $({}^-2, 3)$ rather than at the origin.

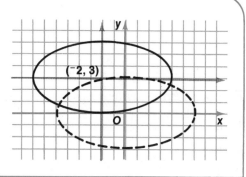

The graph of $x^2 + 2y^2 - 2x + 8y - 11 = 0$ is an ellipse. To write the equation in the form $\dfrac{(x - h)^2}{a^2} + \dfrac{(y - k)^2}{b^2} = 1$, complete the square for each variable.

$$x^2 + 2y^2 - 2x + 8y - 11 = 0$$
$$x^2 - 2x + \square + 2(y^2 + 4y + \square) = 11 + \square + 2\square$$
$$x^2 - 2x + \left(\frac{-2}{2}\right)^2 + 2\left(y^2 + 4y + \left(\frac{4}{2}\right)^2\right) = 11 + \left(\frac{-2}{2}\right)^2 + 2\left(\frac{4}{2}\right)^2$$
$$(x - 1)^2 + 2(y + 2)^2 = 20$$
$$\frac{(x - 1)^2}{20} + \frac{(y + 2)^2}{10} = 1$$

The ellipse has center $(1, {}^-2)$. Since a^2 is 20, the major axis is horizontal and is $2(\sqrt{20})$ or $4\sqrt{5}$ units long. Since b^2 is 10, the minor axis is $2\sqrt{10}$ units long.

4 An ellipse has equation $y^2 - 8y + 3x^2 + 30x + 85 = 0$. Find the coordinates of the center and foci of the ellipse. Then draw the graph.

$$y^2 - 8y + 3x^2 + 30x + 85 = 0$$
$$y^2 - 8y + \square + 3(x^2 + 10x + \square) = {}^-85 - \square + 3\square$$
$$y^2 - 8y + \left(\frac{-8}{2}\right)^2 + 3\left(x^2 + 10x + \left(\frac{10}{2}\right)^2\right) = {}^-85 + \left(\frac{-8}{2}\right)^2 + 3\left(\frac{10}{2}\right)^2$$
$$(y - 4)^2 + 3(x + 5)^2 = 6$$
$$\frac{(y - 4)^2}{6} + \frac{(x + 5)^2}{2} = 1$$

The ellipse has center $({}^-5, 4)$.

To determine coordinates of the foci, first find c.
$$b^2 = a^2 - c^2$$
$$2 = 6 - c^2 \qquad \text{\textit{a} is } \sqrt{6} \text{ and \textit{b} is } \sqrt{2}.$$
$$c = 2$$

Thus, the foci are 2 units above and below the center $({}^-5, 4)$. The coordinates of the foci are $({}^-5, 6)$ and $({}^-5, 2)$. The coordinates of the endpoints of the major axis are $({}^-5, 4 + \sqrt{6}), ({}^-5, 4 - \sqrt{6})$.

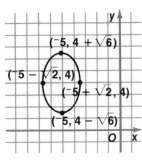

$({}^-5, 4 + \sqrt{6})$
$({}^-5 - \sqrt{2}, 4)$
$({}^-5 + \sqrt{2}, 4)$
$({}^-5, 4 - \sqrt{6})$

exercises

Exploratory Name the center of each ellipse with the given equation.

1. $\dfrac{x^2}{9} + \dfrac{y^2}{4} = 1$

2. $\dfrac{x^2}{16} + \dfrac{y^2}{1} = 1$

3. $\dfrac{x^2}{9} + \dfrac{y^2}{25} = 1$

4. $\dfrac{x^2}{10} + \dfrac{y^2}{36} = 1$

5. $\dfrac{x^2}{81} + \dfrac{(y - 5)^2}{49} = 1$

6. $\dfrac{(x + 3)^2}{25} + \dfrac{y^2}{9} = 1$

7. $\dfrac{(x - 2)^2}{36} + \dfrac{(y + 5)^2}{16} = 1$

8. $\dfrac{(x - 4)^2}{16} + \dfrac{(y - 4)^2}{121} = 1$

9. $\dfrac{(x + 2)^2}{81} + \dfrac{(y - 3)^2}{144} = 1$

Name the foci of each ellipse with the given equation.

10. $\dfrac{x^2}{9} + \dfrac{y^2}{4} = 1$ **11.** $\dfrac{x^2}{16} + \dfrac{y^2}{1} = 1$ **12.** $\dfrac{x^2}{9} + \dfrac{y^2}{25} = 1$

13. $\dfrac{x^2}{10} + \dfrac{y^2}{36} = 1$ **14.** $\dfrac{x^2}{81} + \dfrac{(y-5)^2}{49} = 1$ **15.** $\dfrac{(x+3)^2}{25} + \dfrac{y^2}{9} = 1$

Written   Find the center, foci, and lengths of the major axis and minor axis of each ellipse whose equation is given. Then draw the graph.

1. $\dfrac{x^2}{4} + \dfrac{y^2}{25} = 1$ **2.** $\dfrac{x^2}{36} + \dfrac{y^2}{16} = 1$ **3.** $\dfrac{x^2}{25} + \dfrac{y^2}{9} = 1$ **4.** $\dfrac{x^2}{10} + \dfrac{y^2}{5} = 1$

5. $9x^2 + 16y^2 = 144$ **6.** $3x^2 + 9y^2 = 27$ **7.** $4x^2 + 9y^2 = 36$ **8.** $4x^2 + y^2 = 4$

9. $36x^2 + 81y^2 = 2916$ **10.** $x^2 + 16y^2 = 16$ **11.** $27x^2 + 9y^2 = 81$

12. $\dfrac{(x+3)^2}{36} + \dfrac{(y-4)^2}{9} = 1$ **13.** $\dfrac{(x+2)^2}{20} + \dfrac{(y+3)^2}{40} = 1$ **14.** $\dfrac{(x-8)^2}{4} + \dfrac{(y+8)^2}{1} = 1$

15. $\dfrac{(x+2)^2}{5} + \dfrac{(y-3)^2}{2} = 1$ **16.** $\dfrac{(x-4)^2}{121} + \dfrac{(y+5)^2}{64} = 1$ **17.** $\dfrac{(x-2)^2}{16} + \dfrac{(y-3)^2}{9} = 1$

18. $9x^2 + 4y^2 - 18x + 16y = 11$ **19.** $3x^2 + 7y^2 - 12x - 28y = {}^-19$

20. $9x^2 + 16y^2 - 18x + 64y = 71$ **21.** $16x^2 + 25y^2 + 32x - 150y = 159$

Write the equation of each ellipse described below.

22. The foci are $(0, 8)$ and $(0, {}^-8)$. The endpoints of the major axis are $(0, 10)$ and $(0, {}^-10)$. The endpoints of the minor axis are $(6, 0)$ and $({}^-6, 0)$.

23. The foci are $(12, 0)$ and $({}^-12, 0)$. The endpoints of the major axis are $(13, 0)$ and $({}^-13, 0)$. The endpoints of the minor axis are $(0, 5)$ and $(0, {}^-5)$.

24. The center has coordinates $(5, 4)$. The major axis is 16 units and parallel to the x-axis. The minor axis is 9 units.

25. The center has coordinates $({}^-2, 3)$. The major axis is 12 units and parallel to the y-axis. The minor axis is 8 units.

26. The endpoints of the major axis are $(2, 12)$ and $(2, {}^-4)$. The endpoints of the minor axis are $(4, 4)$ and $(0, 4)$.

27. The foci are $(5, 4)$ and $({}^-3, 4)$. The major axis is 10 units.

The Capitol   excursions in algebra

If rays of light or sound are emitted from one focus of an elliptical reflector, these rays are concentrated at the other focus.

The elliptical chamber of the United States Capitol has this property. A person standing at one focus and whispering is easily heard by a person standing at the other focus.

8–5   Hyperbolas

When the light from a table lamp hits the wall, curves called **hyperbolas** are formed.

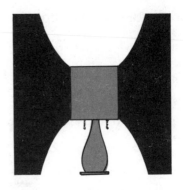

> **A hyperbola is the set of all points in the plane such that the absolute value of the difference of the distances from two given points, called the *foci*, is constant.**

Definition of Hyperbola

The hyperbola at the right has foci ($^-5$, 0) and (5, 0). The difference of the distances from the two foci is 8. You can use the distance formula and the definition of a hyperbola to find the equation of this hyperbola.

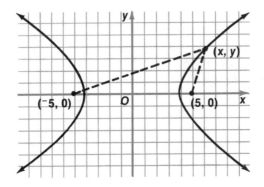

Let (x, y) be a point on the hyperbola. The distance between (x, y) and ($^-5$, 0) *minus* the distance between (x, y) and (5, 0) is $^\pm 8$.

$$\underset{\substack{\text{distance between}\\(x,\,y)\text{ and }(^-5,\,0)}}{} \quad - \quad \underset{\substack{\text{distance between}\\(x,\,y)\text{ and }(5,\,0)}}{} \quad = {}^\pm 8$$

$$\sqrt{(x - {}^-5)^2 + (y - 0)^2} - \sqrt{(x - 5)^2 + (y - 0)^2} = {}^\pm 8$$

$$\sqrt{(x + 5)^2 + y^2} = {}^\pm 8 + \sqrt{(x - 5)^2 + y^2}$$

$$(x + 5)^2 + y^2 = 64 \pm 16\sqrt{(x - 5)^2 + y^2} + (x - 5)^2 + y^2$$

$$5x - 16 = {}^\pm 4\sqrt{(x - 5)^2 + y^2}$$

$$25x^2 - 160x + 256 = 16[(x - 5)^2 + y^2]$$

$$9x^2 - 16y^2 = 144$$

$$\frac{x^2}{16} - \frac{y^2}{9} = 1$$

The equation of a hyperbola with foci ($^-5$, 0) and (5, 0), and with 8 as the absolute value of the difference between the distances from the two foci is $\dfrac{x^2}{16} - \dfrac{y^2}{9} = 1$.

The **center** of a hyperbola is the midpoint of the segment connecting the foci. The point on each branch of the hyperbola nearest the center is called a **vertex**. The **asymptotes** of a hyperbola are lines that the branches of the curve approach as the curve recedes from the center. Like the ellipse, the distance from the center to a vertex is a units and the distance from the center to a focus is c units.

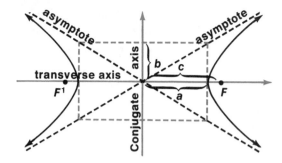

A hyperbola has two axes of symmetry, as shown at the right. The line segment of length $2a$ which has its endpoints at the vertices is called the **transverse axis**. The segment of length $2b$ perpendicular to the transverse axis at its center is called the **conjugate axis**. For a hyperbola, the lengths a, b, and c are related by the formula $a^2 + b^2 = c^2$. *The relationship between a, b, and c is different for ellipses and hyperbolas.*

The method used to find the equation of the hyperbola on the previous page also can be used to find the general equation of a hyperbola.

The asymptotes pass through the center of the hyperbola and form the diagonals of the rectangles whose sides are a and b units.

The general equation of a hyperbola with foci (^{-}c, 0) and (c, 0), and with the absolute value of the difference between distances from the two foci $2a$ units, can be written in the following form.

$$\frac{x^2}{a^2} - \frac{y^2}{b^2} = 1 \text{ where } c^2 = a^2 + b^2$$

The general equation of a hyperbola with foci (0, ^{-}c) and (0, c), and with the absolute value of the difference between distances from the two foci $2a$ units, can be written in the following form.

$$\frac{y^2}{a^2} - \frac{x^2}{b^2} = 1 \text{ where } c^2 = a^2 + b^2$$

Equation of Hyperbola

example

1   **Write the equation of the hyperbola shown below.**

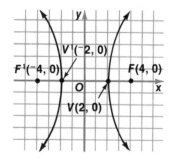

The distance from the center to a vertex is a units.
$$a = 2$$
The distance from the center to a focus is c units.
$$c = 4$$
Now find b.
$$c^2 = a^2 + b^2$$
$$4^2 = 2^2 + b^2$$
$$b = \sqrt{12}$$

The equation is $\dfrac{x^2}{2^2} - \dfrac{y^2}{(\sqrt{12})^2} = 1$ or $\dfrac{x^2}{4} - \dfrac{y^2}{12} = 1$.

Before graphing a hyperbola, it is helpful to sketch the asymptotes. The equations of the asymptotes are as follows.

$$y = \frac{b}{a}x \text{ and } y = -\frac{b}{a}x \text{ for } \frac{x^2}{a^2} - \frac{y^2}{b^2} = 1, \text{ or}$$

$$y = \frac{a}{b}x \text{ and } y = -\frac{a}{b}x \text{ for } \frac{y^2}{a^2} - \frac{x^2}{b^2} = 1$$

example

2 **Find the equations for the asymptotes of the graph of $\frac{y^2}{16} - \frac{x^2}{9} = 1$. Then find the coordinates of the foci and vertices and draw the graph.**

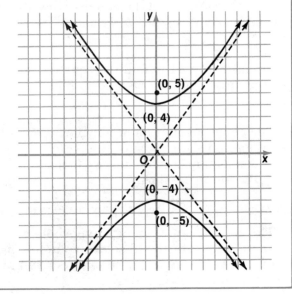

The hyperbola has a vertical transverse axis. Its center has coordinates $(0, 0)$. Since a is 4 and b is 3, the equations of the asymptotes are $y = \frac{4}{3}x$ and $y = -\frac{4}{3}x$.

Since a is 4, the distance from the center to a vertex is 4 units. Thus, the vertices are $(0, 4)$ and $(0, -4)$.

To locate the foci, find the value of c.

$$c^2 = a^2 + b^2$$
$$c^2 = 4^2 + 3^2$$
$$c = 5$$

Therefore, the foci are $(0, 5)$ and $(0, -5)$.

An equation of the form $\frac{x^2}{a^2} - \frac{y^2}{b^2} = 1$ represents a hyperbola with center $(0, 0)$ and a horizontal transverse axis. A hyperbola with the same shape but center at (h, k) has an equation of the form $\frac{(x - h)^2}{a^2} - \frac{(y - k)^2}{b^2} = 1$. Likewise, a hyperbola with center at (h, k) and vertical transverse axis has an equation of the form $\frac{(y - k)^2}{a^2} - \frac{(x - h)^2}{b^2} = 1$. The equations of the asymptotes of a hyperbola with center at (h, k) are as follows.

$$y - k = \frac{b}{a}(x - h) \text{ and } y - k = -\frac{b}{a}(x - h) \qquad \textit{horizontal transverse axis}$$

$$y - k = \frac{a}{b}(x - h) \text{ and } y - k = -\frac{a}{b}(x - h) \qquad \textit{vertical transverse axis}$$

3 **Draw the graph of** $\dfrac{(y-1)^2}{16} - \dfrac{(x+2)^2}{9} = 1.$

The graph has the same shape as the graph of $\dfrac{y^2}{16} - \dfrac{x^2}{9} = 1$, but has center at $(^-2,\ 1)$ rather than at the origin.

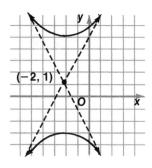

The graph of $x^2 - 4y^2 + 6x + 16y - 11 = 0$ is a hyperbola. To write the equation in the form $\dfrac{(x-h)^2}{a^2} - \dfrac{(y-k)^2}{b^2} = 1$, complete the square for each variable.

$$x^2 - 4y^2 + 6x + 16y - 11 = 0$$
$$x^2 + 6x + \square - 4(y^2 - 4y + \square) = 11 + \square - 4\square$$
$$x^2 + 6x + \left(\tfrac{6}{2}\right)^2 - 4\left(y^2 - 4y + \left(\tfrac{-4}{2}\right)^2\right) = 11 + \left(\tfrac{6}{2}\right)^2 + (^-4)\left(\tfrac{-4}{2}\right)^2$$
$$(x+3)^2 - 4(y-2)^2 = 4$$
$$\dfrac{(x+3)^2}{4} - \dfrac{(y-2)^2}{1} = 1$$

The hyperbola has center $(^-3,\ 2)$. Since a^2 is 4, the transverse axis is horizontal and is $2(\sqrt{4})$ or 4 units long. Since $b^2 = 1$, the conjugate axis is $2\sqrt{1}$ or 2 units long.

4 **A hyperbola has equation $9x^2 - 4y^2 - 54x - 40y - 55 = 0$. Find the coordinates of the vertices and the equations of the asymptotes. Then draw the graph.**

$$9x^2 - 4y^2 - 54x - 40y - 55 = 0$$
$$9(x^2 - 6x + \square) - 4(y^2 + 10y + \square) = 55 + 9\square - 4\square$$
$$9\left(x^2 - 6x + \left(\tfrac{-6}{2}\right)^2\right) - 4\left(y^2 + 10y + \left(\tfrac{10}{2}\right)^2\right) = 55 + 9\left(\tfrac{-6}{2}\right)^2 + (^-4)\left(\tfrac{10}{2}\right)^2$$
$$9(x-3)^2 - 4(y+5)^2 = 36$$
$$\dfrac{(x-3)^2}{4} - \dfrac{(y+5)^2}{9} = 1$$

The hyperbola has a horizontal transverse axis. Its center has coordinates $(3,\ ^-5)$. The equations of the asymptotes are

$y + 5 = \dfrac{3}{2}(x-3)$ and $y + 5 = -\dfrac{3}{2}(x-3)$.

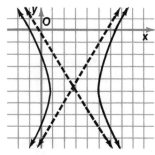

Since a is 2, the distance from the center to a vertex is 2 units. Thus, the coordinates of the vertices are $(5,\ ^-5)$ and $(1,\ ^-5)$.

exercises

Exploratory State whether the graph of each of the following equations is an ellipse or a hyperbola.

1. $\dfrac{x^2}{9} + \dfrac{y^2}{4} = 1$

2. $\dfrac{x^2}{16} - \dfrac{y^2}{4} = 1$

3. $\dfrac{y^2}{18} - \dfrac{x^2}{20} = 1$

4. $\dfrac{x^2}{5} + \dfrac{y^2}{5} = 1$

5. $\dfrac{x^2}{36} - \dfrac{y^2}{1} = 1$

6. $\dfrac{x^2}{10} + \dfrac{y^2}{36} = 1$

7. $\dfrac{y^2}{25} + \dfrac{x^2}{9} = 1$

8. $\dfrac{x^2}{81} - \dfrac{y^2}{36} = 1$

9. $\dfrac{y^2}{100} - \dfrac{x^2}{144} = 1$

Written Find the vertices, foci, and equations of the asymptotes for each hyperbola whose equation is given. Then draw the graph.

1. $\dfrac{x^2}{9} - \dfrac{y^2}{25} = 1$

2. $\dfrac{x^2}{16} - \dfrac{y^2}{4} = 1$

3. $\dfrac{x^2}{36} - \dfrac{y^2}{1} = 1$

4. $\dfrac{y^2}{6} - \dfrac{x^2}{2} = 1$

5. $\dfrac{y^2}{81} - \dfrac{x^2}{25} = 1$

6. $\dfrac{y^2}{18} - \dfrac{x^2}{20} = 1$

7. $\dfrac{x^2}{4} - \dfrac{y^2}{9} = 1$

8. $\dfrac{y^2}{16} - \dfrac{x^2}{25} = 1$

9. $\dfrac{x^2}{81} - \dfrac{y^2}{36} = 1$

10. $\dfrac{y^2}{100} - \dfrac{x^2}{144} = 1$

11. $\dfrac{x^2}{9} - \dfrac{y^2}{16} = 1$

12. $\dfrac{x^2}{9} - \dfrac{y^2}{4} = 1$

13. $25x^2 - 4y^2 = 100$

14. $x^2 - y^2 = 4$

15. $x^2 - 2y^2 = 2$

16. $y^2 - 4x^2 = 4$

17. $y^2 = 36 + 4x^2$

18. $36y^2 - 81x^2 = 2916$

19. $\dfrac{(x + 6)^2}{36} - \dfrac{(y + 3)^2}{9} = 1$

20. $\dfrac{(y - 3)^2}{25} - \dfrac{(x - 2)^2}{16} = 1$

21. $\dfrac{(y - 4)^2}{16} - \dfrac{(x + 2)^2}{9} = 1$

22. $\dfrac{(x + 1)^2}{4} - \dfrac{(y - 4)^2}{9} = 1$

23. $5(x - 4)^2 - 4(y + 2)^2 = 100$

24. $x^2 - 4y^2 + 6x + 16y - 11 = 0$

25. $y^2 - 3x^2 + 6y + 6x = 18$

26. $y^2 - 4x^2 - 2y - 16x = {}^-1$

Write the equation of each hyperbola described below.

27. Center (0, 0), $a = 1$, $b = 4$, horizontal transverse axis

28. Center (5, 4), $a = 2$, $b = 6$, vertical transverse axis

29. Center ($^-2$, 2), $a = 6$, $c = 10$, vertical transverse axis

30. The equations of asymptotes are $3x - 2y = 0$ and $3x + 2y = 0$. The transverse axis is horizontal.

An equation of the form $xy = k$ when $k \neq 0$ represents a hyperbola having the x-axis and y-axis as asymptotes.

31. Complete the following table of values for $xy = 2$.

x	1	2	4	8	$^-1$	$^-4$	$^-8$
y							

32. Find the domain for $xy = 2$.

33. Find the range for $xy = 2$.

34. Sketch the graph of $xy = 2$.

8-6   Conic Sections

Parabolas, circles, ellipses, and hyperbolas can be formed by slicing a hollow double cone in different directions. The curves, therefore, are called **conic sections.**

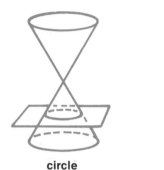

circle

ellipse

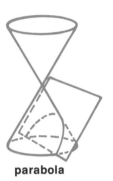

parabola

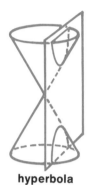

hyperbola

The conic sections are related in another way, too. Each conic section can be described by a quadratic equation in two variables.

> **The equation of a conic section can be written in the form $Ax^2 + Bxy + Cy^2 + Dx + Ey + F = 0$ where A, B, and C are not all zero.**

Equation for Conic Sections

To identify the conic section a quadratic equation in two variables represents, rewrite the equation in the forms you have learned. The following table summarizes these forms.

Often this involves completing the square.

Most of the conic sections you have studied have equations with $B = 0$.

Conic Section	Standard Form of Equation
parabola	$y = a(x - h)^2 + k$ or $x = a(y - k)^2 + h$
circle	$(x - h)^2 + (y - k)^2 = r^2$
ellipse	$\dfrac{(x - h)^2}{a^2} + \dfrac{(y - k)^2}{b^2} = 1$ or $\dfrac{(x - h)^2}{b^2} + \dfrac{(y - k)^2}{a^2} = 1$
hyperbola	$\dfrac{(x - h)^2}{a^2} - \dfrac{(y - k)^2}{b^2} = 1$ or $\dfrac{(y - k)^2}{a^2} - \dfrac{(x - h)^2}{b^2} = 1$ or $xy = k$

1 **Is the graph of $(y - 4)^2 = 9(x - 4)$ a parabola, circle, ellipse, or hyperbola?**

$$(y - 4)^2 = 9(x - 4)$$

$$\frac{1}{9}(y - 4)^2 = x - 4$$

$$\frac{1}{9}(y - 4)^2 + 4 = x \qquad a \text{ is } \frac{1}{9}, k \text{ is } 4, h \text{ is } 4$$

The graph is a parabola.

2 **Is the graph of $x^2 + y^2 = x + 2$ a parabola, circle, ellipse, or hyperbola?**

$$x^2 + y^2 = x + 2$$

$$x^2 - x + \square + y^2 = 2 + \square$$

$$x^2 - x + \left(-\frac{1}{2}\right)^2 + y^2 = 2 + \left(-\frac{1}{2}\right)^2 \qquad \textit{Complete the square.}$$

$$x^2 - x + \frac{1}{4} + y^2 = 2 + \frac{1}{4}$$

$$\left(x - \frac{1}{2}\right)^2 + y^2 = \frac{9}{4}$$

$$\left(x - \frac{1}{2}\right)^2 + (y - 0)^2 = \left(\frac{3}{2}\right)^2 \qquad h \text{ is } \frac{1}{2}, k \text{ is } 0, r \text{ is } \frac{3}{2}$$

The graph is a circle. The graph is also an ellipse with a and b both $\frac{3}{2}$.

A circle is a special kind of ellipse.

3 **Is the graph of $x^2 - 4x - 1 = \frac{5}{6}(y - 1)^2$ a parabola, circle, ellipse, or hyperbola?**

$$x^2 - 4x - 1 = \frac{5}{6}(y - 1)^2$$

$$x^2 - 4x + \square = \frac{5}{6}(y - 1)^2 + 1 + \square$$

$$x^2 - 4x + \left(\frac{-4}{2}\right)^2 = \frac{5}{6}(y - 1)^2 + 1 + \left(\frac{-4}{2}\right)^2 \qquad \textit{Complete the square.}$$

$$(x - 2)^2 = \frac{5}{6}(y - 1)^2 + 5$$

$$\frac{(x - 2)^2}{5} = \frac{(y - 1)^2}{6} + 1 \qquad \textit{Divide both sides by 5.}$$

$$\frac{(x - 2)^2}{5} - \frac{(y - 1)^2}{6} = 1 \qquad h \text{ is } 2, k \text{ is } 1, a \text{ is } \sqrt{5}, b \text{ is } \sqrt{6}$$

The graph is a hyperbola.

Consider an equation of the form $Ax^2 + Bxy + Cy^2 + Dx + Ey + F = 0$ when $B = 0$. By comparing A and C, you can determine the type of conic section the equation represents. If $A = C$, the equation represents a circle. If A and C have the same sign, the equation represents an ellipse. If A and C have opposite signs, the equation represents a hyperbola. If either A or C is zero, the equation represents a parabola.

exercises

Exploratory State whether the graph of each of the following equations is a parabola, a circle, an ellipse, or a hyperbola.

1. $x^2 + y^2 = 9$

2. $\dfrac{y^2}{8} - \dfrac{x^2}{10} = 1$

3. $\dfrac{x^2}{4} + \dfrac{y^2}{6} = 1$

4. $x^2 + y^2 = 4$

5. $y = (x - 3)^2 + 25$

6. $x = \left(y + \dfrac{1}{2}\right)^2$

7. $\dfrac{(x + 3)^2}{1} - \dfrac{(y - 4)^2}{9} = 1$

8. $\dfrac{(y - 7)^2}{3} + \dfrac{(x + 2)^2}{2} = 1$

Written Write the standard form of each equation. State whether the graph of each equation is a parabola, a circle, an ellipse, or a hyperbola. Then graph each equation.

1. $x^2 = 8y$

2. $4x^2 + 2y^2 = 8$

3. $3x^2 + 3y^2 = 81$

4. $9x^2 - 4y^2 = 4$

5. $3x^2 + 4y^2 + 8y = 8$

6. $13x^2 - 49 = {}^-13y^2$

7. $y^2 - 2x^2 - 16 = 0$

8. $y = x^2 + 3x + 1$

9. $x^2 - 8y + y^2 = {}^-11$

10. $\dfrac{(y - 5)^2}{4} - (x + 1)^2 = 4$

11. $x^2 + y = x + 2$

12. $x^2 - 4y^2 + 10x - 16y = {}^-5$

13. $9x^2 + 25y^2 - 54x - 50y = 119$

14. $(y - 4)^2 = 9(x - 4)$

15. $3y^2 + 24y - x^2 - 2x = {}^-41$

16. $x^2 + y^2 + 6y - 8x = {}^-24$

Skills Review Simplify.

1. $\sqrt{242}$

2. $2\sqrt{80}$

3. $(5\sqrt{2})(\sqrt{8})$

4. $(4\sqrt{2})^2$

5. $(5\sqrt{3})(2\sqrt{15})$

6. $\sqrt{3} + \sqrt{27}$

7. $3\sqrt{8} + 5\sqrt{2}$

8. $2\sqrt{5}(\sqrt{8} - \sqrt{2})$

9. $\sqrt{\dfrac{2}{9}}$

10. $2\sqrt{\dfrac{27}{4}}$

11. $\dfrac{4\sqrt{7} - 10\sqrt{2}}{\sqrt{2}}$

12. $\dfrac{3\sqrt{7}}{\sqrt{5}}$

Area of an Ellipse

excursions in algebra

The graph of the ellipse shown at the right has the equation $\dfrac{x^2}{a^2} + \dfrac{y^2}{b^2} = 1$. The ellipse has intercepts at $(a, 0)$, $({}^-a, 0)$, $(0, b)$, and $(0, {}^-b)$. The area of this ellipse is given by the formula $A = \pi ab$.

Exercises Find the area of each of the following.

1. $\dfrac{x^2}{25} + \dfrac{y^2}{16} = 1$

2. $\dfrac{x^2}{9} + \dfrac{y^2}{49} = 1$

3. $25x^2 + 16y^2 = 400$

4. $32x^2 + 72y^2 = 1152$

5. The ellipse with intercepts $(0, 8)$, $(0, {}^-8)$, $(2, 0)$, and $({}^-2, 0)$

6. The ellipse with intercepts $(6, 0)$ and $({}^-6, 0)$ and foci $(2\sqrt{5}, 0)$ and $({}^-2\sqrt{5}, 0)$

$$\frac{x^2}{a^2} + \frac{y^2}{b^2} = 1$$

8–7　Graphing Quadratic Systems

Consider the following system of equations.

$$y = x^2 - 4$$
$$y = {}^-2x - 1$$

To solve this system you must find the
ordered pairs that satisfy *both* equations. One way is to graph each equation and find the intersection of the two
graphs.

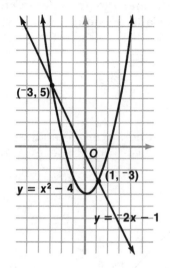

　The graph of $y = x^2 - 4$ is a parabola.
The graph of $y = {}^-2x - 1$ is a line. The
parabola and the line intersect at two
points, $(^-3, 5)$ and $(1, {}^-3)$. The solutions
of the system are $(^-3, 5)$ and $(1, {}^-3)$.

　If the graphs of a system of equations are a conic section and a
straight line, the system will have zero, one, or two solutions.

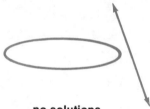

no solutions

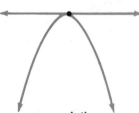

one solution

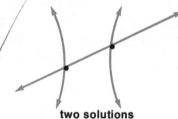

two solutions

example

1　**Graph the following system. Then state the solutions of the system of
equations.**

$$x^2 + y^2 = 25$$
$$y - x = 1$$

The graph of $x^2 + y^2 = 25$ is a
circle centered at the origin with
radius 5 units.

The graph of $y - x = 1$ is a line
with slope 1 and y-intercept 1.

The solutions of the system are
$(3, 4)$ and $(^-4, {}^-3)$.

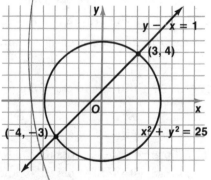

If the graphs of a system of equations are two conic sections, the system will have zero, one, two, three or four solutions.

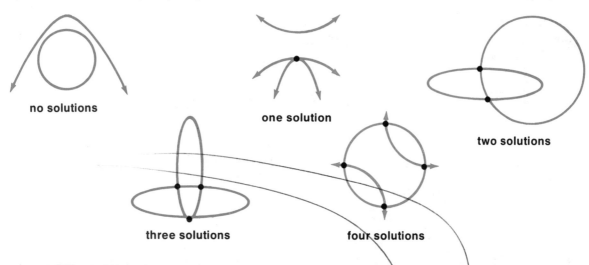

no solutions

one solution

two solutions

three solutions

four solutions

2 Graph the following system. Then state the solutions of the system of equations.

$$x^2 + y^2 = 25$$
$$4y + x^2 = 25$$

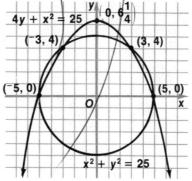

The graph of $x^2 + y^2 = 25$ is a circle centered at the origin with radius 5 units. The graph of $4y + x^2 = 25$ is a parabola which opens downward, has vertex $\left(0, 6\frac{1}{4}\right)$, and x-intercepts 5 and $^-5$. The solutions of the system are $(5, 0)$, $(^-5, 0)$, $(3, 4)$, and $(^-3, 4)$.

3 Graph the following system. Then state the solutions of the system of equations.

$$y^2 - x^2 = 16$$
$$x^2 - y^2 = 16$$

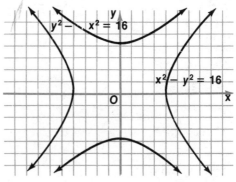

The graph of $y^2 - x^2 = 16$ is a hyperbola with y-intercepts 4 and $^-4$. The graph of $x^2 - y^2 = 16$ is a hyperbola with x-intercepts 4 and $^-4$. The system has *no* solutions.

exercises

Written Graph each system of equations.
Then state the solutions of each system.

1. $x^2 + y^2 = 16$
   $y = 2$

2. $y = x^2$
   $y - 2 = x$

3. $x = y$
   $\dfrac{x^2}{20} + \dfrac{y^2}{5} = 1$

4. $x^2 - y = 4$
   $y = 3x$

5. $\dfrac{x^2}{9} - \dfrac{y^2}{9} = 1$
   $\dfrac{2}{3}y = \dfrac{1}{3}x - 1$

6. $x^2 + y^2 = 25$
   $x + y = {}^-7$

7. $(y - 1)^2 = x + 4$
   $y + x = {}^-1$

8. $\dfrac{x^2}{16} + \dfrac{y^2}{4} = 1$
   $3y + 5x = 6$

9. $y^2 - x^2 = 9$
   $y = 6$

10. $x^2 + y^2 = 100$
    $x - y = 2$

11. $x^2 + y^2 = 9$
    $x + y = 7$

12. $\dfrac{x^2}{4} + \dfrac{y^2}{1} = 1$
    $x - y = 6$

13. $\dfrac{x^2}{16} - \dfrac{y^2}{4} = 1$
    $y = 3x - 3$

14. $x^2 + 4y^2 = 25$
    $2y = 1 - x$

15. $\dfrac{(x - 2)^2}{16} + \dfrac{y^2}{16} = 1$
    $y - x = 2$

16. $y = {}^-x^2$
    $y = {}^-x - 2$

17. $(x - 1)^2 + 4(y - 1)^2 = 20$
    $x = y$

18. $\dfrac{x^2}{36} - \dfrac{y^2}{4} = 1$
    $y = x$

19. $\dfrac{(x - 3)^2}{25} + \dfrac{(y - 4)^2}{9} = 1$
    $5y + 3x = 44$

20. $(x - 3)^2 + (y + 6)^2 = 36$
    $y + 3 = x$

21. $5x^2 + y^2 = 30$
    $y^2 - 16 = 9x^2$

22. $x^2 + y^2 = 5$
    $2x^2 + y = 0$

23. $2y^2 = 10 - x^2$
    $3x^2 - 9 = y^2$

24. $4x^2 + 9y^2 = 36$
    $4x^2 - 9y^2 = 36$

25. $x^2 + 4y^2 = 4$
    $(x - 10)^2 + (y - 11)^2 = 1$

26. $x^2 + 4y^2 = 36$
    $y = {}^-x^2 + 3$

27. $x^2 - y^2 = 25$
    $x^2 - y^2 = 7$

28. $x^2 + y^2 = 16$
    $x^2 + y^2 = 9$

29. $x^2 + y^2 = 64$
    $x^2 + 64y^2 = 64$

30. $x^2 - y^2 = 16$
    $y^2 - x^2 = 16$

The first step in solving some problems is to organize the given information in one of several ways. Sometimes making a list to organize the information is helpful. Another way to classify information is to make a table or chart. Consider the following example.

Example Rachel is beginning to jog. The first week she jogs 1 block each day. The second week she jogs 3 blocks each day. The third week she jogs 5 blocks each day, and so on. That is, on each successive week she jogs 2 more blocks per day than each day of the previous week. How many blocks will she jog each day of the twelfth week? How many blocks will she have jogged altogether after the twelfth week?

Make a table of the information given. Notice the pattern that develops.

Week	Blocks Jogged Each Day	Total Blocks Jogged
1	1	$7 \times 1 = 7$ or $7 \cdot 1$
2	3	$7 + (7 \times 3) = 28$ or $7 \cdot 4$
3	5	$28 + (7 \times 5) = 63$ or $7 \cdot 9$
4	7	$63 + (7 \times 7) = 112$ or $7 \cdot 16$
.	.	.
n	$2n - 1$	$7n^2$

Thus, the twelfth week she will jog $2(12) - 1$ or 23 blocks each day. After the twelfth week she will have jogged a total of $7 \cdot 12^2$ or 1008 blocks.

Exercises Solve each problem.

1. A large sheet of paper is 0.15 mm thick. Suppose it is torn in half and the two pieces are placed together and torn in half again. Suppose this process continues for a total of 20 tears. How many pieces are in the stack of paper? How high is the stack of paper?

2. Classic Cleaners must clean 105 apartments in 5 days. Each day the owner puts 2 more employees on the job. However, each day after the first, each employee cleans 1 less apartment than each did on the previous day. What is the greatest number of apartments cleaned on any one day?

3. Lou Ann Mathena has a box of oranges to be divided among her seven piano students, who are all of different ages. Lou Ann gives each student the number of oranges by which his age can be divided into the total number of oranges. All the oranges are to be distributed. Tara, who is the middle child in terms of age, receives 18 oranges. How many years older is she than the youngest students?

4. Paul questions Bill about the ages of his three children. Bill replies, "The product of their ages is 36 and the sum of their ages is the same as today's date." But Paul says he still needs more information. Then Bill tells him that the oldest child has blonde hair. Paul says that he now can determine their ages. How old are the three children?

8–8 Solving Quadratic Systems

You can use graphs to help find the solutions of a quadratic system. Often you must use algebra to find the exact solutions.

1 **Find the solutions of the following system of equations.**

$$x^2 + y^2 = 25$$
$$y - x = 1$$

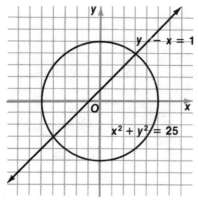

The graphs of the equations are a circle and a straight line. The graphs show that there are two solutions to the system. Also, the values of x are between $^-5$ and 5. And the values of y are between $^-5$ and 5.

Use the substitution method to find the exact solutions. First rewrite $y - x = 1$ as $y = x + 1$.

$$x^2 + y^2 = 25$$
$$x^2 + (x + 1)^2 = 25 \qquad \textit{Substitute } x + 1 \textit{ for } y.$$
$$x^2 + x^2 + 2x + 1 = 25$$
$$2x^2 + 2x - 24 = 0$$
$$2(x + 4)(x - 3) = 0$$

$x + 4 = 0$	or	$x - 3 = 0$
$x = {}^-4$		$x = 3$
$y = x + 1$		$y = x + 1$
$= {}^-4 + 1$ or $^-3$		$= 3 + 1$ or 4

The solutions are $(^-4, {}^-3)$ and $(3, 4)$.

2 **Find the solutions of the following system of equations.**

$$x^2 + 2y^2 = 10$$
$$3x^2 - y^2 = 9$$

The graphs of the equations are an ellipse and a hyperbola. The graphs show that there are four solutions to the system.

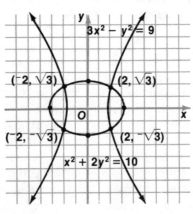

Use the substitution method to find the exact solutions.
First rewrite $x^2 + 2y^2 = 10$ as $x^2 = 10 - 2y^2$.

$$3x^2 - y^2 = 9$$
$$3(10 - 2y^2) - y^2 = 9 \qquad \textit{Substitute } 10 - 2y^2 \textit{ for } x^2.$$
$$30 - 7y^2 = 9$$
$$21 = 7y^2$$
$$3 = y^2$$
$$\pm\sqrt{3} = y$$
$$x^2 = 10 - 2y^2$$

$$x^2 = 10 - 2(\sqrt{3})^2 \quad \text{or} \quad x^2 = 10 - 2(^-\sqrt{3})^2$$
$$x^2 = 4 \qquad\qquad\qquad x^2 = 4$$
$$x = {}^\pm 2 \qquad\qquad\qquad x = {}^\pm 2$$

The solutions are $(2, \sqrt{3})$, $(^-2, \sqrt{3})$, $(2, {}^-\sqrt{3})$, and $(^-2, {}^-\sqrt{3})$.

exercises

Written Find the solutions of each system of equations.

1. $x^2 + y^2 = 16$
   $y = 2$

2. $y = x^2$
   $y - 2 = x$

3. $x = y$
   $\dfrac{x^2}{20} + \dfrac{y^2}{5} = 1$

4. $x^2 - y = 4$
   $y = 3x$

5. $x^2 - y^2 = 9$
   $8y = 4x - 12$

6. $x^2 + y^2 = 25$
   $x + y = {}^-7$

7. $(y - 1)^2 = x + 4$
   $y + x = {}^-1$

8. $\dfrac{x^2}{16} + \dfrac{y^2}{4} = 1$
   $2y + 5x = 4$

9. $y^2 - x^2 = 9$
   $y = 6$

10. $x^2 + y^2 = 100$
    $x - y = 2$

11. $x^2 + y^2 = 9$
    $x + y = 7$

12. $x^2 + 4y^2 = 4$
    $x - y = 6$

13. $x^2 - 4y^2 = 16$
    $y = 3x - 3$

14. $x^2 + 4y^2 = 25$
    $2y = 1 - x$

15. $(x - 2)^2 + y^2 = 16$
    $y - x = 2$

16. $y = {}^\top x^2$
    $y = {}^-x - 2$

17. $x^2 - 4y = 0$
    $y - 2x = {}^-3$

18. $x^2 - 9y^2 = 36$
    $y = x$

19. $\dfrac{(x - 3)^2}{25} + \dfrac{(y - 4)^2}{9} = 1$
    $5y + 3x = 44$

20. $(x - 3)^2 + (y + 6)^2 = 36$
    $y + 3 = x$

21. $5x^2 + y^2 = 30$
    $y^2 - 16 = 9x^2$

22. $x^2 + y^2 = 5$
    $2x^2 + y = 0$

23. $2y^2 = 10 - x^2$
    $3x^2 - 9 = y^2$

24. $4x^2 + 9y^2 = 36$
    $4x^2 - 9y^2 = 36$

25. $x^2 + y^2 = 16$
    $x^2 + y^2 = 9$

26. $x^2 + y^2 = 64$
    $x^2 + 64y^2 = 64$

27. $x^2 - y^2 = 25$
    $x^2 - y^2 = 7$

Challenge Find the solutions of each system of equations.

1. $x^2 + 4y^2 = 4$
   $(x - 10)^2 + (y - 11)^2 = 1$

2. $x = {}^-y^2 + 2$
   $2y - 2\sqrt{2} = x(\sqrt{2} + 2)$

8-9　Systems with Quadratic Inequalities

To graph the solutions of a system of inequalities, you graph each inequality and find the intersection of the two graphs. Consider the following system.

$$x^2 + y^2 \geq 16$$
$$x + y = 2$$

The graph of $x^2 + y^2 \geq 16$ consists of all points on or outside the circle $x^2 + y^2 = 16$. This region is shaded.

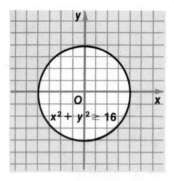

The graph of $x + y = 2$ is a straight line with slope $^-1$ and y-intercept 2.

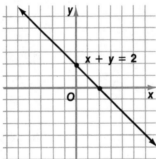

The intersection of the shaded region and the straight line is the graph of the solutions. The graph of the solutions is indicated by the thick rays.

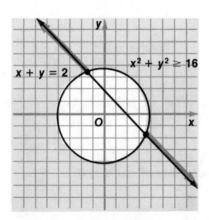

1 **Graph the solutions for the following system of inequalities.**

$$x^2 + y^2 \le 25$$
$$4y + x^2 \le 25$$

The graph of $x^2 + y^2 \le 25$ consists of all points on or within the circle $x^2 + y^2 = 25$. This region is shaded with color. The graph of $4y + x^2 \le 25$ consists of all points on or within the parabola $4y + x^2 = 25$. This region is shaded with gray.

The intersection of these two graphs represents the solutions for the system of inequalities.

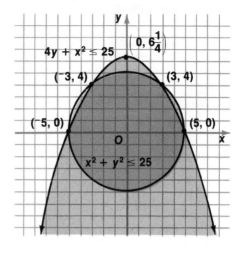

---

exercises

Written Graph the solutions for each system of inequalities.

1. $x^2 + y^2 < 9$
$y < {}^-x^2$

2. $\dfrac{x^2}{9} - \dfrac{y^2}{4} < 1$
$x^2 + y^2 < 25$

3. $\dfrac{x^2}{16} - \dfrac{y^2}{1} \ge 1$
$x^2 + y^2 \ge 49$

4. $\dfrac{x^2}{25} - \dfrac{y^2}{16} \ge 1$
$x - y \ge 2$

5. $x^2 + y^2 > 16$
$81x^2 + 9y^2 < 729$

6. $x^2 - 4y^2 < 16$
$x > y^2$

7. $9x^2 + 4y^2 \le 36$
$4x^2 + 9y^2 \ge 36$

8. $x + 2y > 1$
$x^2 + y^2 < 25$

9. $x^2 + y^2 \ge 4$
$x^2 + y^2 \le 36$

10. $y \ge x^2 - 4$
$(y - 3)^2 \ge x + 2$

11. $x + 3 = y$
$x^2 + y^2 < 25$

12. $4x^2 + 9y^2 \le 36$
$x = 2$

13. $9x^2 - 4y^2 \ge 36$
$x + y = 4$

14. $5x^2 + 5y^2 \ge 25$
$2x - 3y = 5$

15. $4x^2 + (y - 3)^2 \le 16$
$2y = x + 1$

16. $y = {}^-x$
$(x + 2)^2 + 16(y + 3)^2 \ge 16$

17. $x^2 + y^2 \ge 16$
$x = 4$

18. $x^2 + y^2 \le 36$
$y = 6$

Chapter Summary

1. **Distance Between Points on a Number Line:** On a number line, the distance between two points whose coordinates are a and b is $|a - b|$ or $|b - a|$. (223)

2. **Distance Formula for Two Points in the Plane:** The distance between two points with coordinates (x_1, y_1) and (x_2, y_2) is given by the following formula.
$$d = \sqrt{(x_2 - x_1)^2 + (y_2 - y_1)^2} \quad (224)$$

3. **Midpoint Formula:** If a line segment has endpoints with coordinates (x_1, y_1) and (x_2, y_2), then the midpoint of the line segment has coordinates $\left(\dfrac{x_1 + x_2}{2}, \dfrac{y_1 + y_2}{2}\right)$. (224)

4. **Definition of Parabola:** A parabola is the set of all points in a plane that are the same distance from a given point and a given line. The point is called the focus. The line is called the directrix. (226)

5.

Information about Parabolas		
form of equation	$y = a(x - h)^2 + k$	$x = a(y - k)^2 + h$
vertex	(h, k)	(h, k)
axis of symmetry	$x = h$	$y = k$
focus	$\left(h, k + \dfrac{1}{4a}\right)$	$\left(h + \dfrac{1}{4a}, k\right)$
directrix	$y = k - \dfrac{1}{4a}$	$x = h - \dfrac{1}{4a}$
direction of opening	upward if $a > 0$ downward if $a < 0$	right if $a > 0$ left if $a < 0$

(226)

6. **Definition of Circle:** A circle is the set of all points in the plane each of which is the same distance from a given point. The given distance is the radius of the circle, and the given point is the center of the circle. (230)

7. **Equation of Circle:** The equation of a circle with center (h, k) and radius r units is $(x - h)^2 + (y - k)^2 = r^2$. (230)

8. **Definition of Ellipse:** An ellipse is the set of all points in the plane such that the sum of the distances from two given points, called the foci, is constant. (233)

9. **Equation of Ellipse:** The general equation of an ellipse with center at $(0, 0)$, whose foci are $(^-c, 0)$ and $(c, 0)$, and the sum of the distances from the two foci is $2a$ units, is $\dfrac{x^2}{a^2} + \dfrac{y^2}{b^2} = 1$ where $b^2 = a^2 - c^2$. (234)

10. **Equation of Ellipse:** The general equation of an ellipse with center at $(0, 0)$, whose foci are $(0, ^-c)$ and $(0, c)$, and the sum of the distances from the two foci is $2a$ units, is $\dfrac{x^2}{b^2} + \dfrac{y^2}{a^2} = 1$ where $b^2 = a^2 - c^2$. (234)

11. **Definition of Hyperbola:** A hyperbola is the set of all points in the plane such that the absolute value of the difference of the distances from two given points, called the foci, is constant. (238)

12. **Equation of Hyperbola:** The general equation of a hyperbola with center at $(0, 0)$ whose foci are $(^-c, 0)$ and $(c, 0)$ and with the absolute value of the difference between distances from the two foci $2a$ units, can be written as $\dfrac{x^2}{a^2} - \dfrac{y^2}{b^2} = 1$ where $c^2 = a^2 + b^2$. (239)

13. **Equation of Hyperbola:** The general equation of a hyperbola with center at $(0, 0)$, whose foci are $(0, ^-c)$ and $(0, c)$, and with the absolute value of the difference between distances from the two foci $2a$ units, can be written as $\dfrac{y^2}{a^2} - \dfrac{x^2}{b^2} = 1$ where $c^2 = a^2 + b^2$. (239)

14. **Equation of Conic Sections:** The equation of a conic section can be written in the form $Ax^2 + Bxy + Cy^2 + Dx + Ey + F = 0$ where $A, B,$ and C are not all zero. (243)

15. If the graph of a system of equations is a conic section and a straight line, the system will have zero, one, or two solutions. (246)

16. If the graph of a system of equations is two conic sections, the system will have zero, one, two, three, or four solutions. (247)

17. You can use graphs to help find the solutions of a quadratic system. Often you must use algebra to find exact solutions. (250)

18. To graph the solutions of a system of inequalities, you graph each inequality and find the intersection of the two graphs. (252)

8-1 Use the distance formula to find the distance between each pair of points whose coordinates are given.

1. $(3, 6), (7, ^-8)$
2. $(^-8, ^-7), (^-2, ^-1)$
3. $(^-2.4, 0.6), (1.7, 0.8)$
4. $(2\sqrt{3}, 4\sqrt{3}), (2\sqrt{3}, ^-\sqrt{3})$

Find the midpoint of each line segment having endpoints with the following coordinates.

5. $(5, 2), (^-3, 1)$
6. $(17, ^-8)(^-13, 1)$
7. $(0.2, 0.6), (0.3, 0.4)$
8. $(2, 2), (\sqrt{2}, \sqrt{2})$

8-2 Name the vertex, axis of symmetry, focus, directrix, and direction of opening of the parabola whose equation is given. Then find the length of the latus rectum and draw the graph.

9. $4y = x^2$
10. $y^2 = ^-8x$
11. $(y - 8)^2 = ^-4(x - 4)$

8-3 Find the center and radius of each circle whose equation is given. Then draw the graph.

12. $x^2 + y^2 = 25$
13. $(x - 3)^2 + (y + 7)^2 = 81$
14. $x^2 + y^2 - 8x + 10y = 1$

8-4 Find the center, foci, and lengths of the major axis and minor axis for each ellipse whose equation is given. Then draw the graph.

15. $\dfrac{x^2}{8} + \dfrac{y^2}{16} = 1$
16. $\dfrac{(x - 3)^2}{25} + \dfrac{(y + 1)^2}{4} = 1$
17. $9x^2 + 16y^2 = 144$

8-5 Find the vertices, foci, and equations of the asymptotes for each hyperbola whose equation is given. Then draw the graph.

18. $\dfrac{x^2}{16} - \dfrac{y^2}{81} = 1$
19. $25(y + 6)^2 - 20(x - 1)^2 = 500$
20. $49x^2 - 16y^2 = 784$

8-6 State whether the graph of each of the following equations is a parabola, a circle, an ellipse, or a hyperbola.

21. $(x - 3)^2 = 4y - 4$
22. $3x^2 - 16 = ^-3y^2$
23. $4x^2 + 5y^2 = 20$
24. $3y^2 - 7x^2 = 21$

8-7 Graph each system of equations. Then state the solutions of each system.

25. $x + y = 1$
$x^2 + y^2 = 9$

26. $x + y = 4$
$y = x^2$

8-8 Find the solutions of each system of equations.

27. $(x - 2)^2 + y^2 = 16$
$y - x = 2$

28. $x^2 - y^2 = 16$
$y^2 - x^2 = 16$

8-9 Graph the solutions for each system of inequalities.

29. $x^2 + y^2 < 25$
$x + y > 5$

30. $y \geq x^2 + 4$
$x^2 + y^2 < 49$

Find the distance between each pair of points whose coordinates are given.

1. $(2, 6), (^-7, ^-2)$

2. $(^-3, 5), (^-11, ^-16)$

Find the midpoint of each line segment having endpoints with the following coordinates.

3. $(6, ^-4), (^-8, 3)$

4. $(^-5.5, ^-7.8), (1.3, ^-9.6)$

State whether the graph of each of the following equations is a parabola, a circle, an ellipse, or a hyperbola. Then draw the graph.

5. $2y = x^2$

6. $x^2 + y^2 + 4x = 6$

7. $9x^2 + 49y^2 = 441$

8. $x^2 - 4y^2 = 4$

9. $(x - 3)^2 = 4(y + 1)$

10. $x^2 + 4x + y^2 - 8y = 2$

11. $6x^2 + 6y^2 = 6$

12. $\dfrac{(x - 3)^2}{81} + \dfrac{(y + 4)^2}{16} = 1$

13. $13y^2 - 2x^2 = 5$

14. $y - x^2 = x + 3$

15. $x^2 + 5y^2 - 16 = 0$

16. $16x^2 - 4y^2 = 64$

Find the solutions of each system of equations.

17. $x^2 + 16y^2 = 16$
$x - y = 3$

18. $x^2 + y^2 = 16$
$\dfrac{x^2}{16} - \dfrac{y^2}{9} = 1$

Graph the solutions for each system of inequalities.

19. $x^2 + y^2 < 49$
$y < ^-x^2 + 2$

20. $x + y = 5$
$x^2 + y^2 \geq 49$

chapter
9 Polynomial Functions

Vincent works at the gift-wrap counter in a department store. Suppose a certain gift box must have a volume of 4000 cm³. The width of the box is half the length and the height is 15 cm less than the width. He can write a polynomial equation and apply the theorems in this chapter to find the dimensions of the gift box.

9-1 Polynomial Functions

The following expressions are examples of polynomials in one variable.

$$3x + 2$$
$$4a^2 + 8a - 7$$
$$19x^3 - 7x^2 + x - 75$$
$$6x^5 + 62x^3 - 12x + 13$$

> A polynomial in one variable, x, is an expression of the form
>
> $$a_nx^n + a_{n-1}x^{n-1} + \cdots + a_2x^2 + a_1x + a_0.$$
>
> The coefficients $a_0, a_1, a_2, \ldots, a_n$ represent real numbers, and n represents a nonnegative integer.

Definition of Polynomial in One Variable

example

1 **Which of the following expressions are polynomials in one variable?**

$7x^4 - 9x^2 + 2x + 1$

$6x^2y^3 - 8xy + 7z + 2$

$x + \dfrac{1}{x} - 2$

$y^2 + 2y + 3$

$7x^4 - 9x^2 + 2x + 1$ is a polynomial in one variable, x.

$6x^2y^3 - 8xy + 7z + 2$ is *not* a polynomial in one variable.   *There are three variables.*

$x + \dfrac{1}{x} - 2$ is *not* a polynomial in one variable.   *$\dfrac{1}{x}$ cannot be written in the form x^n where n is a nonnegative integer.*

$y^2 + 2y + 3$ is a polynomial in one variable, y.

The degree of a polynomial in one variable is the greatest exponent of its variable.

5	has degree 0.
$3x + 2$	has degree 1.
$4x^2 + 8x + 7$	has degree 2.
$6x^5 + 62x^3 - 12x + 13$	has degree 5.
$a_nx^n + a_{n-1}x^{n-1} + \ldots + a_1x + a_0$	has degree n.

A polynomial of degree 0 is called a **constant.**
A polynomial of degree 1 is called a **linear expression.**
A polynomial of degree 2 is called a **quadratic expression.**

Polynomial equations can be used to represent functions. In general, a **polynomial function** is in the form

$$p(x) = a_n x^n + a_{n-1} x^{n-1} + \cdots + a_1 x + a_0.$$

The coefficients $a_0, a_1, a_2, \ldots, a_{n-1}, a_n$ represent real numbers, and n represents a nonnegative integer.

The equation $p(x) = 3x^2 - 8x + 7$ represents a polynomial function. If 2 is an element of the domain of the function, then $p(2)$ is the corresponding element of the range. To show that the value of $p(2)$ is 3, you write $p(2) = 3$.

examples

2 **Find $p(2) + p(^-2)$ if $p(x) = 3x^2 - 8x + 7$.**

$$p(2) + p(^-2) = [3(2)^2 - 8(2) + 7] + [3(^-2)^2 - 8(^-2) + 7]$$
$$= \quad 3 \quad + \quad 35$$
$$= \quad 38$$

3 **Find $p(m + 2)$ if $p(x) = 3x - 8x^2 + x^3$.**

$$p(m + 2) = 3(m + 2) - 8(m + 2)^2 + (m + 2)^3$$
$$= 3m + 6 - 8m^2 - 32m - 32 + m^3 + 6m^2 + 12m + 8$$
$$= m^3 - 2m^2 - 17m - 18$$

4 **Find $3p(x) + 2p(x - 1)$ if $p(x) = x^3 - 3x^2 + 3x + 1$.**

$$3p(x) + 2p(x - 1)$$
$$= 3[x^3 - 3x^2 + 3x + 1] + 2[(x - 1)^3 - 3(x - 1)^2 + 3(x - 1) + 1]$$
$$= [3x^3 - 9x^2 + 9x + 3] + [2x^3 - 6x^2 + 6x - 2 - 6x^2 + 12x - 6 + 6x - 6 + 2]$$
$$= 5x^3 - 21x^2 + 33x - 9$$

exercises

Exploratory Which of the following expressions are polynomials in one variable?

1. $8x + y + 1$

2. $3x - 2$

3. $xy\sqrt{2} + 3$

4. $x^2 + 8x + 7$

5. $\dfrac{9}{x} + x + 3$

6. $5 + \sqrt{x} + 8y$

7. $x^3 + 5x^2 + x\sqrt{3} + 2$

8. $x^3 + 9x^2 + 8x + 1$

9. $9x^2 + ix^2 + 8x + 3i$

10. $(6 + 2i)x^2 + 3ix + 7i^2$

11. $5x^4 - 2$

12. $9m^2 + \dfrac{3i}{m} + 7$

13. $9x^3 + 6x^3 - 5x^3$

14. $6y^2 + 7y - 3$

Written Find $p(1)$ for each of the following.

1. $p(x) = 3x + 1$

2. $p(x) = 4x^2 + 3x - 3$

3. $p(x) = {}^-2x^3 + 4x - 1$

4. $p(x) = 5x^4 - 8x^3$

5. $p(x) = 3x - 8x^2 + x^3$

6. $p(x) = 2x^4 - 3x^3 + 8$

7. $p(x) = \frac{5}{2}x^3 - 8$

8. $p(x) = 7x^3 + \frac{7}{3}x + 1$

9. $p(x) = \frac{x^2}{3} + 2x + 4$

Find $f(2)$ for each of the following.

10. $f(x) = 4x - 3$

11. $f(x) = x^2 - 7x + 5$

12. $f(x) = {}^-3x^3 + 2$

13. $f(x) = -\frac{x^4}{4} - 2$

14. $f(x) = x^2 - 4x$

15. $f(x) = 5x^2 + 7x - 6$

16. $f(x) = 6x^3 + 11x^2 + 4x$

17. $f(x) = 9x - 6x^2 + x^3$

18. $f(x) = x^5 - x^3$

Find $g({}^-3)$ for each of the following.

19. $g(x) = 4 - 3x$

20. $g(x) = 2x + x^2$

21. $g(x) = 15x^2 - 4x - 3$

22. $g(x) = (x - 3)^2$

23. $g(x) = -\frac{x^3}{3} + 2x^2 - \frac{8}{3}x$

24. $g(x) = 25 - \frac{x^3}{6}$

25. $g(x) = x^2 + 2x - 15$

26. $2g(x) = 6x^3 - 20x + 18$

27. $3g(x) = 3x^4 + 7x$

Find $f(x + h)$ for each of the following.

28. $f(x) = 5x - 10$

29. $f(x) = x$

30. $f(x) = 6x^2$

31. $f(x) = x^3 + 4x$

32. $f(x) = x^2 - \frac{2}{5}x$

33. $f(x) = \frac{4}{3}x^3 - 1$

34. $f(x) = x^2 - 7x + 4$

35. $f(x) = x^3 - 4x^2$

36. $f(x) = 2x^3 - x^2 + 4$

Find $3p(x - 1)$ for each of the following.

37. $p(x) = 3x + 5$

38. $p(x) = x^2 - 4$

39. $p(x) = x^3$

40. $p(x) = x^2 - 2x + 3$

41. $p(x) = \frac{5}{3}x^2 - \frac{5}{6}$

42. $p(x) = \frac{x^3}{4} + \frac{x^2}{2} - x - 2$

Find $2f(x) - 3f(x + 1)$ for each of the following.

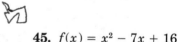

43. $f(x) = 5x - 3$

44. $f(x) = x^2 - 4$

45. $f(x) = x^2 - 7x + 16$

46. $f(x) = \frac{5}{2}x^3 + 1$

47. $f(x) = \frac{4}{5}x^3 + \frac{x^2}{2} - 2$

48. $f(x) = (x - 2)^3$

49. Write a computer program that will evaluate $p(x) = x^4 - x^3 + x^2 - x + 1$ for integer values of x between ${}^-6$ and 6, inclusive.

Challenge If $f(x) = \frac{x^2 - 4}{2x + 4}$ and $g(x) = \frac{x^2 + 4x + 4}{3x - 6}$, find the value of each of the following.

1. $f(x) \cdot g(x)$

2. $\frac{f(x)}{g(x)}$

3. $\frac{g(x)}{f(x)}$

If $f(x) = \frac{x^3 - 1}{x + 1}$, $g(x) = \frac{x^2 + 2x + 1}{x^2 + x + 1}$, and $h(x) = \frac{x^2 + 2x - 3}{x + 1}$, find the value of each of the following.

4. $\frac{f(x) \cdot g(x)}{h(x)}$

5. $\frac{f(x)}{g(x)} \cdot h(x)$

6. $\frac{f(x)}{g(x) \cdot h(x)}$

9–2 The Remainder and Factor Theorems

You can divide polynomials by using either long division or synthetic division.

1 **Divide $x^3 + 4x^2 + 3x - 2$ by $x - 3$.**

Long Division

$$\begin{array}{r} x^2 + 7x + 24 \\ x - 3 \overline{\smash{)}x^3 + 4x^2 + 3x - 2} \\ \underline{x^3 - 3x^2} \\ 7x^2 + 3x \\ \underline{7x^2 - 21x} \\ 24x - 2 \\ \underline{24x - 72} \\ 70 \end{array}$$

Synthetic Division

$$\begin{array}{r|rrrr} 3 & 1 & 4 & 3 & -2 \\ & & 3 & 21 & 72 \\ \hline & 1 & 7 & 24 & | \ 70 \end{array}$$

The numbers 1, 7, and 24 are the coefficients of the quotient $x^2 + 7x + 24$. The remainder is 70.

The quotient is $x^2 + 7x + 24$ with a remainder of 70.

Check: Multiply $x^2 + 7x + 24$ by $x - 3$ and then add 70.

$$\underset{\text{dividend}}{} \quad = \quad \underset{\text{quotient} \cdot \text{divisor}}{} \quad + \underset{\text{remainder}}{}$$
$$x^3 + 4x^2 + 3x - 2 = (x^2 + 7x + 24)(x - 3) + \quad 70$$

Consider $f(x) = x^3 + 4x^2 + 3x - 2$. The value of $f(3)$ is 70. As shown in the previous example when $f(x)$ is divided by $x - 3$, the remainder is 70.

> If a polynomial $f(x)$ is divided by $x - a$, the remainder is a constant, $f(a)$, and
>
> $$\text{dividend} = \text{quotient} \cdot \text{divisor} + \text{remainder}$$
> $$f(x) \quad = \quad q(x) \quad \cdot (x - a) + \quad f(a)$$
>
> where $q(x)$ is a polynomial with degree one less than the degree of $f(x)$.

The Remainder Theorem

2 **Let $f(x) = x^4 + 3x^2 + 4x - 1$. Show that $f(1)$ is the remainder when $f(x)$ is divided by $x - 1$.**

$$\begin{array}{r|rrrrr} 1 & 1 & 0 & 3 & 4 & -1 \\ & & 1 & 1 & 4 & 8 \\ \hline & 1 & 1 & 4 & 8 & | \ 7 \end{array}$$ *Use synthetic division.*

The quotient is $x^3 + x^2 + 4x + 8$ with a remainder of 7.

$$\underset{\text{dividend}}{} \quad = \quad \underset{\text{quotient} \cdot \text{divisor}}{} \quad + \underset{\text{remainder}}{}$$
$$x^4 + 3x^2 + 4x - 1 = (x^3 + x^2 + 4x + 8)(x - 1) + \quad 7$$

Now evaluate $f(1)$.

$$f(1) = (1)^4 + 3(1)^2 + 4(1) - 1$$
$$= 7 \quad \text{The result is the same as the remainder.}$$

The Remainder Theorem and synthetic division can be used to find the value of a function. This process called *synthetic substitution* is convenient especially when large powers are involved.

For any polynomial $f(x)$, $f(a)$ is always the same as the remainder when dividing by $(x - a)$.

example

3 **If $f(x) = x^4 - 2x^3 - x^2 - 15x + 2$, find $f(12)$.**

The Remainder Theorem says that $f(12)$ is the remainder when $f(x)$ is divided by $x - 12$.

$$\begin{array}{r|rrrrr} 12 & 1 & ^-2 & ^-1 & ^-15 & 2 \\ & & 12 & 120 & 1428 & 16{,}956 \\ \hline & 1 & 10 & 119 & 1413 & 16{,}958 \end{array}$$ $f(12) = 16{,}958$

Check by using direct substitution.
$$f(12) = 12^4 - 2(12^3) - 12^2 - 15(12) + 2$$
$$= 20{,}736 - 3456 - 144 - 180 + 2 \text{ or } 16{,}958$$

Consider the polynomial defined by $f(x) = x^3 + 7x^2 + 2x - 40$. If $f(x)$ is divided by $x - 2$, the remainder is zero.

$$\begin{array}{r|rrrr} 2 & 1 & 7 & 2 & ^-40 \\ & & 2 & 18 & 40 \\ \hline & 1 & 9 & 20 & 0 \end{array}$$ $f(2) = (2)^3 + 7(2)^2 + 2(2) - 40 \text{ or } 0$

dividend $\quad = \quad$ quotient $\cdot$ divisor $\quad +$ remainder

$$x^3 + 7x^2 + 2x - 40 = (x^2 + 9x + 20)(x - 2) + \quad 0$$
$$= (x^2 + 9x + 20)(x - 2)$$

In other words, $x - 2$ is a factor of $x^3 + 7x^2 + 2x - 40$. This example illustrates the factor theorem, a special case of the remainder theorem.

If the divisor is a factor of a polynomial, then the remainder upon division is zero.

> **The binomial $x - a$ is a factor of the polynomial $f(x)$ if and only if $f(a) = 0$.**

The Factor Theorem

The Factor Theorem can be used to identify the factors of a polynomial.

example

4 **Is $x - 4$ a factor of $x^4 + x^3 - 13x^2 - 25x - 12$?**

Let $f(x) = x^4 + x^3 - 13x^2 - 25x - 12$.
If $f(4) = 0$, then $x - 4$ is a factor.
$$f(4) = (4)^4 + (4)^3 - 13(4)^2 - 25(4) - 12 \qquad a \text{ is } 4.$$
$$= 256 + 64 - 208 - 100 - 12 \text{ or } 0$$
Since $f(4) = 0$, the binomial $x - 4$ is a factor of $f(x)$.

5 Is $y + 5$ a factor of $3y^5 + y^3 - 2y^2 - 6y + 550$?

Use synthetic division.

$$
\begin{array}{r|rrrrrr}
-5 & 3 & 0 & 1 & ^-2 & ^-6 & 550 \\
   &   & ^-15 & 75 & ^-380 & 1910 & ^-9520 \\
\hline
   & 3 & ^-15 & 76 & ^-382 & 1904 & \,|\, ^-8970
\end{array}
$$

Since the remainder is not 0, the binomial $y + 5$ is *not* a factor of $f(y)$.

If a factor of a polynomial is known, the *depressed polynomial* sometimes can be factored to find the remaining factors. Study how this technique is used in the following example.

6 Show that $x + 1$ is a factor of $x^3 - x^2 - 10x - 8$. Then find the remaining factors.

$$
\begin{array}{r|rrrr}
-1 & 1 & ^-1 & ^-10 & ^-8 \\
   &   & ^-1 & 2 & 8 \\
\hline
   & 1 & ^-2 & ^-8 & \,|\, 0
\end{array}
$$
The remainder of 0 shows that $x + 1$ is a factor of $x^3 - x^2 - 10x - 8$.

Thus, $x^3 - x^2 - 10x - 8 = (x^2 - 2x - 8)(x + 1)$.
The quotient, $x^2 - 2x - 8$, is called the depressed polynomial.
$x^2 - 2x - 8 = (x - 4)(x + 2)$ *Factor.*
Thus, $x^3 - x^2 - 10x - 8 = (x + 1)(x - 4)(x + 2)$.

exercises

Exploratory Divide using synthetic division. Write your answer in the form *dividend = quotient · divisor + remainder.*

1. $(x^2 - 3x + 1) \div (x - 2)$

2. $(x^3 - 4x^2 + 2x - 6) \div (x - 4)$

3. $(x^3 - 8x^2 + 2x - 1) \div (x + 1)$

4. $(x^2 + 8x - 1) \div (x + 3)$

5. $(x^5 + x^4 + 2x - 1) \div (x - 2)$

6. $(2x^4 - x^2 + 1) \div (x + 1)$

7. $(x^5 + 32) \div (x + 2)$

8. $(x^5 - 3x^2 - 20) \div (x - 2)$

Written Divide. Write your answer in the form *dividend = quotient · divisor + remainder.*

1. $(2x^3 + 8x^2 - 3x - 1) \div (x - 2)$

2. $(x^3 - 64) \div (x - 4)$

3. $(x^4 - 16) \div (x - 2)$

4. $(x^3 + 27) \div (x + 3)$

5. $(4x^4 + 3x^3 - 2x^2 + x + 1) \div (x - 1)$

6. $(6x^3 + 9x^2 - 6x + 2) \div (x + 2)$

7. $(3x^3 + 2x^2 - 4x - 1) \div \left(x + \dfrac{1}{2} \right)$

8. $(x^4 - 2x^3 + 4x^2 + 6x - 8) \div \left(x - \dfrac{1}{2} \right)$

Use synthetic substitution to find $f(3)$ for each of the following.

9. $f(x) = x^3 + 2x^2 - 3x + 1$

10. $f(x) = 2x^2 - 8x + 6$

11. $f(x) = x^3 - 8x^2 + 2x + 5$

12. $f(x) = x^3 + 8x + 1$

13. $f(x) = 3x^4 + 8x^2 - 1$

14. $f(x) = x^4 + x^3 + x^2 + x + 1$

15. $f(x) = x^5 + 8x^3 + 2$

16. $f(x) = 2x^3 + 2x^2 - 2x - 2$

Show that the binomial given after each polynomial below is a factor of the polynomial. Then find the remaining factors of the polynomial. (Some factors may not be binomials.)

17. $x^3 + x^2 - 4x - 4;\ x + 1$

18. $x^3 - 6x^2 + 11x - 6;\ x - 2$

19. $x^3 + 2x^2 - x - 2;\ x - 1$

20. $2x^3 + 17x^2 + 23x - 42;\ x + 6$

21. $x^3 - 3x + 2;\ x - 1$

22. $x^3 - x^2 - 5x - 3;\ x - 3$

23. $x^4 + 2x^3 - 8x - 16;\ x + 2$

24. $8x^4 + 32x^3 + x + 4;\ x + 4$

25. $x^5 + x^4 - x - 1;\ x + 1$

26. $16x^5 - 32x^4 - 81x + 162;\ x - 2$

Find values for k so that each remainder is 3.

27. $(x^2 + 8x + k) \div (x - 2)$

28. $(x^2 + kx + 3) \div (x - 1)$

29. $(x^3 + 8x^2 + kx + 4) \div (x + 2)$

30. $(x^3 + 4x^2 - kx + 1) \div (x + 1)$

31. Write a computer program that uses synthetic division to divide a polynomial by a linear polynomial.

Synthetic Division

The calculator may be used to perform synthetic division. At each step, the result should be written in place.

Example   Find $p(9)$ if $p(x) = 2x^3 + 3x^2 - x - 79$.

The value of $p(9)$ is the remainder when $2x^3 + 3x^2 - x - 79$ is divided by $x - 9$. Use synthetic division.

$$
\begin{array}{r|rrrr}
9 & 2 & 3 & ^-1 & ^-79 \\
  &   & 18 & 189 & 1692 \\
\hline
  & 2 & 21 & 188 & 1613
\end{array}
$$

ENTER: 9 $\boxed{\times}$ 2 $\boxed{=}$ $\boxed{+}$ 3 $\boxed{=}$ $\boxed{\times}$ 9 $\boxed{=}$ $\boxed{+}$ 1 $\boxed{+/-}$ $\boxed{=}$ $\boxed{\times}$ 9 $\boxed{=}$ $\boxed{+}$ 79 $\boxed{+/-}$ $\boxed{=}$

DISPLAY: 9   2 18   3 21   9 189   1 -1 188   9 1692   79 -79 1613

Exercises   If $g(x) = 3x^3 - 2x^2 + x - 1$, find each of the following using the calculator and synthetic division.

1. $g(^-2)$ 2. $g(5)$ 3. $g(4.6)$ 4. $g(^-11.9)$ 5. $g(\sqrt{41})$

Find $h(17) - h(16.5)$ for each of the following using the calculator and synthetic division.

6. $h(x) = x^4 - x^3 + x^2 - x + 1$ 7. $h(x) = 7x^3 + \frac{7}{3}x + 1$ 8. $h(x) = 10x^5 - x^3 - 93x$

9–3 Zeros

If $f(x) = x^3 - 4x^2 + x + 6$ represents a polynomial function and $f(a) = 0$, then a is called a **zero** of the function. For example, $f(x)$ has three zeros, namely 3, 2, and $^-1$. These zeros are also solutions of the equation $x^3 - 4x^2 + x + 6 = 0$. In general, the zeros of a function defined by $y = f(x)$ are solutions to the equation $f(x) = 0$.

example

1 **Find the zeros of the function defined by**
$f(x) = (x - 3)(x + 8)(3x - 7)(2x + 5).$

Solve $(x - 3)(x + 8)(3x - 7)(2x + 5) = 0.$

$x - 3 = 0$ or $x + 8 = 0$ or $3x - 7 = 0$ or $2x + 5 = 0$ *Why?*
$x = 3$ $x = ^-8$ $3x = 7$ $2x = ^-5$
                           $x = \dfrac{7}{3}$ $x = -\dfrac{5}{2}$

The zeros of the function are 3, $^-8$, $\dfrac{7}{3}$, and $-\dfrac{5}{2}$.   *How can you check the solutions?*

Suppose you wish to find the zeros of $f(x) = x^3 - 4x^2 - 7x + 10$. The polynomial $x^3 - 4x^2 - 7x + 10$ cannot be easily factored. Synthetic division can be used to find factors of the polynomial. A combined and shortened form of synthetic division is shown below for binomial divisors of $x^3 - 4x^2 - 7x + 10$. The value of r in $x - r$ is shown at the left. Beside each value is the last line of the synthetic division procedure. The last numeral in each row is the remainder. Notice how this procedure can be used to determine factors of a polynomial.

r	1	$^-4$	$^-7$	10	
1	1	$^-3$	$^-10$	0	*x − 1 is a factor.*
2	1	$^-2$	$^-11$	$^-12$	
3	1	$^-1$	$^-10$	-20	
4	1	0	$^-7$	$^-18$	
5	1	1	$^-2$	0	*x − 5 is a factor.*
$^-1$	1	$^-5$	$^-2$	12	
$^-2$	1	$^-6$	5	0	*x − $^-$2, or x + 2 is a factor.*

Thus, the zeros of the function $f(x) = x^3 - 4x^2 - 7x + 10$ are 1, 5, and $^-2$. Notice that they are all factors of 10.

The Rational Zero Theorem can be used to identify possible zeros of polynomial equations that have integral coefficients.

Let $f(x) = a_n x^n + a_{n-1} x^{n-1} + \cdots + a_1 x + a_0$ represent a polynomial with integer coefficients and n be a non-negative integer. If $\frac{p}{q}$ is a rational number in simplest form and is a zero of $y = f(x)$, then p is a factor of a_0 and q is a factor of a_n.

Rational Zero Theorem

The Rational Zero Theorem can be proven as follows.

Assume $\frac{p}{q}$ is a zero and p and q have no common factors.

$$a_0 \frac{p^n}{q^n} + a_1 \frac{p^{n-1}}{q^{n-1}} + \cdots + a_{n-1} \frac{p}{q} + a_n = 0 \qquad \textit{Substitute } \frac{p}{q} \textit{ for x.}$$

$$a_0 p^n + a_1 p^{n-1} q + \cdots + a_{n-1} p q^{n-1} + a_n q^n = 0 \qquad \textit{Multiply both sides by } q^n.$$

$$a_0 p^n + a_1 p^{n-1} q + \cdots + a_{n-1} p q^{n-1} = {}^- a_n q^n \qquad \textit{Subtract } a_n q^n \textit{ from both sides.}$$

$$p(a_0 p^{n-1} + a_1 p^{n-2} q + \cdots + a_{n-1} q^{n-1}) = {}^- a_n q^n \qquad \textit{Factor p from the terms on the left side.}$$

Since p is a factor of the left side, it is also a factor of the right side. But p and q have no common factors, so p is a factor of a_n rather than q^n. Using a similar approach but factoring q from the last n terms, you can prove that q is a factor of a_0. Therefore p is a factor of a_n and q is a factor of a_0.

example

2 **Find all rational zeros of $f(x) = 2x^3 + 3x^2 - 8x + 3$.**

According to the Rational Zero Theorem, if $\frac{p}{q}$ is a zero of the function, then p is a factor of 3 and q is a factor of 2.

$$p \text{ is } \pm 1, \pm 3. \qquad q \text{ is } \pm 1, \pm 2.$$

The possible rational zeros are ± 1, ± 3, $\pm \frac{1}{2}$, and $\pm \frac{3}{2}$. You can test each possible zero using substitution or synthetic division.

$\frac{p}{q}$	2	3	⁻8	3	
1	2	5	⁻3	0	*1 is a zero.*
⁻1	2	1	⁻9	12	
3	2	9	19	60	
⁻3	2	⁻3	1	0	*⁻3 is a zero.*
$\frac{1}{2}$	2	4	⁻6	0	*$\frac{1}{2}$ is a zero.*
$-\frac{1}{2}$	2	2	⁻9	$7\frac{1}{2}$	
$\frac{3}{2}$	2	6	1	$4\frac{1}{2}$	
$-\frac{3}{2}$	2	0	⁻8	15	

The rational zeros of $f(x) = 2x^3 + 3x^2 - 8x + 3$ are 1, ⁻3, and $\frac{1}{2}$.

It is not always necessary to complete the entire chart. Once a zero is found, the depressed polynomial may be factored.

3 **Find all zeros of $f(x) = 6x^3 + 4x^2 - 14x + 4$.**

According to the Rational Zero Theorem, if $\frac{p}{q}$ is a zero of the function, then p is a factor of 4 and q is a factor of 6.

p is $\pm1, \pm2$, or ±4. q is $\pm1, \pm2, \pm3$, or ±6.

$\frac{p}{q}$	6	4	⁻14	4
1	6	10	⁻4	0

1 is a zero.

The depressed polynomial is $6x^2 + 10x - 4$.   *How do you know this?*

$6x^2 + 10x - 4 = 2(3x^2 + 5x - 2)$
$= 2(3x - 1)(x + 2)$

Solve $2(3x - 1)(x + 2) = 0$.

$3x - 1 = 0$ or $x + 2 = 0$
$x = \frac{1}{3}$ or $x = {}^-2$

The zeros are $1, \frac{1}{3}$, and $^-2$.

4 **Find all zeros of $f(x) = x^4 + x^3 - 13x^2 - 25x - 12$.**

p is $\pm1, \pm2, \pm3, \pm4, \pm6, \pm12$. q is ±1.

$\frac{p}{q}$	1	1	⁻13	⁻25	⁻12
1	1	2	⁻11	⁻36	⁻48
⁻1	1	0	⁻13	⁻12	0

⁻1 is a zero.

The depressed polynomial is $x^3 - 13x - 12$.

p is $\pm1, \pm2, \pm3, \pm4, \pm6, \pm12$. q is ±1.

$\frac{p}{q}$	1	0	13	⁻12
1	1	1	⁻12	⁻24
⁻1	1	⁻1	⁻12	0

⁻1 is a zero.

The depressed polynomial is $x^2 - x - 12$.   *This depressed polynomial is of degree two.*

$x^2 - x - 12 = (x - 4)(x + 3)$ *Factor the polynomial, if possible. If not, use the quadratic formula to find the two remaining zeros.*

Solve $(x - 4)(x + 3) = 0$.

$x - 4 = 0$ or $x + 3 = 0$
$x = 4$ or $x = {}^-3$

The zeros are $^-1, {}^-1, 4$, and $^-3$.

exercises

Exploratory   State all *possible* rational zeros for each function.

1. $f(x) = x^4 + x^2 - 2$
2. $f(x) = x^3 + 2x^2 - 3x + 5$
3. $f(x) = x^2 - 8x + 6$
4. $f(x) = x^3 + 5x^2 - 3$
5. $f(x) = x^3 - 2x^2 + 3x - 8$
6. $f(x) = x^3 - 4x + 10$
7. $f(x) = x^3 + 8x^2 - 3x + 1$
8. $f(x) = x^3 - 2x^2 - 5x - 9$
9. $f(x) = x^3 - 8x^2 - 11x + 20$
10. $f(x) = x^4 + 2x + 15$
11. $f(x) = 6x^4 + 35x^3 - x^2 - 7x - 1$
12. $f(x) = 6x^3 + 4x^2 - 14x - 2$
13. $f(x) = 3x^4 - 5x^2 + 4$
14. $f(x) = 2x^3 + x^2 + 5x - 3$

Find all rational zeros for each function.

15. $f(x) = (x - 3)(x + 5)(2x + 5)$
16. $f(x) = (x - 8)(7x - 5)(x + 3)$
17. $f(x) = (x - 3)^2(x + 2)(2x - 1)(3x - 2)$
18. $f(x) = (x + 5)^3(4x - 1)^2(5x + 3)$
19. $f(x) = 2(3x - 2)(x - 5)(x + 1)$
20. $f(x) = (x + 1)(2x + 3)(x - 5)$

Written   Find all rational zeros for each function.

1. $f(x) = x^3 - x^2 - 34x - 56$
2. $f(x) = x^3 + x^2 - 80x - 300$
3. $f(x) = 2x^3 - 11x^2 + 12x + 9$
4. $f(x) = x^3 - 3x - 2$
5. $f(x) = x^3 - 3x^2 + x - 3$
6. $f(x) = x^3 - 3x^2 - 53x - 9$
7. $f(x) = x^4 + 10x^3 + 33x^2 + 38x + 8$
8. $f(x) = x^4 + x^3 - 9x^2 - 17x - 8$
9. $f(x) = x^4 + x^2 - 2$
10. $f(x) = x^4 - 6x^3 - 3x^2 - 24x - 28$
11. $f(x) = 8x^2 - 6x + 1$
12. $f(x) = 2x^2 - 7x + 3$
13. $f(x) = x^3 - 2x^2 - 13x - 10$
14. $f(x) = x^3 + 4x^2 - 3x - 18$
15. $f(x) = x^3 - x^2 - 40x + 12$
16. $f(x) = x^4 - 13x^2 + 36$
17. $f(x) = 12x^4 + 4x^3 - 3x^2 - x$
18. $f(x) = 48x^4 - 52x^3 + 13x - 3$
19. $f(x) = x^4 - 6x^2 + 8$
20. $f(x) = 2x^5 - x^4 - 2x + 1$

Solve each problem.

21. A box is to have a volume of 72 m³. The width is 2 m longer than the height, and the length is 7 m longer than the height. Find the dimensions of the box.

22. A box is to have a volume of 144 cm³. The width is 3 cm longer than the height, and the length is 2 cm longer than the width. Find the dimensions of the box.

Skills Review   Solve each equation by using factoring or the quadratic formula.

1. $x^2 - 9 = 0$
2. $y^2 - 5y - 6 = 0$
3. $x^2 + 11x + 24 = 0$
4. $b^2 - 10b = 24$
5. $a^2 - 25a + 24 = 0$
6. $2x^2 - 9x - 5 = 0$
7. $2x^2 + 7x - 4 = 0$
8. $2c^2 + 7c = {}^-3$
9. $5b^2 - 4b - 1 = 0$
10. $6x^2 = 9 - 25x$
11. $x^2 - 3x - 2 = 0$
12. $2y^2 - y - 3 = 0$

9–4   Nature of Solutions

Some polynomial equations like $4x^2 - 1 = 0$ have no integral solutions. Some like $x^2 - 2 = 0$ have no rational solutions. Some like $x^2 + 1 = 0$ have no real solutions. All polynomial equations have *at least one solution* in the set of complex numbers.

> **Every polynomial equation with degree greater than zero has at least one solution in the set of complex numbers.**

The Fundamental Theorem of Algebra

Another interesting theorem comes from The Fundamental Theorem of Algebra. It states that a polynomial equation has n complex solutions if its polynomial has degree n.

For example, $x^3 + 5x^2 + 4x + 20 = 0$ has three solutions in the set of complex numbers, $2i$, $-2i$, and -5. The equation $x^3 + 7x^2 + 15x + 9 = 0$ has three solutions since -3 is a double root.

Karl Friedrich Gauss (1777–1855) is credited with the first proof of the Fundamental Theorem of Algebra.

$$x^3 + 5x^2 + 4x + 20 = 0$$
$$(x - 2i)(x + 2i)(x + 5) = 0$$

$x - 2i = 0$ or $x + 2i = 0$ or $x + 5 = 0$
$\qquad x = 2i \qquad\qquad x = -2i \qquad\qquad x = -5$

$$x^3 + 7x^2 + 15x + 9 = 0$$
$$(x + 1)(x + 3)^2 = 0$$

$x + 1 = 0$ or $(x + 3)^2 = 0$
$\qquad x = -1 \qquad\qquad x = -3$

You may have noticed that imaginary solutions to quadratic equations come in pairs. In general, if an imaginary number is a solution, then its conjugate is also a solution.

> **Suppose a and b are real numbers with $b \neq 0$. Then, if $a + bi$ is a solution of a polynomial equation, $a - bi$ is also a solution of the equation.**

Complex Conjugates Theorem

---

example

1 Find all zeros of $f(x) = x^3 - 7x^2 + 17x - 15$ if $2 - i$ is one solution to $f(x) = 0$.

Since $2 - i$ is a solution, $2 + i$ also is a solution. Thus, both $x - (2 - i)$ and $x - (2 + i)$ are factors of the polynomial.

$$f(x) = [x - (2 - i)][x - (2 + i)][\ \ ?\ \ ]$$
$$= (x^2 - 4x + 5)(\ \ ?\ \ )$$

Use division to find the other factor.

$f(x) = (x^2 - 4x + 5)(x - 3)$

Since $x - 3$ is a factor, 3 is a solution.

The polynomial has degree 3, so it has 3 zeros.

The zeros are $2 - i$, $2 + i$, and 3.

$$\begin{array}{r} x\ -\ 3 \\ x^2 - 4x + 5\overline{)x^3 - 7x^2 + 17x - 15} \\ \underline{x^3 - 4x^2 +\ \ 5x} \\ -3x^2 + 12x - 15 \\ \underline{-3x^2 + 12x - 15} \\ 0 \end{array}$$

More information about the zeros of a polynomial function was developed by Rene Descartes (1596–1650), a French mathematician.

> Suppose $p(x)$ is a polynomial whose terms are arranged in descending powers of the variable. The number of positive real zeros of $y = p(x)$ is the same as the number of changes in sign of the coefficients of the terms, or is less than this number by an even multiple. The number of negative real zeros is the same as the number of changes in sign of $p(^-x)$, or is less than this number by an even multiple.

Descartes' Rule of Signs

Zero coefficients are ignored.

example

2 State the number of positive and negative real zeros for $p(x) = 2x^4 - x^3 + 5x^2 + 3x - 9$.

The signs, in order, are as follows.
$$2x^4 - x^3 + 5x^2 + 3x - 9$$

There are 3 sign changes, so there are 3 or 1 positive real zeros.

Next, evaluate the polynomial for ^-x.
$$p(^-x) = 2(^-x)^4 - (^-x)^3 + 5(^-x)^2 + 3(^-x) - 9$$
$$= 2x^4 + x^3 + 5x^2 - 3x - 9$$

The signs, in order, are as follows.
$$2x^4 + x^3 + 5x^2 - 3x - 9$$

There is 1 sign change, so there is 1 negative real zero.

The polynomial equation in the previous example has degree 4. Thus, it has four solutions or zeros. The possibilities for the nature of these solutions can be given in a table.

Number of Positive Real Zeros	Number of Negative Real Zeros	Number of Imaginary Zeros
3	1	0
1	1	2

$3 + 1 + 0 = 4$
$1 + 1 + 2 = 4$

example

3 Write the simplest polynomial equation with integral coefficients whose roots are 4 and $2 - 3i$.

If $2 - 3i$ is a root, then $2 + 3i$ is also a root. *Why?*

$$[x - (2 - 3i)][x - (2 + 3i)](x - 4) = [(x - 2) + 3i][(x - 2) - 3i](x - 4)$$
$$= [(x - 2)^2 - 9i^2](x - 4)$$
$$= (x^2 - 4x + 13)(x - 4)$$
$$= x^3 - 8x^2 + 29x - 52$$

Exploratory State the number of positive real zeros and negative real zeros for each function.

1. $f(x) = x^4 - 2x^3 + x^2 - 1$

2. $f(x) = 3x^5 + 7x^2 - 8x + 1$

3. $f(x) = 4x^4 - 3x^3 + 2x^2 - x + 1$

4. $f(x) = x^7 - x^3 + 2x - 1$

5. $f(x) = x^4 - x^3 + x^2 + x + 1$

6. $f(x) = {}^-x^4 - x^2 - x - 1$

7. $f(x) = x^6 - 2x^5 + 3x^4 - 8x^3 + 7x^2 - 1$

8. $f(x) = x^3 + x^2 + x + 1$

9. $f(x) = x^4 + x^3 - 7x - 1$

10. $f(x) = x^{10} - 1$

Written Complete the chart.

	Function	No. Positive Real Zeros	No. Negative Real Zeros	No. Imaginary Zeros
	$f(x) = {}^-x^3 + x^2 - x + 1$	3 or 1	0	0 or 2
1.	$f(x) = 3x^4 + 2x^3 - 3x^2 - 4x + 1$			
2.	$f(x) = 3x^4 - 8x + 1$			
3.	$f(x) = {}^-7x^3 - 6x + 1$			
4.	$f(x) = x^{10} - x^8 + x^6 - x^4 + x^2 - 1$			
5.	$f(x) = x^5 - x^3 - x + 1$			
6.	$f(x) = 3x^4 - x^2 + x - 1$			
7.	$f(x) = 4x^5 - x^2 + 1$			
8.	$f(x) = x^3 + 1$			
9.	$f(x) = x^{14} + x^{10} - x^9 + x - 1$			
10.	$f(x) = x^4 + x^3 + 2x^2 - 3x - 1$			

11. Let $f(x) = x^3 - 10x^2 + 34x - 40$. Find all zeros if $3 + i$ is one solution to $x^3 - 10x^2 + 34x - 40 = 0$.

12. Let $f(x) = x^3 - 3x^2 + 9x + 13$. Find all zeros if $2 - 3i$ is one solution to $x^3 - 3x^2 + 9x + 13 = 0$.

13. Let $f(x) = x^3 + 2x^2 - 3x + 20$. Find all zeros if $1 + 2i$ is one solution to $x^3 + 2x^2 - 3x + 20 = 0$.

14. Let $f(x) = x^4 - 6x^3 + 12x^2 + 6x - 13$. Find all zeros if $3 - 2i$ is one solution to $x^4 - 6x^3 + 12x^2 + 6x - 13 = 0$.

15. Let $f(x) = x^3 + 6x^2 + 21x + 26$. Find all zeros if $^-2$ is one solution to $x^3 + 6x^2 + 21x + 26 = 0$.

16. Let $f(x) = 2x^3 - x^2 + 28x + 51$. Find all zeros if $-\dfrac{3}{2}$ is one solution to $2x^3 - x^2 + 28x + 51 = 0$.

Write the simplest polynomial equation that has the given roots. Express the equation using integral coefficients.

17. $2, 1 - i, 1 + i$

18. $^-1, 1, 2 + i, 2 - i$

19. $3, 2i$

20. $^-2, 2 + 3i$

21. $^-2 - i, 1 + 3i$

22. $3, 3, {}^-2i$

23. Explain why $4x^3 + 2x^2 + 1 = 0$ must have two complex roots.

The function $f(x) = x^3 - 7x + 6$ has real zeros 1, 2, and $^-3$. An **upper bound** for the zeros of a function is a number for which no real zero *greater* than that number exists. For example 2, 3, and 10.9 are upper bounds for the zeros of f. A **lower bound** for the zeros of a function is a number for which no real zero *less* than that number exists. Some lower bounds for the zeros of f are $^-3$, $^-17$, and $^-125.4$.

Upper and lower bounds may be found by using synthetic division and applying the theorem below.

> **Suppose c is a positive number and $P(x)$ is divided by $x - c$ (using synthetic division). If the resulting quotient and remainder have no change in sign, then $P(x)$ has no real zeros greater than c. Thus, c, is an upper bound of the zeros of $P(x)$.**

Notice that there can be more than one upper bound. Therefore, it is helpful to find the least integral upper bound of the zeros of a function. The least positive integral upper bound of the zeros of $f(x) = x^3 - 7x + 6$ is 2.

Example Find the least positive integral upper bound of the zeros of the function $f(x) = x^4 - 3x^3 - 2x^2 + 3x - 5$ using synthetic division.

Divide by increasing values of c until the depressed polynomial and the remainder have no change in sign.

c	1	$^-3$	$^-2$	3	$^-5$
1	1	$^-2$	$^-4$	$^-1$	$^-6$
2	1	$^-1$	$^-4$	$^-5$	$^-15$
3	1	0	$^-2$	$^-3$	$^-14$
4	1	1	2	11	39

This row has no changes in sign.

Thus, 4 is the least positive integral upper bound.

Any value greater than 4 is also an upper bound.

A lower bound of the zeros of $f(x)$ can be found by using synthetic division. Suppose c is a nonpositive number and $P(x)$ is divided by $(x - c)$. If the resulting quotient and remainder have alternating signs, then c is a lower bound of $P(x)$.

Divide by decreasing values of c until the depressed polynomial and the remainder have alternating signs.

Exercises Find the least positive integral upper bound and the greatest negative integral lower bound of the zeros of each function using synthetic division.

1. $f(x) = x^3 + 3x^2 - 5x - 10$
2. $f(x) = x^4 - 8x + 2$
3. $f(x) = 3x^3 - 2x^2 + 5x - 1$
4. $f(x) = x^5 + 5x^4 - 3x^3 + 20x^2 - 15$
5. $f(x) = x^3 - 4x + 6$
6. $f(x) = 2x^3 - 4x^2 - 3$

9–5 Approximating Zeros

The graph of a continuous curve drawn from a lower point to a higher point must *cross* every horizontal line in between. Thus, if the graph of a polynomial function is in part below the x-axis and in part above the x-axis, it must also *cross* the x-axis.

> **Suppose $y = f(x)$ represents a polynomial function. And suppose a and b are two numbers with $f(a)$ negative and $f(b)$ positive. Then the function has at least one real zero between a and b.**

The Location Principle

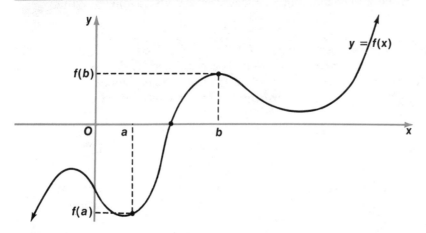

You can use the location principle to approximate zeros of a polynomial function.

examples

1 **Approximate to the nearest tenth the real zeros of the function with equation $f(x) = x^4 + x^2 - 6$.**

By Descartes' Rule of Signs, there is one positive real zero and one negative real zero. The other zeros are imaginary. By the Rational Zero Theorem, the possible rational zeros are $^-6$, $^-3$, $^-2$, $^-1$, 1, 2, 3, or 6.

Use synthetic substitution to evaluate $f(x)$ for these values.

x	1	0	1	0	$^-6$	$f(x)$
$^-6$	1	$^-6$	37	$^-222$	1326	1326
$^-3$	1	$^-3$	10	$^-30$	84	84
$^-2$	1	$^-2$	5	$^-10$	14	14
$^-1$	1	$^-1$	2	$^-2$	$^-4$	$^-4$
1	1	1	2	2	$^-4$	$^-4$
2	1	2	5	10	14	14
3	1	3	10	30	84	84
6	1	6	37	222	1326	1326

By the Location Principle there is a zero between $^-1$ and $^-2$, and a zero between 1 and 2.

Locate the negative zero.

It is convenient to use a calculator to find f(x).

x	$f(x)$
$^-1.5$	1.3125
$^-1.4$	$^-0.1984$
$^-1.3$	$^-1.4539$
$^-1.2$	$^-2.4864$
$^-1.1$	$^-3.3259$
$^-1.0$	$^-4$

$\longleftarrow f(^-1.45) \approx 0.5$

The zero is "closer" to $^-1.4$.

Locate the positive zero.

x	$f(x)$
1.0	$^-4$
1.1	$^-3.3259$
1.2	$^-2.4864$
1.3	$^-1.4539$
1.4	$^-0.1984$
1.5	1.3125

The zero is "closer" to 1.4.

$\longleftarrow f(1.45) \approx 0.5$

Why aren't values less than $^-1.5$ tested?　　　*Why aren't values greater than 1.5 tested?*

The real zeros are approximately $^-1.4$ and 1.4.

2 **Approximate to the nearest tenth the real zeros of the function with equation $f(x) = x^4 - x^3 - 4x^2 + 8x - 4$.**

By Descartes' Rule of Signs, there are three or one positive real zeros and one negative real zero. By the Rational Zero Theorem, the possible rational zeros are $^-4$, $^-2$, $^-1$, 1, 2, or 4.

x	1	$^-1$	$^-4$	8	$^-4$	$f(x)$
$^-4$	1	$^-5$	16	$^-56$	220	220
$^-2$	1	$^-3$	2	4	$^-12$	$^-12$
$^-1$	1	$^-2$	$^-2$	10	$^-14$	$^-14$
1	1	0	$^-4$	4	0	0
2	1	1	$^-2$	4	4	4
4	1	3	8	40	156	156

$\longleftarrow$ *By the Location Principle there is a zero between $^-4$ and $^-2$.*

$\longleftarrow$ *1 is a zero.*

Locate the zero between $^-4$ and $^-2$.

First, find $f(^-3)$.

$$\begin{array}{r|rrrr|r} ^-3 & 1 & ^-1 & ^-4 & 8 & ^-4 \\ & & 1 & ^-4 & 8 & ^-16 & 44 \end{array}$$

By the Location Principle, the zero is between $^-3$ and $^-2$.

x	$f(x)$
$^-2.5$	5.6875
$^-2.4$	0.7616
$^-2.3$	$^-3.4089$

$f(^-2.35) \approx ^-1.414$
The zero is "closer" to $^-2.4$.

The real zeros are 1 and approximately $^-2.4$.

Written Approximate to the nearest tenth the real zeros of functions with the following equations. Use a calculator as necessary.

1. $f(x) = x^3 - 2x^2 + 6$
2. $f(x) = x^4 - 4x^2 + 3$
3. $f(x) = 2x^5 + 3x - 2$
4. $f(x) = x^4 - x^2 + 6$
5. $f(x) = x^3 + 2x^2 - 3x - 5$
6. $f(x) = x^3 - 5$
7. $f(x) = x^5 - 6$
8. $f(x) = 3x^3 - 16x^2 + 12x + 6$
9. $f(x) = x^3 - x^2 + 1$
10. $f(x) = x^4 - 4x^2 + 6$
11. $f(x) = 3x^2 - 8x + 1$
12. $f(x) = {}^-7x^3 - 6x + 1$
13. $f(x) = x^5 - x^3 - x + 1$
14. $f(x) = 3x^4 - x^2 + x - 1$
15. $f(x) = x^3 + 1$
16. $f(x) = x^4 - x^2 - 6$
17. $f(x) = x^3 - 4x + 4$
18. $f(x) = x^3 - 3$

Bisection Method

excursions in algebra

You can approximate real zeros of a function like $f(x) = x^4 + 5x^3 + 8x^2 + 45x - 9$ by using the **bisection method.** The function has a real zero between 0 and 1 since $f(0) = {}^-9$ and $f(1) = 50$. It also has a real zero between $^-6$ and $^-5$ since $f(^-6) = 225$ and $f(^-5) = {}^-34$.

Suppose you wish to approximate the zero between 0 and 1.

First divide or "bisect" the interval from 0 to 1.

$$\frac{0 + 1}{2} = 0.5$$

Evaluate the function for 0.5 to determine which half the zero lies in.

$$f(0.5) = 16.1875$$

Using the location principle you know that the zero must lie between 0 and 0.5.

Repeat the same procedure.

$$\frac{0 + 0.5}{2} = 0.25$$

$$f(0.25) = 2.8320313$$

Using the location principle you know that the zero must lie between 0 and 0.25.

This procedure can be repeated until the desired accuracy of the zero is obtained. A computer is very convenient when using the bisection method, especially when a complicated function is involved or when a high degree of accuracy is desired.

Exercises Use the bisection method to approximate the real zeros of each function to three decimal places.

1. $f(x) = x^3 - 2x - 3$
2. $f(x) = x^3 - x - 5$
3. $f(x) = x^3 + x^2 + 1$
4. $f(x) = x^4 + 2x^3 - 3$

5. Write a computer program that uses the bisection method to approximate real zeros of polynomial functions. Apply the bisection process five times.

9–6   Graphing Polynomials

The simplest polynomial graphs are those with equations of the form $f(x) = x^n$ where n is a positive integer.

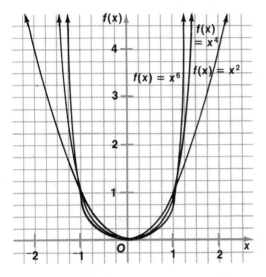
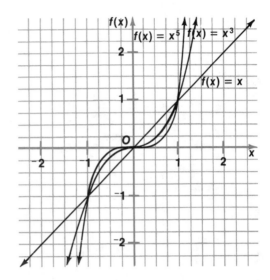

Notice that each graph has only one x-intercept, the origin. The graphs are completed by finding points on the graphs and connecting them with smooth continuous curves.

If a polynomial $f(x)$ can be factored into linear factors, much information about the graph of $y = f(x)$ is available. For example, consider $y = (x - 2)(x - 3)(x + 5)$.

1. The function has three zeros, 2, 3, and $^-5$.
2. The function has negative values when x is less than $^-5$ and when x is between 2 and 3.
3. The function has positive values when x is between $^-5$ and 2 and when x is greater than 3.

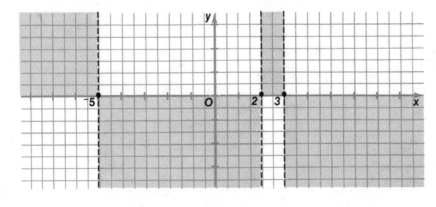

The graph crosses the x-axis at $^-5$, 2, and 3. The shaded regions contain no points of the graph.

To complete the graph, find and plot points on the graph. Connect them with a smooth continuous curve. *Use a calculator and/or synthetic substitution to find the y-coordinates.*

x	y
⁻6	⁻72
⁻5	0
⁻4	42
⁻3	60
⁻2.5	61.875
⁻2	60
⁻1	48
0	30
1	12
2	0
2.3	⁻1.533
2.5	⁻1.875
2.7	⁻1.617
3	0
4	18
5	60

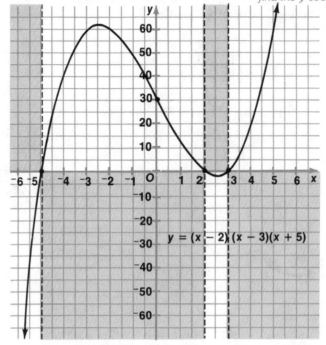

$y = (x - 2)(x - 3)(x + 5)$

Notice how the vertical scale has been "condensed" so the graph will fit the space provided.

1 Graph $f(x) = {}^-x^3 + 2x^2 + 4x - 8$.

First, factor the polynomial.

$$f(x) = {}^-(x - 2)^2(x + 2)$$

1. The function has two zeros, 2 and ⁻2.
2. The function has positive values when x is less than ⁻2.
3. The function has negative or zero values when x is greater than ⁻2.

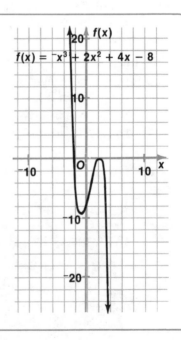

$f(x) = {}^-x^3 + 2x^2 + 4x - 8$

x	⁻4	⁻3	⁻2	⁻1	0	1	2	3	4
f(x)	72	25	0	⁻9	⁻8	⁻3	0	⁻5	⁻24

In general, the graph of a cubic polynomial function has a *sideways S* shape. Point A on each graph is called a **relative maximum** since there are no nearby points that are greater than A. Likewise, each point B is called a **relative minimum**. You can use this information to help graph functions that have imaginary zeros.

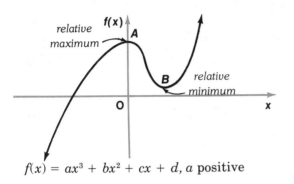

$f(x) = ax^3 + bx^2 + cx + d$, a positive

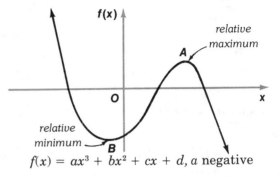

$f(x) = ax^3 + bx^2 + cx + d$, a negative

example

2 **Graph $f(x) = x^3 - 6x - 9$.**

First, factor the polynomial.

$f(x) = (x - 3)(x^2 + 3x + 3)$

The function has one real zero, 3.

The graph of this cubic polynomial function has a *sideways S* shape. Thus it has one relative maximum and one relative minimum.

x	$f(x)$
$^-3$	$^-18$
$^-2$	$^-5$
$^-1.5$	$^-3.375$
$^-1$	$^-4$
$^-0.5$	$^-6.125$
0	$^-9$
1	$^-14$
1.5	$^-14.625$
2	$^-13$
3	0
4	31

indicates a relative maximum

indicates a relative minimum

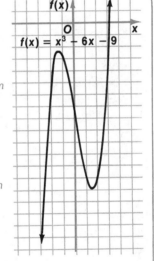
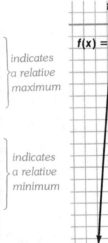

$f(x) = x^3 - 6x - 9$

exercises

Written **Graph each of the following. Use a calculator or synthetic substitution to help find points of the graph.**

1. $f(x) = x^3$
2. $f(x) = x^6$
3. $f(x) = 4x^6$
4. $f(x) = 3x^5$
5. $f(x) = (x - 1)(x - 2)(x + 2)$
6. $f(x) = (x + 4)(x - 1)(x + 1)$
7. $f(x) = (x - 2)^2(x + 3)$
8. $f(x) = (x - 3)^2(x + 1)$
9. $f(x) = x^3 - x$
10. $f(x) = {}^-x^3 - x$
11. $f(x) = x^3 - x^2 - 8x + 12$
12. $f(x) = x^4 - 81$
13. $f(x) = x^4 - 10x^2 + 9$
14. $f(x) = x^3 + 5$
15. $f(x) = 15x^3 - 16x^2 - x + 2$
16. $f(x) = x^3 - 3x - 4$
17. $f(x) = {}^-x^3 - 13x - 12$
18. $f(x) = {}^-x^3 - 4x^2 - 8x - 8$

9–7   Composition of Functions

Scientists often use the Kelvin temperature scale. Kelvin temperature readings and Celsius temperature readings are related in the following way.

$$K = C + 273$$

Celsius readings and Fahrenheit readings are related in the following way.

$$C = \frac{5}{9}(F - 32)$$

Using these equations, you can write a new equation which shows how Kelvin readings and Fahrenheit readings are related.

$$
\begin{aligned}
K &= C + 273 \\
&= \frac{5}{9}(F - 32) + 273 \qquad \text{\textit{Substitute} } \frac{5}{9}(F-32) \text{ \textit{for} C.} \\
&= \frac{5}{9}F + \frac{2297}{9}
\end{aligned}
$$

The above example illustrates **composition of functions**.

> **Given functions f and g, the composite function $f \circ g$ can be described by the following equation.**
> $$[f \circ g](x) = f[g(x)]$$

The range of g is a subset of the domain of f.

Composition of Functions

The symbol $f \circ g$ is read "f composition g" or "the composite of f and g."

examples

1   **If $f(x) = x + 273$ and $g(x) = \frac{5}{9}(x - 32)$, find $[f \circ g](x)$.**

$$
\begin{aligned}
[f \circ g](x) &= f[g(x)] \\
&= f\!\left[\frac{5}{9}(x - 32)\right] & \text{\textit{Substitute} } \frac{5}{9}(x-32) \text{ \textit{for} g(x).} \\
&= \left[\frac{5}{9}(x - 32)\right] + 273 & \text{\textit{Evaluate} f \textit{when} x \textit{ is} } \frac{5}{9}(x-32). \\
&= \frac{5}{9}x + \frac{2297}{9} & \text{\textit{Simplify.}}
\end{aligned}
$$

2   **If $f(x) = x^2 + 3$ and $h(x) = 2x - 1$, find $[f \circ h](2)$.**

$$
\begin{aligned}
[f \circ h](2) &= f[h(2)] \\
&= f[2(2) - 1] & \text{\textit{Substitute} } 2(2) - 1 \text{ \textit{for} h(2).} \\
&= f[3] & \text{\textit{Substitute} 3 \textit{for} } 2(2) - 1. \\
&= 12 & \text{\textit{Evaluate} f \textit{when} x \textit{ is} 3.}
\end{aligned}
$$

Mappings can be used to show composition of functions. Suppose $f = \{(1, 2), (2, 3), (3, 4)\}$ and $g = \{(2, 3), (3, 1), (4, 2)\}$.

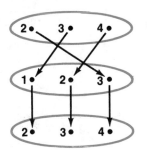

domain of g

range of g
domain of f

range of f

$f \circ g = \{(2, 4), (3, 2), (4, 3)\}$

Notice that in the example above, $f \circ g \neq g \circ f$. In general, composition of functions is not a commutative operation.

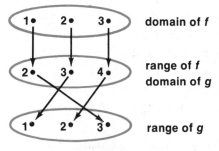

domain of f

range of f
domain of g

range of g

$g \circ f = \{(1, 3), (2, 1), (3, 2)\}$

3 **If $f(x) = x + 7$ and $g(x) = 3 + 2x$, find $[f \circ g](x)$ and $[g \circ f](x)$.**

$$[f \circ g](x) = f[g(x)]$$
$$= f[3 + 2x]$$
$$= (3 + 2x) + 7$$
$$= 2x + 10$$

$$[g \circ f](x) = g[f(x)]$$
$$= g[x + 7]$$
$$= 3 + 2(x + 7)$$
$$= 2x + 17$$

In some cases, given two functions h and k, the composite functions $h \circ k$ or $k \circ h$ may *not* even exist. For example, let $h = \{(2, 4), (4, 6), (6, 8), (8, 10)\}$ and $k = \{(4, 5), (6, 5), (8, 12), (10, 12)\}$. The range of k is *not* a subset of the domain of h. So, $h \circ k$ *does not exist.* The range of h is a subset of the domain of k. So, $k \circ h$ *does exist.*

domain of k

range of k

domain of h

range of h

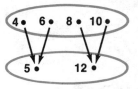
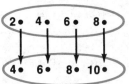

$h \circ k$ does *not* exist. The range of k is not in the domain of h.

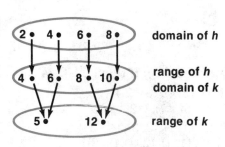

domain of h

range of h
domain of k

range of k

$k \circ h = \{(2, 5), (4, 5), (6, 12), (8, 12)\}$

exercises

Exploratory In each exercise find $f(2)$, $f(^-2)$, and $f(0)$.

1. $f(x) = x - 3$
2. $f(x) = x^2 + 4$
3. $f(x) = x^2 - 2x + 1$
4. $f(x) = |x + 2|$
5. $f(x) = |x| + 2$
6. $f(x) = x^3 - x^2 + x - 1$
7. $f(x) = x^4 - 6$
8. $f(x) = x^2 - 8x + 4$
9. $f(x) = x^5 - x^2 + 2$
10. $f(x) = x^2 - x^3$
11. $f = \{(0, 3), (2, 4), (^-2, 9)\}$
12. $f = \{(0, 2), (^-2, 2), (5, 2)\}$

Written In each exercise, find $[f \circ g](3)$ and $[g \circ f](3)$.

1. $f(x) = x + 2$
   $g(x) = x - 1$
2. $f(x) = x^2 + 8$
   $g(x) = x - 3$
3. $f(x) = x^3 - 1$
   $g(x) = x + 1$
4. $f(x) = x$
   $g(x) = x$
5. $f(x) = 2x^2 + 1$
   $g(x) = x^2 - 1$
6. $f(x) = x^2$
   $g(x) = x^3$

In each exercise, find $f[g(x)]$ and $g[f(x)]$.

7. $f(x) = 2x + 1$
   $g(x) = x - 3$
8. $f(x) = 3x - 4$
   $g(x) = 2x + 5$
9. $f(x) = x^2 + 3$
   $g(x) = 2x - 1$
10. $f(x) = x + 2$
    $g(x) = 3x^2 - 1$
11. $f(x) = ^-x^2 - 8$
    $g(x) = x^2 - 1$
12. $f(x) = x + 2$
    $g(x) = x - 2$

In each exercise, find $f[g(^-1)]$ and $g[f(^-1)]$.

13. $f(x) = x - 1$
    $g(x) = x + 1$
14. $f(x) = x^2 + 2x + 1$
    $g(x) = ^-2x^2 - 1$
15. $f(x) = 3x^2 + 2$
    $g(x) = x - 3$
16. $f(x) = 2x^2 + 4x^3 + 1$
    $g(x) = x^2 + 1$
17. $f(x) = x - 8$
    $g(x) = |x|$
18. $f(x) = |x + 1|$
    $g(x) = |x + 1|$

If $f(x) = x^2$, $g(x) = 3x$, and $h(x) = x - 1$, find each of the following.

19. $[f \circ g](1)$
20. $[g \circ f](1)$
21. $[h \circ f](3)$
22. $[f \circ h](3)$
23. $g[f(^-2)]$
24. $f[h(^-3)]$
25. $g[h(^-2)]$
26. $h[g(^-2)]$
27. $f\left[h\left(-\frac{1}{2}\right)\right]$
28. $g\left[f\left(-\frac{1}{2}\right)\right]$
29. $f[h(\sqrt{2} + 3)]$
30. $f[g(1 + \sqrt{2})]$
31. $f[g(x)]$
32. $g[h(x)]$
33. $[f \circ (g \circ h)](x)$

Express $g \circ f$ and $f \circ g$, if they exist, as sets of ordered pairs.

34. $f = \{(2, 1), (3, 4), (6, ^-2)\}$
    $g = \{(1, 5), (4, ^-7), (^-2, ^-3)\}$
35. $f = \{(3, 8), (4, 0), (6, 3), (7, ^-1)\}$
    $g = \{(8, 6), (0, 4), (3, 6), (^-1, ^-8)\}$
36. $f = \{(0, 2), (1, 1), (3, 3), (4, ^-1)\}$
    $g = \{(0, 0), (1, 1), (2, 4), (3, 9)\}$
37. $f = \{(1, 0), (^-1, 7), (5, 0), (9, 1)\}$
    $g = \{(6, 5), (0, ^-8), (7, ^-2), (1, ^-3)\}$

38. Write a computer program that will find $f[g(x)]$ for values of x from $^-6$ to 6 for the functions $f(x) = x^2 + 8x - 1$ and $g(x) = x^2 + 2$.

9-8   Inverse Functions

You have learned that two numbers are additive inverses if their sum is 0, the additive identity. Two numbers are multiplicative inverses if their product is 1, the multiplicative identity. The function $I(x) = x$ is called the **identity function** since, for any function f, $[f \circ I](x) = f(x)$ and $[I \circ f](x) = f(x)$. Two functions are **inverse functions** if both their compositions are the identity function.

Suppose $f(x) = 3x - 2$ and $g(x) = \frac{x + 2}{3}$. You can determine if they are inverse functions by finding both their compositions.

$$[f \circ g](x) = f[g(x)] \qquad\qquad [g \circ f](x) = g[f(x)]$$
$$= f\left[\frac{x + 2}{3}\right] \qquad\qquad\qquad = g[3x - 2]$$
$$= 3\left(\frac{x + 2}{3}\right) - 2 \qquad\qquad = \frac{(3x - 2) + 2}{3}$$
$$= x \qquad\qquad\qquad\qquad\qquad = x$$

Since both their compositions are the identity function, they are inverse functions.

> **Two polynomial functions f and g are inverse functions if and only if both their compositions are the identity function. That is,**
>
> $$[f \circ g](x) = [g \circ f](x) = x.$$

Definition of Inverse Functions

A special notation often is used to show that two functions f and g are inverse functions.

$$g = f^{-1} \quad \text{and} \quad f = g^{-1}$$

The notation f^{-1} is read "f inverse," or "the inverse of f." The -1 is <u>not</u> an exponent.

The ordered pairs of a function and its inverse are related in a special way. Consider $f(x) = 3x - 2$ and its inverse $f^{-1}(x) = \frac{x + 2}{3}$.

$$f(5) = 3 \cdot 5 - 2 \qquad\qquad f^{-1}(13) = \frac{13 + 2}{3}$$
$$= 13 \qquad\qquad\qquad\qquad\qquad = 5$$

The ordered pair $(5, 13)$ belongs to f.

The ordered pair $(13, 5)$ belongs to f^{-1}.

> **Suppose f and f^{-1} are inverse functions. Then $f(a) = b$ if and only if $f^{-1}(b) = a$.**

Property of Inverse Functions

The inverse of a function can be found by reversing the order of each pair in the given function. For example, if $f = \{(1, 2), (2, 7), (3, 12), (4, 17)\}$, then $f^{-1} = \{(2, 1), (7, 2), (12, 3), (17, 4)\}$.

Suppose you wish to find the inverse of function f. By interchanging the variables in the equation for f, the order of each pair in f is interchanged. Thus, you can obtain the ordered pairs in f^{-1} and the equation for f^{-1}.

1 **Suppose $f(x) = 3x - 5$. Find $f^{-1}(x)$. Also, show that f and f^{-1} are inverse functions.**

Rewrite the function $f(x)$ as $y = 3x - 5$.

Next, interchange the variables x and y and solve the equation for y.

$$x = 3y - 5$$
$$3y = x + 5$$
$$y = \frac{x + 5}{3}$$

Thus, $f^{-1}(x) = \frac{x + 5}{3}$.

Now show that the compositions of f and f^{-1} are identity functions.

$$[f \circ f^{-1}](x) = f[f^{-1}(x)] \qquad\qquad [f^{-1} \circ f](x) = f^{-1}[f(x)]$$
$$= f\left[\frac{x + 5}{3}\right] \qquad\qquad\qquad = f^{-1}[3x - 5]$$
$$= 3\left(\frac{x + 5}{3}\right) - 5 \qquad\qquad = \frac{(3x - 5) + 5}{3}$$
$$= x \qquad\qquad\qquad\qquad\qquad = x$$

So, $[f \circ f^{-1}](x) = [f^{-1} \circ f](x) = x$.

Not all functions have inverses which are functions.

2 **Given $f(x) = x^2 + 3$, find $f^{-1}(x)$.**

Rewrite the function $f(x)$ using y. Interchange the variables and solve for y.

$$y = x^2 + 3$$
$$x = y^2 + 3$$
$$y^2 = x - 3$$
$$y = \pm\sqrt{x - 3} \quad \text{or} \quad f^{-1}(x) = \pm\sqrt{x - 3}$$

This equation does *not* define a function. For a given value of x, there is more than one value of $f^{-1}(x)$. For example, $f^{-1}(7) = 2$ or $^-2$.

The following example shows how the graphs of a function and its inverse are related.

3 If $f(x) = 2x + 1$, find $f^{-1}(x)$. Then graph $f(x)$ and $f^{-1}(x)$ on the same coordinate system.

$$f(x) = 2x + 1 \rightarrow y = 2x + 1$$

$$x = 2y + 1 \qquad \text{Interchange the variables.}$$

$$y = \frac{x - 1}{2} \qquad \text{Solve for } y.$$

$$f^{-1}(x) = \frac{x - 1}{2} \qquad \text{Rewrite using function notation.}$$

Now graph both $f(x)$ and $f^{-1}(x)$. Suppose the plane containing the graphs were folded along the line $f(x) = x$. Then the graphs would coincide.

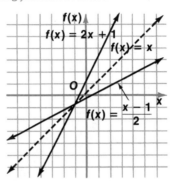

In general, the graphs of a function and its inverse are mirror images of each other with respect to the graph of the identity function, $f(x) = x$.

exercises

Exploratory Write the inverse of each function and determine if its inverse is a function.

1. $f = \{(3, 1), (2, 4), (1, 5)\}$
2. $f = \{(3, 2), (4, 2)\}$
3. $g = \{(3, 8), (4, ^-2), (5, ^-3)\}$
4. $g = \{(^-1, ^-2), (^-3, ^-2), (^-1, ^-4), (0, 6)\}$
5. $h = \{(^-3, 1), (2, 4), (7, 8)\}$
6. $h = \{(4, ^-2), (3, 7), (5, 7), (3, 8)\}$

Written Write the equation for the inverse of each function.

1. $y = 2x$
2. $f(x) = x + 2$
3. $f(x) = ^-6x - 5$
4. $y = 3x - 7$
5. $y = 3$
6. $f(x) = \frac{1}{2}x + 4$
7. $f(x) = 0$
8. $f(x) = ^-3x - 1$
9. $y = x^2$
10. $y = x^2 - 4$

Graph each function and its inverse.

11. $f = \{(2, 1), (3, {}^-4), (0, 1)\}$

12. $f = \left\{\left(\frac{1}{2}, 3\right), (0, {}^-2), (7, 6)\right\}$

13. $y = x$

14. $y = {}^-2x - 1$

15. $y = 3x$

16. $f(x) = x + 2$

17. $f(x) = \dfrac{3x + 1}{2}$

18. $y = \dfrac{x - 3}{5}$

19. $y = x^2 + 1$

20. $f(x) = (x - 4)^2$

Determine if the inverse of each relation graphed below is a function.

21.
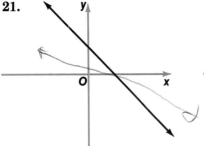

22.
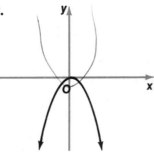

23.
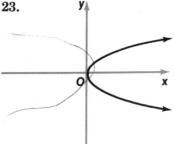

24.
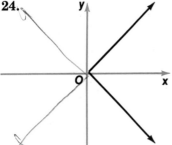

25.
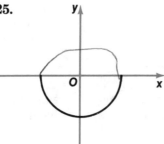

26.
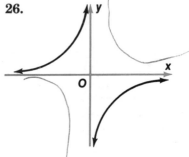

Determine whether the given functions are inverses of one another.

27. $y = 2x + 1$
$y = \dfrac{x - 1}{2}$

28. $y = {}^-2x + 3$
$y = 2x - 3$

29. $y = x + 4$
$y = x - 4$

30. $f(x) = x + 1$
$f(x) = x - 1$

31. $f(x) = 4x - 5$
$f(x) = \dfrac{x + 5}{4}$

32. $f(x) = x - \dfrac{1}{2}$
$f(x) = 2x + 1$

33. $f(x) = x$
$f(x) = {}^-x$

34. $f(x) = {}^-2x + 3$
$f(x) = 2x - 3$

Solve each problem. In each case, assume f is a function.

35. If $f(3) = 4$, find $f^{-1}(4)$.

36. If $f\left(\frac{1}{2}\right) = 6$, find $f^{-1}(6)$.

37. If $f(a) = b$, find $f^{-1}(b)$.

38. If $f(r) = s$, find $f^{-1}(s)$.

39. If $f(a + 1) = 2$, find $f^{-1}(2)$.

40. If $f(m + n) = p$, find $f^{-1}(p)$.

Chapter Summary

1. A polynomial in one variable, x, is an expression of the form $a_n x^n + a_{n-1}x^{n-1} + \cdots + a_2 x^2 + a_1 x + a_0$. The coefficients $a_0, a_1, a_2, \ldots, a_n$ represent real numbers, and n represents a nonnegative integer. (259)

2. The Remainder Theorem: If a polynomial $f(x)$ is divided by $x - a$, the remainder is a constant, $f(a)$, and $f(x) = q(x) \cdot (x - a) + f(a)$ where $q(x)$ is a polynomial with degree one less than the degree of $f(x)$. (262)

3. The Factor Theorem: The binomial $x - a$ is a factor of the polynomial $f(x)$ if and only if $f(a) = 0$. (263)

4. The Rational Zero Theorem: Let $f(x) = a_n x^n + a_{n-1}x^{n-1} + \cdots + a_1 x + a_0$ represent a polynomial with integral coefficients and n be a nonnegative integer. If $\frac{p}{q}$ is a rational number in simplest form and a zero of $y = f(x)$, then p is a factor of a_0 and q is a factor of a_n. (267)

5. The Fundamental Theorem of Algebra: Every polynomial equation with degree greater than zero has at least one solution in the set of complex numbers. (270)

6. Complex Conjugates Theorem: Suppose a and b are real numbers with $b \neq 0$. Then, if $a + bi$ is a solution to a polynomial equation, $a - bi$ is also a solution to the equation. (270)

7. Descartes' Rule of Signs: Suppose $p(x)$ is a polynomial whose terms are arranged in descending powers of the variable. The number of positive real zeros of $y = p(x)$ is the same as the number of changes in sign of the coefficients of the terms, or is less than this number by an even multiple. The number of negative real zeros is the same as the number of changes in sign of $p(^-x)$ or is less than this number by an even multiple. (271)

8. The Location Principle: Suppose $y = f(x)$ represents a polynomial function. And suppose a and b are two numbers with $f(a)$ negative and $f(b)$ positive. Then the function has at least one real zero between a and b. (274)

9. Composition of Functions: Given functions f and g, the composite function $f \circ g$ can be described by the equation $[f \circ g](x) = f[g(x)]$. (280)

10. **Definition of Inverse Functions:** Two polynomial functions f and g are inverse functions if and only if both their compositions are the identity function. That is, $[f \circ g](x) = [g \circ f](x) = x$. (283)

11. **Property of Inverse Functions:** Suppose f and f^{-1} are inverse functions. Then $f(a) = b$ if and only if $f^{-1}(b) = a$. (283)

Chapter Review

9-1 Find $p(^-2)$ for each of the following.

1. $p(x) = 2x^3 + x^2 - 1$

2. $p(x) = 2x^4 - 3x^3 + 8$

Find $f(m + 2)$ for each of the following.

3. $f(x) = x^2 + 3x - 7$

4. $f(x) = {}^-4x^3 - 5$

9-2 Find the remainder for each of the following.

5. $(x^2 + 5x + 6) \div (x + 1)$

6. $(x^3 + 8x + 1) \div (x - 2)$

7. $(x^5 + 8x^3 + 2) \div (x + 2)$

8. $(x^4 + 3x^2 - 1) \div (x - 4)$

Factor each polynomial by using synthetic division.

9. $x^3 + 2x^2 - x - 2$

10. $x^3 + 5x^2 + 8x + 4$

11. $x^3 - 3x + 2$

12. $x^3 - 6x^2 + 11x - 6$

9-3 Find all rational zeros for each function.

13. $f(x) = (x - 1)^2(2x - 3)^2$

14. $f(x) = (x + 2)(x - 2)(x + 5)^3$

15. $f(x) = 6x^3 - 41x^2 + 58x - 15$

16. $f(x) = 2x^3 - 5x^2 - 28x + 15$

9-4 For each function, state the number of positive real zeros, negative real zeros, and imaginary zeros.

17. $f(x) = 2x^4 - x^3 + 5x^2 + 3x - 9$

18. $f(x) = {}^-x^4 - x^2 - x - 1$

19. $f(x) = 7x^3 + 6x - 1$

20. $f(x) = x^4 + x^3 - 7x + 1$

21. Find all zeros of $f(x) = x^3 - 7x^2 + 17x - 15$ if $2 + i$ is one solution to $f(x) = 0$.

9-5 Approximate to the nearest tenth the real zeros of functions with the following equations.

22. $f(x) = x^3 - x^2 + 1$

23. $f(x) = 3x^4 - x^2 + x - 1$

24. $f(x) = x^3 - 2x^2 + 6$

25. $f(x) = 4x^3 + x^2 - 20$

9-6 Graph each of the following.

26. $f(x) = (x - 3)^2(x + 2)$

27. $f(x) = x^3 - 3x - 4$

9-7 In each exercise, find $[f \circ g](3)$, $[g \circ f](4)$, and $[f \circ g](x)$.

28. $f(x) = x^2 + 2$
    $g(x) = x - 3$

29. $f(x) = x^2 + 2x + 1$
    $g(x) = 2x^2 - 1$

30. $f(x) = |x|$
    $g(x) = x - 8$

31. $f(x) = |x + 1|$
    $g(x) = 2|x - 3|$

9–8 Graph each function and its inverse.

32. $f(x) = 1 - 4x$

33. $f(x) = \dfrac{3x + 2}{2}$

34. $f(x) = (x - 6)^2$

Determine whether the given functions are inverses of each other.

35. $f(x) = 3x - 4$ and $g(x) = \dfrac{x - 4}{3}$

36. $f(x) = \dfrac{x + 5}{4}$ and $g(x) = 4x - 5$

Chapter Test

Find $p(3)$ for each of the following.

1. $p(x) = x^4 - x^3 + x - 1$

2. $p(x) = x^3 - 27$

Find $f(m - 1)$ for each of the following.

3. $f(x) = 3x^2 - 4x + 5$

4. $f(x) = x^3 - x + 7$

Find the remainder for each of the following.

5. $(x^2 + 4x + 4) \div (x + 2)$

6. $(x^3 + 8x + 1) \div (x + 2)$

7. $(x^5 + 8x^3 + 2) \div (x - 2)$

8. $(x^4 + x^3 + x^2 + x + 1) \div (x + 1)$

Factor each polynomial by using synthetic division.

9. $x^4 - 5x^2 + 4$

10. $x^3 - 3x - 2$

11. $x^3 - x^2 - 5x - 3$

12. $x^4 - 3x^3 - 7x^2 - 27x - 24$

Find all rational zeros for each function.

13. $f(x) = x^4 + x^3 - 9x^2 - 17x - 8$

14. $f(x) = x^3 - 3x^2 - 53x - 9$

15. $f(x) = 2x^3 - 5x^2 - 28x + 15$

16. $f(x) = 6x^3 + 4x^2 - 14x + 4$

17. Find all zeros of $f(x) = x^3 - 10x^2 + 34x - 40$ if $3 + i$ is one solution to $f(x) = 0$.

18. Approximate to the nearest tenth the real zeros of $f(x) = x^3 - 3x - 4$. Then draw the graph.

If $f(x) = 2x$ and $g(x) = x^2 - 1$, find each of the following.

19. $[f \circ g](^-2)$

20. $g[f(3)]$

21. $[g \circ f](x)$

Find the inverse of each function.

22. $f(x) = 3x - 4$

23. $f(x) = x^2 + 2$

24. Show that $f(x) = 2x - 3$ and $g(x) = \dfrac{x + 3}{2}$ are inverses of each other.

25. Graph $f(x) = 3x - 2$ and its inverse.

cumulative review

Solve each open sentence.

1. $2x + 4 = 13$
2. $19 - 2b = 13$
3. $4(2y - 3) = 3(2y + 4)$
4. $\frac{2}{3}(x + 1) = -\frac{4}{5}$
5. $x = 2 + \frac{x^2 - 4}{x}$
6. $\frac{2a - 4}{a - 2} = 2$
7. $|3 + 2r| = 3$
8. $|2x| + 1 = 5$
9. $x \le 5(x - 2)$
10. $2x \le 5(x - 3)$
11. $\frac{b}{2} - 1 > 3 - b$
12. $\frac{2t - 5}{2} > \frac{5t + 4}{5}$

Graph each equation or inequality.

13. $2x + y = 4$
14. $x - y = 5$
15. $x - 2y = {}^-1$
16. $x = {}^-2$
17. $y = \frac{3}{4}x - 3$
18. $4y = x + 2$
19. $2x - y \ge 4$
20. $x - 3y \le 6$
21. ${}^-2x + 3y < {}^-6$

Solve each system of equations.

22. $3x - 2y = 8$
    $4x + y = 7$
23. $2y - 3x = 0$
    $x - y = {}^-2$
24. $2x + 3y = 7$
    $\frac{1}{4}x - \frac{1}{6}y = \frac{1}{3}$

Solve each system of inequalities by graphing.

25. $x > 0$
    $x + y \le {}^-6$
26. $x + 2y \ge 8$
    $3x - 5y < 6$

Simplify.

27. $2({}^-5a)(a^2)$
28. $ab(a^3 - ab + b)$
29. $(x + 5)(x - 3)$
30. $(2x + 4y)(x - y)$
31. $-\frac{a^3b}{ab}$
32. $\frac{x^{10}}{x^2} \cdot \frac{x^5}{x^3}$

Factor.

33. $3x^2 - 3xy + x$
34. $5ax + 15ay$
35. $9x^2 - 36$
36. $8x^3 - 27y^3$
37. $y^2 - 8y + 16$
38. $2x^2 - 11x + 5$

Simplify.

39. $\sqrt{72x^2}$
40. $\sqrt[3]{-54}$
41. $\sqrt{\frac{2}{3}}$
42. $4\sqrt{7} - \sqrt{7}$
43. $\frac{\sqrt{10}}{\sqrt{2}}$
44. $(5\sqrt{2} + 1)^2$
45. $({}^-1 - 2i) - (3 - i)$
46. $(5 + 3i)({}^-6 + i)$
47. $\sqrt{-20} + 2\sqrt{5} - 3i - 4^2$

Solve each equation.

48. $6x^2 - x - 1 = 0$
49. $x^2 = 4x$
50. $x(2x - 3) = {}^-1$
51. $x^2 - 8x = 5$
52. $x^2 - 2\sqrt{2}x + 3 = 0$
53. $2x^2 + 3x - 2 = 0$

54. $x^2 - 3x + 1 = 0$ **55.** $3x^2 - 5x = 1$ **56.** $x^2 - x + 2 = 0$

Graph each equation. Name the vertex, axis of symmetry, and direction of opening.

57. $y = 5(x - 2)^2 - 4$

58. $\frac{1}{8}(y + 2)^2 + 3 = x$

59. $x^2 - 2x + 4y + 5 = 0$

60. $y^2 - 12x + 2y + 1 = 0$

Graph the solutions for the following systems of inequalities.

61. $x^2 + y^2 \geq 16$
$y = 6$

62. $(y - 3)^2 \leq x + 2$
$y \geq x^2 - 4$

State whether the graph of each of the following equations is a parabola, a circle, an ellipse, or a hyperbola. Then draw the graph.

63. $4x^2 - y^2 = 4$

64. $x^2 + y^2 = 9$

65. $\frac{x^2}{9} + \frac{y^2}{25} = 1$

66. $y^2 = 8x$

67. $x^2 + y^2 - 4x + 2y - 4 = 0$

68. $\frac{(y + 2)^2}{9} - \frac{(x - 1)^2}{16} = 1$

Find $p(1)$ and $p(^-2)$ for each of the following.

69. $p(x) = x^2 - 2x + 6$

70. $p(x) = x^3 + 2x^2 - 11x - 12$

Find all rational zeros for each function.

71. $f(x) = (x + 1)(x - 3)(2x - 5)$

72. $f(x) = 2x^3 + 3x^2 - 5x - 6$

73. $f(x) = 2x^3 + 7x^2 - 42x - 72$

74. $f(x) = 3x^3 - 8x^2 - 5x - 6$

If $f(x) = 2x + 3$, $g(x) = x - 1$, and $h(x) = x^2 + 4$, find each of the following.

75. $[f \circ g](3)$

76. $[g \circ h](2)$

77. $g[f(^-1)]$

78. $h[f(x)]$

Solve each problem.

79. The sum of three consecutive integers is 105. Find the integers.

80. A jar of pennies and nickels contains 110 coins worth $2.50. How many nickels are in the jar?

81. Six years ago, Marty was four times as old as Joseph. In ten more years Marty will be twice as old as Joseph. Find their ages now.

82. The carpet in Sang Lee's living room is 9 feet by 12 feet. If the area of the room is 154 square feet, how wide is a strip of uniform width around the carpet?

chapter
10
Rational Polynomial Expressions

Terry and Fran own Riegle's Custom Painting and Paper Hanging. Terry can paint the interior of an average-size house in three days. Fran can do the same job in four days. Suppose they work together. The rational equation $\frac{x}{3} + \frac{x}{4} = 1$ can be used to determine how many days it would take them to complete the job.

10–1   Multiplying Rational Expressions

Rational numbers and **rational algebraic expressions** are similar.

A rational number can be expressed as the quotient of two integers.

$$\frac{2}{3} \qquad \frac{415}{100} \qquad \frac{^-6}{11}$$

A rational algebraic expression can be expressed as the quotient of two polynomials.

$$\frac{2x}{x-5} \qquad \frac{p^2-25}{p^2+4p+1}$$

To simplify a rational algebraic expression, divide both numerator and denominator by their greatest common factor (GCF).

All polynomials, including constants are rational expressions. But not all rational expressions are polynomials.

examples

1 Simplify $\dfrac{2x(x-5)}{(x-5)(x^2-1)}$.

$$\frac{2x(x-5)}{(x-5)(x^2-1)} = \frac{2x}{x^2-1} \qquad \text{\textit{The GCF is }} (x-5).$$

2 Simplify $\dfrac{x^2y-x^2}{x^3-x^3y}$.

$$\begin{aligned} \frac{x^2y-x^2}{x^3-x^3y} &= \frac{x^2(y-1)}{x^3(1-y)} \\ &= \frac{^-1 \cdot x^2(1-y)}{x \cdot x^2(1-y)} \qquad y-1 = {^-1}(1-y) \\ &= -\frac{1}{x} \qquad\qquad \text{\textit{The GCF is }} x^2(1-y). \end{aligned}$$

Both rational numbers and rational expressions are multiplied the same way. Multiply numerators and multiply denominators.

$$\frac{2}{3} \cdot \frac{4}{5} = \frac{2 \cdot 4}{3 \cdot 5} \quad \text{or} \quad \frac{8}{15}$$

$$\frac{(x+1)}{(x-4)} \cdot \frac{(2x+3)}{(3x-1)} = \frac{(x+1)(2x+3)}{(x-4)(3x-1)} \quad \text{or} \quad \frac{2x^2+5x+3}{3x^2-13x+4}$$

This method can be generalized as follows.

For all rational expressions $\dfrac{a}{b}$ **and** $\dfrac{c}{d}$, $b \neq 0$ **and** $d \neq 0$,

$$\frac{a}{b} \cdot \frac{c}{d} = \frac{ac}{bd}.$$

Multiplying Rational Expressions

3 Find $\dfrac{4a}{5b} \cdot \dfrac{15b}{16a}$.

$$\dfrac{4a}{5b} \cdot \dfrac{15b}{16a} = \dfrac{60ab}{80ab}$$

$$= \dfrac{3 \cdot 20ab}{4 \cdot 20ab}$$

$$= \dfrac{3}{4} \qquad \text{The GCF is 20ab.}$$

4 Find $\dfrac{x^2 - 9}{x^2 + x - 12} \cdot \dfrac{x + 2}{x + 3}$.

$$\dfrac{x^2 - 9}{x^2 + x - 12} \cdot \dfrac{x + 2}{x + 3} = \dfrac{(x^2 - 9)(x + 2)}{(x^2 + x - 12)(x + 3)}$$

$$= \dfrac{(x - 3)(x + 3)(x + 2)}{(x - 3)(x + 4)(x + 3)} \qquad \text{Factor.}$$

$$= \dfrac{x + 2}{x + 4} \qquad \text{The GCF is } (x - 3)(x + 3).$$

exercises

Exploratory For each expression, find the greatest common factor (GCF) of the numerator and denominator. Then simplify each expression.

1. $\dfrac{24}{72}$

2. $\dfrac{99}{132}$

3. $\dfrac{33}{303}$

4. $\dfrac{37}{81}$

5. $\dfrac{13x}{39x^2}$

6. $\dfrac{42y}{18xy}$

7. $\dfrac{34x^2}{42x^5}$

8. $\dfrac{42y^3x}{18y^7}$

9. $\dfrac{38a^2}{42ab}$

10. $\dfrac{79a^2b}{158a^3bc}$

11. $\dfrac{-3x^2y^5}{18x^5y^2}$

12. $\dfrac{14y^2z}{49yz^3}$

13. $\dfrac{(-2x^2y)^3}{4x^5y}$

14. $\dfrac{a^3b^2}{(-ab)^3}$

15. $\dfrac{(2xy)^4}{(x^2y)^2}$

16. $\dfrac{(-3t^2u)^3}{(6tu^2)^2}$

17. $\dfrac{m + 5}{2m + 10}$

18. $\dfrac{4x}{x^2 - x}$

19. $\dfrac{a + b}{a^2 - b^2}$

20. $\dfrac{1 - x^2}{x + 1}$

21. $\dfrac{8x^2 - x^3}{16 - 2x}$

22. $\dfrac{2y^2 - 18}{2y - 6}$

23. $\dfrac{y^2 - 9}{y^2 + 6y + 9}$

24. $\dfrac{y^2 + 8y - 20}{y^2 - 4}$

25. $\dfrac{2x^2 + 8x}{x^2 + x - 12x}$

26. $\dfrac{6y^3 - 9y^2}{2y^2 + 5y - 12}$

27. $\dfrac{x^2 - x - 20}{x^2 + 7x + 12}$

28. $\dfrac{y^2 + 4y + 4}{3y^2 + 5y - 2}$

29. $\dfrac{a^2 + 2a + 1}{2a^2 + 3a + 1}$

30. $\dfrac{2b^2 - 9b + 9}{b^2 - 6b + 9}$

Written Find each product. Write each answer in simplest form.

1. $\dfrac{3}{8} \cdot \dfrac{16}{7}$

2. $\dfrac{21}{35} \cdot \dfrac{56}{42}$

3. $\dfrac{18x}{8y} \cdot \dfrac{3x}{27z}$

4. $\dfrac{3ab}{4ac} \cdot \dfrac{6a^2}{3b^2}$

5. $\dfrac{7a}{14b} \cdot \dfrac{6b^2}{a}$

6. $\dfrac{^-4ab}{21c} \cdot \dfrac{14c^2}{18a^2}$

7. $\dfrac{7xy}{16z} \cdot \dfrac{^-4z^2}{21x^2}$

8. $\dfrac{x}{3y} \cdot \dfrac{9y^4}{3x^5}$

9. $\dfrac{3a^2b^3c}{4ab^2} \cdot \dfrac{6c}{1}$

10. $\dfrac{4a^2xy}{12bc} \cdot \dfrac{24bc^2}{6xy}$

11. $\dfrac{^-3abc}{9abd} \cdot \dfrac{7d}{18c^2}$

12. $\dfrac{11xy}{5xz} \cdot \dfrac{^-15z}{^-66y^2}$

13. $\dfrac{(cd)^3}{a} \cdot \dfrac{ax^2}{xc^2d}$

14. $\dfrac{(3a)^3}{18b^3} \cdot \dfrac{12a^4b^5}{(3a)^2}$

15. $\left(\dfrac{x^2}{y}\right)^2 \cdot \dfrac{5}{3x}$

16. $\left(\dfrac{3a^3}{b^2}\right)^3 \cdot \dfrac{4b^2}{3a^7}$

17. $\dfrac{y+2}{x} \cdot \dfrac{x^2}{(y+2)^2}$

18. $\dfrac{3(y+4)^2}{x^2} \cdot \dfrac{2x^3}{9(y+4)}$

19. $\dfrac{x-3}{x+4} \cdot \dfrac{x+4}{2}$

20. $\dfrac{2n-4}{5} \cdot \dfrac{10}{n-2}$

21. $\dfrac{4x+40}{3x} \cdot \dfrac{9x}{3x+30}$

22. $\dfrac{4y^2-9}{4y^2} \cdot \dfrac{8y}{2y-3}$

23. $\dfrac{^-(2-b)}{x} \cdot \dfrac{x^2}{b-2}$

24. $\dfrac{a+b}{14} \cdot \dfrac{7}{b+a}$

25. $\dfrac{x^2-y^2}{y^2} \cdot \dfrac{y^3}{y-x}$

26. $\dfrac{x^2-y^2}{x+y} \cdot \dfrac{11}{x-y}$

27. $-\dfrac{x^2-y^2}{x+y} \cdot \dfrac{1}{x-y}$

28. $\dfrac{(y-2)^2}{(x-4)^2} \cdot \dfrac{x-4}{y-2}$

29. $\dfrac{a^2-b^2}{14} \cdot \dfrac{35}{a+b}$

30. $\dfrac{x^2-y^2}{70} \cdot \dfrac{56}{4x-4y}$

31. $\dfrac{3x+15}{2} \cdot \dfrac{8}{x^2+4x-5}$

32. $\dfrac{y^2+8y+15}{y} \cdot \dfrac{y^2}{2y+10}$

33. $\dfrac{a^3-b^3}{b^2-a^2} \cdot \dfrac{a+b}{a^2+ab+b^2}$

34. $\dfrac{x^2-3x-10}{x+2} \cdot \dfrac{y^3}{5-x}$

35. $\dfrac{3m^2-m}{5m+10} \cdot \dfrac{4-m^2}{6m}$

36. $\dfrac{x^2-8x-48}{2(12-x)} \cdot \dfrac{4x+4y}{x+y}$

37. $\dfrac{x^2+7x+12}{x^2-9} \cdot \dfrac{8x}{16y}$

38. $\dfrac{c^2-4cd}{3a} \cdot \dfrac{18a^2b}{c-4d}$

39. $\dfrac{x^2+3x-10}{x^2+8x+15} \cdot \dfrac{x^2+5x+6}{x^2+4x+4}$

40. $\dfrac{x^3+y^3}{x^2-y^2} \cdot \dfrac{3a}{9ab} \cdot \dfrac{6xb}{7x}$

41. $\dfrac{x^3+3x^2+3x+1}{x+5} \cdot \dfrac{x^2-25}{x+1}$

42. $\dfrac{x^4-1}{x+2} \cdot \dfrac{x^2-4}{x-1}$

43. $\dfrac{a^3-b^3}{a+b} \cdot \dfrac{a^2-b^2}{a^2+ab+b^2}$

44. $\dfrac{y^2-y-12}{y+12} \cdot \dfrac{y^2-4y-12}{y-4}$

45. $\dfrac{w^2-11w+24}{w^2-18w+80} \cdot \dfrac{w^2-15w+50}{w^2-9w+20}$

46. $\dfrac{2x^2+x-15}{4x^2+2x-30} \cdot \dfrac{6x^2-8x+2}{3x^2+8x-3}$

10–2 Dividing Rational Expressions

Recall that dividing by a fraction is the same as multiplying by its multiplicative inverse.

$$\frac{3}{8} \div \frac{3}{4} = \frac{3}{8} \cdot \frac{4}{3} \qquad \text{\textit{The inverse of } } \frac{3}{4} \text{ \textit{is} } \frac{4}{3}.$$

$$= \frac{12}{24}$$

$$= \frac{1}{2} \qquad \text{\textit{The GCF is 12.}}$$

Similarly, dividing by a rational algebraic expression is the same as multiplying by its multiplicative inverse.

Recall that a fraction names a rational number.

For all rational expressions $\frac{a}{b}$ and $\frac{c}{d}$, b, c, and $d \neq 0$,

$$\frac{a}{b} \div \frac{c}{d} = \frac{a}{b} \cdot \frac{d}{c}.$$

Dividing Rational Expressions

examples

1 Find $\dfrac{4x^2y}{15a^3b^3} \div \dfrac{2xy^2}{5ab^3}$.

$$\frac{4x^2y}{15a^3b^3} \div \frac{2xy^2}{5ab^3} = \frac{4x^2y}{15a^3b^3} \cdot \frac{5ab^3}{2xy^2} \qquad \text{\textit{The inverse of } } \frac{2xy^2}{5ab^3} \text{ \textit{is} } \frac{5ab^3}{2xy^2}.$$

$$= \frac{20x^2yab^3}{30xy^2a^3b^3}$$

$$= \frac{2x}{3ya^2} \qquad \text{\textit{The GCF is } } 10xyab^3.$$

2 Find $\dfrac{x^2}{x^2 - 25y^2} \div \dfrac{x}{x + 5y}$.

$$\frac{x^2}{x^2 - 25y^2} \div \frac{x}{x + 5y} = \frac{x^2}{x^2 - 25y^2} \cdot \frac{x + 5y}{x} \qquad \text{\textit{The inverse of } } \frac{x}{x + 5y} \text{ \textit{is} } \frac{x + 5y}{x}.$$

$$= \frac{x^2(x + 5y)}{x(x^2 - 25y^2)}$$

$$= \frac{x^2(x + 5y)}{x(x + 5y)(x - 5y)} \qquad \text{\textit{Factor } } x^2 - 25y^2.$$

$$= \frac{x}{x - 5y} \qquad \text{\textit{The GCF is } } x(x + 5y).$$

A complex rational expression, also called a **complex fraction**, is an expression whose numerator or denominator, or both, contain rational expressions.

$$\frac{\dfrac{x^2 + y^2}{x - y}}{\dfrac{x^2 - y^2}{x + y}} \qquad \frac{\dfrac{1}{x} + 3}{\dfrac{2}{x} + 5} \qquad \frac{8}{\dfrac{x}{3 - y}}$$

To simplify a complex fraction, treat it as a division problem.

example

3 **Simplify** $\dfrac{\frac{4-x^2}{2}}{\frac{2-x}{5}}$.

$$\frac{\frac{4-x^2}{2}}{\frac{2-x}{5}} = \frac{4-x^2}{2} \div \frac{2-x}{5}$$

$$= \frac{4-x^2}{2} \cdot \frac{5}{2-x} \qquad \textit{The inverse of } \frac{2-x}{5} \textit{ is } \frac{5}{2-x}.$$

$$= \frac{5(4-x^2)}{2(2-x)}$$

$$= \frac{5(2+x)(2-x)}{2(2-x)} \qquad \textit{Factor.}$$

$$= \frac{5(2+x)}{2} \qquad \textit{The GCF is 2 } - \textit{ x.}$$

exercises

Exploratory State the multiplicative inverse of each expression.

1. $\dfrac{3}{8}$

2. $-\dfrac{7}{43}$

3. $\dfrac{7x}{9y}$

4. $\dfrac{18x}{7}$

5. 16

6. $-\dfrac{3}{22}$

7. $\dfrac{x+y}{2}$

8. $\dfrac{x^2-8}{x-1}$

9. $\dfrac{(x+4)^2}{(x-3)^2}$

10. $x+a$

11. $\dfrac{1}{x-y}$

12. $-\dfrac{2x}{a^2-b^2}$

State a multiplication expression for each of the following.

13. $\dfrac{3}{8} \div \dfrac{1}{2}$

14. $-\dfrac{5}{6} \div \dfrac{1}{3}$

15. $\dfrac{a^2}{b^2} \div \dfrac{b^2}{a^2}$

16. $\dfrac{p^3}{2q} \div \dfrac{^-p^2}{4q}$

17. $\dfrac{3m}{m+1} \div (m-2)$

18. $\dfrac{y^2}{x+2} \div \dfrac{y}{x+2}$

Written Find the multiplicative inverse of each expression and simplify.

1. $\dfrac{14}{a^2}$

2. $-\dfrac{9}{15ab}$

3. $\dfrac{x+y}{ab}$

4. $\dfrac{3x}{x^2+7x}$

5. $\dfrac{a^2+ab+b^2}{a^2-b^2}$

6. $\dfrac{y-4}{y^2-4y-12}$

7. $\dfrac{3x+3}{x^2+2x-3}$

8. $\dfrac{3x-21}{x^2-49}$

Find each quotient. Write each answer in simplest form.

9. $-\dfrac{46}{90} \div \dfrac{23}{10}$

10. $-\dfrac{16.8}{7} \div \dfrac{8.4}{35}$

11. $\dfrac{7}{a} \div \dfrac{14}{a^2}$

12. $-\dfrac{3}{5a} \div -\dfrac{9}{15ab}$

13. $\dfrac{1}{x} \div -\dfrac{3}{x^2}$

14. $-\dfrac{b^3c}{d} \div \dfrac{bc}{d^2}$

15. $\dfrac{a^2b}{2c} \div \dfrac{a^2b^2}{c^2}$

16. $\dfrac{3d^3c}{a^4} \div -\dfrac{6dc}{a^5}$

17. $\dfrac{(ab)^3}{d^3} \div \dfrac{a^2b^4}{(cd)^4}$

18. $\dfrac{13a^2}{14c} \div \dfrac{26a^3}{70c^2}$

19. $\dfrac{(x+y)^2}{a} \div \dfrac{x+y}{ab}$

20. $\dfrac{x+y}{a} \div \dfrac{x+y}{a^2}$

21. $\dfrac{5}{m-3} \div \dfrac{10}{m-3}$

22. $\dfrac{11}{m+6} \div \dfrac{22}{(m+6)^2}$

23. $\dfrac{a^2-b^2}{2a} \div \dfrac{a-b}{6a}$

24. $\dfrac{y-5}{6} \div \dfrac{y-5}{18}$

25. $\dfrac{2x+2}{x^2+5x+6} \div \dfrac{3x+3}{x^2+2x-3}$

26. $\dfrac{3x-21}{x^2-49} \div \dfrac{3x}{x^2+7x}$

27. $\dfrac{a^2+2a-15}{a-3} \div \dfrac{a^2-4}{2}$

28. $\dfrac{y^2-y}{w^2-y^2} \div \dfrac{y^2-2y+1}{1-y}$

Simplify each expression.

29. $\dfrac{\dfrac{x^2-y^2}{2}}{\dfrac{x-y}{4}}$

30. $\dfrac{\dfrac{w^2+2w+1}{w+1}}{3}$

31. $\dfrac{\dfrac{5a^2-20}{2a+2}}{\dfrac{10a-20}{4a}}$

32. $\dfrac{\dfrac{x^2-1}{x^2-3x-10}}{\dfrac{x^2-12x+35}{x^2+3x+2}}$

33. $\dfrac{\dfrac{2y}{y^2-4}}{\dfrac{3}{y^2-4y+4}}$

34. $\dfrac{\dfrac{c^2+2c-3}{3c+3}}{\dfrac{c^2+5c+6}{2c+2}}$

35. $\dfrac{\dfrac{p^2+7p}{3p}}{\dfrac{49-p^2}{3p-21}}$

36. $\dfrac{\dfrac{9-4t^2}{t^2+6t+9}}{\dfrac{8t-12}{2t^2+5t-3}}$

37. $\dfrac{\dfrac{3+10t^2-17t}{5t^2+4t-1}}{\dfrac{4t^2-9}{3+5t+2t^2}}$

38. Write a computer program to find the multiplicative inverse of any nonzero rational number. Print out the results in fraction form and in decimal form.

The position of symbols is very important in algebra. Study the list of expressions below.

$$2x \qquad 2 - x \qquad x - 2 \qquad \frac{x}{2} \qquad \frac{2}{x} \qquad x^2 \qquad \frac{x^2}{x + 2}$$

Each expression contains the symbols 2 and x. However, each expression says something different. The same expressions are listed below. The arrows indicate the order in which the symbols usually are read, and the words on the right are English translations of the expressions.

$2x$	two times x
$2 - x$	two minus x
$x - 2$	x minus two
$\frac{x}{2}$	x divided by two
$\frac{2}{x}$	two divided by x
x^2	x squared
$\frac{x^2}{x + 2}$	x squared divided by the quantity x plus two.

Exercises   As quickly as possible, look at each list of expressions. Which expressions in the list are the same as the first expression?

1. $\dfrac{x^3}{3}$ a. $\dfrac{x}{3}$ b. $\dfrac{x^3}{3}$ c. $\dfrac{x}{3^3}$ d. $\dfrac{3x}{3}$

2. $\dfrac{(cd)^3}{a}$ a. $\dfrac{(cd)^3}{a}$ b. $\dfrac{cd^3}{a}$ c. $\dfrac{3(cd)}{a}$ d. $\dfrac{(cd)^3}{a}$

3. $\dfrac{1}{x - y}$ a. $\dfrac{1}{y - x}$ b. $\dfrac{1}{x + y}$ c. $\dfrac{x}{1 - y}$ d. $\dfrac{1}{x - y}$

4. $\dfrac{x^2 - 4}{x - 1}$ a. $\dfrac{x - 4}{x - 1}$ b. $\dfrac{x^2 - 4}{x - 1}$ c. $\dfrac{x^2 - 4}{x^2 - 1}$ d. $\dfrac{4 - x^2}{x^2 - 1}$

5. $\dfrac{8x^2 - x^3}{16 - 2x}$ a. $\dfrac{8x^2 - x^3}{2x - 16}$ b. $\dfrac{8x^3 - x^2}{16 - 2x}$ c. $\dfrac{8x^2 - x^3}{16 - 2x}$ d. $\dfrac{8x^3 - x^2}{2x - 16}$

6–10. In problems **1–5,** which expressions are different than the first expression? How are they different?

11. Turn to page 297 in this textbook. Copy each expression in Exploratory Exercises **1–12.** Draw an arrow to indicate the order you would read the symbols in each expression.

12. Write an English translation for each expression in problem **11.**

10–3   Adding and Subtracting Rational Expressions

You add rational numbers like $\frac{7}{13}$ and $\frac{4}{13}$ in the following way.

$$\frac{7}{13} + \frac{4}{13} = \frac{7+4}{13} \quad \text{or} \quad \frac{11}{13}$$

The sum of two rational numbers with a common denominator is the sum of the numerators over the common denominator.

If two rational expressions have common denominators, add them in a similar fashion.

$$\frac{7x}{13y^2} + \frac{4x}{13y^2} = \frac{7x+4x}{13y^2} \quad \text{or} \quad \frac{11x}{13y^2}$$

The sum of two rational expressions with a common denominator is the sum of the numerators over the common denominator.

To add two rational numbers with different denominators, first find two equivalent rational numbers with common denominators. Then add the equivalent fractions.

$$\frac{3}{8} + \frac{2}{3} = \frac{3 \cdot 3}{8 \cdot 3} + \frac{2 \cdot 8}{3 \cdot 8} \qquad \textit{The least common denominator is } 8 \cdot 3.$$
$$= \frac{9}{24} + \frac{16}{24}$$
$$= \frac{9+16}{24}$$
$$= \frac{25}{24}$$

One way to find the least common denominator (LCD) is first to factor each denominator into its prime factors. For example, suppose you wish to add $\frac{5}{36}$ and $\frac{7}{24}$.

The prime factors of 36 and 24 are shown below.

$$36 = 2 \cdot 2 \cdot 3 \cdot 3$$
$$24 = 2 \cdot 2 \cdot 2 \cdot 3$$

The least common denominator of 36 and 24 contains each prime factor the greatest number of times that it appears.

$$\text{LCD} = 2 \cdot 2 \cdot 2 \cdot 3 \cdot 3 \text{ or } 72$$

Now, add the fractions.

$$\frac{5}{36} + \frac{7}{24} = \frac{10}{72} + \frac{21}{72} \qquad \frac{5}{36} = \frac{5 \cdot 2}{36 \cdot 2} \quad \text{or} \quad \frac{10}{72} \text{ and } \frac{7}{24} = \frac{7 \cdot 3}{24 \cdot 3} \quad \text{or} \quad \frac{21}{72}$$
$$= \frac{31}{72}$$

To add rational expressions with different denominators, follow the same procedure. First find two equivalent expressions with a common denominator. Then add the equivalent expressions.

1 Find $\dfrac{7x}{15y^2} + \dfrac{y}{18xy}$.

First find the LCD of $15y^2$ and $18xy$.

$$15y^2 = 3 \cdot 5 \cdot y \cdot y \qquad\qquad 18xy = 2 \cdot 3 \cdot 3 \cdot x \cdot y$$

The LCD is $2 \cdot 3 \cdot 3 \cdot 5 \cdot x \cdot y \cdot y$ or $90xy^2$.

Rewrite each term using the LCD and add.

$$\begin{aligned}
\frac{7x}{15y^2} + \frac{y}{18xy} &= \frac{7x \cdot 6x}{15y^2 \cdot 6x} + \frac{y \cdot 5y}{18xy \cdot 5y} \\
&= \frac{42x^2}{90xy^2} + \frac{5y^2}{90xy^2} \\
&= \frac{42x^2 + 5y^2}{90xy^2}
\end{aligned}$$

2 Find $\dfrac{1}{x^2 - 2x - 15} + \dfrac{3x + 1}{2x - 10}$.

$$\begin{aligned}
\frac{1}{x^2 - 2x - 15} + \frac{3x + 1}{2x - 10} &= \frac{1}{(x - 5)(x + 3)} + \frac{3x + 1}{2(x - 5)} \\
&= \frac{2}{2(x - 5)(x + 3)} + \frac{(3x + 1)(x + 3)}{2(x - 5)(x + 3)} \qquad \textit{The LCD is } 2(x - 5)(x + 3). \\
&= \frac{2 + (3x + 1)(x + 3)}{2(x - 5)(x + 3)} \\
&= \frac{2 + 3x^2 + 9x + x + 3}{2(x - 5)(x + 3)} \\
&= \frac{3x^2 + 10x + 5}{2(x - 5)(x + 3)} \qquad \textit{Simplify the numerator.}
\end{aligned}$$

Use a similar method to subtract rational expressions.

3 Find $\dfrac{x + 4}{2x - 8} - \dfrac{x + 12}{4x - 16}$.

$$\begin{aligned}
\frac{x + 4}{2x - 8} - \frac{x + 12}{4x - 16} &= \frac{x + 4}{2(x - 4)} - \frac{x + 12}{4(x - 4)} \qquad \textit{Factor each denominator.} \\
&= \frac{2(x + 4)}{4(x - 4)} - \frac{x + 12}{4(x - 4)} \qquad \textit{The LCD is } 4(x - 4). \\
&= \frac{(2x + 8) - (x + 12)}{4(x - 4)} \qquad \textit{Remember that } {}^-(x + 12) = {}^-x - 12. \\
&= \frac{x - 4}{4(x - 4)} \quad \textit{or} \quad \frac{1}{4} \qquad \textit{Simplify.}
\end{aligned}$$

Complex fractions may involve sums or differences.

4 **Simplify** $\dfrac{\dfrac{1}{x} - \dfrac{1}{y}}{1 + \dfrac{1}{x}}$.

$$\dfrac{\dfrac{1}{x} - \dfrac{1}{y}}{1 + \dfrac{1}{x}} = \dfrac{\dfrac{y}{xy} - \dfrac{x}{xy}}{\dfrac{x}{x} + \dfrac{1}{x}}$$ *Simplify the numerator and denominator.*

$$= \dfrac{\dfrac{y - x}{xy}}{\dfrac{x + 1}{x}}$$

$$= \dfrac{y - x}{xy} \div \dfrac{x + 1}{x}$$ *Write the complex fraction as a division problem.*

$$= \dfrac{y - x}{xy} \cdot \dfrac{x}{x + 1}$$

$$= \dfrac{y - x}{y(x + 1)} \text{ or } \dfrac{y - x}{xy + y}$$

exercises

Exploratory Find the least common denominator (LCD) for each pair of denominators given below.

1. $54, 28$
2. $78, 39$
3. $80, 125$
4. $12, 27$
5. $7a^2, 14ab$
6. $36x^2y, 20xyz$
7. $x(x - 2), x^2 - 4$
8. $(x + 2)(x + 1), x^2 - 1$
9. $x^2 + 2x + 1, x^2 - 9$
10. $3x + 15, x^2 + 3x - 15$
11. $x^2 - 8x, y^2 - 8y$
12. $96x^2, 16(x + 9)$

Written Find each sum. Write each answer in simplest form.

1. $\dfrac{5}{6a} + \dfrac{7}{4a}$
2. $\dfrac{7}{ab} + \dfrac{9}{b}$
3. $\dfrac{5}{a} + 7$

4. $\dfrac{2x}{3y} + 5$
5. $\dfrac{3x}{x - y} + \dfrac{4x}{y - x}$
6. $\dfrac{3a + 2}{a + b} + \dfrac{4}{2a + 2b}$

7. $-\dfrac{18}{9xy} + \dfrac{21}{6x}$
8. $-\dfrac{37a}{42b} + \dfrac{17b}{6a}$
9. $\dfrac{x}{x^2 - 9} + \dfrac{1}{2x + 6}$

10. $y - 1 + \dfrac{1}{y - 1}$
11. $\dfrac{3}{a - 2} + \dfrac{2}{a - 3}$
12. $\dfrac{6}{x^2 + 4x + 4} + \dfrac{5}{x + 2}$

13. $\dfrac{3}{x^2 - 25} + \dfrac{6}{x - 5}$
14. $\dfrac{x - 1}{x^2 - 1} + \dfrac{3}{5x + 5}$
15. $\dfrac{5}{x^2 - 3x - 28} + \dfrac{7}{2x - 14}$

16. $\dfrac{a}{a + 4} + \dfrac{2}{a^2 + 8a + 16}$
17. $\dfrac{2}{y^2 - 4y - 5} + \dfrac{5}{y^2 - 2y - 15}$

18. $\dfrac{2a}{3a - 15} + \dfrac{-16a + 20}{3a^2 - 12a - 15}$
19. $\dfrac{m^2 + n^2}{m^2 - n^2} + \dfrac{m}{n - m} + \dfrac{n}{m + n}$

20. $\dfrac{x}{x - y} + \dfrac{y}{y^2 - x^2} + \dfrac{2x}{x + y}$
21. $\dfrac{x + 1}{x - 1} + \dfrac{x + 2}{x - 2} + \dfrac{x}{x^2 - 3x + 2}$

Find each difference. Write each answer in simplest form.

22. $\dfrac{3}{4a} - \dfrac{2}{5a} - \dfrac{1}{2a}$

23. $\dfrac{11}{9} - \dfrac{7}{2a} - \dfrac{6}{5a}$

24. $\dfrac{9}{y-2} - \dfrac{2}{1-y}$

25. $\dfrac{7}{y-8} - \dfrac{6}{8-y}$

26. $\dfrac{y}{y-9} - \dfrac{^-9}{9-y}$

27. $\dfrac{8}{2y-16} - \dfrac{y}{8-y}$

28. $\dfrac{^-4y}{y^2-4} - \dfrac{y}{y+2}$

29. $\dfrac{x}{x+3} - \dfrac{6x}{x^2-9}$

30. $3m + 1 - \dfrac{2m}{3m+1}$

31. $\dfrac{y-2}{y-4} - \dfrac{y-8}{y-4}$

32. $\dfrac{6-y}{y-2} - \dfrac{3+y}{2-y}$

33. $\dfrac{x}{x^2+2x+1} - \dfrac{x+2}{x+1}$

34. $\dfrac{x-4}{2x-8} - \dfrac{x+5}{4x-16}$

35. $\dfrac{m}{m-3} - \dfrac{8m}{9-m^2}$

36. $\dfrac{x}{x+y} - \dfrac{x}{x^2-y^2}$

Simplify.

37. $\dfrac{\dfrac{x}{2} - \dfrac{x}{5}}{\dfrac{x}{3} - \dfrac{x}{6}}$

38. $\dfrac{\dfrac{2x}{ab} - \dfrac{5x}{4}}{\dfrac{3x}{a} - \dfrac{6x}{5}}$

39. $\dfrac{\dfrac{x+y}{x}}{\dfrac{1}{x} + \dfrac{1}{y}}$

40. $\dfrac{\dfrac{x}{y} - \dfrac{y}{x}}{\dfrac{1}{x} + \dfrac{1}{y}}$

41. $\dfrac{\dfrac{2}{x} + \dfrac{9}{x^2} - \dfrac{5}{x^3}}{2x - \dfrac{1}{2x}}$

42. $\dfrac{\dfrac{1}{a} - \dfrac{1}{a^2} - \dfrac{20}{a^3}}{\dfrac{1}{a} + \dfrac{8}{a^2} - \dfrac{16}{a^3}}$

43. $\dfrac{3 + \dfrac{5}{a+2}}{3 - \dfrac{10}{a+7}}$

44. $\dfrac{\dfrac{2x}{2x+1} - 1}{1 + \dfrac{2x}{1-2x}}$

Euclidean Algorithm　　　　excursions in algebra

The Greek mathematician Euclid (300 B.C.) is credited with developing a method for finding the greatest common factor (GCF) of two integers. This method is called the *Euclidean Algorithm*.

Example　Find the GCF of 232 and 136.

First, divide the greater number by the lesser and express the division in the form dividend = quotient · divisor + remainder.

dividend = quotient · divisor + remainder

$$232 \;=\; 1 \;\cdot\; 136 \;+\; 96$$

Then, divide the divisor by the remainder.

$$136 \;=\; 1 \;\cdot\; 96 \;+\; 40$$

Continue this process until a zero remainder is obtained.

$$96 \;=\; 2 \;\cdot\; 40 \;+\; 16$$
$$40 \;=\; 2 \;\cdot\; 16 \;+\; 8 \qquad \textit{Last nonzero remainder is 8.}$$
$$16 \;=\; 2 \;\cdot\; 8 \;+\; 0$$

The last nonzero remainder is the GCF. Thus, the GCF of 232 and 136 is 8.

Exercises　Find the GCF for each pair of integers.

1. 187, 221　　**2.** 182, 1690　　**3.** 4807, 5083　　**4.** 1078, 1547　　**5.** 714, 2030

10–4   Solving Rational Equations

An equation that contains one or more rational expressions is called a **rational equation.** One way to solve a rational equation is to multiply both sides of the equation by the least common denominator (LCD).

1 **Solve $\frac{x}{9} + \frac{x}{7} = 1$.**

$$\frac{x}{9} + \frac{x}{7} = 1$$

$$63\left(\frac{x}{9} + \frac{x}{7}\right) = 63(1) \qquad \textit{The LCD is } 3 \cdot 3 \cdot 7 \textit{ or } 63.$$

$$63 \cdot \frac{x}{9} + 63 \cdot \frac{x}{7} = 63 \qquad \textit{Use the distributive property.}$$

$$7x + 9x = 63$$

$$16x = 63$$

$$x = \frac{63}{16}$$

The solution is $\frac{63}{16}$.

2 **Solve $\frac{3}{4} - \frac{3}{y + 2} = \frac{9}{28}$.**

$$\frac{3}{4} - \frac{3}{y + 2} = \frac{9}{28}$$

$$28(y + 2)\left[\frac{3}{4} - \frac{3}{y + 2}\right] = 28(y + 2)\left[\frac{9}{28}\right] \qquad \textit{The LCD is } 2 \cdot 2 \cdot 7 \cdot (y + 2)$$
$$\textit{or } 28(y + 2).$$

$$28(y + 2)\left(\frac{3}{4}\right) - 28(y + 2)\left(\frac{3}{y + 2}\right) = 9(y + 2)$$

$$21y + 42 - 84 = 9y + 18$$

$$12y = 60$$

$$y = 5$$

Check: $\dfrac{3}{4} - \dfrac{3}{y + 2} = \dfrac{9}{28}$

$$\frac{3}{4} - \frac{3}{5 + 2} \overset{?}{=} \frac{9}{28} \qquad \textit{Substitute 5 for y.}$$

$$\frac{3}{4} - \frac{3}{7} \overset{?}{=} \frac{9}{28}$$

$$\frac{21}{28} - \frac{12}{28} \overset{?}{=} \frac{9}{28}$$

$$\frac{9}{28} = \frac{9}{28}$$

The solution is 5.

Always notice the values of the variables for which a rational equation is *not* defined. After multiplying both sides of the equation by the LCD, some of these values may appear as results.

examples

3 Solve $\dfrac{7}{x-3} = \dfrac{x+4}{x-3}$.

$$\frac{7}{x-3} = \frac{x+4}{x-3}$$

$$(x-3)\left[\frac{7}{x-3}\right] = (x-3)\left[\frac{x+4}{x-3}\right] \qquad \text{The LCD is } x-3.$$

$$7 = x+4$$

$$3 = x$$

If x is 3, the denominator, $x-3$, is 0. But division by zero is not defined. Thus, the original equation is *not* defined for 3 and the equation has *no* solution.

4 Solve $w + \dfrac{w}{w-1} = \dfrac{4w-3}{w-1}$.

$$w + \frac{w}{w-1} = \frac{4w-3}{w-1}$$

$$(w-1)\left[w + \frac{w}{w-1}\right] = (w-1)\left[\frac{4w-3}{w-1}\right] \qquad \text{The LCD is } w-1.$$

$$(w-1)w + w = 4w-3$$

$$w^2 - w + w = 4w-3$$

$$w^2 - 4w + 3 = 0$$

$$(w-3)(w-1) = 0$$

$$w = 3 \quad \text{or} \quad w = 1$$

The only solution is 3 because the original equation is *not* defined for 1.   *Why?*

exercises

Exploratory Find the least common denominator (LCD) for the expressions in each equation.

1. $\dfrac{1}{x} + \dfrac{1}{2} = \dfrac{2}{x}$

2. $\dfrac{3}{x+2} = \dfrac{4}{x-1}$

3. $\dfrac{1}{5} = \dfrac{2}{10y}$

4. $\dfrac{1}{4} = \dfrac{s-3}{8s}$

5. $\dfrac{6}{x} = \dfrac{9}{x^2}$

6. $\dfrac{7}{3a} + \dfrac{6}{5a^2} = 1$

7. $\dfrac{4}{x-3} = \dfrac{7}{x-2}$

8. $\dfrac{9}{x+5} = \dfrac{6}{x-3}$

9. $\dfrac{3}{m-5} = \dfrac{1}{6}$

10. $\dfrac{11}{2y} - \dfrac{2}{3y} = \dfrac{1}{6}$

11. $\dfrac{3m}{2+m} - \dfrac{5}{7} = 4$

12. $\dfrac{1-b}{1+b} + \dfrac{2b}{2b+3} = \dfrac{19}{6}$

Written Solve and check each equation.

1. $\dfrac{2}{x} + \dfrac{1}{4} = \dfrac{11}{12}$

2. $\dfrac{x^2}{6} - \dfrac{x}{3} = \dfrac{1}{2}$

3. $r^2 + \dfrac{17r}{6} = \dfrac{1}{2}$

4. $\dfrac{2y}{3} - \dfrac{y+3}{6} = 2$

5. $\dfrac{y+1}{3} + \dfrac{y-1}{3} = \dfrac{4}{3}$

6. $\dfrac{2y+1}{5} - \dfrac{2+7y}{15} = \dfrac{2}{3}$

7. $\dfrac{2y-5}{6} - \dfrac{y-5}{4} = \dfrac{3}{4}$

8. $\dfrac{4t-3}{5} - \dfrac{4-2t}{3} = 1$

9. $\dfrac{5+7p}{8} - \dfrac{3(5+p)}{10} = 2$

10. $\dfrac{2q-1}{3} - \dfrac{4q+5}{8} = -\dfrac{19}{24}$

11. $8 - \dfrac{2-5x}{4} = \dfrac{4x+9}{3}$

12. $\dfrac{3x+1}{4} - \dfrac{x+5}{5} = -2$

13. $x + 5 = \dfrac{6}{x}$

14. $a + 1 = \dfrac{6}{a}$

15. $\dfrac{1}{y^2-1} = \dfrac{2}{y^2+y-2}$

16. $\dfrac{x}{x^2-3} = \dfrac{5}{x+4}$

17. $x + \dfrac{12}{x} - 8 = 0$

18. $\dfrac{a}{a-1} + a = \dfrac{4a-3}{a-1}$

19. $x + \dfrac{x}{x-1} = \dfrac{4x-3}{x-1}$

20. $\dfrac{q}{q-5} + \dfrac{q}{q-5} = 3$

21. $1 + \dfrac{3}{y-1} = \dfrac{4}{3}$

22. $\dfrac{5}{6} - \dfrac{2m}{2m+3} = \dfrac{19}{6}$

23. $\dfrac{5}{2x} - \dfrac{3}{10} = \dfrac{1}{x}$

24. $\dfrac{1}{9} + \dfrac{1}{2a} = \dfrac{1}{a^2}$

25. $\dfrac{1}{x-1} + \dfrac{2}{x} = 0$

26. $\dfrac{1}{1-x} = 1 - \dfrac{x}{x-1}$

27. $\dfrac{4t}{3t-2} + \dfrac{2t}{3t+2} = 2$

28. $\dfrac{2p}{2p+3} - \dfrac{2p}{2p-3} = 1$

29. $\dfrac{12}{x^2-16} - \dfrac{24}{x-4} = 3$

30. $\dfrac{4}{x-2} - \dfrac{x+6}{x+1} = 1$

31. $\dfrac{9}{x-3} = \dfrac{x-4}{x-3} + \dfrac{1}{4}$

32. $\dfrac{x-4}{x-2} = \dfrac{x-2}{x+2} + \dfrac{1}{x-2}$

33. $\dfrac{3x-3}{4x} = \dfrac{6x-9}{6x} + \dfrac{1}{3x}$

34. $\dfrac{x-3}{2x} = \dfrac{x-2}{2x+1} - \dfrac{1}{2}$

35. $\dfrac{5}{x+2} = \dfrac{5}{x} + \dfrac{2}{3x}$

36. $\dfrac{6}{a-7} = \dfrac{a-49}{a^2-7a} + \dfrac{1}{a}$

37. $\dfrac{-2}{x-1} = \dfrac{2}{x+2} - \dfrac{4}{x-3}$

38. $\dfrac{2}{y+2} - \dfrac{y}{2-y} = \dfrac{y^2+4}{y^2-4}$

39. $\dfrac{4x^2}{x^2-9} - \dfrac{2x}{x+3} = \dfrac{3}{x-3}$

40. $\dfrac{t+4}{t} + \dfrac{3}{t-4} = \dfrac{-16}{t^2-4t}$

41. $\dfrac{y}{y-5} + \dfrac{17}{25-y^2} = \dfrac{1}{y+5}$

42. $\dfrac{x+3}{x+2} = 2 - \dfrac{3}{x^2+5x+6}$

43. $\dfrac{1}{n-2} = \dfrac{2n+1}{n^2+2n-8} + \dfrac{2}{n+4}$

44. $\dfrac{x}{x^2-1} + \dfrac{2}{x+1} = \dfrac{1}{2x-2}$

Challenge Solve and check each equation.

1. $\dfrac{6}{x^2-9} + \dfrac{4}{6+x-x^2} + \dfrac{2}{x^2+5x+6} = 0$

2. $\dfrac{y+2}{y+1} - \dfrac{y+3}{y+2} = \dfrac{y+4}{y+3} - \dfrac{y+5}{y+4}$

Contest Problem excursions in algebra

This problem appeared in a high school mathematics contest sponsored by the Mathematical Association of America.

The fraction $\dfrac{5x-11}{2x^2+x-6}$ was obtained by adding the two fractions $\dfrac{A}{x+2}$ and $\dfrac{B}{2x-3}$. Find the values of A and B.

Connie Hardesty is a photographer. To take sharp, clear pictures she must focus the camera.

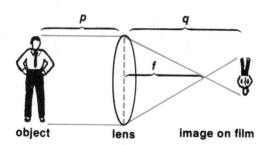

object lens image on film

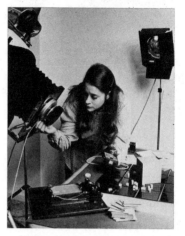

The following formula can be used to determine the distance the lens must be from the film for the camera to be focused.

$$\frac{1}{p} + \frac{1}{q} = \frac{1}{f}$$

p is the distance from the lens to the object.
q is the distance from the lens to the image on the film.
f is the focal length of the lens.

Example A camera has a lens with a focal length of 10 cm. Connie wants to photograph a flower that is 80 cm away. What must the distance be from the lens to the film for the camera to be in focus?

$$\frac{1}{p} + \frac{1}{q} = \frac{1}{f}$$

$$\frac{1}{80} + \frac{1}{q} = \frac{1}{10} \qquad p = 80, f = 10$$

$$q + 80 = 8q \qquad \textit{Multiply both sides by 80q.}$$

$$80 = 7q \quad \text{or} \quad q \approx 11.4$$

The lens must be about 11.4 cm from the film.

Exercises For the following values of p and f, find q.

1. $p = 45$ cm, $f = 5$ cm

2. $p = 600$ mm, $f = 60$ mm

3. $p = 28$ in., $f = 6$ in.

4. $p = 50$ cm, $f = 0.5$ cm

Solve each problem.

5. A camera has a lens with a focal length of 10 in. When Usha has the lens 12 in. from the film, the camera is focused to take a picture of her dog. How far from the lens is the dog?

6. Carl wants to take a picture of his house which is 10 m away. When the camera is focused the lens is 5 cm from the film. What is the focal length of the lens?

10–5   Using Rational Equations

Jake Qualls owns two tractors. With his older tractor, his front field can be plowed in 10 hours. With his newer tractor, the same field can be plowed in 6 hours. How long will it take to plow the field using both tractors at once? This question can be answered by solving a rational equation.

Let h stand for the number of hours it will take to plow the field.

What fraction of the field can the older tractor plow in 1 hour?	$\dfrac{1}{10}$
What fraction of the field can the newer tractor plow in 1 hour?	$\dfrac{1}{6}$
What fraction of the field can the older tractor plow in h hours?	$\dfrac{h}{10}$
What fraction of the field can the newer tractor plow in h hours?	$\dfrac{h}{6}$

Now write an equation.

$$\underset{\substack{\text{fraction older tractor} \\ \text{plows in h hours} \\ \frac{h}{10}}}{} \;+\; \underset{\substack{\text{fraction newer tractor} \\ \text{plows in h hours} \\ \frac{h}{6}}}{} \;=\; \underset{\substack{\text{both tractors plow the} \\ \text{entire job in h hours} \\ 1}}{}$$

Solve the equation.

$$\frac{h}{10} + \frac{h}{6} = 1$$

$$30\left(\frac{h}{10} + \frac{h}{6}\right) = 30(1) \qquad \textit{The LCD is } 2 \cdot 3 \cdot 5 \textit{ or } 30.$$

$$30 \cdot \frac{h}{10} + 30 \cdot \frac{h}{6} = 30 \qquad \textit{Use the distributive property.}$$

$$3h + 5h = 30$$

$$8h = 30$$

$$h = \frac{30}{8} \text{ or } 3\frac{3}{4}$$

It will take $3\frac{3}{4}$ hours to plow the field using both tractors.

The following is another example of how rational expressions can be used to solve verbal problems.

1 **A car travels 300 kilometers in the same time that a train travels 200 kilometers. The speed of the car is 20 kilometers per hour more than the speed of the train. Find the speed of the car and the speed of the train.**

Define a variable.   Let r stand for the speed of the car.

Write an equation.

$$\text{time car travels} \quad = \quad \text{time train travels}$$

$$\frac{\text{distance car travels}}{\text{rate car travels}} = \frac{\text{distance train travels}}{\text{rate train travels}}$$

$$\frac{300}{r} \quad = \quad \frac{200}{r - 20}$$

Solve the equation. $r(r - 20)\dfrac{300}{r} = r(r - 20)\dfrac{200}{r - 20}$ *The LCD is $r(r - 20)$.*

$$300(r - 20) = 200(r)$$
$$300r - 6000 = 200r$$
$$^{-}6000 = {}^{-}100r$$
$$60 = r \quad \text{and} \quad 40 = r - 20$$

Answer the problem.   The car's speed is 60 kilometers per hour, and the train's speed is 40 kilometers per hour.

exercises

Written   **Solve each problem.**

1. One computer can schedule classes for the students at John F. Kennedy High School in 5 hours. Another computer can do the job in 4 hours. If the computers work together, how long will it take to do the job?

2. One hose can fill the Sunshine's small swimming pool in 6 hours. A second, newer hose can fill the pool in 4 hours. If both hoses are used, how long will it take to fill the pool?

3. Jan Zeiss can tile a floor in 14 hours. Together Jan and her helper Bill can tile the same size floor in 9 hours. How long would it take Bill to do the job alone?

4. Elena Dias can paint a 9 by 12 room in $1\frac{1}{2}$ hours. If Luisa Alicea helps, they can paint the same size room in 1 hour. How long would it take Luisa to paint such a room by herself?

5. A painter works on a job for 10 days and is then joined by her helper. Together they finish the job in 6 more days. Her helper could have done the job alone in 30 days. How long would it have taken the painter to do the job alone?

6. A tank can be filled by a hose in 10 hours. The tank can be emptied by a drain pipe in 20 hours. If the drain pipe is open while the tank is filling, how long will it take to fill?

7. The denominator of a fraction is 1 less than twice the numerator. If 7 is added to both numerator and denominator, the resulting fraction has a value of $\frac{7}{10}$. Find the original fraction.

8. Five times the multiplicative inverse of a number is added to the number and the result is $10\frac{1}{2}$. What is the number?

9. The ratio of 4 less than a number to 26 more than that number is 1 to 3. What is the number?

10. Two numbers are in a ratio of 6 to 7. If the first is increased by 2 and the second is increased by 1, the resulting numbers are in the ratio of 4 to 5. Find the original numbers.

11. A boat travels at a rate of 15 kilometers per hour in still water. It travels 60 kilometers upstream in the same time that it travels 90 kilometers downstream. What is the rate of the current?

12. A plane flies from Chicago to Los Angeles, a distance of 2000 miles, in 4 hours. It flies against a 50 mph wind. It returns in $3\frac{1}{3}$ hours. Find the speed of the plane in still air.

13. Increasing the average speed of the Pickerington Express Bus by 13 km/h resulted in the 260 km trip taking an hour less than before. What was the original average speed of the bus?

14. The speed of the current in the Mississippi River is 5 miles per hour. A boat travels downstream 26 miles and returns in $10\frac{2}{3}$ hours. What is its speed in still water?

15. Conrad can jog to Chris' house in 10 minutes. Chris can ride her bike to Conrad's house in 6 minutes. If they start from their houses at the same time, in how many minutes do they meet?

16. The simple interest for one year on a sum of money is $108. Suppose the interest rate is increased by 2%. Then $450 less than the original sum could be invested and yield the same annual interest. How much is the original sum of money, and what is the original rate of interest?

17. The load capacities of two trucks are in the ratio of 5 to 2. The smaller truck has a capacity 3 tons less than that of the larger truck. What is the capacity of the larger truck?

18. Two candles are the same length. One burns up in 6 hours and the other in 9 hours. If they are both lit at the same time, how long is it before one is twice as long as the other?

19. At what time between 5 o'clock and 6 o'clock do the hands of a clock coincide?

20. Write a computer program to find all the times in a day that the hands of a clock coincide.

Skills Review Draw the graph of each equation. Then name the vertex, axis of symmetry, and direction of opening.

1. $y = (x - 3)^2$
2. $y = (x + 3)^2 + 1$
3. $y = {}^-(x - 3)^2 - 1$
4. $y = 3(x - 2)^2 + 5$
5. $y = x^2 + 4x + 3$
6. $y = {}^-2x^2 - 4x + 5$

Credit cards can be used to make purchases and to pay for services at many businesses. They enable you to buy now, but pay later.

If you pay your bill *in full* within the allotted time, usually 25 days, there are no additional charges. However, if you do not, you are assessed an additional charge called credit or *finance charges*. Some of these charges are at the rate of 1.75% per month or 21% per year.

Example   Cecilia used a credit card to purchase a coat for $90. She decided to pay $30 a month plus the finance charge for that month. Find the total finance charges and the total amount paid.

First Monthly Bill   The bill is for $90. Cecilia makes a $30 payment. There is no finance charge on the first monthly bill.

Second Monthly Bill

$$balance - payment = new\ balance$$
$$\$90 - \$30 = \$60$$

Multiply the new balance by 1.75%.

$$60 \cdot 1.75\% = 60 \cdot 0.0175$$
$$= 1.05 \qquad \textit{Her second payment is \$31.05}$$

The finance charge is $1.05 the second month.

Third Monthly Bill

$$balance + finance\ charge - payment = new\ balance$$
$$\$60 + \$1.05 - \$31.05 = \$30$$

Multiply the new balance by 1.75%.

$$30 \cdot 1.75\% = 30 \cdot 0.0175$$
$$= 0.53 \qquad \textit{Her third, and last payment, is \$30.53}$$

The finance charge is $0.53 the third month.

The total finance charges are $1.05 + $0.53 or $1.58.
The total amount paid is $91.58

Exercises   **Find the total finance charges and total amount paid for each of the following credit card purchases.**

1. Suit: $150 to pay, $30 per month, rate of 1.5% per month.

2. Tune-up: $60 to pay, $15 per month, rate of 1.75% per month.

3. Luggage: $125 to pay, $25 per month, rate of 21% per year.

4. Glasses: $75 to pay, $15 per month, rate of 24% per year.

10–6   Graphing Rational Functions

Before graphing a rational function, it is often helpful to find values for which the function is undefined. The graph of the rational function approaches lines that contain these values. However, they do not intersect these lines. These lines are called **asymptotes.**

examples

1   Graph $y = \frac{x}{x-1}$.

The function is undefined when x is 1. The graph of the equation $x = 1$ is a vertical asymptote.

Now solve for x.

$$y = \frac{x}{x-1}$$
$$y(x-1) = x$$
$$xy - y = x$$
$$xy - x = y$$
$$x(y-1) = y$$
$$x = \frac{y}{y-1}$$

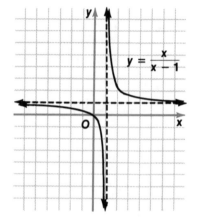

The function is also undefined when y is 1. The graph of the equation $y = 1$ is a horizontal asymptote.

Then sketch the graph by plotting points. Be sure to test values that are close to and on either side of the asymptotes.

2   Graph $y = \frac{2}{(x-2)^2}$.

The graph of the equation $x = 2$ is a vertical asymptote. If y is 0, no value of x exists. Thus, the graph of the equation $y = 0$ is a horizontal asymptote. Also note that the value of y could never be negative.   *Why?*

Sketch the graph by plotting points.

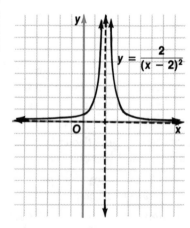

3 Graph $y = \dfrac{4}{(x + 2)(x - 3)}$.

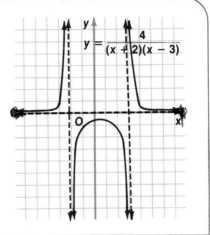

There are two vertical asymptotes, the graph of the equations $x = {}^-2$ and $x = 3$.

If y is 0, no value of x exists. Thus, the graph of the equation $y = 0$ is a horizontal asymptote.

Plot points on either side of each asymptote and sketch the graph.

A calculator or computer is helpful in determining points on the graph.

exercises

Exploratory   State the equations of the vertical and horizontal asymptotes for each rational function.

1. $y = \dfrac{3}{x - 1}$

2. $y = \dfrac{1}{x}$

3. $y = \dfrac{1}{x - 3}$

4. $y = \dfrac{4}{x + 2}$

5. $y = \dfrac{6}{(x - 6)^2}$

6. $y = \dfrac{3}{(x + 1)^3}$

7. $y = \dfrac{4}{(x - 1)(x + 5)}$

8. $y = \dfrac{{}^-6}{x - 3}$

9. $y = \dfrac{{}^-2}{(x - 1)(x - 4)}$

Written   Sketch the graph of each rational function. Be sure to sketch the asymptotes on each graph.

1. $y = \dfrac{x - 1}{x - 4}$

2. $y = \dfrac{3}{x + 2}$

3. $y = \dfrac{x - 5}{x + 1}$

4. $y = \dfrac{1}{x}$

5. $y = \dfrac{x}{x^2 - 4}$

6. $y = \dfrac{x - 1}{x^2 - 9}$

7. $y = \dfrac{x}{x - 2}$

8. $y = \dfrac{{}^-4}{x - 1}$

9. $y = \dfrac{{}^-2}{(x - 3)^2}$

10. $y = \dfrac{2}{(x - 2)(x + 1)}$

11. $y = \dfrac{{}^-1}{x - 6}$

12. $y = \dfrac{{}^-5}{(x - 3)(x + 1)}$

13. $y = \dfrac{4x}{x - 1}$

14. $y = \dfrac{x}{x + 1}$

15. $y = \dfrac{3}{(x - 4)^2}$

16. $y = \dfrac{1}{(x + 2)^2}$

17. $y = \dfrac{8}{(x - 1)(x + 3)}$

18. $y = \dfrac{{}^-8}{(x - 1)(x + 3)}$

10-7   Direct and Inverse Variation

Recall that direct variation is a linear function. Direct variation can be described by an equation of the form $y = kx$ where k is a constant *not* equal to zero. For example, gravity on earth is about six times as great as the gravity on the moon. Thus, weight on earth varies directly with weight on the moon. This relationship can be described by the following equation.

$$y = 6x$$

y stands for weight on earth
x stands for weight on moon
6 is the constant of variation

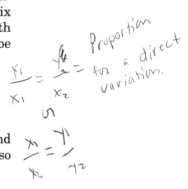

Direct variation can be related to proportion. Suppose that x_1 and y_1 satisfy the equation $y = kx$. And suppose that x_2 and y_2 also satisfy the equation $y = kx$.

$$y_1 = kx_1 \quad \text{and} \quad y_2 = kx_2$$

$$\frac{y_1}{y_2} = \frac{kx_1}{kx_2} \qquad \text{Division Property of Equality}$$

$$\frac{x_1}{x_2} = \frac{y_1}{y_2} \qquad \text{Simplify.}$$

Thus, direct variation can be written as a proportion.

What are other forms of this proportion?

---

example

1   **If y varies directly as x and $y = 12$ when $x = 15$, find x when $y = 21$.**

Use the proportion $\dfrac{x_1}{x_2} = \dfrac{y_1}{y_2}$.

$$\frac{15}{x_2} = \frac{12}{21} \qquad \text{Substitute. } x_1 = 15, \, y_1 = 12, \, y_2 = 21$$

$$x_2 = 26.25 \qquad \text{Solve for } x_2.$$

Many quantities are said to be **inversely proportional** or to **vary inversely** with each other. For example, the amount of current in a circuit is inversely proportional to the amount of resistance in the circuit. That is, as the amount of resistance decreases, the amount of current increases proportionally. The following chart shows several corresponding values.

Current (amps)	0.5	1.0	1.5	2.0	2.5	3.0	4.0	5.0
Resistance (ohms)	12	6.0	4.0	3.0	2.4	2.0	1.5	1.2

Let c stand for the amount of current.
Let r stand for the amount of resistance.

The relationship between these quantities can be described by the following equation.

$$c = \frac{6}{r}$$

A rational equation in two variables of the form $y = \frac{k}{x}$, where k is a constant, is called an **inverse variation**. The constant k is called the **constant of variation**, and y is said to **vary inversely** as x.

Definition of
Inverse Variation

Inverse variation can also be related to proportions or products. Suppose x_1 and y_1 satisfy the equation $y = \frac{k}{x}$. And suppose that x_2 and y_2 also satisfy the equation $y = \frac{k}{x}$.

$$y_1 = \frac{k}{x_1} \quad \text{and} \quad y_2 = \frac{k}{x_2}$$
$$x_1 y_1 = k \qquad x_2 y_2 = k$$
$$x_1 y_1 = x_2 y_2 \qquad \text{Substitution Property of Equality}$$
$$\frac{x_1}{x_2} = \frac{y_2}{y_1} \qquad \text{Divide both sides by } y_1 x_2 \text{ and simplify.}$$

Note that inverse variation yields a different proportion than direct variation.

examples

2 If y varies inversely as x and $y = 3$ when $x = 4$, find y when $x = 18$.

Use the proportion $\frac{x_1}{x_2} = \frac{y_2}{y_1}$.

$$\frac{4}{18} = \frac{y_2}{3} \qquad \text{Substitute, } x_1 = 4, x_2 = 18, \text{ and } y_1 = 3.$$
$$4 \cdot 3 = 18 \cdot y_2$$
$$\frac{12}{18} = y_2$$
$$y_2 = \frac{2}{3}$$

3 The volume of any gas varies inversely with its pressure as long as the temperature remains constant. The volume of a particular gas is 1600 milliliters when the pressure is 25 centimeters of mercury. What is the volume of the gas at the same temperature when the pressure is 40 centimeters of mercury?

Let V_1 stand for the first volume of gas, 1600 ml.
Let P_1 stand for the first gas pressure, 25 cm of mercury.
Let P_2 stand for the second gas pressure, 40 cm of mercury.

Since volume and pressure are inversely proportional, $V_1 P_1 = V_2 P_2$.

$$1600 \cdot 25 = V_2 \cdot 40$$
$$\frac{40,000}{40} = V_2$$
$$1000 = V_2 \qquad \text{The volume is 1000 milliliters.}$$

exercises

Exploratory State whether each equation represents direct variation or inverse variation. Then name the constant of variation.

1. $x = 4y$
2. $xy = {}^-3$
3. $y = {}^-4x$
4. $y = \dfrac{7}{x}$
5. $5 = \dfrac{y}{x}$
6. $\dfrac{x}{y} = {}^-6$
7. $\dfrac{3}{4}y = x$
8. $\dfrac{x}{2} = y$
9. $x = \dfrac{9}{y}$
10. $y = \dfrac{3}{x}$
11. $a = 4b$
12. $\dfrac{3}{5}a = -\dfrac{5}{4}b$

Written In each of the following, y varies directly as x.

1. If $y = 8$, then $x = 2$. Find y when $x = 9$.
2. If $y = 10$, then $x = {}^-3$. Find x when $y = 4$.
3. If $x = 4$, then $y = 0.5$. Find y when $x = 9$.
4. If $y = 11$, then $x = \dfrac{1}{5}$. Find y when $x = \dfrac{2}{5}$.

In each of the following, y varies inversely as x.

5. If $x = 14$, then $y = {}^-6$. Find x when $y = {}^-11$.
6. If $y = \dfrac{1}{5}$, then $x = 9$. Find y when $x = {}^-3$.
7. If $y = 11$, then $x = 44$. Find x when $y = 40$.
8. If $x = 20$, then $y = 10$. Find x when $y = 14$.
9. If $y = {}^-2$, then $x = {}^-8$. Find x when $y = \dfrac{2}{3}$.
10. If $y = 7$, then $x = {}^-3$. Find y when $x = 4$.

Solve each problem.

11. A map is scaled so that 1 cm represents 15 km. How far apart are two towns if they are 7.9 cm apart on the map?

12. A 75-foot tree casts a 40-foot shadow. How tall is a tree that casts a 10-foot shadow at the same time of day?

13. Six feet of steel wire weighs 0.7 kilograms. How much does 100 feet of steel wire weigh?

14. Alan Tokashira invested $5000 at 7% interest. How much must he invest at $6\frac{1}{2}\%$ interest to obtain the same income?

15. The time to drive a certain distance varies inversely according to the rate of speed. Mary Bronson drives 47 mph for 4 hours. How long would it take her to make the same trip at 55 mph?

16. A volume of gas is 120 cubic feet under 6 pounds of pressure. What is the volume at the same temperature when the pressure is 8 pounds?

17. When air is pumped into an automobile tire, the pressure required varies inversely as the volume. If the pressure is 30 pounds when the volume is 140 cubic inches, find the pressure when the volume is 100 cubic inches.

18. In a closed room, the number of hours of safe oxygen level varies inversely as the number of people in the room. If there are 2 hours of safe oxygen level when there are 100 people, how many hours of safe oxygen level are there for 600 people?

19. If y varies directly as x^2 and $y = 7$ when $x = 9$, then find y when $x = 7$.

20. If y^2 varies inversely as x and $y = 4$ when $x = 2$, find y when $x = 11$.

rational algebraic expression (293)   asymptote (312)
complex fraction (296)   inverse variation (315)
rational equation (304)   constant of variation (315)

Chapter Summary

1. To simplify a rational algebraic expression, divide both numerator and denominator by their greatest common factor (GCF). (293)
2. Multiplying Rational Expressions: For all rational expressions $\frac{a}{b}$ and $\frac{c}{d}$, $b \neq 0$ and $d \neq 0$, $\frac{a}{b} \cdot \frac{c}{d} = \frac{ac}{bd}$. (293)
3. Dividing Rational Expressions: For all rational expressions $\frac{a}{b}$ and $\frac{c}{d}$, b, c, and $d \neq 0$, $\frac{a}{b} \div \frac{c}{d} = \frac{a}{b} \cdot \frac{d}{c}$. (296)
4. A complex rational expression, usually called a complex fraction, is an expression whose numerator or denominator, or both, contain rational expressions. (296)
5. The sum of rational expressions with common denominators is the sum of the numerators over the common denominator. (300)
6. To add or subtract two rational expressions with different denominators, first find two equivalent rational expressions with common denominators. Then add or subtract the equivalent fractions. (300)
7. An equation that contains one or more rational expressions is called a rational equation. (304)
8. Before graphing a rational function, it is helpful to graph the asymptotes of the function. (312)
9. Direct variation is a linear function described by $y = kx$ or $f(x) = kx$ where k is a constant *not* equal to zero. (314)
10. Definition of Inverse Variation: A rational equation in two variables of the form $y = \frac{k}{x}$ where k is a constant is called an inverse variation. The constant k is called the constant of variation, and y is said to vary inversely as x. (315)

Chapter Review

10–1 **Simplify each expression.**

1. $\dfrac{25a^4}{80a}$

2. $\dfrac{(4xy)^3}{xy^4}$

3. $\dfrac{2y^3 + 12y^2}{y^2 + 3y - 18}$

Find each product. Write each answer in simplest form.

4. $\dfrac{^-4ab}{21c} \cdot \dfrac{14c^2}{22a^2}$

5. $\dfrac{y - 2}{a - x}(a - 3)$

6. $\dfrac{3a + b}{4c} \cdot \dfrac{16c^2d}{3a^2 + ab}$

10–2 **Find each quotient. Write each answer in simplest form.**

7. $\dfrac{x+y}{a} \div \dfrac{x+y}{a^3}$

8. $\dfrac{a^2-b^2}{6b} \div \dfrac{a+b}{36b^2}$

9. $\dfrac{y^2-y-12}{y+2} \div \dfrac{y-4}{y^2-4y-12}$

Simplify each expression.

10. $\dfrac{\dfrac{1}{n^2-6n+9}}{\dfrac{n+3}{2n^2-18}}$

11. $\dfrac{\dfrac{x^2-y^2}{10x^2}}{\dfrac{x-y}{25xy}}$

12. $\dfrac{\dfrac{x^2+7x+10}{x+2}}{\dfrac{x^2+2x-15}{x+2}}$

10–3 **Perform the indicated operation for each of the following. Write each answer in simplest form.**

13. $-\dfrac{9}{4a} + \dfrac{7}{3b}$

14. $\dfrac{x-1}{x^2-1} + \dfrac{2}{5x+5}$

15. $\dfrac{x+2}{x-5} + 6$

16. $\dfrac{7}{y} - \dfrac{2}{3y}$

17. $\dfrac{7}{y-2} - \dfrac{11}{2-y}$

18. $\dfrac{14}{x+y} - \dfrac{9}{y^2-x^2}$

Simplify each expression.

19. $\dfrac{\dfrac{5x}{4} + \dfrac{2x}{ab}}{\dfrac{6x}{5} + \dfrac{3x}{a}}$

20. $\dfrac{x - \dfrac{1}{x}}{\dfrac{1}{x} + 1}$

21. $\dfrac{\dfrac{2a+4}{a}}{6 + \dfrac{2}{a^2}}$

10–4 **Solve each equation.**

22. $\dfrac{3}{y} + \dfrac{7}{y} = 9$

23. $1 + \dfrac{5}{y-1} = \dfrac{7}{6}$

24. $\dfrac{3x+2}{4} = \dfrac{9}{4} - \dfrac{3-2x}{6}$

25. $\dfrac{1}{r^2-1} = \dfrac{2}{r^2+r-2}$

26. $\dfrac{x}{x^2-1} + \dfrac{2}{x+1} = 1 + \dfrac{1}{2x-2}$

10–5 **Solve each problem.**

27. Bob Lopatka can paint his house in 15 hours. His friend, Jack, can paint the house in 20 hours. If they work together, how long will it take them to paint the house?

28. One integer is 2 less than another integer. Three times the reciprocal of the lesser integer plus five times the reciprocal of the greater integer is $\dfrac{7}{8}$. What are the two integers?

10–6 **Sketch the graph of each rational function.**

29. $y = \dfrac{4}{x-2}$

30. $y = \dfrac{x}{x-1}$

31. $y = \dfrac{5}{(x+1)(x-3)}$

10–7 **Solve each problem.**

32. Suppose y varies inversely as x, and $y = 9$ when $x = 2\dfrac{1}{2}$. Find y when x is $-\dfrac{3}{5}$.

33. Suppose y varies directly as x, and $x = 7$ when $y = 21$. Find x when y is $^{-}5$.

Perform the indicated operation for each of the following. Write each answer in simplest form.

1. $\dfrac{7ab}{9c} \cdot \dfrac{81c^2}{91a^2b}$

2. $\dfrac{x^2 - y^2}{a^2 - b^2} \cdot \dfrac{a + b}{x - y}$

3. $\dfrac{a^2 - ab}{3a} \div \dfrac{a - b}{15b^2}$

4. $\dfrac{x^2 - 2x + 1}{y - 5} \div \dfrac{x - 1}{y^2 - 25}$

5. $\dfrac{7}{5a} - \dfrac{10}{3ab}$

6. $\dfrac{6}{x - 5} + 7a$

7. $\dfrac{x - y}{a - b} - \dfrac{x + y}{a + b}$

8. $\dfrac{x + 2}{x - 1} + \dfrac{6}{7x - 7}$

George's make-up test. →

Simplify each expression.

9. $\dfrac{\dfrac{2}{x - 4} + \dfrac{5}{x + 1}}{\dfrac{3x}{x^2 - 3x - 4}}$

10. $\dfrac{\dfrac{1}{x} - \dfrac{1}{2x}}{\dfrac{2}{x} + \dfrac{4}{3x}}$

Solve each equation.

11. $\dfrac{3}{x} - \dfrac{7}{x} = 9$

12. $a - \dfrac{5}{a} = 4$

13. $\dfrac{y}{y - 3} + \dfrac{6}{y + 3} = 1$

14. $\dfrac{3}{x} + \dfrac{x}{x + 2} = \dfrac{-2}{x + 2}$

Sketch the graph of each rational function.

15. $y = \dfrac{2}{x - 1}$

16. $y = \dfrac{3x}{x + 2}$

Solve each problem.

17. Joni Mills can type 75 pages of manuscript in 8 hours. Ted Szatro can type the same number of pages in 13 hours. If Joni and Ted work together, how long will it take them to type 75 pages?

18. A fraction has a value of $\dfrac{3}{4}$. If 5 is subtracted from its numerator, its value is $\dfrac{4}{7}$. Find the original fraction.

19. Suppose y varies directly as x. If $y = 10$, then $x = {}^-3$. Find y when x is 20.

20. Suppose y varies inversely as x. If $y = 9$, then $x = -\dfrac{2}{3}$. Find x when y is $^-7$.

chapter
11 Exponents

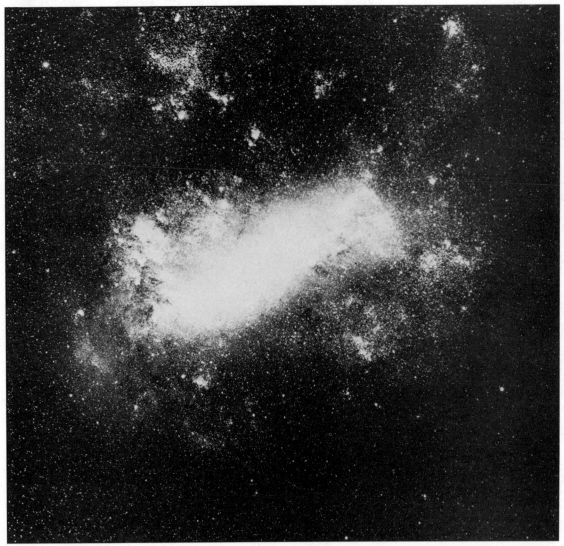

We live in the Milky Way galaxy. The galaxy closest to us is the Large Magellanic Cloud. It is about 160,000 light years or 1,500,000,000,000,000,000 kilometers from Earth. The number 1,500,000,000,000,000,000 can be expressed more concisely by using exponents.

11–1   Negative Exponents

The following pattern shows how negative integers can be used as exponents.

$$\frac{4^3}{4^1} = 4^{3-1} \text{ or } 4^2$$

$$\frac{4^2}{4^1} = 4^{2-1} \text{ or } 4^1 \qquad \textit{Notice that the exponent decreases}$$

$$\frac{4^1}{4^1} = 4^{1-1} \text{ or } 4^0 \qquad \textit{by one in each step.}$$

What number does $\frac{4^0}{4^1}$ represent? The pattern suggests that $\frac{4^0}{4^1} = 4^{0-1}$ or 4^{-1}. Since $4^0 = 1$ and $4^1 = 4$, you also know that $\frac{4^0}{4} = \frac{1}{4}$. Therefore, the value of 4^{-1} must be $\frac{1}{4}$. Continue the pattern.

$$\frac{4^{-1}}{4^1} = 4^{-1-1} \text{ or } 4^{-2}$$

But, the following is also true.

$$\frac{4^{-1}}{4^1} = \frac{\frac{1}{4}}{4} \qquad \textit{Recall that 4 can be written } \frac{4}{1}.$$

$$= \frac{1}{4} \cdot \frac{1}{4} \text{ or } \frac{1}{4^2} \qquad \textit{To divide, invert the } \frac{4}{1} \textit{ to } \frac{1}{4} \textit{ and multiply.}$$

Therefore, the value of 4^{-2} is $\frac{1}{4^2}$. The example above and other similar examples suggest the following.

> **For any number a, except $a = 0$, and for any positive integer n,**
>
> $$a^{-n} = \frac{1}{a^n}.$$

Negative Integer Exponents

To simplify an expression, find an equivalent form which uses only positive exponents.

examples

1   Simplify $(3 \cdot 4)^{-2}$.

$$(3 \cdot 4)^{-2} = \frac{1}{(3 \cdot 4)^2} \text{ or } \frac{1}{3^2 4^2} \qquad \textit{Recall that for any numbers a, b, and m, } (ab)^m = a^m b^m.$$

2   Simplify $\frac{1}{y^{-3}}$.

$$\frac{1}{y^{-3}} = \frac{1}{\frac{1}{y^3}}$$

$$= 1 \div \frac{1}{y^3}$$

$$= 1 \cdot \frac{y^3}{1} \text{ or } y^3$$

3 Simplify $\left(\frac{2}{3}\right)^{-4}$.

$$\left(\frac{2}{3}\right)^{-4} = \frac{1}{\left(\frac{2}{3}\right)^4}$$
$$= 1 \div \left(\frac{2}{3}\right)^4$$
$$= 1 \cdot \left(\frac{3}{2}\right)^4 \quad \text{or} \quad \left(\frac{3}{2}\right)^4$$

4 Simplify $\frac{5^{2k}}{5^{2k-3}}$.

$$\frac{5^{2k}}{5^{2k-3}} = 5^{2k-(2k-3)} \text{ or } 5^3$$

5 Simplify $(a^2 + 2ab + b^2)(a + b)^{-1}$.

$$(a^2 + 2ab + b^2)(a + b)^{-1} = \frac{a^2 + 2ab + b^2}{a + b}$$
$$= \frac{(a + b)^2}{a + b}$$
$$= a + b$$

exercises

Exploratory Simplify.

1. 4^{-3}

2. m^{-1}

3. $\left(\frac{1}{2}\right)^{-2}$

4. $\left(\frac{3}{r}\right)^{-4}$

5. 8^{-9}

6. y^{-3}

7. $\frac{1}{y^{-3}}$

8. $\frac{4}{x^{-2}}$

9. $\left(\frac{7}{x}\right)^{-5}$

10. $\left(\frac{1}{4}\right)^{-4}$

11. $\frac{1}{m^{-2}}$

12. $\frac{x^6}{x^8}$

13. $\left(\frac{1}{r}\right)^{-6}$

14. $\frac{z^5}{y^{-2}}$

15. $\frac{1}{y^{-4}}$

16. $\frac{y^{10}}{y^{13}}$

17. $\frac{x^4}{x^{y-1}}$

18. $\frac{w^3}{w^7}$

19. $\frac{q^8}{q^3}$

20. $\frac{1}{q^{-2}}$

Evaluate.

21. 3^0

22. 2^{-3}

23. 6^{-2}

24. $\left(\frac{1}{3}\right)^{-3}$

25. 4^{-1}

26. $\left(\frac{1}{5}\right)^{-2}$

27. $\frac{8^7}{8^9}$

28. $\left(\frac{2}{3}\right)^{-1}$

29. $3^{-2} \cdot 3^{-1}$

30. $\left(\frac{2}{3}\right)^0$

31. $\frac{2^6}{4^2}$

32. $\left(\frac{3}{5}\right)^{-2}$

Written Evaluate.

1. $\left(\frac{1}{3}\right)^{-2}$

2. $\left(\frac{1}{6}\right)^{-1}$

3. $\left(\frac{3}{2}\right)^{-2}$

4. $(-3)^{-3}$

5. $\dfrac{1}{3^{-1}}$

6. $\dfrac{1}{4^{-2}}$

7. $2^{-1} \cdot 2^{-3}$

8. $3^2 \cdot 7^0$

9. $\dfrac{6^{-2}}{6^{-4}}$

10. $\dfrac{3^{-3}}{3^{-2}}$

11. $\dfrac{1}{4^{-1}} \cdot \dfrac{1}{3^{-1}}$

12. $3^2 \cdot \dfrac{1}{3^{-3}}$

13. $(4^{-1})^{-2}$

14. $\left(\dfrac{3}{2}\right)^{-4}\left(\dfrac{3}{2}\right)^2$

15. $\dfrac{1}{5^{-2}} + \dfrac{1}{4^{-1}}$

16. $\dfrac{1}{2^{-2}} + \dfrac{1}{3^2}$

Simplify, expressing the results with positive exponents only.

17. $\left(\dfrac{1}{y}\right)^{-5}$

18. $\left(\dfrac{1}{m}\right)^{-4}$

19. $\dfrac{1}{r^{-3}}$

20. $\dfrac{1}{y^{-8}}$

21. $\left(\dfrac{2}{b}\right)^{-7}$

22. $\left(\dfrac{3}{a}\right)^{-5}$

23. $\left(\dfrac{x}{4}\right)^{-2}$

24. $\left(\dfrac{y}{x}\right)^{-3}$

25. $\dfrac{2x^6}{16x^{10}}$

26. $\dfrac{3r^7}{-18r^{12}}$

27. $\dfrac{-24s^8}{2s^5}$

28. $\dfrac{125r}{-5r^3}$

29. $\dfrac{(x+4)^3}{(x+4)^7}$

30. $\dfrac{3(x-7)^6}{(x-7)^{10}}$

31. $\dfrac{2(x+3)^4}{10(x+3)^2}$

32. $\dfrac{2(y^2-5)^3}{8(y^2-5)^5}$

33. $(x^3y^2)^{-1}$

34. $(m^4n^5)^{-2}$

35. $5^{-3}b^3x^4y^{-1}$

36. $\left(\dfrac{2}{3}\right)^{-1}x^3y^0z^{-4}$

37. $\dfrac{1}{x^0+y^0}$

38. $\dfrac{-6}{m^0+n^0}$

39. $\dfrac{2m}{n^{-1}}$

40. $\dfrac{5x}{y^{-1}}$

41. $\dfrac{5^{2x}}{5^{2x+2}}$

42. $\dfrac{3^{xy+5}}{3^{xy}}$

43. $\dfrac{r^{2a}}{r^{2a-3}}$

44. $\dfrac{x^{3a}}{x^{3a-2}}$

45. $\dfrac{3m^{-4}}{4^{-1}m^{-2}}$

46. $\dfrac{2^{-1}x^5}{3x^{-2}}$

47. $\left(\dfrac{-3y^4}{2y^2}\right)^{-2}$

48. $\left(\dfrac{3^2x^3}{2^3x^8}\right)^0$

49. $\left(\dfrac{1}{d^{-1}}\right)^{-2}$

50. $\left(\dfrac{3}{2x^{-2}}\right)^{-1}$

51. $\dfrac{(-2r^3)^2(r^{-2})^{-1}}{(r^2)^{-3}}$

52. $\dfrac{(4x^3y)(4^2x^{-1}y)}{4^3xy^2}$

53. $\dfrac{(3^2m^3n^2)(3mn)^2}{3m^{-3}n^4}$

54. $\dfrac{(x+y)^3}{(x+y)^{-1}}$

55. $\dfrac{(p+q)^{-2}}{(p+q)^3}$

56. $m^{-3}(m^2+m^4-m^{-1})$

57. $a^3(a^{-2}+a^{-5}+a)$

58. $(18-12x)(9-6x)^{-1}$

59. $(2a^2b-4ab^2)(a-2b)^{-1}$

60. $(c^2-c^3)(c^2-1)^{-1}$

61. $(a^3-b^3)(a-b)^{-2}$

Challenge Simplify.

1. $\left(\dfrac{y^2+2y-15}{y^2+3y-10}\right)\left(\dfrac{y^2-9}{y^2-9y+14}\right)^{-1}$

2. $\left(\dfrac{x^3-y^3}{x^2+xy+y^2}\right)\left(\dfrac{(x-y)^2}{4x+4y}\right)^{-1}$

Show why each statement is, or is not, true.

3. $2^5 + 2^5 = 2^6$

4. $3^5 + 3^5 = 3^6$

5. $3^5 + 3^5 + 3^5 = 3^6$

In most problems, a set of conditions or facts is given and you must arrive at a solution. However, in some cases, you are given the final solution or goal and then asked for an intermediate condition. In other cases, it may be faster to determine how the problem ends and then work backwards rather than to start from the beginning. Consider the following example.

Example   If the sum of two numbers is 2 and the product of these same two numbers is 3, find the sum of the reciprocals of these two numbers.

A first reaction might be to set up the following system of equations.
$$x + y = 2$$
$$xy = 3$$

But solving this system is very complicated, involving complex numbers. Rather than using this approach, work backwards. The desired outcome is $\frac{1}{x} + \frac{1}{y}$.

$$\frac{1}{x} + \frac{1}{y} = \frac{y}{xy} + \frac{x}{xy} \qquad \textit{The LCD is xy.}$$
$$= \frac{x + y}{xy}$$

The two original equations immediately reveal the numerator and denominator of this fraction.

$$\frac{x + y}{xy} = \frac{2}{3} \qquad \textit{Substitute.}$$

The sum of the reciprocals is $\frac{2}{3}$.

Exercises   Solve each problem.

1. A pirate found a treasure chest containing silver coins. He buried half of them and gave half of the remaining coins to his mother. If he was left with 4550 coins, how many were in the treasure chest that he found?

2. Tim collects model cars. He decides to give them away. First he gives half of them plus half a car more to Amy. Then he gives half of what is left plus half a car more to Tina. Then he has one car left which he gives to Aaron. How many cars did Tim start with? (Assume that no car is cut in half.)

3. Paul, Eric, and Garnet are playing a card game. They have a rule that when a player loses a hand, he must subtract enough points from his score to double each of the other players' scores. First Paul loses a hand, then Eric, and then Garnet. Each player now has 8 points. Who lost the most points?

4. If the sum of two numbers is 2 and the product of the same two numbers is 3, find the sum of the squares of the reciprocals of these numbers.

11–2   Scientific Notation

The table below contains the mean distances in kilometers from the sun to each of the planets in our solar system.

Planet	Mean Distance from Sun			
Mercury	58,000,000	or	5.8	$\times$	10^7
Venus	108,000,000	or	1.08	$\times$	10^8
Earth	150,000,000	or	1.5	$\times$	10^8
Mars	228,000,000	or	2.28	$\times$	10^8
Jupiter	779,000,000	or	7.79	$\times$	10^8
Saturn	1,428,000,000	or	1.428	$\times$	10^9
Uranus	2,872,000,000	or	2.872	$\times$	10^9
Neptune	4,501,000,000	or	4.501	$\times$	10^9
Pluto	5,906,000,000	or	5.906	$\times$	10^9

Writing very large or very small numbers in decimal notation can lead to serious errors if the number of places is misread. You can avoid this problem by using scientific notation.

> **A number is expressed in scientific notation when it is in the form**
> $$a \times 10^n$$
> **where $1 \le a < 10$ and n is an integer.**

Definition of Scientific Notation

Scientific notation is based on the powers of ten.

$10^6 = 1,000,000.$
$10^5 = 100,000.$
$10^4 = 10,000.$
$10^3 = 1,000.$
$10^2 = 100.$
$10^1 = 10.$
$10^0 = 1.$

These powers of ten have exponents that are nonnegative integers. Compare each exponent to the number of places between the decimal point and the one.

$10^{-1} = \frac{1}{10}$ or 0.1

$10^{-2} = \frac{1}{100}$ or 0.01

$10^{-3} = \frac{1}{1,000}$ or 0.001

$10^{-4} = \frac{1}{10,000}$ or 0.0001

These powers of ten have exponents that are negative integers. Compare the absolute value of each exponent and the number of places to the right of the decimal point.

The mean distance from the sun to Saturn is 1,428,000,000 kilometers. To write this number in scientific notation, you must find an expression such that $1{,}428{,}000{,}000 = a \times 10^n$. As shown below, you can move the decimal point to the left to get a number between one and ten.

$$1{,}428{,}000{,}000$$
$$1.428\ 000\ 000$$

$a = 1.428$ *How do you find a?*

$n = 9$ *How do you find n?*

In scientific notation, $1{,}428{,}000{,}000 = 1.428 \times 10^9$.

---

examples

1 **Express 72,500 in scientific notation.**

$72{,}500 \longrightarrow 7.25 \times 10 \times 10 \times 10 \times 10$

$a = 7.25$

$n = 4$ *How do you find n?*

In scientific notation, $72{,}500 = 7.25 \times 10^4$.

2 **Express 0.001325 in scientific notation.**

Move the decimal point to the right to get a number between one and ten.

$0.001325 \longrightarrow 0.001325$

$a = 1.325$ *How do you find a?*

$n = {}^-3$ *Why?*

In scientific notation, $0.001325 = 1.325 \times 10^{-3}$.

3 **Express 3.102×10^5 in decimal notation.**

$3.102 \times 10^5 = 3.102 \times 100{,}000$

$= 310{,}200$ *The decimal point is moved 5 places to the right.*

4 **Express 4.37×10^{-3} in decimal notation.**

$4.37 \times 10^{-3} = 4.37 \times 0.001$

$= 0.00437$ *The decimal point is moved 3 places to the left.*

Scientific notation is useful in computation. Study the following examples.

examples

5 **Multiply 0.543 by 617,000.**

$0.543 \times 617{,}000 = (5.43 \times 10^{-1})(6.17 \times 10^5)$ *Express 0.543 and 617,000 in scientific*

$= 5.43 \times 6.17 \times 10^4$ or $335{,}031$ *notation.*

6 Divide 0.00086 by 0.031.

$$\frac{0.00086}{0.031} = \frac{8.6 \times 10^{-4}}{3.1 \times 10^{-2}}$$ *Express 0.00086 and 0.031 in scientific notation.*

$$= \frac{8.6}{3.1} \times 10^{-2} \text{ or approximately } 0.028.$$

exercises

Exploratory   Find the value of n in each equation.

1. $40000 = 4 \times 10^n$ **2.** $0.0057 = 5.7 \times 10^n$ **3.** $0.00004 = 4 \times 10^n$ **4.** $600 = 6 \times 10^n$

Express each of the following in scientific notation.

5. 67,530   **6.** 146,000   **7.** 0.000075   **8.** 0.0014

Express each of the following in decimal notation.

9. 5.8×10^4 **10.** 6.7×10^6 **11.** 5.4×10^{-3} **12.** 1.82×10^{-4}

Evaluate. Express each answer both in scientific and in decimal notation.

13. $(6 \times 10^3)^2$

15. $\frac{3 \times 10^{-2}}{5 \times 10^2}$

14. $(7 \times 10^4)(8 \times 10^{-6})$

16. $\frac{6 \times 10^3}{4 \times 10^{-2}}$

Written   Express each of the following in scientific notation.

1. 618   **2.** 723   **3.** 0.0021   **4.** 0.0692
5. 810.4   **6.** 482.09   **7.** 9,000,000,000   **8.** 786,500,000
9. 0.00016   **10.** 0.000003   **11.** 0.000000721   **12.** 0.0000528

Express each of the following in decimal notation.

13. 6×10^3 **14.** 9.8×10^4 **15.** 5.7×10^{-4}
16. 3.21×10^6 **17.** 7.2×10^{-5} **18.** 4.27×10^{-2}

Evaluate. Express each answer both in scientific and in decimal notation.

19. $(7.2 \times 10^5)(8.1 \times 10^3)$

21. $\frac{8 \times 10^{-1}}{16 \times 10^{-2}}$

20. $(9.5 \times 10^3)^2$

22. $\frac{15 \times 10^4}{6 \times 10^{-2}}$

23. $(4,300)(0.02)$

25. $\frac{0.000000036}{0.00011}$

27. $\frac{(93,000,000)(0.0005)}{0.0015}$

24. $(34,000)(0.0056)$

26. $\frac{5,600,000,000}{60,000}$

28. $\frac{(84,000,000)(0.00004)}{0.0016}$

Solve each problem.

29. Light from a laser travels about 300,000 km per second. How many kilometers can this light travel in a day?

30. In astronomy, a light year is the distance light travels in one year. If light travels about 186,000 miles per second, how many miles are in a light year?

31. Wavelengths of light are measured in Angstrom units. An Angstrom unit is 10^{-8} cm. The wavelength of cadmium's green line is 5085.8 Angstrom units. How many wavelengths of cadmium's green line are there in one meter?

32. The mass of a proton is 1.672×10^{-24} grams. If the mass of the earth's moon is 7.35×10^{22} kilograms, how many times larger is its mass than that of a proton?

33. Metal expands and contracts with changes in temperature. The change in the length of steel per degree Celsius is given by the constant 11×10^{-6}. A steel bridge 200 meters long varies in temperature 70° Celsius. What is the change in the length of the bridge in centimeters?

34. Newton's law of gravitation can be used to compute the mass of the earth in grams. His formula applied is:

$$908 = \frac{6.67 \times 10^{-8} \times 1 \times M}{(6.37 \times 10^8)^2}$$

If M represents mass, what is the mass of the earth in grams?

The Exponential Shift Key

Many calculators have an exponential shift key $\boxed{\text{EE↓}}$. Any number less than $\pm 1 \times 10^{-8}$ or greater than ± 99999999 must be entered in the calculator in scientific notation. To do this you can use the exponential shift key.

Example   Enter 7158×10^{19}.

ENTER:	7158	$\boxed{\text{EE↓}}$		19		$\boxed{=}$	*Any operation*
DISPLAY:	7158.	7158. 00	7158. 19		7.158 22		*key can be used.*

The display 7.158 22 means 7.158×10^{22}. The number 7158×10^{19} expressed in scientific notation is 7.158×10^{22}. While 7.158 22 is in the display, press the $\boxed{\text{EE↓}}$ key once. What do you notice? Press the $\boxed{\text{EE↓}}$ key several times in succession, what do you notice about the display each time? *The exponent decreases by 1 and the decimal point moves 1 place to the right.*

Now press $\boxed{\text{INV}}$ $\boxed{\text{EE↓}}$ several times in succession, what do you notice about the display each time? *The exponent increases by 1 and the decimal point moves 1 place to the left.*

Exercises   Use the exponential shift key to enter each of the following in scientific notation.

1. 80.01×10^7 **2.** 0.789×10^{25} **3.** 0.05×10^{20} **4.** 7562×10^{15}
5. $^-25.38 \times 10^{10}$ **6.** $^-0.00891 \times 10^{16}$ **7.** 6504×10^{-11} **8.** $^-0.00915 \times 10^{-6}$

Compute each of the following.

9. $(0.65 \times 10^6) + (2.99 \times 10^7)$ **10.** $(75.21 \times 10^8) - (20.08 \times 10^6)$
11. $(21.5 \times 10^{-4})(150.2 \times 10^{-3})$ **12.** $(0.008 \times 10^{-2}) \div (54.6 \times 10^{-15})$

11–3 Rational Exponents

The properties of exponents can also be extended to include rational number exponents. Study the examples below.

$$5^{\frac{1}{2}} \cdot 5^{\frac{1}{2}} = 5^{\frac{1}{2}+\frac{1}{2}}$$
$$= 5$$

But, it is also true that $\sqrt{5} \cdot \sqrt{5} = 5$. Therefore, the values of $5^{\frac{1}{2}}$ and $\sqrt{5}$ must be the same.

$$4^{\frac{1}{3}} \cdot 4^{\frac{1}{3}} \cdot 4^{\frac{1}{3}} = 4^{\frac{1}{3}+\frac{1}{3}+\frac{1}{3}}$$
$$= 4$$

But, it is also true that $\sqrt[3]{4} \cdot \sqrt[3]{4} \cdot \sqrt[3]{4} = 4$. Therefore, the values of $4^{\frac{1}{3}}$ and $\sqrt[3]{4}$ must be the same.

These examples and other similar examples suggest the following definition.

> **For any number b and for any integer n, with n greater than one, $b^{\frac{1}{n}} = \sqrt[n]{b}$, except when $b < 0$ and n is even.**

Rational Numbers as Exponents

From the definition you can conclude that $7^{\frac{1}{2}} = \sqrt{7}$ and $(^-8)^{\frac{1}{3}} = \sqrt[3]{^-8}$ or $^-2$. Since $^-16 < 0$, the expression $(^-16)^{\frac{1}{4}}$ is not defined.

examples

1 **Evaluate $27^{\frac{1}{3}}$.**

$27^{\frac{1}{3}} = \sqrt[3]{27}$ or 3   *Recall that $3^3 = 3 \cdot 3 \cdot 3$ or 27.*

2 **Evaluate $32^{\frac{1}{5}}$.**

$32^{\frac{1}{5}} = \sqrt[5]{32}$ or 2   *Recall that $2^5 = 2 \cdot 2 \cdot 2 \cdot 2 \cdot 2$ or 32.*

3 **Evaluate $1000^{-\frac{1}{3}}$.**

$$1000^{-\frac{1}{3}} = \frac{1}{1000^{\frac{1}{3}}}$$
$$= \frac{1}{\sqrt[3]{1000}} \text{ or } \frac{1}{10}$$ *Recall that $10^3 = 10 \cdot 10 \cdot 10$ or 1000.*

4 **Evaluate $16^{\frac{1}{4}}$.**

$16^{\frac{1}{4}} = (2^4)^{\frac{1}{4}}$ *Rewrite 16 as 2^4.*
$= 2^1$ or 2   *Recall that $(a^m)^n = a^{mn}$.*

The following results show how the properties of exponents can be extended even further.

$$5^{\frac{3}{2}} = (5^{\frac{1}{2}})^3 \text{ or } (\sqrt{5})^3$$
$$5^{\frac{3}{2}} = (5^3)^{\frac{1}{2}} \text{ or } \sqrt{5^3}$$

Therefore, the values of $(\sqrt{5})^3$ and $\sqrt{5^3}$ must be the same.

$$7^{\frac{2}{3}} = (7^{\frac{1}{3}})^2 \text{ or } (\sqrt[3]{7})^2$$
$$7^{\frac{2}{3}} = (7^2)^{\frac{1}{3}} \text{ or } \sqrt[3]{7^2}$$

Therefore, the values of $(\sqrt[3]{7})^2$ and $\sqrt[3]{7^2}$ must be the same. These and other similar examples suggest the following definition.

> **For any nonzero number b, and any integers m and n, with $n > 1$**
> $$b^{\frac{m}{n}} = \sqrt[n]{b^m} = (\sqrt[n]{b})^m$$
> **except when $\sqrt[n]{b}$ does not represent a real number.**

Definition of Rational Exponents

Study the following examples to see how to apply this definition.

example

5 **Evaluate each of the following.**

a. $27^{\frac{2}{3}}$

$$27^{\frac{2}{3}} = (\sqrt[3]{27})^2$$
$$= (3)^2 \quad \text{or} \quad 9$$

b. $8^{\frac{1}{3}} \cdot 8^{\frac{4}{3}}$

$$8^{\frac{1}{3}} \cdot 8^{\frac{4}{3}} = 8^{\frac{5}{3}}$$
$$8^{\frac{5}{3}} = (\sqrt[3]{8})^5$$
$$= (2)^5 \quad \text{or} \quad 32$$

When a radical is in simplest form, its index is as small as possible.

examples

6 **Express $\sqrt[6]{25}$ in simplest radical form.**

$$\sqrt[6]{25} = 25^{\frac{1}{6}} \qquad \textit{The index is 6. Is it possible to find a smaller index?}$$
$$= (25^{\frac{1}{2}})^{\frac{1}{3}}$$
$$= (\sqrt{25})^{\frac{1}{3}} \qquad \textit{Note that } 25^{\frac{1}{2}} = \sqrt{25}.$$
$$= 5^{\frac{1}{3}} \quad \text{or} \quad \sqrt[3]{5}$$

7 **Express $3^{\frac{1}{2}}x^{\frac{2}{3}}y^{\frac{1}{6}}$ in simplest radical form.**

$$3^{\frac{1}{2}}x^{\frac{2}{3}}y^{\frac{1}{6}} = 3^{\frac{3}{6}}x^{\frac{4}{6}}y^{\frac{1}{6}} \qquad \textit{Rewrite all exponents using the same denominator.}$$
$$= (3^3x^4y^1)^{\frac{1}{6}}$$
$$= \sqrt[6]{27x^4y}$$

example

8 Express $\sqrt[5]{(32x)^2}$ using rational exponents.

$$\sqrt[5]{(32x)^2} = (32x)^{\frac{2}{5}}$$
$$= 32^{\frac{2}{5}} \cdot x^{\frac{2}{5}}$$
$$= (32^{\frac{1}{5}})^2 \cdot x^{\frac{2}{5}}$$
$$= 2^2 x^{\frac{2}{5}} \quad \text{or} \quad 4x^{\frac{2}{5}}$$

exercises

Exploratory   Evaluate.

1. $4^{\frac{3}{2}}$
2. $9^{\frac{3}{2}}$
3. $8^{-\frac{1}{3}}$
4. $16^{-\frac{3}{4}}$
5. $(16^{\frac{1}{2}})^{-\frac{1}{2}}$
6. $27^{-\frac{2}{3}}$
7. $64^{\frac{5}{6}}$
8. $64^{-\frac{1}{3}}$
9. $\sqrt[3]{8^2}$
10. $16^{-\frac{1}{4}}$
11. $\sqrt[4]{81}$
12. $\sqrt[3]{216}$
13. $(6^{\frac{2}{3}})^3$
14. $9^{\frac{1}{3}} \cdot 9^{\frac{5}{3}}$
15. $\dfrac{36^{\frac{3}{4}}}{36^{\frac{1}{4}}}$
16. $16^{-\frac{3}{2}}$

Express each of the following in simplest radical form.

17. $\sqrt[4]{36}$
18. $\sqrt[6]{49}$
19. $\sqrt[6]{81}$
20. $\sqrt[4]{25}$

Written   Express each of the following using exponents.

1. $\sqrt{21}$
2. $\sqrt[3]{30}$
3. $\sqrt[6]{32}$
4. $\sqrt[4]{x}$
5. $\sqrt[3]{y}$
6. $\sqrt{25x^3y^4}$
7. $\sqrt[3]{8m^3r^6}$
8. $\sqrt[4]{8x^3y^5}$
9. $\sqrt[4]{27}$
10. $\sqrt[3]{16a^5b^7}$
11. $\sqrt[3]{n^2}$
12. $\sqrt[6]{b^3}$

Express each of the following in simplest radical form.

13. $64^{\frac{1}{6}}$
14. $5^{\frac{1}{2}}$
15. $6^{\frac{1}{3}}$
16. $x^{\frac{3}{4}}$
17. $a^{\frac{3}{2}}b^{\frac{5}{2}}$
18. $4^{\frac{1}{3}}x^{\frac{2}{3}}y^{\frac{4}{3}}$
19. $2^{\frac{1}{3}}x^{\frac{7}{3}}$
20. $(2x)^{\frac{1}{2}}x^{\frac{1}{2}}$
21. $5^{\frac{1}{3}}p^{\frac{2}{3}}q^{\frac{1}{3}}$
22. $(3m)^{\frac{2}{5}}n^{\frac{3}{5}}$
23. $r^{\frac{5}{2}}q^{\frac{3}{4}}$
24. $w^{\frac{4}{7}}y^{\frac{1}{7}}$
25. $x^{\frac{1}{3}}y^{\frac{1}{2}}$
26. $a^{\frac{5}{6}}b^{\frac{1}{2}}c^{\frac{7}{3}}$
27. $5^2b^{\frac{1}{2}}c^{\frac{1}{4}}$
28. $x^{\frac{3}{4}}y^{\frac{1}{3}}z^{\frac{5}{6}}$
29. $\sqrt[4]{9}$
30. $\sqrt[4]{49}$
31. $\sqrt[6]{8}$
32. $\sqrt[8]{16}$

Evaluate each expression.

33. $121^{\frac{1}{2}}$
34. $\left(\dfrac{1}{32}\right)^{\frac{1}{5}}$
35. $\sqrt[3]{12^3}$
36. $\sqrt[4]{256}$
37. $\left(\dfrac{343}{64}\right)^{\frac{1}{3}}$
38. $\left(\dfrac{216}{729}\right)^{\frac{2}{3}}$
39. $(6^{\frac{2}{3}})^3$
40. $(9^{\frac{3}{4}})^{\frac{2}{3}}$
41. $(0.125)^{\frac{2}{3}}$
42. $(0.008)^{\frac{1}{3}}$
43. $(0.027)^{\frac{1}{3}}$
44. $(0.0016)^{\frac{1}{4}}$

Challenge   Express each of the following in simplest radical form.

1. $\sqrt[3]{2^5} \cdot \sqrt[4]{2}$
2. $\sqrt[3]{2^2} \cdot \sqrt[6]{2^7}$
3. $\sqrt{3} \cdot \sqrt[3]{3^2}$
4. $\sqrt[3]{5^2} \cdot \sqrt{5}$
5. $\sqrt[5]{16} \cdot \sqrt[5]{2}$
6. $\sqrt[3]{32} \cdot \sqrt[3]{2}$
7. $\sqrt[3]{\sqrt{27}}$
8. $\sqrt{\sqrt[3]{36}}$
9. $\sqrt[3]{\sqrt{8}}$

11–4   Simplifying Expressions

The process of changing the form of a rational expression to one without radicals in the denominator is called *rationalizing the denominator*.

1   Simplify $\dfrac{1}{\sqrt{2}}$.

$$\dfrac{1}{\sqrt{2}} = \dfrac{1}{\sqrt{2}} \cdot 1$$

$$= \dfrac{1}{\sqrt{2}} \cdot \dfrac{\sqrt{2}}{\sqrt{2}} \qquad \textit{Notice that 1 is renamed as } \dfrac{\sqrt{2}}{\sqrt{2}}. \textit{ Why was } \dfrac{\sqrt{2}}{\sqrt{2}} \textit{ chosen?}$$

$$= \dfrac{\sqrt{2}}{2}$$

2   Simplify $\dfrac{^-3}{\sqrt{y}+1}$.

$$\dfrac{^-3}{\sqrt{y}+1} = \dfrac{^-3}{\sqrt{y}+1} \cdot 1$$

$$= \dfrac{^-3}{\sqrt{y}+1} \cdot \dfrac{\sqrt{y}-1}{\sqrt{y}-1} \qquad \textit{What is the conjugate of } (\sqrt{y}+1)?$$

$$= \dfrac{^-3\sqrt{y}+3}{y-1} \qquad \textit{What happens when conjugates appear in a product?}$$

A rational expression that contains a fractional exponent in the denominator must also be rationalized.

3   Simplify $\dfrac{1}{3^{\frac{1}{2}}}$.

$$\dfrac{1}{3^{\frac{1}{2}}} = \dfrac{1}{3^{\frac{1}{2}}} \cdot 1$$

$$= \dfrac{1}{3^{\frac{1}{2}}} \cdot \dfrac{3^{\frac{1}{2}}}{3^{\frac{1}{2}}} \qquad \textit{Why is } \dfrac{3^{\frac{1}{2}}}{3^{\frac{1}{2}}} \textit{ chosen?}$$

$$= \dfrac{3^{\frac{1}{2}}}{3^{\frac{1}{2}+\frac{1}{2}}}$$

$$= \dfrac{3^{\frac{1}{2}}}{3}$$

It is important to choose a multiplier carefully. Study the following ways to simplify $\dfrac{1}{5^{\frac{3}{2}}}$.

$$\dfrac{1}{5^{\frac{3}{2}}} = \dfrac{1}{5^{\frac{3}{2}}}\left(\dfrac{5^{\frac{3}{2}}}{5^{\frac{3}{2}}}\right)$$

$$= \dfrac{5^{\frac{3}{2}}}{5^3}$$

$$= \dfrac{5 \cdot 5^{\frac{1}{2}}}{5 \cdot 5^2} \text{ or } \dfrac{5^{\frac{1}{2}}}{5^2}$$

$$\dfrac{1}{5^{\frac{3}{2}}} = \dfrac{1}{5^{\frac{3}{2}}}\left(\dfrac{5^{\frac{1}{2}}}{5^{\frac{1}{2}}}\right)$$

$$= \dfrac{5^{\frac{1}{2}}}{5^2} \text{ or } \dfrac{5^{\frac{1}{2}}}{25}$$

Notice that there are fewer steps in simplifying $\dfrac{1}{5^{\frac{3}{2}}}$ when 1 is written in the form $\dfrac{5^{\frac{1}{2}}}{5^{\frac{1}{2}}}$.

An expression is simplified when it meets these conditions.

1. **It has no negative exponents.**
2. **It has no fractional exponents in the denominator.**
3. **It is not a complex fraction.**
4. **The index of any remaining radical is as small as possible.**

Conditions for Simplified Expressions

When you simplify an expression, be sure your answer meets all of the above conditions. In some problems, the simplest form may not always be the most convenient to use. Sometimes the content of a problem determines the most appropriate form for the answer.

examples

4 Simplify $r^{-\frac{1}{9}}$.

This expression is not in simplest form because it contains a negative exponent.

$$r^{-\frac{1}{9}} = \dfrac{1}{r^{\frac{1}{9}}}$$

$$= \dfrac{1}{r^{\frac{1}{9}}}\left(\dfrac{r^{\frac{8}{9}}}{r^{\frac{8}{9}}}\right) \qquad \textit{Why choose to multiply by } \dfrac{r^{\frac{8}{9}}}{r^{\frac{8}{9}}}?$$

$$= \dfrac{r^{\frac{8}{9}}}{r}$$

5 Simplify $\dfrac{a^{\frac{1}{2}} - b^{\frac{1}{2}}}{a^{\frac{1}{2}} + b^{\frac{1}{2}}}$.

This expression is not in simplest form because it contains fractional exponents in the denominator.

$$\dfrac{a^{\frac{1}{2}} - b^{\frac{1}{2}}}{a^{\frac{1}{2}} + b^{\frac{1}{2}}} = \dfrac{a^{\frac{1}{2}} - b^{\frac{1}{2}}}{a^{\frac{1}{2}} + b^{\frac{1}{2}}} \cdot \dfrac{a^{\frac{1}{2}} - b^{\frac{1}{2}}}{a^{\frac{1}{2}} - b^{\frac{1}{2}}} \qquad \textit{Why choose to multiply by } \dfrac{a^{\frac{1}{2}} - b^{\frac{1}{2}}}{a^{\frac{1}{2}} - b^{\frac{1}{2}}}?$$

$$= \dfrac{a - 2a^{\frac{1}{2}}b^{\frac{1}{2}} + b}{a - b}$$

exercises

Exploratory State a factor that can be used to rationalize each expression.

1. $\dfrac{6}{3^{\frac{1}{2}}}$

2. $\dfrac{10}{5^{\frac{2}{3}}}$

3. $\dfrac{16}{4^{\frac{3}{2}}}$

4. $\dfrac{18}{3^{\frac{3}{2}}}$

5. $\dfrac{1}{x^{\frac{1}{3}}}$

6. $\dfrac{1}{y^{\frac{2}{3}}}$

7. $\dfrac{2}{m^{\frac{3}{4}}}$

8. $\dfrac{5a}{a^{\frac{5}{6}}}$

9. $a^{-\frac{1}{5}}$

10. $p^{-\frac{3}{2}}$

11. $\dfrac{1}{x^{\frac{1}{2}} + 1}$

12. $\dfrac{m + p}{m^{\frac{1}{2}} + p}$

13. $\dfrac{r}{r^{\frac{1}{2}} - s^{\frac{1}{2}}}$

14. $\dfrac{2}{t^{\frac{3}{2}} + s^{\frac{1}{2}}}$

15. $\dfrac{1}{b^{\frac{3}{2}} + b^{\frac{1}{2}}}$

Written 1–15. Simplify each expression in Exploratory Exercises 1–15.

Simplify each expression.

16. $\dfrac{1}{y^{\frac{2}{5}}}$

17. $\dfrac{3}{r^{\frac{4}{5}}}$

18. $b^{-\frac{1}{4}}$

19. $m^{-\frac{5}{6}}$

20. $\dfrac{15}{5^{\frac{2}{3}}}$

21. $\dfrac{24}{6^{\frac{2}{3}}}$

22. $\dfrac{rm^{\frac{1}{2}}}{b^{\frac{3}{2}}}$

23. $\dfrac{pq}{\sqrt[3]{a}}$

24. $\dfrac{b^{\frac{3}{2}} + 3b^{-\frac{1}{2}}}{b^{\frac{1}{2}}}$

25. $\dfrac{a^{\frac{5}{3}}m + 3a^{-\frac{1}{3}}}{a^{\frac{2}{3}}}$

26. $\dfrac{3x + 4x^2}{x^{-\frac{2}{3}}}$

27. $\dfrac{3m}{b^{-\frac{3}{2}} \cdot \sqrt[3]{a}}$

28. $(r^{-\frac{1}{6}})^{-\frac{2}{3}}$

29. $(y^{\frac{1}{3}})^{-\frac{3}{4}}$

30. $\dfrac{r^{\frac{3}{2}}}{r^{\frac{3}{2}} + 2}$

31. $\dfrac{x^{\frac{1}{2}} + y^{\frac{1}{2}}}{x^{\frac{1}{2}} - y^{\frac{1}{2}}}$

32. $\dfrac{a^{\frac{1}{2}} - b^{\frac{1}{2}}}{a^{\frac{1}{2}} + b^{\frac{1}{2}}}$

33. $\dfrac{x^{\frac{1}{2}} + 1}{x^{\frac{1}{2}} - 1}$

34. $\dfrac{rs}{r^{\frac{1}{2}} + r^{\frac{3}{2}}}$

35. $\dfrac{x^{\frac{1}{3}}}{x^{\frac{2}{3}} - x^{-\frac{1}{3}}}$

36. $\dfrac{b^{\frac{1}{2}}}{b^{\frac{3}{2}} - b^{\frac{1}{2}}}$

37. $\dfrac{a^{-\frac{2}{3}}b^{\frac{1}{2}}}{b^{-\frac{3}{2}}\sqrt[3]{a}}$

38. $\left(\dfrac{x^{-2}y^6}{9}\right)^{-\frac{1}{2}}$

39. $\left(\dfrac{z^{-\frac{2}{3}}}{5^{-1}z^{\frac{1}{3}}}\right)^{-2}$

40. $(\sqrt[6]{5}\,x^{\frac{7}{4}}y^{-\frac{2}{3}})^{12}$

41. $\dfrac{8^{\frac{1}{6}} - 9^{\frac{1}{4}}}{\sqrt{3} + \sqrt{2}}$

42. $\dfrac{9x^{-\frac{4}{3}} - 4x^0y^{-2}}{3x^{-\frac{2}{3}} + 2y^{-1}}$

43. $\dfrac{a^{\frac{5}{3}}b^0 - a^{\frac{1}{3}}b^{\frac{4}{3}}}{a^{\frac{2}{3}} + b^{\frac{2}{3}}}$

Evaluate the following expressions.

44. $-\dfrac{4}{9}x^9\left(\dfrac{3}{x^2} - \dfrac{1}{\sqrt[3]{2}}\right)$ when $x = \sqrt[6]{2}$

45. $\dfrac{3^0y + 4y^{-1}}{y^{-\frac{2}{3}}}$ when $y = 8$

Challenge Simplify each of the following.

1. $\dfrac{1}{x^{\frac{1}{3}} - y^{\frac{1}{3}}}$

2. $\dfrac{a}{a^{\frac{1}{3}} - b^{\frac{2}{3}}}$

3. $\dfrac{1}{a^{\frac{2}{3}} - b^{\frac{2}{3}}}$

4. $\dfrac{z^{\frac{1}{3}}}{z^{\frac{2}{3}} - z^{\frac{1}{3}}}$

William Sheppard works as an energy analyst at a large research institute. He uses scientific notation regularly in his work. He is involved in energy research planning and in the analysis of economic and environmental impacts of possible approaches to provided more energy. This energy may come from fossil fuels, solar energy, and agricultural residues.

The rates of energy and fuel production and consumption can be reported in a number of different ways. For example, they can be expressed in quadrillion Btu per year, millions of barrels of oil per day, and thousands of cubic feet of natural gas per hour.

1 barrel of oil = 5.8×10^6 Btu
1 cubic foot of natural gas = 1.0×10^3 Btu
1 ton of coal = 2.4×10^7 Btu

One Btu is the energy required to raise the temperature of 1 pound of water 1 degree Fahrenheit.

How many tons of coal per year are equivalent to the rate of production of 1 barrel of oil per day?

$$\frac{(5.8 \times 10^6)(3.65 \times 10^2)}{(2.4 \times 10^7)} = 8.8 \times 10^1 \text{ tons of coal per year.}$$

How many Btu per year are equivalent to the U.S. 1976 coal production rate of 1.8 million tons per day?

$$(1.8 \times 10^6)(3.65 \times 10^2)(2.4 \times 10^7) = 1.6 \times 10^{16} \text{ Btu per year}$$

Exercises   Solve each problem.

1. How many barrels of oil per day are equivalent to the rate of the U.S. total consumption in 1976 (leap year) of 74 quadrillion Btu per year?

2. How many cubic feet of natural gas per hour are equivalent to the U.S. 1977 rate of oil production of 8.4 million barrels per day?

11-5   Solving Equations in Quadratic Form

Many equations can be solved using the following property of exponents. For any number a, and any rational numbers m and n,

$$(a^m)^n = a^{mn}.$$

examples

1   **Solve $x^{\frac{3}{2}} = 8$.**

$x^{\frac{3}{2}} = 8$

$(x^{\frac{3}{2}})^{\frac{2}{3}} = 8^{\frac{2}{3}}$ *Raise each side of the equation to the $\frac{2}{3}$ power. Why $\frac{2}{3}$?*

$x = 8^{\frac{2}{3}}$

$x = (8^{\frac{1}{3}})^2$ *How is the property of exponents listed above used here?*

$x = 2^2$ or 4

2   **Solve $y^{-2} - 64 = 0$.**

$y^{-2} - 64 = 0$

$y^{-2} = 64$

$(y^{-2})^{-\frac{1}{2}} = 64^{-\frac{1}{2}}$ *Raise each side of the equation to the $-\frac{1}{2}$ power. Why $-\frac{1}{2}$?*

$y = 64^{-\frac{1}{2}}$

$y = \pm\dfrac{1}{8}$

Some equations are written in quadratic form as described below.

> **For any numbers a, b, and c, except $a = 0$, an equation written as $a[f(x)]^2 + b[f(x)] + c = 0$ is in quadratic form.**

Definition of Quadratic Form

In an equation such as $x^2 + 2x + 1 = 0$, the expression $f(x)$ is just x.

example

3   **Find $f(x)$ in each equation.**

a. $x^{\frac{1}{2}} - 6x^{\frac{1}{4}} + 8 = 0$

$x^{\frac{1}{4}\cdot 2} - 6x^{\frac{1}{4}} + 8 = 0$

$(x^{\frac{1}{4}})^2 - 6(x^{\frac{1}{4}}) + 8 = 0$

Then $f(x)$ is $x^{\frac{1}{4}}$.

b. $x^{-4} + 2x^{-2} + 7 = 0$

$x^{-2\cdot 2} + 2x^{-2} + 7 = 0$

$(x^{-2})^2 + 2(x^{-2}) + 7 = 0$

Then $f(x)$ is x^{-2}.

Equations in quadratic form can be solved by the same methods used for solving quadratic equations.

4 **Solve $x^{\frac{1}{2}} - 6x^{\frac{1}{4}} + 8 = 0$.**

$$x^{\frac{1}{2}} - 6x^{\frac{1}{4}} + 8 = 0$$
$$(x^{\frac{1}{4}})^2 - 6(x^{\frac{1}{4}}) + 8 = 0 \qquad \text{So } f(x) \text{ is } x^{\frac{1}{4}}.$$
$$(x^{\frac{1}{4}} - 2)(x^{\frac{1}{4}} - 4) = 0 \qquad \text{Factor to solve for } f(x).$$

$$x^{\frac{1}{4}} - 2 = 0 \qquad \text{or} \qquad x^{\frac{1}{4}} - 4 = 0$$
$$x^{\frac{1}{4}} = 2 \qquad\qquad\qquad x^{\frac{1}{4}} = 4$$

To solve for x, continue as shown.

$$x^{\frac{1}{4}} = 2 \qquad\qquad \text{or} \qquad\qquad x^{\frac{1}{4}} = 4$$
$$(x^{\frac{1}{4}})^4 = (2)^4 \qquad\qquad\qquad\qquad (x^{\frac{1}{4}})^4 = 4^4$$
$$x = 2^4 \text{ or } 16 \qquad\qquad\qquad x = 4^4 \text{ or } 256$$

Check: $x^{\frac{1}{2}} - 6x^{\frac{1}{4}} + 8 = 0$

$$16^{\frac{1}{2}} - 6(16^{\frac{1}{4}}) + 8 \stackrel{?}{=} 0 \qquad 256^{\frac{1}{2}} - 6(256^{\frac{1}{4}}) + 8 \stackrel{?}{=} 0$$
$$4 - 6(2) + 8 \stackrel{?}{=} 0 \qquad\qquad 16 - 6(4) + 8 \stackrel{?}{=} 0$$
$$12 - 12 \stackrel{?}{=} 0 \qquad\qquad\qquad 24 - 24 \stackrel{?}{=} 0$$
$$0 = 0 \qquad\qquad\qquad\qquad 0 = 0$$

The solutions are 16 and 256.

5 **Solve $4z^{\frac{4}{3}} - 25z^{\frac{2}{3}} + 36 = 0$.**

$$4z^{\frac{4}{3}} - 25z^{\frac{2}{3}} + 36 = 0$$
$$4(z^{\frac{2}{3}})^2 - 25(z^{\frac{2}{3}}) + 36 = 0 \qquad \text{So } f(z) \text{ is } z^{\frac{2}{3}}.$$
$$(4z^{\frac{2}{3}} - 9)(z^{\frac{2}{3}} - 4) = 0 \qquad \text{Factor to solve for } f(z).$$

$$4z^{\frac{2}{3}} - 9 = 0 \qquad \text{or} \qquad z^{\frac{2}{3}} - 4 = 0$$
$$z^{\frac{2}{3}} = \frac{9}{4} \qquad\qquad\qquad z^{\frac{2}{3}} = 4$$
$$(z^{\frac{2}{3}})^{\frac{3}{2}} = \left(\frac{9}{4}\right)^{\frac{3}{2}} \qquad\qquad (z^{\frac{2}{3}})^{\frac{3}{2}} = 4^{\frac{3}{2}}$$
$$z = \left(\frac{9}{4}\right)^{\frac{3}{2}} \qquad\qquad\qquad z = 4^{\frac{3}{2}}$$
$$z = \frac{27}{8} \qquad\qquad\qquad\qquad z = 8$$

Check: $4z^{\frac{4}{3}} - 25z^{\frac{2}{3}} + 36 = 0$

$$4\left(\frac{27}{8}\right)^{\frac{4}{3}} - 25\left(\frac{27}{8}\right)^{\frac{2}{3}} + 36 \stackrel{?}{=} 0 \qquad 4(8)^{\frac{4}{3}} - 25(8)^{\frac{2}{3}} + 36 \stackrel{?}{=} 0$$
$$4\left(\frac{81}{16}\right) - 25\left(\frac{9}{4}\right) + 36 \stackrel{?}{=} 0 \qquad\qquad 4(16) - 25(4) + 36 \stackrel{?}{=} 0$$
$$\frac{81}{4} - \frac{225}{4} + \frac{144}{4} \stackrel{?}{=} 0 \qquad\qquad\qquad 64 - 100 + 36 \stackrel{?}{=} 0$$
$$0 = 0 \qquad\qquad\qquad\qquad\qquad 0 = 0$$

The solutions are $\frac{27}{8}$ and 8.

exercises

Exploratory   Solve each equation.

1. $r^{\frac{1}{3}} = 2$

2. $x^{\frac{1}{3}} = 3$

3. $y^{\frac{1}{2}} = 5$

4. $x^{-\frac{1}{2}} = 4$

5. $z^{-2} = 25$

6. $r^{-3} = 27$

7. $y^{\frac{3}{2}} - 8 = 0$

8. $z^{-\frac{1}{3}} - 2 = 0$

9. $p^{-2} = 169$

10. $a^{\frac{2}{3}} = \frac{4}{9}$

11. $y^{\frac{1}{3}} - 4 = 0$

12. $x^{-\frac{1}{2}} + 1 = 2$

Express each equation in quadratic form.

13. $x^{\frac{4}{3}} - 7x^{\frac{2}{3}} + 12 = 0$

14. $x^{-6} - 8x^{-3} + 16 = 0$

15. $x - 10x^{\frac{1}{2}} + 25 = 0$

16. $x^{\frac{1}{2}} + 7x^{\frac{1}{4}} + 12 = 0$

17. $x^{\frac{1}{2}} - 8x^{\frac{1}{4}} + 15 = 0$

18. $y^{\frac{1}{2}} - 10y^{\frac{1}{4}} + 16 = 0$

19. $r^{\frac{2}{3}} - 5r^{\frac{1}{3}} + 6 = 0$

20. $s^{\frac{2}{3}} - 9s^{\frac{1}{3}} + 20 = 0$

21. $a^{-\frac{2}{3}} - 11a^{-\frac{1}{3}} + 28 = 0$

22. $k^{-\frac{4}{3}} - 10k^{-\frac{2}{3}} + 21 = 0$

23. $2m + 5m^{\frac{1}{2}} + 3 = 0$

24. $2b^{-\frac{1}{3}} - 17b^{-\frac{1}{6}} + 30 = 0$

Written   Solve each equation.

1. $x^{\frac{1}{2}} - 10x^{\frac{1}{4}} + 16 = 0$

2. $x^{\frac{2}{3}} - 8x^{\frac{1}{3}} + 15 = 0$

3. $r^{\frac{2}{3}} - 12r^{\frac{1}{3}} + 20 = 0$

4. $b^{\frac{2}{3}} - 7b^{\frac{1}{3}} + 10 = 0$

5. $m - 11m^{\frac{1}{2}} + 30 = 0$

6. $s - 5s^{\frac{1}{2}} + 6 = 0$

7. $x^{\frac{4}{3}} - 8x^{\frac{2}{3}} + 16 = 0$

8. $y^{\frac{4}{3}} - 13y^{\frac{2}{3}} + 36 = 0$

9. $a^{-\frac{2}{3}} - 10a^{-\frac{1}{3}} + 21 = 0$

10. $y^{-\frac{2}{5}} - 4y^{-\frac{1}{5}} + 4 = 0$

11. $y^{-1} - 5y^{-\frac{1}{2}} + 6 = 0$

12. $y^{3} - 16y^{\frac{3}{2}} + 64 = 0$

13–24. Solve each equation in Exploratory Exercises 13–24.

Solve each equation.

25. $3g^{\frac{2}{3}} - 10g^{\frac{1}{3}} + 8 = 0$

26. $2a^{\frac{1}{2}} - 13a^{\frac{1}{4}} + 20 = 0$

27. $6x - 19x^{\frac{1}{2}} + 15 = 0$

28. $3m + m^{\frac{1}{2}} - 2 = 0$

29. $2r^{\frac{1}{2}} + r^{\frac{1}{4}} - 15 = 0$

30. $2y^{\frac{2}{3}} - 5y^{\frac{1}{3}} - 12 = 0$

History   excursions in algebra

Mary Fairfax Somerville (1780–1872) wrote several books aimed at popularizing current scientific theories. As did many others, she began studying mathematics with Euclid's *Geometry*. She later taught herself subjects such as conic sections, trigonometry, and calculus.

11-6   Solving Radical Equations

Some equations can be written using either rational exponents or radicals. The methods of solving such equations are similar.

Rational Exponents   Radicals

Solve $x^{\frac{1}{3}} = 2$ *Solve each*   Solve $\sqrt[3]{x} = 2$

$\qquad x^{\frac{1}{3}} = 2$ *equation by* $\qquad \sqrt[3]{x} = 2$

$\quad (x^{\frac{1}{3}})^3 = 2^3$ *raising both* $\quad (\sqrt[3]{x})^3 = 2^3$
                                         sides to the
$\qquad x = 2^3$ or 8 *same power.* $\qquad x = 2^3$ or 8

$\qquad 8^{\frac{1}{3}} \stackrel{?}{=} 2$ *Check the* $\qquad \sqrt[3]{8} \stackrel{?}{=} 2$

$\qquad 2 = 2$ *solution.* $\qquad 2 = 2$

The following examples illustrate techniques for solving radical equations.

examples

1 **Solve $\sqrt[3]{x + 4} = {}^-5$.**

$\qquad \sqrt[3]{x + 4} = {}^-5$

$\quad (\sqrt[3]{x + 4})^3 = ({}^-5)^3$ *How do you know to raise both sides of the equation*

$\qquad\quad x + 4 = {}^-125$ *to the third power?*

$\qquad\qquad x = {}^-129$

Check: $\sqrt[3]{x + 4} = {}^-5$

$\qquad\quad \sqrt[3]{{}^-129 + 4} \stackrel{?}{=} {}^-5$

$\qquad\qquad \sqrt[3]{{}^-125} \stackrel{?}{=} {}^-5$

$\qquad\qquad\quad {}^-5 = {}^-5$

The solution is ${}^-129$.

2 **Solve $x + \sqrt{3x - 2} = 4$.**

$\qquad x + \sqrt{3x - 2} = 4$

$\qquad\quad \sqrt{3x - 2} = 4 - x$ *Isolate the radical so that when each side is*

$\quad (\sqrt{3x - 2})^2 = (4 - x)^2$ *squared there are no extra terms containing radicals.*
                                                    Square each side.
$\qquad\quad 3x - 2 = x^2 - 8x + 16$

$\qquad\qquad 0 = x^2 - 11x + 18$ *Combine terms.*

$\qquad\qquad 0 = (x - 2)(x - 9)$ *Factor to solve for x.*

$x - 2 = 0 \qquad$ or $\qquad x - 9 = 0$

$\quad x = 2 \qquad\qquad\qquad x = 9$

Check: $x + \sqrt{3x - 2} = 4$

$\qquad 2 + \sqrt{3(2) - 2} \stackrel{?}{=} 4 \qquad\qquad 9 + \sqrt{3(9) - 2} \stackrel{?}{=} 4$

$\qquad\qquad 2 + \sqrt{4} \stackrel{?}{=} 4 \qquad\qquad\qquad 9 + \sqrt{25} \stackrel{?}{=} 4$

$\qquad\qquad\qquad 4 = 4 \qquad\qquad\qquad\qquad 14 \neq 4$ *Does not check.*

The solution is 2.

You must check all possible solutions in the original equation. Squaring both sides of an equation may produce solutions that do not satisfy the equation.

examples

3 **Solve $\sqrt{2y - 3} - \sqrt{y - 2} = 1$.**

$$\sqrt{2y - 3} - \sqrt{y - 2} = 1$$
$$\sqrt{2y - 3} = \sqrt{y - 2} + 1 \qquad \textit{Isolate one radical.}$$
$$(\sqrt{2y - 3})^2 = (\sqrt{y - 2} + 1)^2 \qquad \textit{Square each side.}$$
$$2y - 3 = y - 2 + 2\sqrt{y - 2} + 1 \qquad \textit{Note middle term from expansion.}$$
$$y - 2 = 2\sqrt{y - 2} \qquad \textit{Isolate the other radical.}$$
$$(y - 2)^2 = (2\sqrt{y - 2})^2$$
$$y^2 - 4y + 4 = 4(y - 2)$$
$$y^2 - 8y + 12 = 0$$
$$(y - 2)(y - 6) = 0$$
$$y - 2 = 0 \quad \text{or} \quad y - 6 = 0$$
$$y = 2 \qquad\qquad y = 6$$

Check: $\sqrt{2y - 3} - \sqrt{y - 2} = 1$

$$\sqrt{2(2) - 3} - \sqrt{2 - 2} \overset{?}{=} 1 \qquad\qquad \sqrt{2(6) - 3} - \sqrt{6 - 2} \overset{?}{=} 1$$
$$\sqrt{1} - \sqrt{0} \overset{?}{=} 1 \qquad\qquad \sqrt{9} - \sqrt{4} \overset{?}{=} 1$$
$$1 = 1 \qquad\qquad 3 - 2 \overset{?}{=} 1$$
$$\qquad\qquad 1 = 1$$

The solutions are 2 and 6.

4 **Solve $\sqrt{2y^2 + 5y} = {}^-y - 10$.**

$$\sqrt{2y^2 + 5y} = {}^-y - 10$$
$$2y^2 + 5y = y^2 + 20y + 100 \qquad \textit{Square each side.}$$
$$y^2 - 15y - 100 = 0$$
$$(y + 5)(y - 20) = 0$$
$$y + 5 = 0 \quad \text{or} \quad y - 20 = 0$$
$$y = {}^-5 \qquad\qquad y = 20$$

Check: $\sqrt{2y^2 + 5y} = {}^-y - 10$

$$\sqrt{2({}^-5)^2 + 5({}^-5)} \overset{?}{=} {}^-({}^-5) - 10 \qquad\qquad \sqrt{2(20)^2 + 5(20)} \overset{?}{=} {}^-(20) - 10$$
$$\sqrt{2(25) - 25} \overset{?}{=} 5 - 10 \qquad\qquad \sqrt{2(400) + 100} \overset{?}{=} {}^-30$$
$$\sqrt{25} \overset{?}{=} {}^-5 \qquad\qquad \sqrt{900} \overset{?}{=} {}^-30$$
$$5 \neq {}^-5 \quad \textit{Does not check.} \qquad\qquad 30 \neq {}^-30 \quad \textit{Does not check.}$$

There are no solutions.

exercises

Exploratory Solve each equation. Check each solution.

1. $\sqrt{x-2} - 7 = 0$
2. $\sqrt{y-3} - 5 = 0$
3. $\sqrt[3]{a+2} = 3$
4. $\sqrt[3]{m-3} = 1$
5. $x - \sqrt{7x} = 0$
6. $k - \sqrt{10k} = 0$
7. $\sqrt[3]{5-a} = 2$
8. $\sqrt[3]{x-2} - 1 = 0$
9. $\sqrt{2y+3} + y = 0$
10. $\sqrt{x+2} - x = 0$

Written Solve each equation. Check each solution.

1. $\sqrt{3x+10} = x + 4$
2. $2\sqrt{k-1} = k - 1$
3. $\sqrt[3]{x+1} = 2$
4. $\sqrt[3]{r-2} = 1$
5. $\sqrt{2x+11} = x - 2$
6. $2m - 3 = \sqrt{7m-3}$
7. $\sqrt[3]{x-1} = 2$
8. $\sqrt[3]{5-y} = 2$
9. $\sqrt{y+3} + 3 = y$
10. $\sqrt{a+2} + 4 = a$
11. $\sqrt{4x+3} = x$
12. $\sqrt{2m} + 4 = m$
13. $\sqrt{b+1} - b = 1$
14. $\sqrt{2r+1} = r + 1$
15. $\sqrt{4x-4} + 4 = x$
16. $\sqrt{3s-2} + 4 = s$
17. $\sqrt{6x+7} - 2x = {}^-1$
18. $\sqrt{5z+4} - z = {}^-2$
19. $\sqrt{x-5} - \sqrt{x} = 1$
20. $\sqrt{m+12} - \sqrt{m} = 2$
21. $\sqrt{b+4} = \sqrt{b+20} - 2$
22. $\sqrt{2k+1} = 2 - \sqrt{k-3}$
23. $\sqrt{2t-1} + \sqrt{t-1} = 1$
24. $\sqrt{2a+1} = 1 + \sqrt{a}$
25. $\sqrt{3x^2 + 11x - 5} = 2x + 1$
26. $\sqrt{4-m} + \sqrt{m+6} = 4$
27. $\sqrt{4r^2 - 11} = r + 8$
28. $\sqrt{2y^2 + 5y} = {}^-y - 10$
29. $\sqrt{y+6} - \sqrt{y} = \sqrt{2}$
30. $\sqrt[3]{3t^2 - 3t + 1} = t$
31. $\sqrt{4x+1} - \sqrt{x-2} = 3$
32. $\sqrt{4m-3} = 2 + \sqrt{2m-5}$
33. $\sqrt{3x-5} = 2 - \sqrt{x-1}$
34. $\sqrt{3x-3} - \sqrt{x} = 1$
35. $\sqrt{2y+3} - \sqrt{y+1} = 1$
36. $\sqrt[3]{4x+5} - \sqrt[3]{x^2} = 0$
37. $\sqrt[4]{m^3 + 8} = 2$
38. $\sqrt[3]{(y+5)^2} = 1$

Challenge Solve each equation.

1. $\sqrt{m} + \sqrt{m-3} = \dfrac{3}{\sqrt{m-3}}$
2. $\sqrt{x+1} = \sqrt{x+6} - \dfrac{2}{\sqrt{x+1}}$

Skills Review State whether the graph of each equation is a parabola, a circle, an ellipse, or a hyperbola. Then draw each graph.

1. $9x^2 + y^2 = 36$
2. $x^2 + y^2 = 16$
3. $x^2 - y^2 = 16$
4. $y = x^2 + x - 6$
5. $y = 2x^2 - 4$
6. $x^2 - 4y^2 = 16$

11–7   Real Exponents

Consider the graph of $y = 2^x$ where x is a rational exponent. The expression $y = 2^x$ represents a function, since for each value of x there is a unique value of y.

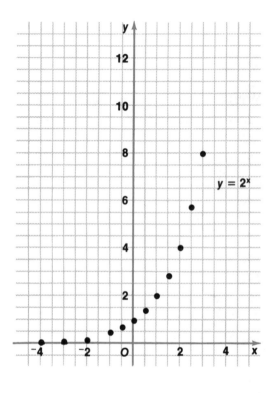

x	2^x or y	y (approximate)
$^-4$	$2^{-4} = \frac{1}{16}$	0.06
$^-3$	$2^{-3} = \frac{1}{8}$	0.12
$^-2$	$2^{-2} = \frac{1}{4}$	0.25
$^-1$	$2^{-1} = \frac{1}{2}$	0.5
$-\frac{1}{2}$	$2^{-\frac{1}{2}} = \frac{1}{2}\sqrt{2}$	0.7
0	$2^0 = 1$	1
$\frac{1}{2}$	$2^{\frac{1}{2}} = \sqrt{2}$	1.4
1	$2^1 = 2$	2
$\frac{3}{2}$	$2^{\frac{3}{2}} = 2\sqrt{2}$	2.8
2	$2^2 = 4$	4
$\frac{5}{2}$	$2^{\frac{5}{2}} = 4\sqrt{2}$	5.7
3	$2^3 = 8$	8

As greater values are selected for x the value of y increases. Thus, the function is increasing.

Since 2^x has not been defined when x is irrational, "holes" still remain in the graph of $y = 2^x$. How could you expand the domain of $y = 2^x$ to include both rational and irrational numbers?

Consider an expression such as $2^{\sqrt{3}}$. Since $1.7 < \sqrt{3} < 1.8$ it follows that $2^{1.7} < 2^{\sqrt{3}} < 2^{1.8}$. By selecting closer approximations for $\sqrt{3}$, closer approximations for $2^{\sqrt{3}}$ are possible.

$$2^{1.7} < 2^{\sqrt{3}} < 2^{1.8}$$
$$2^{1.73} < 2^{\sqrt{3}} < 2^{1.74}$$
$$2^{1.732} < 2^{\sqrt{3}} < 2^{1.733}$$
$$2^{1.7320} < 2^{\sqrt{3}} < 2^{1.7321}$$
$$2^{1.73205} < 2^{\sqrt{3}} < 2^{1.73206}$$

Therefore, it is possible to determine an approximate value for 2^x when x represents an irrational number by using rational approximations for x.

Definition of Irrational Exponents

Since 2^x is defined when x represents an irrational number, the domain of $y = 2^x$ has been expanded to the set of real numbers.

By using a large, accurate graph of $y = 2^x$ you could estimate the value of $2^{\sqrt{3}}$.

Study the following examples.

The "holes" have been filled and the graph is now a smooth curve.

example

1 **Use the graph of $y = 2^x$ to evaluate y to the nearest tenth.**

a. $y = 2^{\sqrt{3}}$ **b.** $y = 2^{1.6}$ **c.** $y = 2^{7.9}$

a. $y = 2^{\sqrt{3}}$

The value of x is $\sqrt{3}$ and $1.7 < \sqrt{3} < 1.8$.
From the graph, the value of y is approximately 3.3.

b. $y = 2^{1.6}$

From the graph, the value of y is approximately 3.

c. $y = 2^{7.9}$

$y = 2^6 \cdot 2^{1.9}$
$y = 64 \cdot 3.7$ $2^{1.9} \approx 3.7$ Why?
$y = 236.8$

The value of y is approximately 236.8

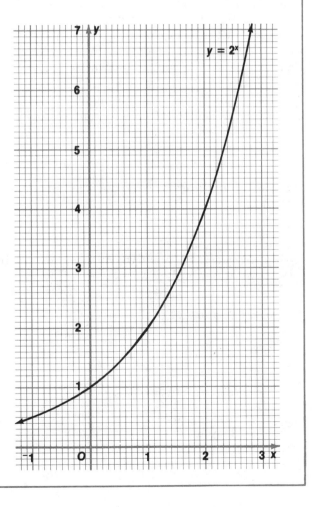

The properties of rational exponents apply to all real exponents.

2   **Simplify $3^{\sqrt{2}} \cdot 3^{\sqrt{5}}$.**

$3^{\sqrt{2}} \cdot 3^{\sqrt{5}} = 3^{\sqrt{2}+\sqrt{5}}$ *Recall that $a^m \cdot a^n = a^{m+n}$.*

3   **Simplify $(4^{\sqrt{3}})^{\sqrt{2}}$.**

$(4^{\sqrt{3}})^{\sqrt{2}} = 4^{\sqrt{3}\cdot\sqrt{2}}$
$\qquad = 4^{\sqrt{6}}$ *Recall that $(a^m)^n = a^{m \cdot n}$.*

An equation of the form $y = a^x$ where a is a positive real number other than 1 is called an **exponential function**. The figure at the right shows graphs of several exponential functions. Compare the graphs of functions where $a > 1$ and those where $a < 1$. What do you notice? When $a > 1$, is the graph of $y = a^x$ increasing or decreasing? When $a < 1$, is the graph increasing or decreasing?

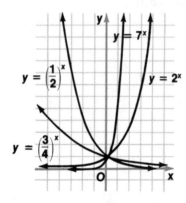

An important property of exponential functions is the property of equality.

Suppose a is a positive number other than 1. Then $a^{x_1} = a^{x_2}$ if and only if $x_1 = x_2$.

Property of Equality for Exponential Functions

What happens when a = 1?

4   **Solve $3^5 = 3^{2n-1}$ for n.**

$$3^5 = 3^{2n-1}$$
Therefore, $5 = 2n - 1$ *Property of Equality for Exponential Functions*
$$6 = 2n$$
$$n = 3$$

example

5 Solve $9^{3r} = 27^{r-2}$ for r.

$$9^{3r} = 27^{r-2}$$
$$(3^2)^{3r} = (3^3)^{r-2} \qquad \text{The bases must be the same. Replace 9 with } 3^2 \text{ and 27 with } 3^3.$$
$$3^{6r} = 3^{3r-6}$$
$$\text{Therefore, } 6r = 3r - 6 \qquad \text{Property of Equality for Exponential Functions}$$
$$3r = {}^-6$$
$$r = {}^-2$$

exercises

Exploratory Use the graph of $y = 2^x$ to evaluate each expression to the nearest tenth.

1. $2^{0.7}$
2. $2^{1.1}$
3. $2^{-0.3}$
4. 2^{-1}
5. $2^{\sqrt{2}}$
6. $2^{\sqrt{5}}$
7. $2^{6.4}$
8. $2^{8.3}$

Use the rules for exponents to simplify each of the following.

9. $2^{\sqrt{5}} \cdot 2^{3\sqrt{5}}$
10. $7^{\sqrt{3}} \cdot 7^{2\sqrt{3}}$
11. $(2^{\sqrt{3}})^{\sqrt{3}}$
12. $(9^{\sqrt{5}})^{\sqrt{5}}$
13. $3(2^{\sqrt{2}})(2^{-\sqrt{2}})$
14. $\dfrac{8^{2\sqrt{3}}}{8^{\sqrt{12}}}$

Solve each equation.

15. $4^x = 4^{-5}$
16. $5^x = 125$
17. $7^t = \dfrac{1}{49}$

Written   Simplify each expression.

1. $(2^{\sqrt{3}})^{\sqrt{12}}$
2. $(3^{\sqrt{8}})^{\sqrt{2}}$
3. $5^{\sqrt{3}} \cdot 5^{\sqrt{27}}$
4. $11^{\sqrt{5}} \cdot 11^{\sqrt{45}}$
5. $16^{\sqrt{7}} \div 2^{\sqrt{7}}$
6. $9^{\sqrt{3}} \div 3^{\sqrt{3}}$
7. $8^{\sqrt{3}} \cdot 16^{\sqrt{5}}$
8. $64^{\sqrt{2}} \cdot 16^{\sqrt{3}}$
9. $y^{\sqrt{5}} \cdot y^{\sqrt{45}}$
10. $(x^{\sqrt{2}})^{\sqrt{8}}$
11. $(y^{\sqrt{3}})^{\sqrt{27}}$
12. $b^{\sqrt{2}} \cdot b^{\sqrt{32}}$
13. $(m^{\sqrt{2}} \cdot p^{\sqrt{2}})^{\sqrt{2}}$
14. $(m^{\sqrt{2}} + n^{\sqrt{2}})^2$
15. $(x^{\sqrt{3}} + y^{\sqrt{2}})^2$
16. $(x^{\sqrt{2}} - y^{\sqrt{2}})(x^{\sqrt{2}} + y^{\sqrt{2}})$

Solve each equation.

17. $2^5 = 2^{2x-1}$
18. $3^y = 3^{3y+1}$
19. $5^{3s+4} = 5^s$
20. $3^x = 9^{x+1}$
21. $9^{3y} = 27^{y+2}$
22. $8^{r-1} = 16^{3r}$
23. $2^{2m-1} = 8^{m+7}$
24. $\left(\dfrac{1}{3}\right)^p = 3^{p-6}$
25. $2^{z+3} = \dfrac{1}{16}$
26. $\dfrac{1}{27} = 3^{x-5}$
27. $25^{2n} = 125^{n-3}$
28. $4^{y-1} = 8^y$

Graph each equation.

29. $y = 3^x$
30. $y = \left(\dfrac{1}{3}\right)^x$
31. $y = \left(\dfrac{1}{4}\right)^x$
32. $y = 4^x$
33. Compare the graphs for exercises 29 and 30. What do you notice?
34. Compare the graphs for exercises 31 and 32. What do you notice?

Tom and Ann Howard want to set up a savings fund for the education of their first child, who will enter college in ten years. They find they can put $1200 each year in a special account for this purpose. The account earns 6% interest, compounded annually.

They calculate how much will be in the account in a certain number of years by using this formula.

$$S = P \cdot \left(\frac{x}{1 - x}\right)(1 - x^k)$$

S is the amount in the account.
P is the amount deposited each year.
x is [1 + (rate of interest)].
k is the number of years.

Exercises   Solve each problem.

1. In the Howards' case, what is the value P?
2. What is the rate of interest, expressed as a decimal?
3. What is the value of x?
4. Suppose $k = 1$. Find the value of S at the end of the first year.
   Hint: $S = 1200\left(\frac{1.06}{1 - 1.06}\right)[1 - (1.06)^1]$
5. Compute $(1.06)^2$.
6. Compute $(1.06)^5$.
7. Compute $[(1.06)^5]^2$ or $(1.06)^{10}$.

Use the formula to find the following.

8. Find the amount in the account at the end of the second year.
9. Find the amount in the account at the end of the fifth year.
10. Find the amount in the account at the end of the tenth year.

Vocabulary

Chapter Summary

1. **Negative Integer Exponents:** For any number a, except $a = 0$, and for any positive integer n, $a^{-n} = \dfrac{1}{a^n}$. (321)

2. **Definition of Scientific Notation:** A number is expressed in scientific notation when it is in the form $a \times 10^n$. Here $1 \le a < 10$ and n is an integer. (325)

3. **Rational Numbers as Exponents:** For any number b and for any integer n, with n greater than one, $b^{\frac{1}{n}} = \sqrt[n]{b}$ except for $b < 0$ and n even. (329)

4. **Definition of Rational Exponents:** For any nonzero number b, and any integers m and n, with $n > 1$,
$b^{\frac{m}{n}} = \sqrt[n]{b^m} = (\sqrt[n]{b})^m$ except when $\sqrt[n]{b}$ does not represent a real number. (330)

5. **Conditions for Simplified Expressions:** An expression is simplified when it meets these conditions.
   1. It has no negative exponents.
   2. It has no fractional exponents in the denominator.
   3. It is not a complex fraction.
   4. The index of any remaining radical is as small as possible. (333)

6. **Definition of Quadratic Form:** For any numbers a, b, and c, except $a = 0$, an equation written as $a[f(x)]^2 + b[f(x)] + c = 0$, where $f(x)$ is some expression in x, is in quadratic form. (336)

7. These steps are usually used to solve a radical equation.
   1. Isolate the radical
   2. Raise both sides to a power
   3. Combine terms.
   4. Solve for the variable.
   5. Check each solution. (339)

8. **Definition of Irrational Exponents:** If x is an irrational number and $a > 0$, then a^x is the real number between a^{x_1} and a^{x_2}, for all possible choices of rational numbers x_1 and x_2 such that $x_1 < x < x_2$. (343)

9. **Property of Equality for Exponential Functions:** Suppose a is a positive number other than 1. Then $a^{x_1} = a^{x_2}$ if and only if $x_1 = x_2$. (344)

11–1 Evaluate.

1. 3^{-2}
2. 11^0
3. $\left(\frac{4}{3}\right)^{-2}$
4. $3^{-3}4^2$

5. $\left(\frac{7}{5}\right)^{-3}$
6. $\left(\frac{2}{3}\right)^0$
7. $(4^2)^{-2}$
8. $\left(\frac{12}{15}\right)^2$

Simplify each expression.

9. y^{-3}
10. $m^3 \cdot m^{-4}$
11. $\frac{s^{-3}}{s^2}$
12. $\frac{1}{x^{-2}}$

13. $\left(\frac{1}{m}\right)^{-6}$
14. $\left(\frac{y}{3}\right)^{-2}$
15. $r^{-3} \cdot r^{-2}$
16. $\left(\frac{2}{3x^{-2}}\right)^{-1}$

11–2 Copy and complete the chart.

	Decimal notation	Scientific notation
17.		1.215×10^3
18.	3,176,000,000	
19.		1.592×10^{-4}
20.	0.00078231	

Evaluate. Express each answer in scientific notation.

21. $\frac{6.921 \times 10^{11}}{8.317 \times 10^3}$

22. $(4,731,000)(0.028)$

11–3 For each of the following evaluate or express using exponents.

23. $6^{\frac{1}{2}} \cdot 6^{\frac{3}{2}}$
24. $125^{\frac{1}{3}}$
25. $(0.008)^{\frac{2}{3}}$
26. $(25^{\frac{3}{4}})^{\frac{2}{3}}$

27. $\sqrt[4]{x^4y^3}$
28. $\sqrt[3]{27m^3n^2}$
29. $\sqrt[5]{32w^{10}r^5}$

Write in simplest radical form.

30. $r^2s^{\frac{1}{3}}y^{\frac{1}{2}}$
31. $\sqrt[6]{27}$
32. $(3x)^{\frac{1}{2}}x^{\frac{1}{4}}$

11–4 Simplify each expression.

33. $\frac{1}{z^{\frac{3}{5}}}$
34. $\frac{w^{-\frac{2}{3}}r^{\frac{1}{2}}}{wr^2}$
35. $\frac{z^{\frac{1}{3}}}{z^{\frac{2}{3}} - z^{-\frac{1}{3}}}$
36. $\frac{x^{\frac{1}{2}} - y^{\frac{1}{2}}}{x^{\frac{1}{2}} + y^{\frac{1}{2}}}$

Evaluate each expression.

37. $\frac{2}{3}x^3\left(\frac{3}{x^2} - \frac{1}{x^{\frac{1}{3}}}\right)$ when $x = 8$

38. $\frac{3r^2 + 2r^{-1}}{r^{-\frac{2}{3}}}$ when $r = 3$

11–5 Solve each equation.

39. $m^{-\frac{2}{5}} - 4m^{-\frac{1}{5}} + 4 = 0$
40. $w^3 - 16w^{\frac{3}{2}} + 64 = 0$
41. $z^{-\frac{2}{3}} - 11z^{-\frac{1}{3}} + 28 = 0$

11–6 Solve each equation.

42. $\sqrt[3]{w} - 3 = 1$
43. $\sqrt{b + 2} + 4 = b$
44. $\sqrt{r + 12} - \sqrt{r} = 2$

11-7 **Solve each equation.**

45. $2^{6x} = 4^{5x+2}$

46. $(\sqrt{3})^{n+1} = 9^{n-1}$

47. $49^{3p+1} = 7^{2p-5}$

Simplify.

48. $3^{\sqrt{2}} \cdot 3^{\sqrt{2}}$

49. $(9^{\sqrt{2}})^{\sqrt{2}}$

50. $\dfrac{49^{\sqrt{2}}}{7^{\sqrt{12}}}$

Chapter Test

Simplify each expression.

1. y^{-5}

2. $\left(\dfrac{m}{4}\right)^{-2}$

3. $\dfrac{x^3}{x^{-4}}$

4. $\dfrac{(x+y)^3}{(x+y)^{-1}}$

5. $\dfrac{1}{y^{\frac{2}{3}}}$

6. $\dfrac{15}{5^{\frac{2}{3}}}$

7. $\dfrac{p^2}{p^{-1}q^0}$

8. $\left(\dfrac{2y^{-2}}{3z}\right)^{-1}\left(\dfrac{m^2 n}{y}\right)^0$

9. $\dfrac{r+s}{r^{\frac{1}{2}}+s^{\frac{1}{2}}}$

10. $\dfrac{7m}{m^{-3}} + \dfrac{3m^3}{m^{-1}}$

11. $\dfrac{-18t^3 s^2}{6t^4 s}$

12. $\dfrac{x^{\frac{5}{3}}y + 3x^{-\frac{1}{3}}}{x^{\frac{2}{3}}}$

Evaluate each expression.

13. $\left(\dfrac{3}{2}\right)^{-4}\left(\dfrac{3}{2}\right)^2$

14. $27^{-\frac{4}{3}}$

15. $(\sqrt[3]{27})^2$

16. $\dfrac{16}{4^{\frac{3}{2}}}$

17. $(0.0081)^{\frac{1}{4}}$

18. $25^{\frac{3}{2}}$

19. $\left(\dfrac{1}{64}\right)^{-\frac{2}{3}}$

20. $243^{\frac{3}{5}}$

Evaluate. Express each answer in scientific notation.

21. $(2.7 \times 10^{11})(3 \times 10^4)$

22. $\dfrac{6.3 \times 10^{-4}}{1.7 \times 10^{-7}}$

23. $\dfrac{72{,}000{,}000 \times 0.005}{0.0015}$

24. $\dfrac{84{,}000{,}000 \times 0.0013}{0.021}$

Express each of the following using exponents.

25. $\sqrt[3]{n^2}$

26. $\sqrt{a^6}$

27. $\sqrt[3]{8m^2 r^7}$

28. $\sqrt[6]{57}$

29. $\sqrt[3]{32} \cdot \sqrt[3]{2}$

30. $\sqrt[4]{x^4 y^6 b^2}$

Express in simplest radical form.

31. $\sqrt[3]{64}$

32. $\sqrt[4]{49}$

33. $4^{\frac{3}{2}}y^{\frac{5}{2}}x^{\frac{1}{2}}$

Solve each equation.

34. $y^{\frac{3}{2}} - 8 = 0$

35. $b^{-\frac{2}{3}} = 9$

36. $t^{-\frac{3}{4}} = \dfrac{1}{8}$

37. $w^{\frac{4}{3}} - 7w^{\frac{2}{3}} + 12 = 0$

38. $x^{\frac{1}{2}} - 10x^{\frac{1}{4}} + 16 = 0$

39. $m + \sqrt{3m-2} = 4$

40. $4^{3x} = 16^{x-\frac{1}{2}}$

41. $9^r = 3^{3r-2}$

chapter
12 Exponential and Logarithmic Functions

Jean Garson needs to determine how long it takes two of a certain strain of bacteria to increase to 1000 bacteria. To find an approximate answer she uses the general formula for growth and decay in nature, $y = ne^{kt}$. This formula is an example of an exponential equation.

12-1   An Inverse Relation

In the table on the left, x is the exponent. Compute the power of 2 to find y.

x	$2^x = y$	y
$^-1$	$2^{-1} = y$	?
2	$2^2 = y$	?
3	$2^3 = y$	?
6	$2^6 = y$	?

y	$2^y = x$	x
?	$2^y = \frac{1}{2}$	$\frac{1}{2}$
?	$2^y = 4$	4
?	$2^y = 8$	8
?	$2^y = 64$	64

Exponent to Power   Exponent from Power

In the table on the right, the emphasis is shifted. You are given x as the value of the power. Work toward finding the exponent, y. In the relation $2^y = x$, y is called the **logarithm** of x. It is more conveniently written as $\log_2 x = y$. The equation $\log_2 x = y$ is read *the log of x to the base 2 equals y*. The logarithm is the exponent.

Exponential Equation   Logarithmic Equation

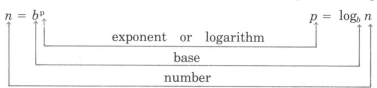

$n = b^p$ $p = \log_b n$

exponent or logarithm

base

number

> **Suppose $b > 0$ and $b \neq 1$. Then for $n > 0$, there is a number p such that $\log_b n = p$ if and only if $b^p = n$.**

Definition of Logarithm

Study the table of corresponding equations.

Exponential Equation	Logarithmic Equation
$6^2 = 36$	$\log_6 36 = 2$
$10^4 = 10{,}000$	$\log_{10} 10{,}000 = 4$
$3^0 = 1$	$\log_3 1 = 0$
$2^{-3} = \frac{1}{8}$	$\log_2 \frac{1}{8} = {}^-3$
$4^{\frac{1}{2}} = 2$	$\log_4 2 = \frac{1}{2}$

1 **Solve the equation $\log_2 64 = y$.**

$\log_2 64 = y$ implies that $2^y = 64$.
Since $2^6 = 64$, $2^y = 2^6$ and $y = 6$. *Property of Equality for Exponential Functions*

The solution is 6.

2 **Solve the equation $\log_9 x = \frac{1}{2}$.**

$\log_9 x = \frac{1}{2}$ implies that $9^{\frac{1}{2}} = x$.
Since $9^{\frac{1}{2}}$ or $\sqrt{9}$ is 3, $x = 3$.

The solution is 3.

3 **Solve the equation $\log_b 16 = 2$.**

$\log_b 16 = 2$ implies that $b^2 = 16$.
Since $4^2 = 16$, $b^2 = 4^2$ and $b = 4$. *Property of Equality for Exponential Functions*

The solution is 4.

exercises

Exploratory   **Change each equation to logarithmic form.**

1. $3^3 = 27$

2. $4^2 = 16$

3. $2^{-3} = \frac{1}{8}$

4. $5^{-2} = \frac{1}{25}$

5. $10^3 = 1000$

6. $10^{-2} = 0.01$

Change each equation to exponential form.

7. $\log_4 64 = 3$

8. $\log_3 9 = 2$

9. $\log_9 27 = \frac{3}{2}$

10. $\log_3 \frac{1}{81} = {}^-4$

11. $\log_{10} 0.1 = {}^-1$

12. $\log_{10} 0.0001 = {}^-4$

Evaluate each expression.

13. $\log_{10} 100$

14. $\log_3 81$

15. $\log_5 625$

16. $\log_{11} 121$

17. $\log_2 \frac{1}{8}$

18. $\log_3 \frac{1}{9}$

19. $\log_7 \frac{1}{343}$

20. $\log_2 \frac{1}{16}$

Written Rewrite each equation in logarithmic form.

1. $3^4 = 81$
2. $2^6 = 64$
3. $5^3 = 125$
4. $8^0 = 1$
5. $4^{-2} = \frac{1}{16}$
6. $3^{-1} = \frac{1}{3}$
7. $2^{-4} = \frac{1}{16}$
8. $7^{-2} = \frac{1}{49}$
9. $3^{\frac{1}{2}} = \sqrt{3}$
10. $9^{\frac{3}{2}} = 27$
11. $36^{\frac{3}{2}} = 216$
12. $\left(\frac{1}{9}\right)^{-2} = 81$

Rewrite each equation in exponential form.

13. $\log_2 32 = 5$
14. $\log_8 64 = 2$
15. $\log_{11} 121 = 2$
16. $\log_{13} 13 = 1$
17. $\log_5 1 = 0$
18. $\log_3 243 = 5$
19. $\log_{\frac{1}{2}} 16 = {}^-4$
20. $\log_8 4 = \frac{2}{3}$
21. $\log_{10} \frac{1}{10} = {}^-1$
22. $\log_5 \frac{1}{25} = {}^-2$
23. $\log_{\frac{1}{3}} 81 = {}^-4$
24. $\log_{27} 3 = \frac{1}{3}$

Evaluate each expression.

25. $\log_{10} 1000$
26. $\log_6 36$
27. $\log_{12} 144$
28. $\log_{10} 0.01$
29. $\log_{\frac{1}{4}} 64$
30. $\log_4 2$
31. $\log_9 27$
32. $\log_8 16$
33. $\log_{\frac{1}{2}} 8$
34. $\log_{10} 0.001$

Solve each equation.

35. $\log_b 49 = 2$
36. $\log_b 64 = 3$
37. $\log_6 x = 2$
38. $\log_9 x = {}^-1$
39. $\log_{\frac{1}{2}} 16 = x$
40. $\log_3 27 = x$
41. $\log_b 81 = 4$
42. $\log_b 18 = 1$
43. $\log_5 x = {}^-2$
44. $\log_3 x = {}^-3$
45. $\log_{10} \sqrt{10} = x$
46. $\log_5 \sqrt{5} = x$
47. $\log_a \frac{1}{27} = {}^-3$
48. $\log_b 36 = {}^-2$
49. $\log_{\frac{1}{2}} x = {}^-6$
50. $\log_4 x = -\frac{1}{2}$
51. $\log_2 x = {}^-4$
52. $\log_{\sqrt{3}} x = 6$
53. $\log_{\sqrt{3}} 27 = x$
54. $\log_x \sqrt{5} = \frac{1}{4}$
55. $\log_x \sqrt[3]{7} = \frac{1}{3}$
56. $\log_{10} \sqrt[3]{10} = x$

Challenge Solve each equation.

1. $\log_{\sqrt{x}} 6 = 2$
2. $\log_{\frac{1}{2}} \frac{1}{16} = x^2$

12–2 Logarithmic Functions

Study the graphs of $y = 2^x$ and $2^y = x$.

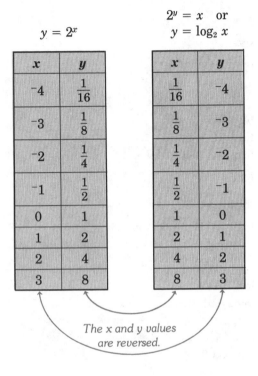

$y = 2^x$

$2^y = x$ or
$y = \log_2 x$

x	y
$^-4$	$\frac{1}{16}$
$^-3$	$\frac{1}{8}$
$^-2$	$\frac{1}{4}$
$^-1$	$\frac{1}{2}$
0	1
1	2
2	4
3	8

x	y
$\frac{1}{16}$	$^-4$
$\frac{1}{8}$	$^-3$
$\frac{1}{4}$	$^-2$
$\frac{1}{2}$	$^-1$
1	0
2	1
4	2
8	3

The x and y values are reversed.

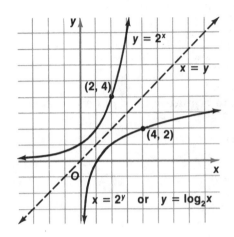

The domain of the logarithmic function is the set of all positive numbers. The range is all real numbers.

From the graph, $y = \log_2 x$ appears to be a function. A vertical line will not intersect the graph in more than one point. Both graphs are symmetrical with respect to the diagonal line $y = x$. For $y = 2^x$, y cannot be negative. For $y = \log_2 x$, x cannot be negative. Both graphs are smooth, unbroken, and continually increasing. By comparing points, such as (2, 4) and (4, 2), you can see that the functions are inverses of each other.

Thus, both $y = b^x$ and its inverse $y = \log_b x$ are functions. Recall that the property of equality holds for exponential functions. That is, $b^{x_1} = b^{x_2}$ if and only if $x_1 = x_2$. A similar property also holds for logarithmic functions.

Suppose $b > 0$ and $b \neq 1$. Then $\log_b x_1 = \log_b x_2$ if and only if $x_1 = x_2$.

Property of Equality for Logarithmic Functions

Study the following examples.

1 Solve the equation $\log_2 (x^2 - 1) = \log_2 8$.

$$\log_2 (x^2 - 1) = \log_2 8$$
$$x^2 - 1 = 8 \qquad \textit{Property of Equality for Logarithmic Functions}$$
$$x^2 - 9 = 0$$
$$(x - 3)(x + 3) = 0$$
$$x - 3 = 0 \qquad \text{or} \qquad x + 3 = 0$$
$$x = 3 \qquad \text{or} \qquad x = {}^-3 \qquad \text{The solutions are 3 and } {}^-3.$$

You know that $y = b^x$ and $y = \log_b x$ are inverse functions. Two applications of the property of inverse functions, $f(f^{-1}(x)) = x$, are given below.

same

$3^{\log_3 9} = 3^2 \text{ or } 9$ and $\log_4 4^2 = \log_4 16 \text{ or } 2$

$b^{\log_b x} = x$ and $\log_b b^x = x$

Find $f(f^{-1}(x))$ and $f^{-1}(f(x))$. Then apply the definition of inverse functions.

2 Evaluate the expression $\log_7 7^4$.

$$\log_7 7^4 = 4$$

The value of the expression is 4.

3 Solve the equation $3^{\log_3 x} = 3x - 4$.

$$3^{\log_3 x} = 3x - 4$$
$$x = 3x - 4$$
$$x = 2 \qquad \text{The solution is 2.}$$

exercises

Exploratory Evaluate each expression.

1. $\log_5 5^2$
2. $\log_9 9^4$
3. $9^{\log_9 2}$
4. $7^{\log_7 3}$
5. $\log_b b^4$
6. $\log_m m^x$
7. $b^{\log_b 5}$
8. $8^{\log_8 x}$

Solve each equation.

9. $\log_2 x = \log_2 4$
10. $\log_4 10 = \log_4 2x$
11. $\log_3 (x + 1) = \log_3 (2x)$
12. $\log_7 (x^2 - 1) = \log_7 3$

Written   Evaluate each expression.

1. $\log_4 4^3$

2. $\log_r r^4$

3. $6^{\log_6 7}$

4. $9^{\log_9 5}$

5. $\log_n n^5$

6. $3^{\log_3 21}$

Solve each equation.

7. $\log_3 (2x + 1) = \log_3 (3x - 6)$

8. $\log_{10} (4 + y) = \log_{10} (2y)$

9. $\log_{10} (3n) = \log_{10} (n + 2)$

10. $\log_4 (2x - 3) = \log_4 (x + 2)$

11. $\log_3 (3y - 1) = \log_3 (y + 4)$

12. $\log_7 (5x - 1) = \log_7 (3x + 7)$

13. $\log_{10} (x^2 + 36) = \log_{10} 100$

14. $\log_{10} (x - 1)^2 = \log_{10} 0.01$

15. $\log_9 (x^2 + 9x) = \log_9 10$

16. $\log_5 (4x - 4) = \log_5 100$

Graph each pair of equations on the same set of axes.

17. $y = 3^x$ and $y = \log_3 x$

18. $y = \left(\dfrac{1}{2}\right)^x$ and $y = \log_{\frac{1}{2}} x$

19. $y = 4^x$ and $y = \log_4 x$

20. $y = 10^x$ and $y = \log_{10} x$

Show that each statement is true.

21. $\log_4 4 + \log_4 16 = \log_4 64$

22. $\log_3 27 + \log_3 3 = \log_3 81$

23. $\log_2 32 - \log_2 4 = \log_2 8$

24. $\log_6 36 - \log_6 6 = \log_6 6$

25. $\log_3 27 = 3 \log_3 3$

26. $\log_4 16 = 2 \log_4 4$

27. $\dfrac{1}{2} \log_3 81 = \log_3 9$

28. $\dfrac{1}{3} \log_5 25 = 2 \log_5 \sqrt[3]{5}$

29. $\log_2 8 \cdot \log_8 2 = 1$

30. $\log_5 25 \cdot \log_{25} 5 = 1$

31. $\log_{10} [\log_3 (\log_4 64)] = 0$

32. $\log_2 64 = 3 \log_8 64$

33. $\log_3 81 = \dfrac{4}{3} \log_2 8$

34. $\log_4 [\log_2 (\log_3 81)] = \dfrac{1}{2}$

Solve each equation.

35. $6^{\log_6 x^2} = x + 30$

36. $3^{\log_3 x^3} = \dfrac{1}{27}$

37. $\log_2 [\log_4 (\log_3 x)] = {}^-1$

38. $\log_{10} [\log_2 (\log_7 x)] = 0$

Skills Review   In each exercise find $f({}^-1)$, $f(1)$, and $f(0)$.

1. $f(x) = 3x^3 - 1$

2. $f(x) = x^2 - 6$

3. $f(x) = -\dfrac{1}{4}x + 3$

4. $f(x) = 2x - 5$

5. $f(x) = x^3 - x^2 - 2$

6. $f(x) = x^4 - 8$

Write the equation for the inverse of each function.

7. $f(x) = {}^-7x - 5$

8. $f(x) = 2x - 3$

9. $f(x) = x^2 - 16$

10. $f(x) = \dfrac{x + 3}{2}$

11. $y = 3x$

12. $y = 4$

A logarithmic scale called the **Richter scale** is used to measure the strength of an earthquake. Each increase of one on the Richter scale corresponds to a ten-times increase in intensity. In other words, an earthquake that registers 8 on the Richter scale is ten times as intense as an earthquake that registers 7. An earthquake that registers 9 is ten times as intense as the one registering 8, and one hundred times as intense as the one registering 7.

The table below gives the effects of earthquakes of various intensities.

Richter Number	Intensity	Effect
1	10^1	only detectable by seismograph
2	10^2	hanging lamps sway
3	10^3	can be felt
4	10^4	glass breaks, buildings shake
5	10^5	furniture collapses
6	10^6	wooden houses damaged
7	10^7	buildings collapse
8	10^8	catastrophic damage

On April 18, 1906, one of the worst California earthquakes in recent history hit San Francisco. It caused a fire that burned more than 4 square miles. Hundreds of people died. There was from 250 to 300 million dollars worth of property damage. It is believed that this earthquake would have measured 8.3 on the Richter scale.

This photograph shows the San Andreas fault. Scientists claim that shifts in the earth's surface along this fault could cause major earthquakes in the near future. Small earthquakes are a common occurrence in California.

Exercises Solve each problem.

1. An earthquake with a rating of 7 is how much stronger than one with a rating of 6?

2. An earthquake with a rating of 7 is how much stronger than one with a rating of 4?

3. Which was stronger, the San Francisco earthquake or the Alaska earthquake that rated 8.4?

4. Which was stronger, the Ecuador earthquake that rated 8.9 or the Alaska earthquake?

5. The San Francisco earthquake was how much weaker than the Ecuador earthquake?

12-3   Properties of Logarithms

Logarithms are exponents. Thus, the properties of logarithms can be derived from the properties of exponents.

For example, to find the product of powers, add exponents. To find the logarithm of a product, add logarithms.

$$\begin{aligned}
\log_2 (8 \cdot 32) &= \log_2 (2^3 \cdot 2^5) \\
&= \log_2 (2^{3+5}) \\
&= 3 + 5 \\
&= \log_2 2^3 + \log_2 2^5 \\
&= \log_2 8 + \log_2 32
\end{aligned}$$

Similarly, to find the quotient of powers, subtract exponents. To find the logarithm of a quotient, subtract logarithms.

$$\begin{aligned}
\log_2 (32 \div 8) &= \log_2 (2^5 \div 2^3) \\
&= \log_2 (2^{5-3}) \\
&= 5 - 3 \\
&= \log_2 2^5 - \log_2 2^3 \\
&= \log_2 32 - \log_2 8
\end{aligned}$$

Finally, to find the power of a power, multiply exponents. Thus, to find the logarithm of a power, multiply by the exponent.

$$\begin{aligned}
\log_2 8^4 &= \log_2 (2^3)^4 \\
&= \log_2 2^{3 \cdot 4} \\
&= 3 \cdot 4 \\
&= (\log_2 2^3) \cdot 4 \\
&= (\log_2 8) \cdot 4 \\
&= 4 \log_2 8
\end{aligned}$$

These properties of logarithms can be summarized in the following way.

> Suppose m and n are positive numbers, b is a positive number other than 1, and p is any number. Then the following properties hold.
>
> **Product Property:** $\log_b mn = \log_b m + \log_b n$
>
> **Quotient Property:** $\log_b \dfrac{m}{n} = \log_b m - \log_b n$
>
> **Power Property:** $\log_b m^p = p \cdot \log_b m$

Properties of Logarithms

Study how these properties are applied in the following examples.

1 **Given $\log_3 5 = 1.465$, estimate $\log_3 45$ and $\log_3 25$.**

$$\begin{aligned}
\log_3 45 &= \log_3 (3^2 \cdot 5) \\
&= \log_3 3^2 + \log_3 5 \\
&= 2 + 1.465 \quad \text{or} \quad 3.465
\end{aligned}$$

$$\begin{aligned}
\log_3 25 &= \log_3 5^2 \\
&= 2 \cdot \log_3 5 \\
&= 2(1.465) \quad \text{or} \quad 2.930
\end{aligned}$$

2 **Solve the equation $\log_{12} 72 - \log_{12} 9 = \log_{12} 4m$.**

$$\log_{12} 72 - \log_{12} 9 = \log_{12} 4m$$
$$\log_{12} \frac{72}{9} = \log_{12} 4m \quad \text{\textit{Quotient Property of Logarithms}}$$
$$8 = 4m \quad \text{\textit{Property of Equality for Logarithmic Functions}}$$
$$2 = m$$

Check: $\quad \log_{12} 72 - \log_{12} 9 = \log_{12} 4m$
$$\log_{12} 72 - \log_{12} 9 \overset{?}{=} \log_{12} 4 \cdot 2$$
$$\log_{12} 8 = \log_{12} 8$$

The solution is 2.

3 **Solve the equation $\log_3 (y + 4) + \log_3 (y - 4) = 2$.**

$$\log_3 (y + 4) + \log_3 (y - 4) = 2$$
$$\log_3 (y + 4)(y - 4) = 2 \quad \text{\textit{Product Property of Logarithms}}$$
$$(y + 4)(y - 4) = 3^2 \quad \text{\textit{Definition of Logarithm}}$$
$$y^2 - 16 = 9$$
$$y^2 - 25 = 0$$
$$(y - 5)(y + 5) = 0$$
$$y - 5 = 0 \quad \text{or} \quad y + 5 = 0$$
$$y = 5 \quad \text{or} \quad y = {}^-5$$

Check: $\quad \log_3 (y + 4) + \log_3 (y - 4) = 2$
$$\log_3 (5 + 4) + \log_3 (5 - 4) \overset{?}{=} 2$$
$$\log_3 9 + \log_3 1 \overset{?}{=} 2$$
$$2 + 0 = 2$$

$\log_3 (y + 4) + \log_3 (y - 4) = 2$
$$\log_3 ({}^-5 + 4) + \log_3 ({}^-5 - 4) \overset{?}{=} 2$$
$$\log_3 ({}^-1) + \log_3 ({}^-9) \overset{?}{=} 2$$
Since log is not defined for negative numbers, ${}^-5$ is not an acceptable solution.

The only solution is 5.

4 **Show that $\log_b mn = \log_b m + \log_b n$ for m, n, and b positive and $b \neq 1$.**

$$b^{\log_b m} = m, \, b^{\log_b n} = n, \, b^{\log_b mn} = mn \quad \text{\textit{Property of Inverse Functions}}$$
$$b^{\log_b mn} = mn$$
$$= b^{\log_b m} \cdot b^{\log_b n} \quad \text{\textit{Substitute} } b^{\log_b m} \text{ \textit{for m and} } b^{\log_b n} \text{ \textit{for n.}}$$
$$b^{\log_b mn} = b^{\log_b m + \log_b n} \quad \text{\textit{Add the exponents.}}$$
$$\log_b mn = \log_b m + \log_b n \quad \text{\textit{Property of Equality for Exponential Functions}}$$

exercises

Exploratory   Solve each equation.

1. $\log_2 3 + \log_2 7 = \log_2 x$

2. $\log_5 4 + \log_5 x = \log_5 36$

3. $\log_4 18 - \log_4 x = \log_4 6$

4. $\log_3 56 - \log_3 8 = \log_3 x$

5. $2 \log_7 3 + 3 \log_7 2 = \log_7 x$

6. $2 \log_6 4 - \frac{1}{3} \log_6 8 = \log_6 x$

Express each logarithm as the sum or difference of simpler logarithmic expressions.

7. $\log_3 (xy)$

8. $\log_4 (rst)$

9. $\log_2 (m^4 y)$

10. $\log_2 \left(\frac{y}{r} \right)$

11. $\log_b \left(\frac{\sqrt{x}}{p} \right)$

12. $\log_4 \left(\frac{xy}{z} \right)$

13. $\log_3 (5 \sqrt[3]{a})$

14. $\log_{10} (ac)^2$

15. $\log_2 (ax^{\frac{1}{2}})$

Evaluate each expression.

16. $5^{\log_5 3 + \log_5 2}$

17. $7^{\log_7 8 - \log_7 4}$

18. $6^{3 \log_6 2}$

Written   Use $\log_{10} 3 = 0.4771$ and $\log_{10} 7 = 0.8451$ to estimate each expression.

1. $\log_{10} 21$

2. $\log_{10} \frac{7}{3}$

3. $\log_{10} 27$

4. $\log_{10} 63$

5. $\log_{10} 30$

6. $\log_{10} 0.03$

7. $\log_{10} (70 \cdot 3)$

8. $\log_{10} 4.9$

9. $\log_{10} 700$

10. $\log_{10} 90$

11. $\log_{10} \left(3\frac{1}{3} \right)$

12. $\log_{10} \left(\frac{1}{9} \right)$

Solve each equation.

13. $\log_3 7 + \log_3 x = \log_3 14$

14. $\log_2 10 - \log_2 t = \log_2 2$

15. $\log_3 y - \log_3 2 = \log_3 12$

16. $\log_3 14 + \log_3 m = \log_3 42$

17. $\log_5 x = 3 \log_5 7$

18. $\log_2 p = \frac{1}{2} \log_2 81$

19. $\log_9 x = \frac{1}{2} \log_9 144 - \frac{1}{3} \log_9 8$

20. $\log_7 m = \frac{1}{3} \log_7 64 + \frac{1}{2} \log_7 121$

21. $\log_{10} 7 + \log_{10} (n - 2) = \log_{10} 6n$

22. $\log_{10} (m + 3) - \log_{10} m = \log_{10} 4$

23. $\log_{10} x + \log_{10} x + \log_{10} x = \log_{10} 27$

24. $4 \log_5 x - \log_5 4 = \log_5 4$

25. $\log_2 15 + \log_2 14 - \log_2 105 = \log_2 x$

26. $2 \log_3 x + \log_3 \frac{1}{10} = \log_3 5 + \log_3 2$

27. $\log_4 (x + 2) + \log_4 (x - 4) = 2$

28. $\log_4 (y - 1) + \log_4 (y - 1) = 2$

29. $\log_{10} (y - 1) + \log_{10} (y + 2) = \log_7 7$

30. $\log_{10} y + \log_{10} (y + 21) = 2$

31. $\log_4 (x + 3) + \log_4 (x - 3) = 2$

32. $\log_2 (9x + 5) - \log_2 (x^2 - 1) = 2$

33. $\log_8 (m + 1) - \log_8 m = \log_8 4$

34. $\log_2 (y + 2) - 1 = \log_2 (y - 2)$

Show that each of the following is true.

35. Quotient Property of Logarithms

36. Power Property of Logarithms

A **cloze test** is one method to test your comprehension of reading material. In a cloze test, a section of text is chosen. The entire first sentence is given. One of the first five words in the second sentence is replaced by a blank. Then every fifth word is replaced by a blank. You must decide which words are missing. You may have to guess at some of the words, but you can find many clues in the material that remains. The following section is taken from this chapter.

Every logarithm has two parts, the characteristic and the mantissa. The _____(a)_____ is the logarithm of _____(b)_____ number between 1 and _____(c)_____. The characteristic is the _____(d)_____ of 10 by which _____(e)_____ number is multiplied when _____(f)_____ number is expressed in _____(g)_____ notation.
The table of _____(h)_____ is really a table _____(i)_____ mantissas. You must supply the characteristic.

From the first sentence, you learn that this section is about logarithms and the two parts of logarithms. The third sentence is talking about the characteristic. Perhaps the blank marked *a* should be *mantissa*. Then the second sentence would read, *The mantissa is the logarithm of* _____(b)_____ *number between 1 and* _____(c)_____ The blank marked *b* could be *a* and the blank marked *c* must be *10*. The characteristic is the power of 10, so the blank marked *d* must be *power*.

Try to fill in the remaining blanks.

Your answers should be (e) that, (f) the, (g) scientific, (h) logarithms, and (i) of.

You may check your comprehension of any lesson by asking a friend to copy a section of that lesson, leaving a blank for every fifth word.

Exercises   Copy the following sentences and fill in each blank.

Logarithms were invented to make computation easier. With logarithms, _____ converts to addition; division _____ to subtraction. What is _____ is a table of _____ for some convenient base. _____ 10 is most useful _____ our numbers are in _____ 10. Logarithms to base _____ are called common logarithms. _____ is written as log *x*.
_____ table of common logarithms _____ numbers between 1 and _____ may be found on _____ 575. To find log 1.23, _____ across the row labeled _____ and down the column _____ 3.
For numbers greater _____ 10 or less than _____, scientific notation and the _____ of logarithms are used _____ find the _____.

12-4   Common Logarithms

Logarithms were invented to make computation easier. With logarithms, multiplication changes to addition and division changes to subtraction. Logarithms to base 10 are most useful because our number system is based upon 10. These logarithms are called **common logarithms.** $\log_{10}x$ is written as $\log x$.

A table of common logarithms for numbers between 1 and 10 may be found on pages 575 and 576. To find $\log 1.23$, read across the row labeled 12 and down the column labeled 3.

Common Logarithms of Numbers

n	0	1	2	3	4
10	0000	0043	0086	0128	0170
11	0414	0453	0492	0531	0569
12	0792	0828	0864	0899	0934

The values in the table are rounded to the nearest ten-thousandth.

$$\log 1.23 = 0.0899$$

For numbers greater than 10 or less than 1, scientific notation and the properties of logarithms are used to find the logarithm.

---

example

1 **Find log 745,000 to the nearest ten-thousandth.**

$$745{,}000 = 7.45 \times 10^5$$ *Scientific notation*
$$\log 745{,}000 = \log(7.45 \times 10^5)$$ *Property of Equality for Logarithmic Functions*
$$= \log 7.45 + \log 10^5$$ *Product Property of Logarithms*
$$= \log 7.45 + 5$$
$$= 0.8722 + 5 \text{ or } 5.8722$$ *From the table, $\log 7.45 = 0.8722$.*

The log of 745,000 is 5.8722

Every logarithm has two parts, the **characteristic** and the **mantissa.** The mantissa is the logarithm of a number between 1 and 10. When the number is expressed in scientific notation, the characteristic is the power of 10.

Mantissas range from 0 to 1.

$$\log 745{,}000 = \underset{\substack{\uparrow \\ \text{characteristic}}}{5}.\underset{\substack{\uparrow \\ \text{mantissa}}}{8722}$$

Since $745{,}000 = 7.45 \times 10^5$ the characteristic is 5.

The table of logarithms is really a table of mantissas. You must supply the characteristic.

2 **Find log 0.000524**

$$\log 0.000524 = \log (5.24 \times 10^{-4}) \quad \textit{Substitution}$$
$$= \log 5.24 + \log 10^{-4} \quad \textit{Product Property}$$
$$= 0.7193 + (^-4)$$
$$= 0.7193 - 4 \quad \text{The logarithm is approximately } 0.7193 - 4.$$

Logarithm tables are tables of positive mantissas. To avoid a negative mantissa, do *not* add the $^-4$ and 0.7193. The negative characteristic may be written in many ways.

$$\log 0.000524 = 0.7193 - 4$$
$$\log 0.000524 = 6.7193 - 10 \quad \textit{Note } 6 - 10 = ^-4.$$

We usually use $6 - 10$ for $^-4$. But, in some cases it may be more convenient to use another difference such as $26 - 30$.

Sometimes a logarithm is given and you must find the number. To find the number, use the table of mantissas in reverse. The number is called the **antilogarithm.** *If log x = a, then x = antilog a.*

3 **If log x = 3.5821, find x.**

$$\log x = 3.5821$$
$$x = \text{antilog } 3.5821 \quad \textit{3 is the characteristic and 0.5821 is the mantissa.}$$
$$= (\text{antilog } 0.5821) \times 10^3$$

Find antilog 0.5821 in the table of mantissas. It is in the row labeled 38 and the column labeled 2.

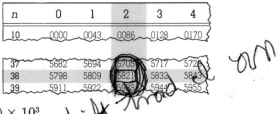

n	0	1	2	3	4
10	0000	0043	0086	0128	0170
37	5682	5694	5705	5717	5729
38	5798	5809	5821	5832	5843
39	5911	5922	5933	5944	5955

$$x = (\text{antilog } 0.5821) \times 10^3$$
$$= 3.82 \times 10^3$$
$$= 3820 \quad \text{The solution is 3820.}$$

exercises

Exploratory   **If log 483 = 2.6839, find each number.**

1. characteristic of log 483
2. mantissa of log 483
3. log 48.3
4. log 4830
5. log 0.004830
6. antilog 0.6839
7. antilog 5.6839
8. antilog (0.6839 − 4)

State the characteristic of the logarithm of each number. Then use the table on pages 575 and 576 to find the logarithm.

9. 47.5   **10.** 370   **11.** 4.61   **12.** 0.076
13. 0.209   **14.** 6870   **15.** 55   **16.** 0.00213

State the characteristic of each logarithm and use the table to find the antilogarithm.

17. 1.5527   **18.** 3.8096   **19.** 0.8376 − 2   **20.** 0.6263 − 3
21. 4.5955   **22.** 0.9513 − 5   **23.** 0.7910 − 1   **24.** 2.1106

Written   Use the table of mantissas to find the logarithm of each number.

1. 58.2   **2.** 715   **3.** 9.58   **4.** 0.000741
5. 7420   **6.** 0.3   **7.** 0.00211   **8.** 841,000
9. 0.0385   **10.** 0.671   **11.** 62,700   **12.** 0.113

Find the antilog of each logarithm.

13. 1.0899   **14.** 0.8727 − 2   **15.** 3.9581   **16.** 0.7846 − 1
17. 0.9542 − 2   **18.** 5.7451   **19.** 9.2014 − 10   **20.** 0.1673
21. 5.7168   **22.** 1.3075   **23.** 3.6656   **24.** 0.6304

Logarithms

Many calculators have keys for logarithmic and exponential functions. For example, you can use the [log] key to find the logarithm of 76,500.

ENTER: 76500   [log]   *The logarithm of 76,500*
DISPLAY: 76500   4.8836614   *is approximately 4.8837.*

Notice that the calculator supplies both the mantissa and the characteristic.

Example   Find the logarithm of 0.00431.

ENTER: .00431   [log]   *The logarithm of 0.00431*
DISPLAY: 0.00431   −2.3655227   *is approximately −2.3655.*

By using the table on pages 575 and 576 to find the mantissa, and by supplying the characteristic, you could express the logarithm of 0.00431 as 0.6345 − 3. Compare this result to your calculator result. What can you conclude about calculator logarithms for numbers less than 1?

From the definition of logarithm you know that $x = 10^a$ if and only if $a = \log x$. Also, if $a = \log x$ then $x = $ antilog a. Therefore, you can find antilog a by finding 10^a. Use the $[y^x]$ key to find the antilog of 1.0899.

ENTER: 10 $[y^x]$ 1.0899 $[=]$ *The antilog of 1.0899*
DISPLAY: 10   10   1.0899   12.299855   *is approximately 12.3.*

Exercises   **1–12.** Use [log] to check your answers to Written Exercises **1–12**.
13–24. Use $[y^x]$ to check your answers to Written Exercises **13–24**.

12–5   Interpolation

The table of logarithms in this text includes mantissas of numbers with 3 significant digits. You can approximate logarithms of numbers with 4 significant digits by a method known as **interpolation.**

1   **Approximate the value of log 1.327.**

n	0	1	2	3	4
10	0000	0043	0086	0128	0170
11	0414	0453	0492	0531	0569
12	0792	0828	0864	0899	0934
13	1139	1173	1206	1239	1271

The logarithm of 1.327 must be between log 1.32 and log 1.33.

Form a proportion of differences.

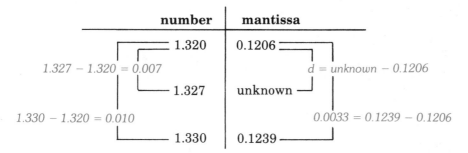

$$\frac{0.007}{0.010} = \frac{d}{0.0033}$$
$$0.00231 = d$$
$$0.0023 = d$$

The log tables are given in 4-place decimals. Round to 4 places.

Since the table is increasing, add 0.0023 to the mantissa of 1.320.

$$\log 1.327 = \log 1.320 + d$$
$$= 0.1206 + 0.0023$$
$$= 0.1229 \qquad \text{The logarithm of 1.327 is approximately 0.1229.}$$

2   **Approximate the value of log 0.001327.**

$$\log 0.001327 = \log (1.327 \times 10^{-3})$$
$$= \log 1.327 + \log 10^{-3}$$
$$= 0.1229 - 3 \qquad \textit{The value of log 1.327 was found in Example 1.}$$

The logarithm of 0.001327 is about $0.1229 - 3$ or $7.1229 - 10$.

Interpolation can also be used to find an antilogarithm that cannot be obtained directly from the table.

example

3 **Find antilog 2.4356.**

antilog 2.4356 = (antilog 0.4356) × 10^2

n	0	1	2	3	4
10	0000	0043	0086	0128	0170

26	4150	4166	4183	4200	4216
27	4314	4330	4346	4362	4378
28	4472	4487	4502	4518	4533

In the table of mantissas 4356 lies between 4346 and 4362.

Again, form a proportion of differences.

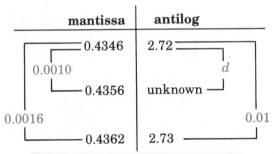

$$\frac{0.0010}{0.0016} = \frac{d}{0.01}$$
$$0.00625 = d$$
$$0.006 = d$$

In finding antilogs, interpolation is accurate for one more digit than given in the table.

Since the table is increasing, add 0.006 to 2.72.

antilog 2.4356 = (antilog 0.4356) × 10^2
          = (2.72 + 0.006) × 10^2
          = 2.726 × 10^2
          = 272.6

The antilog of 2.4356 is about 272.6.

exercises

Exploratory State the two numbers whose logarithms you would use to find the logarithm of each number below.

1. 7.413

2. 32,520

3. 0.0007463

4. 0.01234

State two numbers between which the antilog of each logarithm lies.

5. 0.6209 **6.** 2.7295 **7.** 3.9788 **8.** 0.7885 − 2

Written   Interpolate to find the logarithm of each number.

1. 5.273 **2.** 7.184 **3.** 27.53
4. 604.7 **5.** 0.1952 **6.** 0.07635
7. 0.003148 **8.** 7.003 **9.** 4167
10. 60.06 **11.** 329.4 **12.** 19.79
13. 0.04729 **14.** 8.871 **15.** 5.008
16. 0.005364 **17.** 80.08 **18.** 0.7214
19. 2148×10^3 **20.** 305.4×10^{-4} **21.** 16.57×10^{-2}

Interpolate to find the antilog of each logarithm.

22. 0.4861 **23.** 0.5506 **24.** 3.5748
25. 2.7792 **26.** 0.3353 − 2 **27.** 0.6173 − 3
28. 0.6409 − 2 **29.** 0.4399 − 3 **30.** 3.4193
31. 4.2173 **32.** 0.5915 − 2 **33.** 0.6778 − 3
34. 0.1177 − 3 **35.** 0.8787 − 2 **36.** 2.5082
37. 5.5958 **38.** 4.6279 **39.** 3.4170
40. 0.9172 − 3 **41.** 0.5688 − 4 **42.** 0.8713 − 2

Computation Using Logarithms   excursions in algebra

Before the invention of handheld calculators, logarithms were often used to do computation.

Example   Evaluate $\dfrac{(673)(549)(13.82)}{147,900}$.

Let $A = \dfrac{(673)(549)(13.82)}{147,900}$.

Then, $\log A = \log \left[\dfrac{(673)(549)(13.82)}{147,900} \right]$

$= \log 673 + \log 549 + \log 13.82 - \log 147{,}900$

$= 2.8280 + 2.7396 + 1.1405 - 5.1700$

$= 1.5381$

And, $A = $ antilog (1.5381)

$= 34.52$

The value is about 34.52.

Exercises   Use logarithms to evaluate each expression.

1. $\dfrac{(812)(41.5)}{431}$ **2.** $\dfrac{(71.63)(313.4)}{(489.2)}$ **3.** $\dfrac{(665)(899)(0.000172)}{(0.00035)(491)}$

12–6   Calculation of Powers and Roots

The development of calculators has greatly reduced the need for logarithmic tables. However, finding powers and roots on some calculators is often complicated or impossible. You may find that some problems are easier to solve if logarithms are used.

examples

1 **Use logarithms to estimate the value of $(47.9)^5$.**

$$\text{Let } A = (47.9)^5$$
$$\begin{aligned} \text{Then, } \log A &= \log (47.9)^5 \\ &= 5 \log(47.9) \\ &= 5(1.6803) \\ &= 8.4015 \\ A &= \text{antilog } 8.4015 \\ &= \text{antilog } (0.4015 + 8) \\ &= (\text{antilog } 0.4015) \times 10^8 \\ &= 2.520 \times 10^8 \\ &= 252{,}000{,}000 \end{aligned}$$

The value of $(47.9)^5$ is about 252,000,000.

2 **Use logarithms to estimate the value of $\sqrt[4]{0.0815}$.**

$$\text{Let } A = \sqrt[4]{0.0815}$$
$$\begin{aligned} \text{Then, } \log A &= \log \sqrt[4]{0.0815} \\ &= \log(0.0815)^{\frac{1}{4}} \\ &= \frac{1}{4} \log 0.0815 \\ &= \frac{1}{4}(0.9112 - 2) \\ &= \frac{1}{4}(2.9112 - 4) \\ &= 0.7278 - 1 \\ A &= \text{antilog } (0.7278 - 1) \\ &= (\text{antilog } 0.7278) \times 10^{-1} \\ &= 5.343 \times 10^{-1} \\ &= 0.5343 \end{aligned}$$

Since the multiplying factor is $\frac{1}{4}$, the negative characteristic should be a multiple of 4.
$0.9112 - 2 = 2.9112 - 4$

The value of $\sqrt[4]{0.0815}$ is about 0.5343.

3   **Estimate the value of $\sqrt[3]{\dfrac{(86.2)(9.1)^2}{43.7}}$ using logarithms.**

Let $A = \sqrt[3]{\dfrac{(86.2)(9.1)^2}{43.7}}$

Then, $\log A = \dfrac{1}{3} \log \left[\dfrac{(86.2)(9.1)^2}{43.71} \right]$

$\qquad\qquad = \dfrac{1}{3} \log 163.3$ *Use a calculator or logarithms to find the radicand.*

$\qquad\qquad = \dfrac{1}{3} (2.2129)$

$\qquad\qquad = 0.7376$

$\qquad A = \text{antilog } 0.7376$

$\qquad\quad = 5.465$

The value is about 5.465.

Logarithms may be used to solve compound interest problems. In the compound interest formula, P is the investment, r is the interest rate per year, n is the number of times the interest is compounded yearly, t is the number of years of the investment, and A is the amount of money accumulated.

Compound Interest Formula

$$A = P \left(1 + \frac{r}{n} \right)^{nt}$$

---

4   **Native Americans were paid \$24 for Manhattan Island in 1626. If this money had been invested at 6% compounded yearly, what would have been the value of this investment at the bicentennial in 1976 (350 years later)?**

$A = 24 \left(1 + \dfrac{0.06}{1} \right)^{1 \cdot 350}$ *Substitute 24 for P, 0.06 for r, 1 for n and 350 for t.*

$\quad = 24(1.06)^{350}$

$\log A = \log [24(1.06)^{350}]$

$\qquad = \log 24 + 350 \log 1.06$

$\qquad = 1.3802 + 350(0.0253)$

$\qquad = 10.2352$

$\quad A = \text{antilog } 10.2352$

$\qquad = (\text{antilog } 0.2352) \times 10^{10}$

$\qquad = 1.719 \times 10^{10}$

$\qquad = 17{,}190{,}000{,}000$

The value would be about \$17,190,000,000.

exercises

Exploratory State the logarithm of each power or root in the form $p \log m$.

1. $(63.9)^3$·
2. $(49.2)^4$
3. $(0.7425)^4$
4. $(0.1783)^5$
5. $(4173)^3$
6. $(1792)^5$
7. $\sqrt{594}$
8. $\sqrt[3]{2079}$
9. $(9.813)^{\frac{1}{4}}$
10. $(2.317)^{\frac{1}{2}}$
11. $\sqrt[3]{46^2}$
12. $\sqrt[5]{82^3}$

Assume each expression is to be evaluated using logarithms. What would be a convenient form for the characteristic?

13. $(0.0017)^{\frac{1}{3}}$
14. $(0.0912)^{\frac{1}{4}}$
15. $(0.00721)^{\frac{3}{8}}$
16. $(0.00219)^{\frac{2}{3}}$
17. $\sqrt[4]{0.0005}$
18. $\sqrt[5]{0.0007}$
19. $\sqrt[3]{-0.294}$
20. $\sqrt[3]{-0.391}$

Written 1–20. Use logarithms to evaluate each expression in Exploratory Exercises 1–20.

Evaluate each expression using logarithms.

21. $\dfrac{\sqrt[3]{4923}}{462.7}$
22. $\dfrac{\sqrt[4]{84.37}}{321.5}$
23. $\sqrt[3]{(82.7)(4.93)}$
24. $\sqrt{(408)(39.6)}$
25. $\sqrt[3]{\dfrac{(82.7)(4.93)}{632}}$
26. $\sqrt[3]{\dfrac{(3.29)(63)^2}{5236}}$

Solve each problem using logarithms.

27. Compute the value of $100 invested for 10 years at 6% annual interest compounded semi-annually.

28. Compute the value of $100 invested for 10 years at 8% annual interest compounded quarterly.

29. If $2500 is invested in a bank paying 6% interest compounded quarterly, how much will be in the account at the end of 5 years?

30. A pendulum of length l feet makes a single swing back and forth in t seconds where $t = \pi\sqrt{\dfrac{l}{32.16}}$. Find t when $l = 4.135$.

31. Which yields more, $275 invested at 10% compounded annually over 15 years, or the same amount invested at 9.5% compounded quarterly over 13 years?

32. Which yields more, $700 invested at 9% compounded semiannually over 20 years or $570 invested at $8\frac{1}{2}$% compounded quarterly over 25 years?

Natural Logarithms　　　excursions in algebra

Frequently, mathematicians and scientists need to solve problems involving a power of e ($e \approx 2.718$). For this reason logarithms to the base e are sometimes more convenient to use than common logarithms. Logarithms to the base e are called **natural logarithms** and are abbreviated ln. Therefore, $\log_e 5$ is written ln 5.

Exercises Solve each equation. Let $e = 2.718$ and $\log_{10} e = 0.4343$.

1. $x = e^{0.05}$
2. $x = e^{0.06}$
3. $x = e^{0.08}$
4. $x = e^{0.09}$

applications Factoring and Compound Interest

Many formulas are used daily in business and science. One such formula is used in finding **compound interest.** Compound interest is interest that is added to an original investment at specified time intervals. Thus, the interest becomes part of a new principal.

Suppose you deposited $500 in a savings account for 3 years at a rate of 6% annual interest.

	amount deposited +	interest	= new principal
End of first year	$500 +	$500 (0.06)	= $530
End of second year	$530 +	$530(0.06)	= $561.80
End of third year	$561.80 +	$561.80(0.06)	= $595.51 *This result is approximate.*

To write a general formula, let P represent the amount deposited or principal and let r represent the annual interest rate. Then, $P \cdot r$ represents the amount of interest earned.

End of first year $\qquad\qquad\qquad P + P \cdot r = P(1 + r)^1$ $\qquad$ *Factor out P.*

End of second year $\qquad P(1 + r) + P(1 + r) \cdot r = P(1 + r)(1 + r)$ $\quad$ *Factor out*
$$= P(1 + r)^2 \qquad\quad P(1 + r).$$

End of third year $\qquad P(1 + r)^2 + P(1 + r)^2 \cdot r = P(1 + r)^2(1 + r)$ $\quad$ *Factor out*
$$= P(1 + r)^3 \qquad\quad P(1 + r)^2.$$
$$\vdots$$

End of t years $\qquad\qquad \Longrightarrow \qquad\qquad P(1 + r)^t$

Therefore, at the end of t years the total amount of savings including interest could be represented by $P(1 + r)^t$.

Suppose that interest is compounded biannually for 1 year at an annual interest rate of 6%. The interest would be computed twice per year at 3% each time. Thus the total amount in savings could be represented by:

$$P\left(1 + \frac{0.06}{2}\right)^{2 \cdot 1} \longleftarrow \text{\textit{interest computed twice per year for 1 year}}$$
$$\underset{\text{\textit{interest computed each time at}} \frac{0.06}{2} \text{\textit{or 0.03}}}{\uparrow}$$

For interest compounded quarterly for 2 years at 8% annual interest the formula is:

$$P\left(1 + \frac{0.08}{4}\right)^{4 \cdot 2} \qquad \text{\textit{Compounded quarterly means 4 times per year.}}$$

The general formula is given below.

$$A = P\left(1 + \frac{r}{n}\right)^{nt} \qquad \text{\textit{What does each variable represent?}}$$

Exercises Use logarithms and your calculator to solve each problem.

1. Gloria invested $750 for 1 year at 8% annual interest. If interest is compounded quarterly, how much will Gloria have at the end of the year?

2. Ann invested $600 in a savings account for 2 years. If the annual interest rate is 12% compounded monthly, what is the total amount Ann will have at the end of 2 years?

12–7   Exponential Equations

Equations in which the variables appear as exponents are called **exponential equations.** Such equations can be solved by using the property of equality for logarithmic functions.

examples

1 **Solve the equation $2^x = 27$.**

$$2^x = 27$$
$$\log 2^x = \log 27$$
$$x \log 2 = \log 27 \qquad \textit{Power Property}$$
$$x = \frac{\log 27}{\log 2}$$
$$= \frac{1.4314}{0.3010} \text{ or } 4.7555$$

The check helps you determine if the solution is reasonable.

Check: $2^4 = 16$, $2^{4.7555} = 27$, and $2^5 = 32$.
Since $16 < 27 < 32$ and $4 < 4.7555 < 5$, the solution is within the proper interval.
The solution is approximately 4.7555.

2 **Express $\log_3 35$ in terms of common logarithms. Then find its value.**

$$\text{Let } x = \log_3 35$$
$$\text{Then, } 3^x = 35$$
$$\log 3^x = \log 35$$
$$x \log 3 = \log 35 \qquad \textit{Power Property}$$
$$x = \frac{\log 35}{\log 3}$$

The logarithm may be expressed as $\dfrac{\log 35}{\log 3}$.

$$\log_3 35 = \frac{\log 35}{\log 3}$$
$$= \frac{1.5441}{0.4771} \text{ or } 3.2364$$

Check: $3^3 = 27$, $3^{3.2364} = 35$, and $3^4 = 81$.
Since $27 < 35 < 81$ and $3 < 3.2364 < 4$, the solution is within the proper interval.
The value of $\log_3 35$ is approximately 3.2364.

In Example **2** notice that $\log_3 35 = \dfrac{\log_{10} 35}{\log_{10} 3}$.

This and other similar examples suggest the following rule.

> Suppose a, b, and n are positive numbers, and neither a nor b is 1. Then the following equation is true.
>
> $$\log_a n = \frac{\log_b n}{\log_b a}$$

Change of Bases

examples

3 **Find the value of $\log_4 8$ using the formula above.**

$\log_4 8 = \dfrac{\log_2 8}{\log_2 4}$ *$\log_2$ was chosen because 8 and 4 are powers of 2.*

$\qquad = \dfrac{3}{2}$

Check: $\log_4 8 \stackrel{?}{=} \dfrac{3}{2}$

$\qquad\quad 4^{\frac{3}{2}} \stackrel{?}{=} 8$

$\qquad\quad \sqrt{4^3} \stackrel{?}{=} 8$

$\qquad\quad \sqrt{64} \stackrel{?}{=} 8$

$\qquad\qquad 8 = 8$

The value of $\log_4 8$ is $\dfrac{3}{2}$.

4 **Solve the equation $2^{3y} = 3^{y+1}$.**

$$2^{3y} = 3^{y+1}$$

$$\log 2^{3y} = \log 3^{y+1}$$

$3y \log 2 = (y + 1) \log 3$ *Power Property*

$3y \log 2 = y \log 3 + \log 3$ *Distributive Property*

$3y \log 2 - y \log 3 = \log 3$

$y(3 \log 2 - \log 3) = \log 3$ *Distributive Property*

$$y = \frac{\log 3}{3 \log 2 - \log 3}$$

$$= \frac{0.4771}{3(0.3010) - 0.4771}$$

$$= 1.1202$$

Check: $2^3 = 8$, $2^{3y} = 2^{3.3}$, and $2^4 = 16$ *Use $y = 1.1$ in check.*

$\qquad\quad 3^2 = 9$, $3^{y+1} = 3^{2.1}$, and $3^3 = 27$

Since $8 < 2^{3.3} < 16$ and $9 < 3^{2.1} < 27$, the solution is within the proper interval.

The solution is approximately 1.1202.

5 **Solve the equation $m^{\frac{3}{2}} = 17$.**

$$m^{\frac{3}{2}} = 17$$

$$(m^{\frac{3}{2}})^{\frac{2}{3}} = 17^{\frac{2}{3}} \quad \textit{Raise both sides of the equation to the } \frac{2}{3} \textit{ power.}$$

$$m = 17^{\frac{2}{3}}$$

$$\log m = \log 17^{\frac{2}{3}}$$

$$= \frac{2}{3} \log 17$$

$$= \frac{2}{3}(1.2305)$$

$$= 0.8203$$

$$m = \text{antilog } 0.8203$$

$$= 6.6115$$

The solution is about 6.61.

exercises

Exploratory   **State x in terms of common logarithms.**

1. $3^x = 55$	**2.** $5^x = 61$	**3.** $7^{2x} = 74$	**4.** $10^{3x} = 191$
5. $x = \log_6 144$	**6.** $x = \log_5 81$	**7.** $x = \log_3 12$	**8.** $x = \log_5 30$
9. $2^{-x} = 10$	**10.** $3^{-x} = 15$	**11.** $3^x = \sqrt{13}$	**12.** $2^x = 3\sqrt{2}$

Written   **1–12. Solve each equation in Exploratory Exercises 1–12.**

Approximate each logarithm to three decimal places.

13. $\log_3 7$	**14.** $\log_7 12$	**15.** $\log_4 22$	**16.** $\log_{3.21} 10$
17. $\log_6 11$	**18.** $\log_4 24$	**19.** $\log_6 72$	**20.** $\log_5 104$

Solve each equation using logarithms.

21. $2.7^x = 52.3$	**22.** $4.3^x = 78.5$	**23.** $7.6^{n-2} = 41.7$
24. $2.1^{x-5} = 9.32$	**25.** $9^{x-4} = 6.28$	**26.** $5^{y+2} = 15.3$
27. $x = \log_4 51.6$	**28.** $x = \log_3 19.8$	**29.** $x^{\frac{3}{2}} = 240$
30. $x^{\frac{3}{4}} = 93.7$	**31.** $5^{x-1} = 3^x$	**32.** $7^{x-2} = 5^x$
33. $5^{2x} = 9^{x-1}$	**34.** $12^{x-4} = 4^{2-x}$	**35.** $7^{x-2} = 5^{3-x}$
36. $3^{3x} = 2^{2x+3}$	**37.** $32^{2y} = 5^{4y+1}$	**38.** $2^{5x-1} = 3^{2x+1}$
39. $4^{5y-6} = 3^{2y+5}$	**40.** $15x^{\frac{5}{3}} = 62$	**41.** $6x^{\frac{3}{2}} = 105$

42. Let x be any real number and n, a, and b be positive real numbers where a and b do not equal 1. Show that if $x = \log_a n$, then $x = \dfrac{\log_b n}{\log_b a}$.

12–8   Solving Problems

The formula for compound interest given on page 369 is one special example of a formula for growth. The general formula for growth and decay in nature has many applications.

$$y = ne^{kt}$$

In the formula, y represents the final amount, n the initial amount, k a constant, and t time. The constant k is greater than 0 for growth and less than 0 for decay. The value of e is approximately 2.718 and $\log e$ is approximately 0.4343.

example 1   **For a certain strain of bacteria, k represents 0.775 when t is measured in hours. How long will it take 2 bacteria to increase to 1000 bacteria?**

$y = ne^{kt}$

$1000 = 2e^{0.775t}$ *Substitute 1000 for y, 2 for n, and 0.775 for k.*

$500 = e^{0.775t}$

$\log 500 = \log e^{0.775t}$

$\log 500 = 0.775t \log e$

$\dfrac{\log 500}{0.775 \log e} = t$ *Solve using logarithms and a calculator.*

$\dfrac{2.6990}{(0.775)(0.4343)} = t$

$8.019 = t$ The solution is approximately 8.019 hours.

Radioactive substances decay with time. Starting with N grams, the number y grams present t years later is given by the equation:

$$y = Ne^{kt}$$

The constant k will be negative.

example 2   **In 10 years, the mass of a 200-gram sample of an element is reduced to 100 grams. This period is called the half-life. Find the constant k for this element.**

$y = Ne^{kt}$

$100 = 200\, e^{k \cdot 10}$ *Substitute 100 for y, 200 for N, and 10 for t.*

$0.5 = e^{k \cdot 10}$

$\log 0.5 = \log e^{k \cdot 10}$

$\dfrac{\log 0.5}{10 \log e} = k$ *Solve using logarithms and a calculator.*

$\dfrac{0.6990 - 1}{10(0.4343)} = k$

$^{-}0.06931 = k$ The solution is approximately $^{-}0.06931$.

When interest is compounded continuously, the formula $A = P\left(1 + \frac{r}{n}\right)^{nt}$ becomes:

$$A = Pe^{rt}$$

In the formula, A represents the final amount, P represents the beginning investment, r represents the annual interest rate, and t represents the time in years.

3 **Assume $100 is deposited in a savings account. The interest rate is 6% compounded continuously. When will the money be double the original amount?**

If the money is to be doubled, the final amount will be $200.

$$A = Pe^{rt}$$
$$200 = 100\,e^{0.06t} \qquad \text{Substitute 200 for A, 100 for P, and 0.06 for r.}$$
$$2 = e^{0.06t}$$
$$\log 2 = \log e^{0.06t}$$
$$\log 2 = 0.06t \log e$$
$$\frac{\log 2}{0.06 \log e} = t$$
$$\frac{0.3010}{(0.06)(0.4343)} = t$$
$$11.55 = t \qquad \text{The solution is approximately 11.55 years}$$

In business, the formula $V_n = P(1 + r)^n$ can be used to find the value of equipment or assets. In the formula, r represents the fixed rate of appreciation or depreciation, P the initial value, and V_n the new value at the end of n years.

Appreciation is an increase in value. Depreciation is a decrease in value.

4 **A piece of machinery valued at $25,000 depreciates at a steady rate of 10% yearly. When will the value be $5000?**

$$V_n = P(1 + r)^n$$
$$5000 = 25{,}000(1 - 0.10)^n$$
$$5000 = 25{,}000(0.9)^n$$
$$0.2 = 0.9^n$$
$$\log 0.2 = \log 0.9^n$$
$$\log 0.2 = n \log 0.9$$
$$\frac{\log 0.2}{\log 0.9} = n$$
$$\frac{0.3010 - 1}{0.9542 - 1} = n$$
$$\frac{^-0.6990}{^-0.0458} = n$$
$$15.26 = n \qquad \text{The solution is approximately 15.26 years.}$$

Substitute 5000 for V_n, 25,000 for P, and $^-0.10$ for r. The value of r is negative since it represents depreciation.

exercises

Exploratory Solve each problem.

1. A certain culture of bacteria will grow from 500 to 4000 bacteria in 1.5 hours. Find the constant k for the growth formula.

2. For a radioactive substance, the constant k is -0.08042. How long will it take 250 grams of the substance to reduce to 50 grams?

3. If $500 is invested at 6% annual interest compounded continuously, when will the investment be tripled?

Written Solve each problem.

1. After 9 years, half of a 20 milligram sample of a radioactive element is left. Find k for this element.

2. For a certain strain of bacteria, $k = 0.782$ when t is measured in hours. How long will it take 10 bacteria to increase to 500 bacteria?

3. For a certain strain of bacteria, $k = 0.783$ when t is measured in hours. How long will it take 10 bacteria to increase to 100 bacteria?

4. Bacteria of a certain type can grow from 80 to 164 bacteria in 3 hours. Find k for the growth formula.

5. Rachel has saved $2000 to buy a car that will cost about $2500. If her money is in a savings account paying 7.25% interest compounded continuously, when will she be able to buy the car?

6. Mr. Sterwin wishes to have $8000 in a savings account in the year 2000. How much should he have deposited in 1980 to have this amount, if the account pays 8% interest compounded continuously?

7. Radium-226 decomposes radioactively. Its half-life (the time half the sample takes to decompose) is 1800 years. Find the constant k for the decay formula. Use 100 grams as the original amount.

8. A piece of machinery valued at $50,000 depreciates 10% per year by the fixed rate method. After how many years will the value have depreciated to $25,000?

9. Susan deposited $500 in the bank. If the interest rate is 10.5% compounded continuously, how much money will she have at the end of $2\frac{1}{2}$ years?

10. Jim and Agnes bought a new house for $95,000. If the value of the house appreciates at a fixed rate of 8% yearly, what will be the value of the house in 10 years?

11. Suppose $1 is invested at 7% interest compounded continuously. When will the investment be worth $10? Worth $100?

12. A radioactive substance decays according to the equation $A = A_0 \times 10^{-0.024t}$ where t is in hours. Find the half-life of the substance (when $A = 0.5A_0$).

13. Mike has $500 in his savings account. He is spending 10% of the balance each week. After how many weeks of this spending will the balance be under $1? Use $V_n = P(1 + r)^n$, where n is the number of weeks.

14. A satellite has a power supply whose output in watts is given by $w(t) = 50e^{-0.004t}$ where t is the time in days. How much power will there be at the end of 500 days?

Chapter Summary

1. A logarithm is an exponent.   (351)
2. Definition of Logarithm: Suppose $b > 0$ and $b \neq 1$. Then for $n > 0$ there is a number p such that $\log_b n = p$ if and only if $b^p = n$.   (351)
3. Both $y = b^x$ and its inverse $y = \log_b x$ are functions.   (354)
4. Property of Equality for Logarithmic Functions: Suppose $b > 0$ and $b \neq 1$. Then $\log_b x_1 = \log_b x_2$ if and only if $x_1 = x_2$.   (354)
5. Because the logarithmic and exponential functions are inverses, $b^{\log_b x} = x$ and $\log_b b^x = x$.   (355)
6. Properties of Logarithms: Suppose m and n are positive numbers, b is a positive number other than 1, and p is any number. Then the following properties hold.

    Product Property: $\log_b mn = \log_b m + \log_b n$

    Quotient Property: $\log_b \dfrac{m}{n} = \log_b m - \log_b n$

    Power Property: $\log_b m^p = p \log_b m$ (358)
7. Common logarithms are logarithms to base 10.   (362)
8. To find the common logarithm of any number, first write the number in scientific notation. If r is the positive number, $r = a \times 10^n$, where $1 \leq a < 10$ and n is an integer. Then, $\log r = \log a + \log 10^n$ and $\log r = \log a + n$. Log a is found in the table of logarithms. It is called the mantissa of log r. The integer n is the characteristic of log r.   (362)
9. To find an antilogarithm, use the table to find the antilog of the mantissa. Multiply by the power of ten corresponding to the characteristic.   (363)
10. Interpolation is a procedure whereby logarithms and antilogarithms *not* directly found in the table may be calculated.   (365)
11. Exponential equations have variables as exponents. They can be solved by using logarithms.   (372)
12. Change of Bases: Suppose a, b, and n are positive numbers, and neither a nor b is 1. Then $\log_a n = \dfrac{\log_b n}{\log_b a}$.   (373)
13. The general formula for growth and decay in nature, $y = ne^{kt}$, has many applications. In the formula, y represents the final amount, n represents the initial amount, k represents a constant, and t represents time.   (375)

12–1 **Change each equation to logarithmic form.**

1. $7^3 = 343$

2. $5^{-2} = \dfrac{1}{25}$

3. $4^0 = 1$

4. $4^{\frac{3}{2}} = 8$

Change each equation to exponential form.

5. $\log_4 64 = 3$

6. $\log_8 2 = \dfrac{1}{3}$

7. $\log_6 \dfrac{1}{36} = {}^-2$

8. $\log_6 1 = 0$

Solve each equation.

9. $\log_b 9 = 2$

10. $\log_b 9 = \dfrac{1}{2}$

11. $\log_{16} 2 = x$

12. $\log_4 x = -\dfrac{1}{2}$

12–2 **Evaluate each expression.**

13. $\log_5 5^7$

14. $6^{\log_6 7}$

15. $\log_n n^3$

16. $n^{\log_n 3}$

Solve each equation.

17. $\log_6 12 = \log_6 (5x - 3)$

18. $\log_3 3y = \log_3 (2y + 5)$

19. $\log_5 y = \log_5 (14 - y)$

20. $\log_3 3x = \log_3 (x + 7)$

21. $\log_2 (3x - 2) = \log_2 (2x + 6)$

22. $\log_4 (1 - 2x) = \log_4 (x + 10)$

23. $\log_7 (x^2 + x) = \log_7 12$

24. $\log_2 (x - 1)^2 = \log_2 7$

12–3 **Use $\log_{10} 7 = 0.8451$ and $\log_{10} 4 = 0.6021$ to estimate each expression.**

25. $\log_{10} \dfrac{7}{4}$

26. $\log_{10} 700$

27. $\log_{10} 0.004$

28. $\log_{10} \dfrac{49}{4}$

Solve each equation.

29. $\log_3 x - \log_3 4 = \log_3 12$

30. $\log_5 x + \log_5 3 = \log_5 15$

31. $\log_2 x = \dfrac{1}{3} \log_2 27$

32. $\log_4 y = 4 \log_4 3$

33. $\log_5 7 + \dfrac{1}{2} \log_5 4 = \log_5 x$

34. $\log_7 (m + 1) + \log_7 (m - 5) = 1$

35. $\log_6 (r - 3) + \log_6 (r + 2) = 1$

36. $\dfrac{1}{2}(2 \log_{10} 4 + 2 \log_{10} 2) = \log_{10} x$

12–4 **Find the logarithm of each number.**

37. 2.65

38. 632

39. 0.0777

40. 51.2

Find the antilog of each logarithm.

41. 0.7364

42. 3.8299

43. 0.4409 − 2

44. 1.5587

12–5 **Interpolate to find the logarithm of each number.**

45. 3.415

46. 463.2

47. 0.04111

48. 2004

Interpolate to find the antilog of each logarithm.

49. 0.3355

50. 0.7963 − 2

51. 1.0725

52. 0.8736 − 3

12–6 **Use logarithms to evaluate each expression.**

53. $\sqrt[4]{36}$

54. 1972^7

55. $\sqrt[3]{\dfrac{321.5}{84.3}}$

56. $\sqrt[5]{(0.43)(0.22)}$

57. $\sqrt{\dfrac{(82)(14.4)}{36}}$

58. $\sqrt[3]{\dfrac{(33.2)(1.64)^2}{(131)}}$

12–7 **Solve each equation using logarithms.**

59. $2^x = 53$

60. $4.5^x = 36.2$

61. $\log_4 11.2 = x$

62. $\log_3 45.2 = x$

63. $3.4^{x-2} = 15.6$

64. $2.3^{x+1} = 66.6$

65. $x^{\frac{3}{4}} = 24$

66. $8^{x-2} = 5^x$

12–8 **Solve each problem.**

67. Assume $200 is deposited in a savings account at 6% annual interest rate compounded continuously. When will the value of the account be $300? Use $A = Pe^{rt}$.

68. A bacterial culture will grow from 400 to 5000 bacteria in $1\frac{1}{4}$ hours. Find the constant k for the growth formula $y = ne^{kt}$ where t is in hours.

Solve problems 1–13 without using a table of logarithms.

1. Change $6^4 = 1296$ to logarithmic form.
2. Change $\log_3 81 = 4$ to exponential form.

Evaluate each expression.

3. $\log_{12} 12^2$

4. $4^{\log_4 3}$

Solve each equation.

5. $\log_m 144 = 2$
6. $\log_7 x = 2$
7. $\log_2 64 = y$
8. $\log_5 (8r - 7) = \log_5 (r^2 + 5)$
9. $\log_9 (x + 4) + \log_9 (x - 4) = 1$

Use $\log_7 5 = 0.8271$ and $\log_7 3 = 0.5645$ to estimate each expression.

10. $\log_7 15$

11. $\log_7 9$

12. $\log_7 45$

13. $\log_7 \dfrac{5}{3}$

Solve problems 14–24 using a table of logarithms.

Find the logarithm of each number.

14. 769,000

15. 0.01473

Find the antilog of each logarithm.

16. 3.2754

17. $(0.8351 - 4)$

Use logarithms to evaluate each expression.

18. $\sqrt[5]{1792}$

19. 9.813^4

20. $\sqrt[3]{36(1.06)^{15}}$

Solve each equation.

21. $3^x = 35$

22. $\log_4 37 = x$

23. $3^x = 5^{x-1}$

24. A Pilgrim ancestor of Agnes Stapleton left $10 in a savings account in the Provident Savings Bank. Interest was compounded continuously at 4%. The account is now worth $75,000. How long ago was the account started? ($A = Pe^{rt}$, $e = 2.718$, and $\log e = 0.4343$)

Graph each equation or inequality.

1. $y = -\frac{1}{2}x - 3$

2. $4x + 5y \leq 10$

Find the slope-intercept form of lines satisfying the following conditions.

3. x-intercept 6 and y-intercept 4

4. passes through $(7, 2)$ and $(0, {}^-3)$

Solve each system of equations.

5. $2x - y = 4$
   $x + y = 5$

6. $2x + 3y = 1$
   $3x + 5y = {}^-4$

Find the value of each determinant.

7. $\begin{vmatrix} 4 & {}^-2 \\ 3 & 2 \end{vmatrix}$

8. $\begin{vmatrix} 1 & 2 & {}^-1 \\ 2 & {}^-1 & 3 \\ {}^-3 & {}^-4 & 5 \end{vmatrix}$

Simplify each expression.

9. $(y - 2)(4y^2 - 7y + 3)$

10. $(5a^3 - 2a^2 + 6a + 5) - (9a^3 - 5a^2 - 11)$

Factor.

11. $16a^4 - 1$

12. $9a^2 + 30ab + 25b^2$

Find the principal root of each expression.

13. $\sqrt{36x^2}$

14. $\sqrt[3]{-64y^{12}}$

Simplify.

15. $\dfrac{5 + i}{2 + 3i}$

16. $\dfrac{\sqrt{2} + i\sqrt{3}}{\sqrt{2} - i\sqrt{3}}$

Solve each equation using the quadratic formula.

17. $3x^2 - 2x - 2 = 0$

18. $3x^2 = {}^-4x - 5$

State the value of the discriminant for each quadratic equation. Describe the nature of the solutions.

19. $3y^2 + 2y + 5 = 0$

20. $6a^2 - a + 2 = 0$

Draw the graph of each quadratic equation. Name the vertex, axis of symmetry, and direction of opening.

21. $f(x) = {}^-3x^2$

22. $f(x) = 5x^2 + 10x + 5$

23. Find the two numbers whose sum is 81 and whose product is a maximum.

State whether the graph of each of the following equations is a parabola, a circle, an ellipse, or a hyperbola. Then draw the graph.

24. $x = y^2 + 8y + 25$

25. $\dfrac{y^2}{16} - \dfrac{x^2}{9} = 1$

26. $\dfrac{x^2}{10} + \dfrac{y^2}{5} = 1$

27. $y^2 + 2 + x^2 + 6x - 12y = 4$

Factor each polynomial by using synthetic division.

28. $x^4 + 8x^3 + 23x^2 + 28x + 12$

29. $x^4 - x^3 - 17x^2 + 21x + 36$

For each function, state the possible number of positive real zeros, negative real zeros, and imaginary zeros.

30. $f(x) = x^3 - 7x^2 + 17x - 15$

31. $f(x) = x^4 + 1$

Find $[f \circ g](x)$ and $[g \circ f](x)$.

32. $f(x) = x^2 + 5$
     $g(x) = x - 2$

33. $f(x) = x^2 + 3x - 8$
     $g(x) = x^2 - 1$

Perform the indicated operation for each of the following.

34. $\dfrac{8x - 8y}{16x - 16y} \cdot \dfrac{(x - y)^2}{2}$

35. $\dfrac{x + 2xy}{3x^2} \div \dfrac{2y + 1}{6x}$

36. Suppose y varies directly as x. If $y = 9$, then $x = {}^-5$. Find y when x is 42.

Simplify each expression.

37. $\dfrac{1}{x^{\frac{2}{3}}}$

38. $\left(\dfrac{x}{5}\right)^{-2}$

39. $\dfrac{x + y}{x^{\frac{1}{2}} - y^{\frac{1}{2}}}$

40. $\dfrac{8x^2}{x^{-5}} + \dfrac{6x}{x^{-6}}$

Evaluate. Express each answer in scientific notation.

41. $(2.1 \times 10^{12})(5.64 \times 10^6)$

42. $\dfrac{64{,}000{,}000 \times 0.0005}{0.00016}$

Express each of the following using exponents.

43. $\sqrt[3]{x^2 y^3 z^4}$

44. $\sqrt{a^8 b^{14}}$

Solve each equation.

45. $\log_{\sqrt{2}} 16 = x$

46. $\log_4 (3x + 2) = \log_4 (6x - 1)$

Solve problems 47–50 using a table of logarithms. Find the logarithm of each number.

47. 25,300

48. 0.0001582

Find the antilog of each logarithm.

49. 4.4232

50. $(0.4600 - 3)$

chapter
13
Sequences and Series

The following sequence of numbers has been discovered in the pattern of beehive construction, in pine cones, and seeds in flowers.

1, 1, 2, 3, 5, 8, 13, 21, 34, . . .

Can you tell what the next number will be?

13–1   Arithmetic Sequences

John Dalton is a race car driver. He enters the straightaway at 91 miles per hour. While on the straightaway he increases his speed by 29.7 mph. After nine seconds, his speed is 120.7 mph.

The speed at each second is shown below.

number of seconds	0	1	2	3	4	5	6	7	8	9
speed	91	94.3	97.6	100.9	104.2	107.5	110.8	114.1	117.4	120.7

These numbers, which represent speeds, are an example of a **sequence**. A set of numbers in a specific order is called a sequence. Each number in a sequence is called a term. The first term is denoted a_1, the second term a_2, and so on to a_n, the nth term.

symbol	a_1	a_2	a_3	a_4	a_5	a_6	a_7	a_8	a_9	$.a_{10}$
term	91	94.3	97.6	100.9	104.2	107.5	110.8	114.1	117.4	120.7

> **An arithmetic sequence is a sequence in which the difference between any two consecutive terms is the same.**

Definition of an Arithmetic Sequence

The common difference is found by subtracting any term from its succeeding term. What is the common difference, d, for the arithmetic sequence of speeds listed above?

Find d for each of the following arithmetic sequences.

$$3, 7, 11, 15, \ldots \quad d = 4$$
$$2, \frac{3}{2}, 1, \frac{1}{2}, 0, -\frac{1}{2}, {}^-1, \ldots \quad d = -\frac{1}{2}$$

The three dots mean that the sequence continues infinitely in the same pattern.

1 **Find the next three terms of the sequence 21, 27, 33, ...**

Find the common difference.

$33 - 27 = 6$ $27 - 21 = 6$ $d = 6$

Add 6 to the third term to get the fourth, and so on.

$33 + 6 = 39$ $39 + 6 = 45$ $45 + 6 = 51$

The next three terms are 39, 45, 51.

There is a pattern in the way the terms of an arithmetic sequence are formed. Consider the terms of the sequence in Example 1.

a_1	a_2	a_3	a_4	a_5
21	27	33	39	45
$21 + 0 \cdot 6$	$21 + 1 \cdot 6$	$21 + 2 \cdot 6$	$21 + 3 \cdot 6$	$21 + 4 \cdot 6$
$a_1 + 0 \cdot d$	$a_1 + 1 \cdot d$	$a_1 + 2 \cdot d$	$a_1 + 3 \cdot d$	$a_1 + 4 \cdot d$

How would you write an addition expression for the term a_n?

The *n*th term, a_n, of an arithmetic sequence with first term a_1 and common difference d is given by the following equation.

$$a_n = a_1 + (n - 1)d$$

Definition of the nth Term of an Arithmetic Sequence

2 **Suppose the race car driver continues to increase his speed at the same rate. What will be his speed after 15 seconds?**

$a_1 = 91$ $d = 3.3$

Find a_{16} using $a_n = a_1 + (n - 1)d$.   *a_{16} is the speed after 15 seconds. Why?*

$a_{16} = 91 + (16 - 1)3.3$

$\phantom{a_{16}} = 91 + 15(3.3)$

$\phantom{a_{16}} = 91 + 49.5$

$\phantom{a_{16}} = 140.5$

His speed will be 140.5 mph.

The terms between any two nonconsecutive terms of an arithmetic sequence are called **arithmetic means**.

$$12, 21, 30, 39, 48, 57, 66, 75, \ldots$$

Thus, 30, 39, and 48 are the three arithmetic means between 21 and 57.

3 Find the four arithmetic means between 12 and 47. Use $a_n = a_1 + (n-1)d$.

$a_1 = 12$ $\qquad$ $12, \underline{\quad}, \underline{\quad}, \underline{\quad}, \underline{\quad}, 47$ $\qquad$ $a_6 = 47$
$a_6 = a_1 + (5)d$
$47 = 12 + 5d$
$\quad 7 = d$ $\qquad$ *The common difference is 7.*
$12 + 7 = 19 \qquad 19 + 7 = 26 \qquad 26 + 7 = 33 \qquad 33 + 7 = 40$

The arithmetic means are 19, 26, 33, and 40.

4 Find the number of multiples of 13 between 29 and 258.

The least and greatest multiples of 13 between 29 and 258 are 39 and 247. A sequence where $a_1 = 39$, $d = 13$, and $a_n = 247$ will have the required number of terms. Use $a_n = a_1 + (n-1)d$.

$247 = 39 + (n-1)13$ $\qquad$ *Here $a_n = 247$, $a_1 = 39$, $d = 13$.*
$208 = (n-1)13$
$\quad 17 = n$

There are 17 multiples of 13 between 29 and 258.

exercises

Exploratory Name the first five terms of each arithmetic sequence described below.

1. $a_1 = 4, d = 3$ $\qquad$ **2.** $a_1 = 7, d = 5$ $\qquad$ **3.** $a_1 = 16, d = -2$ $\qquad$ **4.** $a_1 = 38, d = -4$

5. $a_1 = \frac{3}{4}, d = -\frac{1}{4}$ $\qquad$ **6.** $a_1 = \frac{3}{8}, d = \frac{5}{8}$ $\qquad$ **7.** $a_1 = 2.3, d = 1.6$ $\qquad$ **8.** $a_1 = 0.88, d = 0$

9. $a_1 = -\frac{1}{3}, d = -\frac{2}{3}$ $\qquad$ **10.** $a_1 = -\frac{4}{5}, d = 1$ $\qquad$ **11.** $a_1 = -4.2, d = -1.3$ $\qquad$ **12.** $a_1 = 2, d = -2.5$

Name the next four terms of each of the following arithmetic sequences.

13. $5, 9, 13, \ldots$ $\qquad$ **14.** $11, 14, 17, \ldots$ $\qquad$ **15.** $2, -3, -8, \ldots$

16. $21, 15, 9, \ldots$ $\qquad$ **17.** $\frac{1}{2}, \frac{3}{2}, \frac{5}{2}, \ldots$ $\qquad$ **18.** $-5.4, -1.4, 2.6, \ldots$

19. $-\frac{5}{4}, -\frac{7}{4}, -\frac{9}{4}, \ldots$ $\qquad$ **20.** $9.9, 13.7, 17.5, \ldots$ $\qquad$ **21.** $-0.06, 2.24, 4.54, \ldots$

Written Use $a_n = a_1 + (n - 1)d$ to find the nth term of each arithmetic sequence described below.

1. $a_1 = 7, d = 3, n = 14$
2. $a_1 = {}^-3, d = {}^-9, n = 11$
3. $a_1 = {}^-1, d = {}^-10, n = 25$
4. $a_1 = {}^-7, d = 3, n = 17$
5. $a_1 = 2, d = \frac{1}{2}, n = 8$
6. $a_1 = \frac{3}{4}, d = -\frac{5}{4}, n = 13$
7. $a_1 = 20, d = 4, n = 100$
8. $a_1 = 13, d = 3, n = 101$
9. $a_1 = 27, d = 16, n = 23$
10. $a_1 = 15, d = 80, n = 10$
11. $a_1 = \sqrt{3}, d = {}^-\sqrt{2}, n = 11$
12. $a_1 = 2i, d = {}^-5i, n = 12$

Find the indicated term in each arithmetic sequence.

13. a_{12} for $^-17, {}^-13, {}^-9, \ldots$
14. a_{21} for $10, 7, 4, \ldots$
15. a_{32} for $4, 7, 10, 13, \ldots$
16. a_{10} for $8, 3, {}^-2, \ldots$
17. a_{12} for $\frac{3}{4}, \frac{3}{2}, \frac{9}{4}, \ldots$
18. a_{10} for $\frac{5}{6}, \frac{7}{6}, \frac{3}{2}, \ldots$

Answer each question by finding n, the number of the term.

19. Which term of $^-2, 5, 12, \ldots$ is 124?
20. Which term of $^-3, 2, 7, \ldots$ is 142?
21. Which term of $7, 2, {}^-3, \ldots$ is $^-28$?
22. Which term of $2\frac{1}{4}, 2, 1\frac{3}{4}, \ldots$ is $-\frac{17}{4}$?

Find the missing terms of the following arithmetic sequences.

23. $55, \underline{\hspace{1em}}, \underline{\hspace{1em}}, \underline{\hspace{1em}}, 115$
24. $^-8, \underline{\hspace{1em}}, \underline{\hspace{1em}}, 3$
25. $^-10, \underline{\hspace{1em}}, \underline{\hspace{1em}}, \underline{\hspace{1em}}, \underline{\hspace{1em}}, 2$
26. $2, \underline{\hspace{1em}}, \underline{\hspace{1em}}, \underline{\hspace{1em}}, \underline{\hspace{1em}}, \underline{\hspace{1em}}, 20$
27. $\underline{\hspace{1em}}, {}^-6, \underline{\hspace{1em}}, \underline{\hspace{1em}}, 15, \underline{\hspace{1em}}$
28. $\underline{\hspace{1em}}, 49, \underline{\hspace{1em}}, \underline{\hspace{1em}}, 28$

Solve each problem.

29. The last term of an arithmetic sequence is 207, the common difference is 3, and the number of terms is 14. What is the first term of the sequence?

30. Mark's salary is $12,500. His raises will be $700 per year. What will be his salary after 8 years?

31. How many multiples of 7 are there between 11 and 391?

32. How many multiples of 12 are there between 16 and 415?

33. During a free fall, a skydiver falls 16 feet in the first second, 48 feet in the second second, and 80 feet in the third second. If she continues to fall at this rate, how many feet will she fall in the 10th second?

34. A salesman receives $25 for every vacuum cleaner he sells. If he sells more than 10 vacuum cleaners he will receive an additional $1.75 for each successive sale until he is paid a maximum of $46 per vacuum cleaner. How many vacuum cleaners must he sell to reach this maximum?

Challenge Solve the following problem.

The 5th term of an arithmetic sequence is 19 and the 11th term is 43. Find the first term and the 87th term of the sequence.

13-2 Arithmetic Series

Dana Thompson is starting a savings program. She plans to save five cents the first day, ten cents the second day, fifteen cents the third day, and so on. How much will she save in the first week using this plan?

If the amount Dana saves each day is listed, the list is a sequence.

$$5, 10, 15, 20, 25, 30, 35$$

The sum of this sequence is written as follows.

$$5 + 10 + 15 + 20 + 25 + 30 + 35$$

Dana has saved $1.40.

The indicated sum of the terms of a sequence is called a series.	*Definition of Series*

The chart below contains examples of arithmetic sequences and their corresponding series.

Arithmetic Sequence	*Arithmetic Series*
$3, 6, 9, 12, 15$	$3 + 6 + 9 + 12 + 15$
$^-4, ^-1, 2$	$^-4 + ^-1 + 2$
$\frac{5}{3}, \frac{8}{3}, \frac{11}{3}, \frac{14}{3}$	$\frac{5}{3} + \frac{8}{3} + \frac{11}{3} + \frac{14}{3}$
$a_1, a_2, a_3, a_4, \ldots a_n$	$a_1 + a_2 + a_3 + a_4 + \ldots + a_n$

The symbol, S_n, is used to represent the *sum of the first n terms of a series*. For example, S_3 represents $2 + 5 + 8$ or 15 for the series $2 + 5 + 8 + 11$.

If a series has a large number of terms, it is not convenient to find the sum by adding its terms. To write a general formula for the sum of a series of n terms, consider S_7 for the series $3 + 7 + 11 + 15 + 19 + 23 + 27$.

Add S_7 and S_7 as follows.

$$\begin{array}{rrrrrrrr}
S_7 = & 3 + & 7 + & 11 + & 15 + & 19 + & 23 + & 27 \\
+\ S_7 = & 27 + & 23 + & 19 + & 15 + & 11 + & 7 + & 3 \\
\hline
2 \cdot S_7 = & 30 + & 30 + & 30 + & 30 + & 30 + & 30 + & 30
\end{array}$$

These terms are written in descending order. Notice that the sum of each column is 30.

$$\underbrace{}_{\text{7 sums}}$$

$2 \cdot S_7 = 7 \cdot 30$

Since $30 = 3 + 27$, each 30 could be written as the sum of the first and last terms of S_7.

$$2 \cdot S_7 = 7(a_1 + a_7)$$
$$S_7 = \frac{7}{2}(a_1 + a_7)$$

The same method can be used to write a formula for an arithmetic series with n terms. Let $S_n = a_1 + a_2 + a_3 + a_4 + \ldots + a_n$. To write an expression for $2 \cdot S_n$, write each term as the sum of the first and last terms of S_n.

$$2 \cdot S_n = \underbrace{(a_1 + a_n) + (a_1 + a_n) + (a_1 + a_n) + \ldots + (a_1 + a_n)}_{n \text{ sums}}$$

$2 \cdot S_n = n(a_1 + a_n)$
$S_n = \frac{n}{2}(a_1 + a_n)$

> **The sum, S_n, of the first n terms of an arithmetic series is given by the following formula.**
>
> $$S_n = \frac{n}{2}(a_1 + a_n)$$

Sum of an Arithmetic Series

1 **Find the sum of the first 50 positive integers.**

$a_1 = 1, a_n = 50, n = 50$

$S_n = \frac{n}{2}(a_1 + a_n)$

$S_{50} = \frac{50}{2}(1 + 50)$ *Substitute 1 for a_1, 50 for a_n, and 50 for n.*

$= 25(51)$

$= 1275$

The sum of the first 50 positive integers is 1275.

You know that $a_n = a_1 + (n - 1)d$. Using substitution gives another formula for S_n.

$$S_n = \frac{n}{2}(a_1 + a_n)$$

$$S_n = \frac{n}{2}\{a_1 + [a_1 + (n - 1)d]\} \qquad \text{Use } a_n = a_1 + (n - 1)d.$$

$$S_n = \frac{n}{2}[2 \cdot a_1 + (n - 1)d]$$

2 **Find the sum of the first 60 terms of an arithmetic series where $a_1 = 15$, $n = 60$, and $d = 80$.**

$$S_n = \frac{n}{2}[2 \cdot a_1 + (n - 1)d]$$

$$S_{60} = \frac{60}{2}[2 \cdot 15 + (59)80]$$

$$S_{60} = 30(30 + 59 \cdot 80)$$

$$S_{60} = 142,500$$

3 **A supermarket display consists of cans stacked as shown at the right. The bottom row has 27 cans. Each row above has one less can than the row below it. The display has 15 rows. How many cans are in the display?**

Find the sum of an arithmetic series where $a_1 = 27$, $d = -1$, and $n = 15$.

$$S_n = \frac{n}{2}[2 \cdot a_1 + (n - 1)d]$$

$$S_n = \frac{15}{2}[2 \cdot 27 + (15 - 1)(-1)]$$

$$= \frac{15}{2}(54 - 14)$$

$$= \frac{15}{2}(40)$$

$$= 300$$

There are 300 cans in the display.

exercises

Exploratory Evaluate each of the following series.

1. $4 + 7 + 10 + 13 + 16 + 19 + 22 + 25$

2. $1 + 5 + 9 + 13 + 17 + 21 + 25 + 29$

Find S_n for each series.

3. $a_1 = 2, a_n = 200, n = 100$
5. $a_1 = 4, n = 15, d = 3$
7. $9 + 11 + 13 + 15 + \ldots$ for $n = 12$
9. Find the sum of the first 100 positive integers.

4. $a_1 = 5, a_n = 100, n = 20$
6. $a_1 = 50, n = 20, d = ^-4$
8. $^-3 + ^-7 + ^-11 + ^-15 + \ldots$ for $n = 10$
10. An arithmetic series has a sum of 77. The first term is 2 and the last term is 12. How many terms are there?

Written Find S_n for each series described below.

1. $a_1 = 11, a_n = 44, n = 23$
3. $a_1 = 5, n = 18, a_n = 73$
5. $a_1 = 3, n = 9, a_n = 27$
7. $a_1 = 9, n = 22, a_n = 101$
9. $a_1 = 5, d = 12, n = 7$
11. $a_1 = 9, d = ^-6, n = 14$

2. $a_1 = 3, a_n = ^-38, n = 8$
4. $a_1 = 85, n = 21, a_n = 25$
6. $a_1 = 34, n = 9, a_n = 2$
8. $a_1 = 76, n = 16, a_n = 31$
10. $a_1 = 4, d = ^-1, n = 7$
12. $a_1 = 5, d = \frac{1}{2}, n = 13$

Find the sum of each series.

13. $7 + 14 + 21 + 28 + \ldots + 98$
15. $10 + 4 + (^-2) + (^-8) + \ldots + (^-50)$

14. $6 + 12 + 18 + \ldots + 96$
16. $34 + 30 + 26 + \ldots + 2$

Find S_n for each series described below.

17. $d = ^-4, n = 9, a_n = 27$
19. $a_1 = ^-2, d = \frac{1}{2}, a_n = 5$

18. $a_1 = 91, d = ^-4, a_n = 15$
20. $d = 5, n = 16, a_n = 72$

Find the first three terms for each series described below.

21. $a_1 = 6, a_n = 306, S_n = 1716$
23. $n = 14, a_n = 53, S_n = 378$

22. $a_1 = 7, a_n = 139, S_n = 876$
24. $n = 21, a_n = ^-78, S_n = 1008$

Solve each problem.

25. Find the sum of the odd integers from 1 to 100.
27. A pile of fireplace logs has 1 log in the top layer, 2 logs in the next layer, and so on. How many logs are in the pile if it contains 21 layers?

29. The auditorium in Milford High has 21 seats in the first row. Each of the other rows has one more seat than the row in front of it. If there are 30 rows of seats, what is the seating capacity of the auditorium?

26. Find the sum of the positive integers less than 100 and divisible by 6.
28. The cost of repairs for a certain automobile increases $60 each year. If the cost of repairs for the first year is $125, what is the total amount spent on repairs for the automobile after 7 years?

30. The prize for the correct solution to a certain crossword puzzle is $100. If the prize is uncollected, it is increased by $5 each week. At the end of 20 weeks, how large is the prize?

Suppose you borrow some money from the local bank. As a general rule, the amount of interest is not the same for each month. You owe more interest the first month than you do the last month. For a one-year loan, the following series is used in figuring the amount of interest for each month.

$$12 + 11 + 10 + 9 + 8 + 7 + 6 + 5 + 4 + 3 + 2 + 1 \text{ or } 78$$

How many months are there in a year? How many addends are there in the series above?

The example below shows how the series is used to figure amounts of interest.

Example What part of the interest is paid during the first month of a one-year loan? What part of the interest is paid during the first three months of a one-year loan? What part of the interest is paid during the first six months of a one-year loan?

$\dfrac{12}{78}$ of the total interest is paid in the first month.

$\dfrac{12 + 11 + 10}{78}$ or $\dfrac{33}{78}$ is paid in the first three months.

$\dfrac{12 + 11 + 10 + 9 + 8 + 7}{78}$ or $\dfrac{57}{78}$ is paid in the first six months.

The above method is called the **rule of 78.** Do you see why?

For a two-year loan, find the number of months in 2 years. The interest series has how many addends? What are the addends?

Exercises **Find the part of the interest owed for each of the following using the rule of 78.**

1. first two months of a one-year loan
2. first four months of a one-year loan
3. last month of a one-year loan
4. first month of a two-year loan
5. first three months of a two-year loan
6. first six months of a two-year loan
7. first month of a three-year loan
8. last month of a three-year loan

13–3 Geometric Sequences

Anne Woodruff read about a *foolproof way to save a million dollars*. The plan is simple. Save a penny the first day. Then each day save double the amount saved on the previous day. How much should Anne save on the fifteenth day? On the twenty-eighth day? How much can be saved in 30 days using this plan?

Day 1	*Day 2*	*Day 3*	*Day 4*	*Day 5*	*Day 6*
1¢	**2¢**	**4¢**	**8¢**	**16¢**	**32¢**

The amounts in the savings program form a geometric sequence.

$$1, 2, 4, 8, 16, 32, 64, \ldots \quad \textit{What is the next term?} \qquad \textit{How is it found?}$$

> **In a geometric sequence, each term after the first is found by multiplying the previous term by a constant.**

Definition of Geometric Sequence

In any geometric sequence, the constant or common ratio is found by dividing any term by the previous term.

example

1 **Find the common ratio and the next two terms of the geometric sequence 4, 12, 36, ...**

36 divided by 12 is 3 and 12 divided by 4 is 3. The common ratio is 3. The next two terms are $36 \cdot 3$ or 108 and $108 \cdot 3$ or 324.

A geometric sequence containing n terms and having common ratio r can be written as follows. The second term, a_2, is found by multiplying the first term, a_1, by the common ratio, r.

a_1	a_2	a_3	a_4	$\cdots$	a_n
a_1	$a_1 r$	$a_2 r$	$a_3 r$	$\cdots$	$a_{n-1} r$
a_1	$a_1 r$	$a_1 r^2$	$a_1 r^3$	$\cdots$	$a_1 r^{n-1}$

> **The nth term, a_n of a geometric sequence with first term, a_1, and common ratio, r, is given by either of the following equations.**
>
> $$a_n = a_1 r^{n-1} \qquad a_n = a_{n-1} r$$

Definition of the nth Term of a Geometric Sequence

2 **Write the first six terms of a geometric sequence in which $a_1 = 4$ and $r = 3$.**

Write each term using the formula $a_n = a_1 r^{n-1}$.

a_1	a_2	a_3	a_4	a_5	a_6
4	$4 \cdot 3$	$4 \cdot 3^2$	$4 \cdot 3^3$	$4 \cdot 3^4$	$4 \cdot 3^5$
4	12	36	108	324	972

The six terms are 4, 12, 36, 108, 324, and 972.

3 **Find the seventh term of a geometric sequence in which $a_3 = 7$ and $r = 2$.**

The seventh term of a sequence beginning with a_3 is the same as the fifth term of a sequence beginning with a_1. *Why?*

Use $a_n = a_1 r^{n-1}$

$$a_5 = a_1 \cdot 2^{5-1} \quad \text{\textit{Substitute 2 for r and 5 for n.}}$$
$$= 7 \cdot 2^4 \quad \text{\textit{Substitute 7 for } a_1.}$$
$$= 7 \cdot 16$$
$$= 112$$

The seventh term is 112.

The terms between any two nonconsecutive terms of a geometric sequence are called **geometric means.** In the sequence 3, 12, 48, 192, 768, 3072, . . . , the three geometric means between 3 and 768 are 12, 48, and 192.

4 **Find the missing geometric means in the sequence 81, ____, ____, 3.**

$$a_n = a_1 r^{n-1}$$
$$a_4 = a_1 \cdot r^3 \quad \text{\textit{Substitute 4 for n.}}$$
$$3 = 81 \cdot r^3 \quad \text{\textit{Substitute 81 for } a_1 \text{ and 3 for } a_4.}$$
$$\frac{1}{27} = r^3$$
$$\frac{1}{3} = r$$

$$a_2 = 81\left(\frac{1}{3}\right) \qquad a_3 = 81\left(\frac{1}{3}\right)^2$$
$$= 27 \qquad\qquad\quad = 9$$

The missing terms are 27 and 9.

Sometimes there is more than one way to supply the missing geometric means for a particular sequence.

5 **Find the missing geometric means in the sequence 6, ——, ——, ——, 96.**

$a_5 = a_1r^4$ $a_n = a_1r^{n-1}$
$96 = 6r^4$
$16 = r^4$
$\pm 2 = r$

$a_2 = 6(2)$	$a_3 = 6(2)^2$	$a_4 = 6(2)^3$
$= 12$	$= 24$	$= 48$
or	or	or
$a_2 = 6(^-2)$	$a_3 = 6(^-2)^2$	$a_4 = 6(^-2)^2$
$= ^-12$	$= 24$	$= ^-48$

The missing terms are 12, 24, and 48 or $^-12$, 24, and $^-48$.

6 **A vacuum pump removes $\frac{1}{5}$ of the air from a sealed container on each stroke of its piston. Thus, $\frac{4}{5}$ of the air remains after the first stroke. How much of the air remains after five strokes of the piston? Let 1 represent the original amount of air.**

The sequence can be indicated as follows.

$\begin{matrix} 0 & 1 & 2 & 3 & 4 & 5 \end{matrix}$ *Number of each stroke*

$1, \dfrac{4}{5}, \dfrac{16}{25},$ ——, ——, ——, *How do you find the third term?*

$\begin{matrix} a_1 & a_2 & a_3 & a_4 & a_5 & a_6 \end{matrix}$ *Number of each term*

Use $a_n = a_1 \cdot r^{n-1}$

$a_6 = 1 \cdot \left(\dfrac{4}{5}\right)^5$ or $\dfrac{4^5}{5^5}$ *Substitute 1 for a_1, 6 for n, and $\dfrac{4}{5}$ for r.*

$= \dfrac{1024}{3125}$ or about 0.328   Thus, about 32.8% of the air remains.

exercises

Exploratory **Tell whether each sequence is geometric. If so, find the common ratio.**

1. 4, 20, 100, 500

2. $9, 6, 4, \dfrac{8}{3}$

3. $\dfrac{3}{2}, \dfrac{9}{4}, \dfrac{27}{8}, \dfrac{81}{16}$

4. 2, 4, 6, 8

5. 7, 14, 21, 28

6. 1, 4, 9, 16, 25

Find the missing terms for each geometric sequence.

7. 5, 15, 45, ——, ——

8. 2, 10, 50, ——, ——

9. ——, ——, 3, 9, 27

Written **Find the next two terms for each geometric sequence.**

1. 2, 6, 18, . . .

2. 729, 243, 81, . . .

3. 20, 30, 45, . . .

4. 90, 30, 10, . . .

5. $\dfrac{1}{27}, \dfrac{1}{9}, \dfrac{1}{3}, \ldots$

6. $-\dfrac{1}{4}, \dfrac{1}{2}, ^-1, \ldots$

Find the first four terms of each geometric sequence described below.

7. $a_1 = \dfrac{3}{2}, r = 2$

8. $a_1 = 3, r = ^-2$

9. $a_1 = 12, r = \dfrac{1}{2}$

10. $a_1 = 27, r = -\dfrac{1}{3}$

Find the nth term of each geometric sequence described below. Use $a_n = a_1 \cdot r^{n-1}$.

11. $a_1 = 7, n = 4, r = 2$

12. $a_1 = 4, n = 3, r = 5$

13. $a_1 = 2, n = 5, r = 2$

14. $a_1 = 243, n = 5, r = -\frac{1}{3}$

15. $a_3 = 32, n = 6, r = -\frac{1}{2}$

16. $a_4 = 16, n = 8, r = \frac{1}{2}$

Find the missing geometric means for each sequence.

17. $3, \underline{\quad}, \underline{\quad}, \underline{\quad}, 48$

18. $1, \underline{\quad}, \underline{\quad}, 8$

19. $8, \underline{\quad}, \underline{\quad}, \underline{\quad}, \underline{\quad}, \frac{1}{4}$

20. $3, \underline{\quad}, 75$

21. $5, \underline{\quad}, \underline{\quad}, \underline{\quad}, 80$

22. $7, \underline{\quad}, \underline{\quad}, \underline{\quad}, 112$

23. $\underline{\quad}, \underline{\quad}, {}^-12, \underline{\quad}, \underline{\quad}, 96$

24. $\underline{\quad}, \underline{\quad}, \underline{\quad}, 24, \underline{\quad}, \underline{\quad}, \underline{\quad}, 384$

Solve each problem.

25. A vacuum pump removes $\frac{1}{10}$ of the air from a space capsule on each stroke of its piston. What percent of the air remains after four strokes of the piston?

26. The population of Sunville increases by 10% each year. It is now 20,000. What will be the expected population after five years (to the nearest 100 people)?

27. Mr. Culligan invested in business equipment worth $40,000. The equipment depreciates at the rate of 20% per year. What will be the value of his equipment at the end of the sixth year (to the nearest dollar)?

28. A piece of paper is cut in half. Then each half is cut in half again. If this process is repeated 8 more times, what is the size of each piece compared to the original?

Challenge   Solve the following problem.

A vacuum pump removes $\frac{1}{20}$ of the air in a sealed jar on each stroke of its piston.
How many strokes of the piston are required to remove 99% of the air from the jar?

Skills Review   Perform the indicated operation for each of the following. Write each answer in simplest form.

1. $\dfrac{8xy}{a - b} \cdot \dfrac{b - a}{32x^3y^2}$

2. $\dfrac{4x^2 - 1}{4x^2 - 4x + 1} \cdot \dfrac{3}{2x + 1}$

3. $\dfrac{x^2 - x - 6}{2x + 4} \div \dfrac{x^2 - 9}{6x^2}$

4. $\dfrac{10x^2 + 13x - 3}{10x - 2} \div \dfrac{2x^2 + 5x + 3}{x^2 - 1}$

5. $\dfrac{3x}{5} + \dfrac{8b}{2x}$

6. $\dfrac{5}{2a} - \dfrac{9}{5ab}$

7. $\dfrac{y + 3}{x - y} - \dfrac{6}{y - x}$

8. $\dfrac{5}{x - 7} + 3y$

Simplify each expression.

9. $\dfrac{\dfrac{b}{a} - \dfrac{a}{b}}{\dfrac{1}{b} + \dfrac{1}{a}}$

10. $\dfrac{x + y}{\dfrac{1}{x} + \dfrac{1}{y}}$

13–4 Geometric Series

Anne began her savings plan by saving a penny the first day, two cents the second day, and so on. On the seventh day, she saved 64 cents. How much had she saved altogether? The amounts saved on each day form a geometric sequence in which $a_1 = 1$ and $r = 2$.

For the sequence and series, the first team is a_1, the second term is a_2, and so on.

The geometric sequence 1, 2, 4, 8, 16, 32, 64 is determined by Anne's plan. The corresponding **geometric series** is shown below.

$$1 + 2 + 4 + 8 + 16 + 32 + 64$$

Let S_7 be the sum of the first seven terms indicated above. The following method can be used to calculate the sum.

$$S_7 = 1 + 2 + 4 + 8 + 16 + 32 + 64$$
$$\underline{-2 \cdot S_7 = 2 + 4 + 8 + 16 + 32 + 64 + 128}$$
$$S_7 - 2S_7 = 1 + 0 + 0 + 0 + 0 + 0 + 0 + {}^-128$$
$$(1 - 2)S_7 = 1 - 128$$
$$S_7 = 127 \qquad \text{Anne saved 127 cents, or \$1.27.}$$

Subtract $2 \cdot S_7$ from S_7.

Factor $S_7 - 2S_7$ to get $(1 - 2)S_7$.

In this case, $S_7 = \dfrac{1 - 128}{1 - 2}$.

Substitute names of terms of sequence, and r for 2.

$$S_7 = \frac{a_1 - a_8}{1 - r}$$

Note that $a_8 = a_1 r^7$.

$$= \frac{a_1 - a_1 r^7}{1 - r}$$

Can r be one? Why or why not?

The same method can be used to write a formula for a geometric series with n terms.

Let $S_n = a_1 + a_1 r + a_1 r^2 + \ldots + a_1 r^{n-1}$.

$$S_n = a_1 + a_1 r + a_1 r^2 + \ldots + a_1 r^{n-1}$$
$$\underline{-r \cdot S_n = a_1 r + a_1 r^2 + \ldots + a_1 r^{n-1} + a_1 r^n}$$
$$S_n - rS_n = a_1 + 0 + 0 + \ldots + 0 - a_1 r^n$$
$$(1 - r)S_n = a_1 - a_1 r^n$$
$$S_n = \frac{a_1 - a_1 r^n}{1 - r}$$

Multiply each term of the series by r. Write the second row so that like terms are in columns. Subtract.

The sum, S_n, of the first n terms of a geometric series is given by the following formula.

$$S_n = \frac{a_1 - a_1 r^n}{1 - r} \qquad \text{where } r \neq 1$$

Sum of a Geometric Series

Study the following examples.

1 Find the sum of the first six terms of a geometric series for which $a_1 = 3$ and $r = {}^-2$. Use the formula $S_n = \dfrac{a_1 - a_1 r^n}{1 - r}$.

$$S_n = \frac{a_1 - a_1 r^n}{1 - r}$$

$$S_6 = \frac{3 - 3({}^-2)^6}{1 - ({}^-2)} \qquad \textit{Substitute 3 for } a_1, \ {}^-2 \textit{ for } r, \textit{ and 6 for } n.$$

$$= {}^-63$$

The sum of the first six terms is ${}^-63$.

You know that $a_n = a_1 r^{n-1}$. Then $a_n \cdot r = a_1 r^{n-1} \cdot r$ or $a_1 r^n$. Replacing $a_1 r^n$ by $a_n r$ gives another formula for finding the value of S_n.

$$S_n = \frac{a_1 - a_1 r^n}{1 - r}$$

$$= \frac{a_1 - a_n r}{1 - r} \qquad \textit{Substitute } a_n r \textit{ for } a_1 r^n.$$

2 Find the sum of a geometric series for which $a_1 = 48$, $a_n = 3$, and $r = -\dfrac{1}{2}$. Use the formula $S_n = \dfrac{a_1 - a_n r}{1 - r}$.

$$S_n = \frac{a_1 - a_n r}{1 - r}$$

$$= \frac{48 - 3\left(-\dfrac{1}{2}\right)}{1 - \left(-\dfrac{1}{2}\right)} \qquad \begin{array}{l} \textit{Substitute 48 for } a_1, \textit{ 3 for} \\ a_n, \textit{ and } -\dfrac{1}{2} \textit{ for } r. \end{array}$$

$$= \frac{\dfrac{99}{2}}{\dfrac{3}{2}}$$

$$= 33$$

The sum S_n is 33.

When $r = 1$, S_n is found by the formula $S_n = n \cdot a_1$. For example, the sum of the series $3 + 3 + 3 + 3 + 3 + 3$ is given by $S_n = 6 \cdot 3$ or 18.

Exploratory For each geometric series described below, state the first term, the common ratio, the last term, and the number of terms.

1. $9 - 18 + 36 - 72 + 144$

2. $3 + 1.5 + 0.75 + 0.375 + 0.1875$

3. $a_1 - 5 + \dfrac{5}{4} - \dfrac{5}{16} + a_5$

4. $a_1 + 6 - 3 + \dfrac{3}{2} + a_5$

5. $a_1 = 2, a_4 = 128, n = 5$

6. $a_2 = 6, a_4 = 24, n = 5$

7. $a_2 = {}^-12, a_4 = {}^-108, n = 6$

8. $a_5 = \dfrac{1}{64}, n = 5, a_3 = \dfrac{1}{8}$

Written Find the sum of each geometric series described below.

1. $2 + ({}^-6) + 18 + \ldots$ to 6 terms.

2. $3 + 6 + 12 + \ldots$ to 6 terms.

3. $8 + 4 + 2 + \ldots$ to 6 terms.

4. $\dfrac{1}{9} - \dfrac{1}{3} + 1 - \ldots$ to 5 terms.

5. $1296 - 216 + 36 - \ldots$ to 5 terms.

6. $7 + 7 + 7 + \ldots$ to 9 terms.

7. $75 + 15 + 3 + \ldots$ to 5 terms.

8. $16 + 16 + 16 + \ldots$ to 11 terms.

9. $a_1 = 7, r = 2, n = 4$

10. $a_1 = 5, r = 3, n = 5$

11. $a_1 = 12, a_5 = 972, r = {}^-3$

12. $a_1 = 256, r = \dfrac{3}{4}, n = 5$

13. $a_1 = 243, r = -\dfrac{2}{3}, n = 5$

14. $a_1 = 16, r = -\dfrac{1}{2}, n = 6$

15. $a_1 = 625, a_5 = 81, r = \dfrac{3}{5}$

16. $a_1 = 625, r = \dfrac{2}{5}, n = 5$

17. $a_1 = 4, a_6 = \dfrac{1}{8}, r = \dfrac{1}{2}$

18. $a_1 = 1, a_5 = \dfrac{1}{16}, r = -\dfrac{1}{2}$

19. $a_1 = 125, a_5 = \dfrac{1}{5}, r = \dfrac{1}{5}$

20. $a_1 = 343, a_4 = {}^-1, r = -\dfrac{1}{7}$

21. $a_3 = \dfrac{3}{4}, a_6 = \dfrac{3}{32}, n = 6$

22. $a_2 = 1.5, a_5 = 0.1875, n = 6$

23. $a_3 = \dfrac{5}{4}, a_4 = -\dfrac{5}{16}, n = 6$

24. $a_2 = {}^-12, a_5 = {}^-324, n = 7$

Find a_1 for each geometric series described below.

25. $S_n = 32, r = 2, n = 6$

26. $S_n = 244, r = {}^-3, n = 5$

27. $a_n = 324, r = 3, S_n = 484$

28. $S_n = 635, a_n = 320, r = 2$

29. $S_n = 1022, r = 2, n = 9$

30. $S_n = 15\dfrac{3}{4}, r = \dfrac{1}{2}, a_n = \dfrac{1}{4}$

Solve each problem.

31. Find the sum of the first nine terms of the geometric series whose 4th term is 20 and whose 8th term is 1620.

32. One minute after it is released, a hot air balloon rises 80 feet. In each succeeding minute the balloon rises only 60% as far as it rose in the previous minute. How far will the balloon rise in 6 minutes?

33. The teaching staff of Fairmeadow High School informs its members of school cancellation by telephone. The principal calls 2 teachers, each of whom in turn calls 2 other members, and so on. This process must be repeated 6 times counting the principal's calls as the first time. How many teachers, including the principal, work at Fairmeadow High?

13-5   Infinite Geometric Series

The first swing of a pendulum measures 25 centimeters. The lengths of the successive swings form the geometric sequence 25, 20, 16, 12.8, ...

Suppose this pendulum continues to swing back and forth infinitely. Then the sequence shown above is called an *infinite geometric sequence.*

The distances traveled by the pendulum can be added.

$$25 + 20 + 16 + 12.8 + \cdots$$

The series can be written as follows.
$$25 + 25(0.8)^1 + 25(0.8)^2 + 25(0.8)^3 + 25(0.8)^4 + 25(0.8)^5 + 25(0.8)^6 + \cdots$$

The sum of these distances is an infinite geometric series with $a_1 = 25$ and $r = \dfrac{20}{25}$ or 0.8.

What happens as 0.8 is raised to various powers?

$(0.8)^1 = 0.8$ $(0.8)^{10} \approx 0.1074$ $(0.8)^{50} \approx 0.00001$

As the values of n become greater, what happens to $(0.8)^n$?

What happens to the terms of the series as the exponents increase?

$a_1 = 25$ $a_{10} \approx 3.3554$ $a_{50} \approx 0.0004$

What happens to the sums S_n as n becomes greater?

$S_1 = 25$ $S_{10} \approx \dfrac{25 - 25(0.1074)}{0.2}$ $S_{50} = \dfrac{25 - 25(0.00001)}{0.2}$

$\approx \dfrac{25 - 2.685}{0.2}$ $\approx \dfrac{25 - 0.00025}{0.2}$

≈ 111.575 ≈ 124.9988

Find S_{100}. Do you think a partial sum of this geometric series is ever greater than 125?

In any geometric series, the sum of the first n terms can be found by using either of the following formulas.

$$S_n = \frac{a_1 - a_1 r^n}{1 - r} \quad \text{or} \quad S_n = \frac{a_1(1 - r^n)}{1 - r}, \, r \neq 1$$

Suppose the value of r^n is very close to zero. Then the value of S_n is very close to the following expression, called the *sum of an infinite series.*

$$\frac{a_1(1 - 0)}{1 - r} \quad \text{or} \quad \frac{a_1}{1 - r}$$

The sum, S, of an infinite geometric series where $^-1 < r < 1$ is given by the following formula.
$$S = \frac{a_1}{1 - r}$$

Sum of an Infinite Geometric Series

An infinite geometric series where r is not between $^-1$ and 1, does not have a sum.

Study the following examples.

1 **Find the sum of the series 25 + 20 + 16 + 12.8 + ...**

$S = \dfrac{a_1}{1 - r}$ *Since $^-1 < 0.8 < 1$, you can use the formula.*

$S = \dfrac{25}{1 - 0.8}$ *Substitute 25 for a_1 and 0.8 for r.*

$= 125$

The sum of the series is 125.

2 **Find the sum of the infinite geometric series $\dfrac{4}{3} - \dfrac{2}{3} + \dfrac{1}{3} - \dfrac{1}{6} + \cdots$.**

First find r.

$a_2 = a_1 r$

$-\dfrac{2}{3} = \left(\dfrac{4}{3}\right) r$ *Substitute $-\dfrac{2}{3}$ for a_2 and $\dfrac{4}{3}$ for a_1.*

$-\dfrac{1}{2} = r$

Next, find the sum using $S = \dfrac{a_1}{1 - r}$.

$S = \dfrac{\dfrac{4}{3}}{1 - \left(-\dfrac{1}{2}\right)}$

$= \dfrac{\dfrac{4}{3}}{\dfrac{3}{2}}$

$= \dfrac{8}{9}$

The sum is $\dfrac{8}{9}$.

3 **Express the repeating decimal 0.11111 . . . or $0.\overline{1}$ as a fraction.**

Write $0.\overline{1}$ as an infinite geometric series.

$0.\overline{1} = 0.1 + 0.01 + 0.001 + \ldots$

Then $a_1 = 0.1$ and $r = 0.1$ since $0.01 = 0.1(r)$.

$S = \dfrac{a_1}{1 - r}$

$S = \dfrac{0.1}{1 - 0.1}$ *Substitute 0.1 for a_1 and 0.1 for r.*

$= \dfrac{0.1}{0.9}$

$= \dfrac{1}{9}$ *The repeating decimal $0.\overline{1}$ is equal to $\dfrac{1}{9}$.*

4 A rubber ball dropped 30 feet bounces $\frac{2}{5}$ of the height from which it fell on each bounce. How far will it travel before coming to rest?

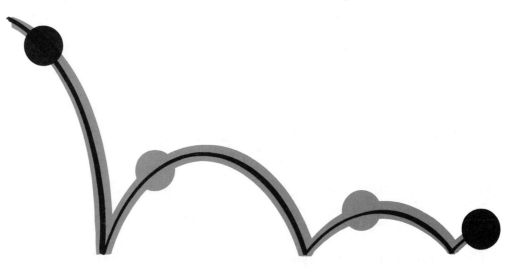

downward distance

$S = \dfrac{30}{1 - 0.4}$ *Note that a_1 is 30 and r is 0.4.*

$\quad = \dfrac{30}{0.6}$

$\quad = 50$

upward distance

$S = \dfrac{12}{1 - 0.4}$ *Note that a_1 is 12 and r is 0.4.*

$\quad = \dfrac{12}{0.6}$

$\quad = 20$

The total distance is 50 + 20 or 70 feet.

exercises

Exploratory Find a_1 and r for each series. Then find the sum, if it exists.

1. $\frac{1}{2} + \frac{1}{3} + \frac{2}{9} + \frac{4}{27} + \cdots$

2. $12 + 3 + \frac{3}{4} + \frac{3}{16} + \cdots$

3. $1 - \frac{1}{3} + \frac{1}{9} - \frac{1}{27} + \cdots$

4. $1 - 3 + 9 - 27 + \cdots$

5. $1 + \frac{3}{2} + \frac{9}{4} + \frac{27}{8} + \cdots$

6. $48 + 16 + \frac{16}{3} + \frac{16}{9} + \cdots$

Express each repeating decimal as an infinite geometric series. State the ratio for each.

7. $0.\overline{7}$

8. $0.\overline{3}$

9. $0.\overline{73}$

10. $0.\overline{8}$

11. $0.\overline{152}$

12. $0.\overline{746}$

13. $0.\overline{93}$

14. $0.\overline{75}$

Written   Find the sum of each infinite geometric series described below.

1. $a_1 = 6, r = \frac{11}{12}$

2. $a_1 = 18, r = -\frac{2}{7}$

3. $a_1 = 7, r = -\frac{3}{4}$

4. $a_1 = 27, r = -\frac{4}{5}$

5. $9 + 6 + 4 + \ldots$

6. $\frac{1}{3} + \frac{1}{9} + \frac{1}{27} + \ldots$

7. $3 - 2 + \frac{4}{3} - \ldots$

8. $\frac{3}{4} + \frac{1}{2} + \frac{1}{3} + \ldots$

9. $12 - 4 + \frac{4}{3} - \frac{4}{9} + \ldots$

10. $1 - \frac{1}{4} + \frac{1}{16} - \ldots$

11. $10 - \frac{5}{2} + \frac{5}{8} - \ldots$

12. $2 + 6 + 18 + 54 + \ldots$

13. $3 - 9 + 27 - \ldots$

14. $12 + 6 + 3 + \ldots$

15. $10 - 1 + 0.1 - \ldots$

16. $100 + 10 + 1 + \ldots$

Find a common fraction equivalent to each repeating decimal below.

17. $0.\overline{3}$

18. $0.\overline{9}$

19. $0.\overline{15}$

20. $0.\overline{31}$

21. $0.\overline{075}$

22. $0.\overline{410}$

23. $0.3\overline{7}$

24. $0.4\overline{5}$

Find the first three terms of each infinite geometric series described below.

25. $S = 9, r = \frac{1}{3}$

26. $S = 16, r = \frac{3}{4}$

27. $S = 28, r = -\frac{2}{7}$

28. $S = \frac{27}{4}, r = -\frac{1}{3}$

Solve each problem.

29. The end of a swinging pendulum 90 cm long moves through 50 cm on its first swing. Each succeeding swing is $\frac{9}{10}$ of the preceding one. How far will the pendulum travel before coming to rest?

30. The end of a swinging pendulum 30 cm long moves through 20 cm on its first swing. Each succeeding swing is $\frac{10}{11}$ of the preceding one. How far will it travel before coming to rest?

31. A silicon ball dropped 12 feet rebounds $\frac{7}{10}$ of the height from which it fell on each bounce. How far will it travel before coming to rest?

32. A hot-air balloon rises 80 feet in the first minute after the balloon is released. If in each succeeding minute the balloon rises only 90 percent as far as in the previous minute, what is the maximum height (altitude) the balloon will reach?

Challenge   Solve each problem.

1. A side of an equilateral triangle is 20 inches. The midpoints of its sides are joined to form an inscribed equilateral triangle. If this process is continued without end, find the sum of the perimeters of the triangles.

2. Find the sum of the areas of the series of triangles in the previous exercise.

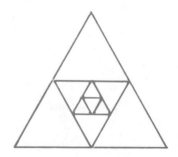

13-6   Sigma Notation

Consider the sum of the first ten positive even integers.

$$2 + 4 + 6 + 8 + \ldots + 20$$

This series can be written in a more concise way. First, notice the following pattern.

$$2(1) + 2(2) + 2(3) + 2(4) + \ldots + 2(10)$$

The Greek letter sigma, Σ, can be used to indicate this sum.

stop at 10 $\longrightarrow$

start n at 1 $\longrightarrow$

$$\sum_{n=1}^{10} 2n$$

This is read *the summation from 1 to 10 of 2n.*

Using sigma to indicate the sum of a series is called sigma or summation notation. When using this notation, the variable defined at the bottom of the sigma is called the *index of summation*. The terms of the series above are generated by successively replacing the index of summation with 1, 2, 3 . . . 10.

Any letter can be used for the index of summation.

examples

1 Write $\sum_{k=1}^{5} 4k$ in expanded form.

Replace k with 1, 2, 3, 4, 5 successively.

$$\sum_{k=1}^{5} 4k = \overset{k=1}{4 \cdot 1} + \overset{k=2}{4 \cdot 2} + \overset{k=3}{4 \cdot 3} + \overset{k=4}{4 \cdot 4} + \overset{k=5}{4 \cdot 5}$$
$$= 4 + 8 + 12 + 16 + 20$$

2 Write $\sum_{n=3}^{7} (3n - 2)$ in expanded form and find the sum.

$$\sum_{n=3}^{7} (3n - 2) = \overset{n=3}{(3 \cdot 3 - 2)} + \overset{n=4}{(3 \cdot 4 - 2)} + \overset{n=5}{(3 \cdot 5 - 2)} + \overset{n=6}{(3 \cdot 6 - 2)} + \overset{n=7}{(3 \cdot 7 - 2)}$$
$$= (9 - 2) + (12 - 2) + (15 - 2) + (18 - 2) + (21 - 2)$$
$$= (7 + 10 + 13 + 16 + 19) \text{ or } 65$$

The sum is 65.

3 Write $\sum_{j=1}^{5} 2(4)^{j-1}$ in expanded form and find the sum.

$$\sum_{j=1}^{5} 2(4)^{j-1} = \overset{j=1}{2 \cdot 4^{1-1}} + \overset{j=2}{2 \cdot 4^{2-1}} + \overset{j=3}{2 \cdot 4^{3-1}} + \overset{j=4}{2 \cdot 4^{4-1}} + \overset{j=5}{2 \cdot 4^{5-1}}$$
$$= 2 \cdot 4^0 + 2 \cdot 4^1 + 2 \cdot 4^2 + 2 \cdot 4^3 + 2 \cdot 4^4$$
$$= 2 \cdot 1 + 2 \cdot 4 + 2 \cdot 16 + 2 \cdot 64 + 2 \cdot 256$$
$$= (2 + 8 + 32 + 128 + 512) \text{ or } 682$$

The sum is 682.

4 **Find the sum of** $\sum\limits_{x=1}^{9} [3 + (x - 1)5]$.

$$\sum_{x=1}^{9} [3 + (x - 1)5] = (3 + 0 \cdot 5) + (3 + 1 \cdot 5) + (3 + 2 \cdot 5) + \ldots + (3 + 8 \cdot 5)$$
$$= \quad 3 \quad + \quad 8 \quad + \quad 13 \quad + \ldots + \quad 43$$

Since this is an arithmetic series, use $S_n = \dfrac{n}{2}(a_1 + a_n)$.

$S_n = \dfrac{9}{2}(3 + 43)$ $a_1 = 3, a_n = 43, n = 9.$

$\quad = \dfrac{9}{2}(46)$

$\quad = 207$

The sum is 207.

5 **Use sigma notation to express $5 + 9 + 13 + 17 + 21$.**

First, search for a pattern.

$$5 \quad + \quad 9 \quad + \quad 13 \quad + \quad 17 \quad + \quad 21$$
$$= (5 + 0 \cdot 4) + (5 + 1 \cdot 4) + (5 + 2 \cdot 4) + (5 + 3 \cdot 4) + (5 + 4 \cdot 4)$$

The pattern is $5 + (n - 1)4$, if n is replaced successively with 1, 2, 3, 4, 5. Therefore, the series can be expressed as:

$$\sum_{n=1}^{5} [5 + (n - 1)4] \quad \text{or} \quad \sum_{n=1}^{5} (4n + 1)$$

6 **Use sigma notation to express $1 - 3 + 9 - 27 + 81 - 243$.**

Since $1 - 3 + 9 - 27 + 81 - 243$ is a geometric series, use $a_n = a_1 r^{n-1}$.

$a_n = 1 \cdot (^-3)^{n-1}$ $a_1 = 1$ and $r = {}^-3$

Therefore the series can be expressed as:

$$\sum_{n=1}^{6} (^-3)^{n-1}$$

exercises

Exploratory For each of the following state the index and the number of terms in the series. Then, state each series in expanded form.

1. $\sum\limits_{j=1}^{4} (j + 2)$
2. $\sum\limits_{k=3}^{5} 4k$
3. $\sum\limits_{r=1}^{3} (r - 1)$
4. $\sum\limits_{k=2}^{6} (3 - k)$

5. $\displaystyle\sum_{i=0}^{4} 2i$ **6.** $\displaystyle\sum_{m=6}^{8} (^-m)$ **7.** $\displaystyle\sum_{p=4}^{7} (p + 2)$ **8.** $\displaystyle\sum_{i=2}^{5} (i + 9)$

Written   Write each expression in expanded form and find the sum.

1. $\displaystyle\sum_{t=0}^{4} (13 + 7t)$ **2.** $\displaystyle\sum_{i=1}^{5} (1 + 7i)$ **3.** $\displaystyle\sum_{p=3}^{7} (2p - 1)$

4. $\displaystyle\sum_{j=0}^{6} (24 - 9j)$ **5.** $\displaystyle\sum_{b=2}^{6} (2b + 1)$ **6.** $\displaystyle\sum_{y=5}^{11} (3y - 5)$

7. $\displaystyle\sum_{i=1}^{7} 2i$ **8.** $\displaystyle\sum_{r=3}^{6} (r + 2)$ **9.** $\displaystyle\sum_{z=1}^{9} (10 - z)$

10. $\displaystyle\sum_{s=3}^{8} (2s - 1)$ **11.** $\displaystyle\sum_{x=6}^{10} (x + 4)$ **12.** $\displaystyle\sum_{j=^-3}^{3} (2j + 2)$

13. $\displaystyle\sum_{n=4}^{8} 4^n$ **14.** $\displaystyle\sum_{k=1}^{7} 2^{k-2}$ **15.** $\displaystyle\sum_{s=1}^{4} 24\left(-\frac{1}{2}\right)^s$

Find the sum of each series.

16. $\displaystyle\sum_{n=1}^{25} 2n$ **17.** $\displaystyle\sum_{n=1}^{30} (2n - 1)$ **18.** $\displaystyle\sum_{n=1}^{40} (3n + 2)$

19. $\displaystyle\sum_{n=10}^{50} (3n - 1)$ **20.** $\displaystyle\sum_{n=21}^{75} (2n + 5)$ **21.** $\displaystyle\sum_{j=1}^{6} (^-2)^j$

22. $\displaystyle\sum_{k=1}^{8} 2^{k-4}$ **23.** $\displaystyle\sum_{s=1}^{5} \left(\frac{3}{10}\right)^s$ **24.** $\displaystyle\sum_{t=1}^{6} \left(\frac{8}{10}\right)^t$

Use sigma notation to express each of the following.
25. $7 + 10 + 13 + 16 + 19$

26. $3 + 10 + 17 + 24 + 31$

27. $15 + 11 + 7 + 3 + (^-1)$

28. $7 + 6\frac{1}{2} + 6 + 5\frac{1}{2} + 5$

29. $1 + 3 + 5 + 7 + \ldots + 25$

30. $5 + 10 + 15 + 20 + \ldots + 50$

31. $8 + 4 + 2 + 1 + \frac{1}{2} + \frac{1}{4}$

32. $2 - 6 + 18 - 54 + 162 - 486$

33. $243 - 162 + 108 - 72 + 48 - 32$

34. $625 + 375 + 225 + 135 + 81$

35. $1^2 + 2^2 + 3^2 + 4^2 + 5^2$

36. $\frac{1}{2} + \frac{1}{3} + \frac{1}{4} + \frac{1}{5} + \frac{1}{6}$

Challenge   Solve each problem.

1. Write a computer program to evaluate the series: $\displaystyle\sum_{k=1}^{100} (3k - 2)$

2. Write a computer program to evaluate the series $\displaystyle\sum_{k=1}^{20} k^3$. Have the program also compute and print $\dfrac{20^2(21)^2}{4}$. Compare the results.

13–7   The General Term

Sequences and series often are described by giving a formula for their general term. This formula may show how to find the nth term.

Sequence type	Formula for the nth term
Arithmetic	$a_n = 7 + (n - 1) \cdot 3$
Geometric	$a_n = 5 \cdot 4^{n-1}$

Sometimes a sequence or series may be described recursively. A **recursive formula** depends on knowing one or more previous terms.

Sequence type	Recursive formula
Arithmetic	$a_{n+1} = a_n + 3, a_1 = 7$
Geometric	$a_{n+1} = a_n \cdot 4, a_1 = 5$

When a sequence or series is described by a formula for its nth term, any term can be computed directly.

1 **Find the 99th term of the sequence in which $a_n = 7 + (n - 1)3$.**

$a_n = 7 + (n - 1)3$
$a_{99} = 7 + (99 - 1)3$ *Substitute 99 for n.*
$\quad = 7 + 98 \cdot 3$
$\quad = 7 + 294$
$\quad = 301$

When a sequence or series is described by a recursive formula, you may need to compute several terms to find the terms desired.

2 **Find the first six terms of the sequence in which $a_1 = 1$, $a_2 = 1$ and $a_{n+2} = a_n + 2 \cdot a_{n+1}$.**

$a_3 = a_{1+2}$ $a_4 = a_{2+2}$
$\quad = a_1 + 2 \cdot a_2$ $\quad = a_2 + 2 \cdot a_3$
$\quad = 1 + 2(1)$ or 3 $\quad = 1 + 2(3)$ or 7

$a_5 = a_{3+2}$ $a_6 = a_{4+2}$
$\quad = a_3 + 2 \cdot a_4$ $\quad = a_4 + 2 \cdot a_5$
$\quad = 3 + 2(7)$ or 17 $\quad = 7 + 2(17)$ or 41

The first six terms are 1, 1, 3, 7, 17, and 41.

3 Find the 51st through the 54th terms of the sequence for which $a_n = 2n + 1$.

These can be written in a chart as follows.

n	$a_n = 2n + 1$
51	$a_{51} = 2(51) + 1$ or 103
52	$a_{52} = 2(52) + 1$ or 105
53	$a_{53} = 2(53) + 1$ or 107
54	$a_{54} = 2(54) + 1$ or 109

4 Find both a recursive formula and a formula for the nth term of the sequence 3, $^-6$, 12, $^-24$, 48, ...

$$3 \qquad ^-6 \qquad 12 \qquad ^-24 \qquad 48$$
$$3 \cdot (^-2) \quad ^-6 \cdot (^-2) \quad 12 \cdot (^-2) \quad ^-24 \cdot (^-2)$$

Consider the ratio of two consecutive terms.

A recursive formula is $a_{n+1} = a_n(^-2)$ and $a_1 = 3$.
A formula for the nth term is $a_n = 3(^-2)^{n-1}$. *Recall $a_n = a_1 r^{n-1}$.*

5 Find a formula for the nth term of the following series and express the series using sigma notation.

$$7 + 9 + 11 + 13 + 15 + 17$$
$$^{+2} \quad ^{+2} \quad ^{+2} \quad ^{+2} \quad ^{+2}$$

What is the difference between any two terms?

$$a_n = a_1 + (n - 1)d$$
$$a_n = 7 + (n - 1)2 \qquad \text{Substitute 7 for } a_1 \text{ and 2 for } d.$$
$$a_n = 5 + 2n$$

$$7 + 9 + 11 + 13 + 15 + 17 = \sum_{n=1}^{6} (5 + 2n)$$

exercises

Exploratory Find the ninth and tenth terms of each sequence.

1. $a_n = n(n + 2)$
2. $a_n = 3n - 4$
3. $a_n = n^2 - 1$
4. $a_n = (^-1)^n$

Find the first four terms of each sequence.

5. $a_1 = 8,\ a_{n+1} = a_n - 1$
6. $a_1 = 13,\ a_{n+1} = a_n + 2$
7. $a_1 = ^-2,\ a_{n+1} = 3a_n$
8. $a_1 = 7,\ a_{n+1} = 2a_n$
9. $a_1 = ^-4,\ a_{n+1} = (^-1)^{n+1}a_n$
10. $a_1 = 3,\ a_{n+1} = (^-1)^n a_n$

11. $a_1 = 3$, $a_2 = 1$, $a_{n+2} = a_n + a_{n+1}$ **12.** $a_1 = 0$, $a_2 = 1$, $a_{n+2} = a_n + a_{n+1}$

Find a formula for the nth term of each sequence.

13. 2, 4, 6, 8, 10, 12, 14, . . .

14. 3, 5, 7, 9, 11, 13, . . .

15. $\dfrac{2}{1}, \dfrac{3}{2}, \dfrac{4}{3}, \dfrac{5}{4}, \dfrac{6}{5}, \ldots$

16. $\dfrac{1}{3}, \dfrac{1}{5}, \dfrac{1}{7}, \dfrac{1}{9}, \dfrac{1}{11}, \dfrac{1}{13}, \ldots$

Find a recursive formula for each sequence.

17. $1, \dfrac{1}{3}, \dfrac{1}{9}, \dfrac{1}{27}, \ldots$

18. 1, 2, 4, 8, . . .

19. 1, ⁻1, 1, ⁻1, . . .

20. $1, -\dfrac{1}{2}, \dfrac{1}{4}, -\dfrac{1}{8}, \ldots$

Written   Find the eighth, ninth, and tenth terms of each sequence.

1. $a_n = 4n - 3$

2. $a_n = \dfrac{n}{n+1}$

3. $a_n = \dfrac{2n+1}{n+2}$

4. $a_n = \dfrac{n(n-1)}{3}$

5. $a_n = \dfrac{2}{n}$

6. $a_n = 4n^2$

7. $a_n = (-1)^{n+1} 2n$

8. $a_n = \dfrac{1}{2}(n^2 + n + 4)$

9. $a_n = n^2 + 2n + 1$

10. $a_n = \dfrac{1}{2} \cdot 2^{n-1}$

Find the first six terms of each sequence.

11. $a_1 = 2$, $a_{n+1} = 3a_n$

12. $a_1 = 7$, $a_{n+1} = a_n + 5$

13. $a_1 = 3$, $a_2 = 5$, $a_{n+2} = a_n + a_{n+1}$

14. $a_1 = 1$, $a_2 = 2$, $a_{n+2} = a_n + a_{n+1}$

15. $a_1 = 2$, $a_2 = 3$, $a_{n+2} = 2a_n + a_{n+1}$

16. $a_1 = 5$, $a_2 = 11$, $a_{n+2} = a_{n+1} - a_n$

Find both a recursive formula and a formula for the nth term of each of the following series.

17. 3, 7, 11, 15, 19, . . .

18. 4, 9, 14, 19, 24, . . .

19. 3, 15, 75, 375, 1875, . . .

20. $\dfrac{3}{2}, \dfrac{3}{4}, \dfrac{3}{8}, \dfrac{3}{16}, \dfrac{3}{32}, \ldots$

21. 5, 10, 15, 20, 25, . . .

22. $\dfrac{7}{2}, \dfrac{7}{10}, \dfrac{7}{50}, \dfrac{7}{250}, \ldots$

Express each series using sigma notation.

23. $3 + 10 + 17 + 24 + 31$

24. $\dfrac{4}{5} + \dfrac{7}{5} + 2 + \dfrac{13}{5} + \dfrac{16}{5}$

25. $\dfrac{3}{3} + \dfrac{6}{4} + \dfrac{9}{5} + 2 + \dfrac{15}{7}$

26. $6 - 2 + \dfrac{2}{3} - \dfrac{2}{9} + \dfrac{1}{27}$

27. $\dfrac{3}{4} + \dfrac{3}{2} + \dfrac{9}{4} + 3 + \dfrac{15}{4} + \dfrac{9}{2}$

28. $2 + 2\dfrac{1}{2} + 3\dfrac{1}{3} + 4\dfrac{1}{4} + 5\dfrac{1}{5} + 6\dfrac{1}{6}$

29. $2 \cdot 5 + 4 \cdot 7 + 6 \cdot 9 + 8 \cdot 11 + 10 \cdot 13$

30. $1 + \left(-\dfrac{1}{3}\right) + \dfrac{1}{5} + \left(-\dfrac{1}{7}\right) + \dfrac{1}{9} + \left(-\dfrac{1}{27}\right)$

Consider the series formed by the first n positive odd integers.

$$1 + 3 + 5 + 7 + \ldots + (2n - 1)$$

Then study the following partial sums.

for $n = 1$ $1 = 1^2$
for $n = 2$ $1 + 3 = 2^2$
for $n = 3$ $1 + 3 + 5 = 3^2$

If this pattern continues for each consecutive value of n, then it seems true that

$$1 + 3 + 5 + 7 + \ldots + (2n - 1) = n^2$$

A method called **mathematical induction** can be used to prove that the sum of this series is indeed n^2. The proof is based on two steps and a conclusion.

Step 1   **First verify that the formula is valid for the first possible case, usually $n = 1$.**

For $n = 1$, it is true that $1 = 1^2$, therefore $S_n = n^2$ is valid for the first case.

Step 2   **Assume that the formula is valid for $n = k$. Using this information, prove that it is also valid for $n = k + 1$.**

Assume that $1 + 3 + 5 + 7 + \ldots + (2k - 1) = k^2$ is true. Then if the $(k + 1)st$ integer is added to both sides the result is an equivalent equation.

$$\underbrace{1 + 3 + 5 + 7 + \ldots + 2k - 1}_{\substack{k \text{ integers} \\ \text{by assumption}}} + \underset{\substack{(k+1)st \\ integer}}{[2(k + 1) - 1]} = k^2 + [2(k + 1) - 1]$$

$$= k^2 + 2k + 1$$

$$= (k + 1)^2$$

By factoring, $k^2 + 2k + 1 = (k + 1)^2$.

The formula is valid for the $(k + 1)st$ integer, since the sum of $(k + 1)$ odd integers is $(k + 1)^2$.

Conclusion   The formula is valid for $n = 1$. Step 2 illustrates that the formula is valid for the next positive integer $n + 1$ or 2. Since the formula is valid when $n = 2$, it is also valid for $n + 1$ or 3, and so on, indefinitely.

Exercises   Show that each statement is true for all natural numbers n.

1. $2 + 4 + 6 + \ldots + 2n = n(n + 1)$ **2.** $1 + 2 + 3 + \ldots + n = \dfrac{n(n + 1)}{2}$

3. $1^2 + 2^2 + 3^2 + \ldots + n^2 = \dfrac{n(n + 1)(2n + 1)}{6}$ **4.** $3 + 6 + 9 + \ldots + 3n = \dfrac{3n(n + 1)}{2}$

13–8 Special Sequences and Series

The base of this pine cone shows an example of a pattern that is often found in nature.
Count the number of strips that spiral to the left.
Count the number of strips that spiral to the right.
These two numbers shown in color below belong to a very special sequence.

This sequence is named after its discoverer, Leonardo Fibonacci.

$$1, 1, 2, 3, 5, 8, 13, 21, 34, 55, 89, 144, \ldots$$

Can you see what the next term will be? What do you think is the pattern used in the Fibonacci sequence?

Let F_n be a term of the sequence.

$F_1 = 1$ $F_2 = 1$ $F_3 = 2$ or $1 + 1$ *How do you find the next*
$F_4 = 3$ or $2 + 1$ $F_5 = 5$ or $3 + 2$ *term from the two*
Then $F_5 = 3 + 2$. Thus, $F_5 = F_4 + F_3$.   *previous terms?*

In general, if F_n is the nth term of the Fibonacci sequence, then

$$F_n = F_{n-1} + F_{n-2}.$$

The Fibonacci sequence is the basis of other sequences as well. One of these is the sequence of ratios found by dividing each term of the Fibonacci sequence by the preceding term.

$$\frac{1}{1}, \frac{2}{1}, \frac{3}{2}, \frac{5}{3}, \frac{8}{5}, \frac{13}{8}, \frac{21}{13}, \frac{34}{21}, \frac{55}{34}, \frac{89}{55}, \frac{144}{89}$$

Notice that the spirals of the pine cone have the ratio $\frac{13}{8}$. Some other pine cones have the ratio $\frac{8}{5}$. Some daisies have the ratio $\frac{34}{21}$. Sunflower heads have spirals of seeds which may have ratios of $\frac{21}{13}, \frac{34}{21}$, or $\frac{55}{34}$.

The following examples illustrate methods for finding patterns.

1 Find the missing terms of the following sequence.

6, 10, 15, 21, 28, ____, ____, ____, . . .

6,   10,   15,   21,   28,   ____,   ____,   ____

+4   +5   +6   +7   +8   +9   +10

Find the difference of consecutive terms.

The difference increases by one for each term.

The missing terms are 36, 45, and 55.

2 Find the missing terms of the sequence 1, 2, 6, 24, 120, ____, ____, ...

1,   2,   6,   24,   120,   ____,   ____

×2   ×3   ×4   ×5   ×? $120 \times 6 = 720$ $720 \times 7 = 5040$

Note that each term is multiplied by an integer.

The integers increase by one each time.

The next two terms are 720 and 5040.

3 Complete the sequence 4, 9, 16, 25, ____, ____, ____, ...

4,   9,   16,   25,   ____,   ____,   ____

↓   ↓   ↓   ↓

2^2 3^2 4^2 5^2

Notice that each term is a perfect square.

The next terms are $6^2 = 36$, $7^2 = 49$, and $8^2 = 64$.

4 Complete the sequence 1, 1, 4, 10, 28, 76, ____, ____, ...

1,   1,   4,   10,   28,   76,   ____,   ____

$2(1 + 1), 2(4 + 1), 2(10 + 4), 2(28 + 10)$

Notice that each term seems to be double the sum of the two previous terms.

The next two terms are 208 and 568.

Some special series often are used in more advanced mathematics. One of these is the Leibniz series for calculating π.

$$\frac{\pi}{4} = 1 + \left(-\frac{1}{3}\right) + \frac{1}{5} + \left(-\frac{1}{7}\right) + \frac{1}{9} + \cdots + \frac{(-1)^{n-1}}{2n-1} + \cdots$$

Multiply both sides by 4 to obtain a value for π.

An approximation for π can be found by taking a finite number of terms in the sum.

Another special series can be used to find natural logarithms (to the base e).

$$\log_e x = \left(\frac{x-1}{x}\right) + \frac{1}{2}\left(\frac{x-1}{x}\right)^2 + \frac{1}{3}\left(\frac{x-1}{x}\right)^3 + \cdots \text{ for } x > \frac{1}{2}$$

What happens to the series if x equals $\frac{1}{2}$? If x is less than $\frac{1}{2}$? Why must x be greater than $\frac{1}{2}$?

Written Find the missing terms of each sequence.

1. 52, 156, 468, ____, ____

2. 1, 2, 4, 7, 11, ____, ____

3. 2, 2.5, 2.75, ____, 2.9375

4. 2, 6, 30, 210, ____

5. 1, 3, 7, 13, 21, ____, ____

6. 64, 32, 8, 1, ____, ____

7. 1, 5, 14, 30, 55, ____, ____

8. 1, 8, 27, 64, 125, ____

9. 1, 3, 4, 7, 11, ____, ____, ____

10. 1, 1, 3, 7, 17, 41, ____, ____

Solve each problem.

11. Find the first twenty terms of the Fibonacci sequence.

12. Find the first 15 terms of the ratios of the Fibonacci sequence $\frac{1}{1}, \frac{2}{1}, \frac{3}{2}, \frac{5}{3} \cdots$. Express each as a decimal.

13. Find the sum of the first 8 terms of the series $\log_e 2$.

14. Find the sum of the first 8 terms of the series $\log_e 10$.

15. The Lucas sequence is 1, 3, 4, 7, 11, 18, 29, 47. Let L_n be a term of the Lucas sequence. Describe L_n in terms of the Fibonacci sequence.

16. Compute e to 4 decimal places by using this series $2 + \frac{1}{2 \cdot 1} + \frac{1}{3 \cdot 2 \cdot 1} + \frac{1}{4 \cdot 3 \cdot 2 \cdot 1} + \frac{1}{5 \cdot 4 \cdot 3 \cdot 2 \cdot 1} + \frac{1}{6 \cdot 5 \cdot 4 \cdot 3 \cdot 2 \cdot 1}$.

Limits of Sequences and Series

Certain types of sequences approach a specific number as more and more terms are found. This number is called a **limit.** You can use your calculator to find the limit of the geometric sequence $1, \frac{1}{2}, \frac{1}{4}, \frac{1}{8}, \frac{1}{16}, \frac{1}{32}, \cdots \left(\frac{1}{2}\right)^n$. Try several values for n to determine what happens as n increases. Use $a_n = a_1 r^{n-1}$ where $a_1 = 1$ and $r = \frac{1}{2}$.

$$a_5 = 1 \cdot \left(\frac{1}{2}\right)^{5-1} = (0.5)^4 \qquad a_{10} = 1 \cdot \left(\frac{1}{2}\right)^{10-1} = (0.5)^9 \qquad a_{20} = 1 \cdot \left(\frac{1}{2}\right)^{20-1} = (0.5)^{19}$$

ENTER: $.5 \boxed{y^x} 4 \boxed{=}$ $.5 \boxed{y^x} 9 \boxed{=}$ $.5 \boxed{y^x} 19 \boxed{=}$

FINAL DISPLAY: 0.0625   .00195313   .00000191

Notice that as n increases, the sequence approaches 0. *The limit is 0.*

Consider the geometric series $1 + \frac{1}{2} + \frac{1}{4} + \frac{1}{8} + \frac{1}{16} + \cdots$. Use your calculator and $S_n = \frac{a_1 - a_1 r^n}{1 - r}$ to find S_5, S_{10}, and S_{20} for this series. Compare these results to the sum of the series found by using $S = \frac{a_1}{1 - r}$. What can you conclude?

Exercises Use your calculator to find the limit of each sequence or series.

1. $\frac{1}{2}, \frac{2}{3}, \frac{3}{4}, \frac{4}{5}, \frac{5}{6}, \cdots \frac{n}{n+1}$

2. $\frac{2}{3}, \frac{4}{9}, \frac{8}{27}, \frac{16}{81}, \cdots \left(\frac{2}{3}\right)^n$

3. $\frac{1}{5}, \frac{2}{7}, \frac{3}{9}, \cdots \frac{n}{2n+3}$

4. $2 + \frac{2}{3} + \frac{2}{9} + \frac{2}{27} + \frac{2}{81} + \cdots$

5. $\frac{1}{3} + \frac{1}{6} + \frac{1}{12} + \frac{1}{24} + \frac{1}{48} + \cdots$

6. $3 + 1 + \frac{1}{3} + \frac{1}{9} + \frac{1}{27} + \cdots$

13–9   The Binomial Theorem

The binomial expression $(a + b)$ can be raised to various powers. There are patterns to be found in the powers of $(a + b)$ listed below.

$$(a + b)^0 = 1$$
$$(a + b)^1 = 1a + 1b$$
$$(a + b)^2 = 1a^2b^0 + 2ab + 1a^0b^2$$
$$(a + b)^3 = 1a^3b^0 + 3a^2b^1 + 3a^1b^2 + 1a^0b^3$$
$$(a + b)^4 = 1a^4b^0 + 4a^3b^1 + 6a^2b^2 + 4a^1b^3 + 1a^0b^4$$

Note that the coefficients are one.

Why can b^0 and a^0 be written here?

What happened to the powers of a?

What about powers of b?

Note the sum of the exponents in any term of $(a + b)^4$
How many terms are in the expansion of $(a + b)^4$?

The following patterns are seen in the expansion of $(a + b)^n$.

1. The exponent of $(a + b)^n$ is the exponent of a in the first term and the exponent of b in the last term.
2. In successive terms, the exponent of a decreases by one. It is n in the first term and zero in the last term.
3. In successive terms, the exponent of b increases by one. It is zero in the first term and n in the last term.
4. The degree of each term is n.
5. Suppose you know one term. The coefficient of the next one is found as follows. Multiply the coefficient of the known term by the exponent of a in that term. Divide by the number of the known term. For example, $5a^4b^1$ is the second term of $(a + b)^5$. The coefficient of the third term is $(4 \cdot 5) \div 2$ or 10.
6. The coefficients are symmetric. They increase at the beginning and decrease at the end of the expansion.

---

example

1   Use the patterns to write $(a + b)^6$ in expanded form.

Indicate expansion with 4 of 7 terms.

$$(a + b)^6 = 1 \cdot a^6b^0 + \frac{6 \cdot 1}{1}a^{6-1}b^{0+1} + \cdots + \frac{6 \cdot 1}{1}a^{0+1}b^{6-1} + 1 \cdot a^0b^6$$

Construct third term and third from last term.

$$= a^6 + 6a^5b^1 + \frac{5 \cdot 6}{2}a^{5-1}b^{1+1} + \cdots + \frac{5 \cdot 6}{2}a^{1+1}b^{5-1} + 6a^1b^5 + 1a^0b^6$$

$$= a^6 + 6a^5b^1 + 15a^4b^2 + \frac{4 \cdot 15}{3}a^{4-1}b^{2+1} + 15a^2b^4 + 6a^1b^5 + 1a^0b^6$$

$$= a^6 + 6a^5b^1 + 15a^4b^2 + 20a^3b^3 + 15a^2b^4 + 6a^1b^5 + b^6$$

The Binomial Theorem is a summary of the patterns found earlier.

If n is a positive integer, then the following is true.

$$(a + b)^n = 1a^n b^0 + \frac{n}{1}a^{n-1}b^1 + \frac{n(n-1)}{1 \cdot 2}a^{n-2}b^2 + \ldots + \frac{n}{1}a^1 b^{n-1} + 1a^0 b^n$$

example

2 **Use the Binomial Theorem to find the terms in the expansion of $(x + y)^8$.**

Find the first 5 terms. Then, use symmetry to find the remaining terms.

$$(x + y)^8 = 1 \cdot x^8 y^0 + \frac{8}{1}x^7 y^1 + \frac{8 \cdot 7}{1 \cdot 2}x^6 y^2 + \frac{8 \cdot 7 \cdot 6}{1 \cdot 2 \cdot 3}x^5 y^3 + \frac{8 \cdot 7 \cdot 6 \cdot 5}{1 \cdot 2 \cdot 3 \cdot 4}x^4 y^4 + \cdots$$

$$= x^8 + 8x^7 y + 28x^6 y^2 + 56x^5 y^3 + 70x^4 y^4 + \cdots$$

$$= x^8 + 8x^7 y + 28x^6 y^2 + 56x^5 y^3 + 70x^4 y^4 + 56x^3 y^5 + 28x^2 y^6 + 8xy^7 + y^8$$

Note that in terms having the same coefficients the exponents are reversed, as in $28x^6 y^2$ and $28x^2 y^6$.

In Example 2, some of the denominators are written as shown below.

$$1 \cdot 2 \cdot 3 \cdot 4 = 4 \cdot 3 \cdot 2 \cdot 1$$
$$1 \cdot 2 \cdot 3 = 3 \cdot 2 \cdot 1$$

The product $4 \cdot 3 \cdot 2 \cdot 1$ is called 4 factorial and is expressed as 4!.

If n is a positive integer, the expression $n!$ (**n factorial**) is defined as follows.

$$n! = n(n - 1)(n - 2) \ldots (1)$$

By definition, $0! = 1$.

example

3 **Evaluate $\frac{8!}{2!6!}$.**

$$\frac{8!}{2!6!} = \frac{8 \cdot 7 \cdot 6 \cdot 5 \cdot 4 \cdot 3 \cdot 2 \cdot 1}{2 \cdot 1 \cdot 6 \cdot 5 \cdot 4 \cdot 3 \cdot 2 \cdot 1}$$

$$= 28$$

Notice that the coefficients in Example 2 are equivalent to the factorial expressions below.

$$\frac{8}{1} = \frac{8!}{1!7!} \qquad \frac{8 \cdot 7}{1 \cdot 2} = \frac{8!}{2!6!} \qquad \frac{8 \cdot 7 \cdot 6}{1 \cdot 2 \cdot 3} = \frac{8!}{3!5!}$$

Thus, another way to write the expansion is:

$$(x + y)^8 = \frac{8!}{0!8!}x^8 + \frac{8!}{1!7!}x^7 y^1 + \frac{8!}{2!6!}x^6 y^2 + \frac{8!}{3!5!}x^5 y^3 + \ldots$$

An equivalent form of the Binomial Theorem uses both sigma and factorial notation.

$$(a + b)^n = \frac{n!}{0!(n - 0)!}a^n + \frac{n!}{1!(n - 1)!}a^{n-1}b^1 + \frac{n!}{2!(n - 2)!}a^{n-2}b^2 + \dots$$

$$= \sum_{k=0}^{n} \frac{n!}{k!(n - k)!}a^{n-k}b^k \qquad \text{Here } n \text{ is a positive integer,}$$
$$k \text{ is a positive integer or}$$
$$\text{zero.}$$

4 Use the equivalent form of the Binomial Theorem to write $(s + t)^4$ in expanded form.

$$(s + t)^4 = \sum_{k=0}^{4} \frac{4!}{k!(4 - k)!}s^{4-k}t^k \qquad \textit{Now construct each term.}$$

$$= \frac{4!}{0!(4 - 0)!}s^{4-0}t^0 + \frac{4!}{1!(4 - 1)!}s^{4-1}t^1 + \frac{4!}{2!(4 - 2)!}s^{4-2}t^2 + \frac{4!}{3!(4 - 3)!}s^{4-3}t^3 + \frac{4!}{4!(4 - 4)!}s^{4-4}t^4$$

$$= \frac{4 \cdot 3 \cdot 2 \cdot 1}{1 \cdot 4 \cdot 3 \cdot 2 \cdot 1}s^4 + \frac{4 \cdot 3 \cdot 2 \cdot 1}{1 \cdot 3 \cdot 2 \cdot 1}s^3t + \frac{4 \cdot 3 \cdot 2 \cdot 1}{2 \cdot 1 \cdot 2 \cdot 1}s^2t^2 + \frac{4 \cdot 3 \cdot 2 \cdot 1}{3 \cdot 2 \cdot 1 \cdot 1}st^3 + \frac{4 \cdot 3 \cdot 2 \cdot 1}{4 \cdot 3 \cdot 2 \cdot 1 \cdot 1}t^4$$

$$= s^4 + 4s^3t + 6s^2t^2 + 4st^3 + t^4$$

5 Find the fifth term of $(p + q)^9$.

$$(p + q)^9 = \sum_{k=0}^{9} \frac{9!}{k!(9 - k)!}p^{9-k}q^k \qquad \textit{In the fifth term, } k \textit{ will be 4 since}$$
$$k \textit{ starts at zero.}$$

The fifth term, $\frac{9!}{4!(9 - 4)!}p^{9-4}q^4$, is $\frac{9 \cdot 8 \cdot 7 \cdot 6}{1 \cdot 2 \cdot 3 \cdot 4}p^5q^4$ or $126p^5q^4$.

exercises

Exploratory Evaluate each of the following.

1. $7!$
2. $9!$
3. $10!$
4. $12!$
5. $\frac{10!}{8!}$
6. $\frac{31!}{28!}$
7. $\frac{6!}{3!}$
8. $\frac{10!}{4!6!}$

State the number of terms for the expanded form of each expression. Then, find the fourth term for each.

9. $(r + s)^4$
10. $(a + b)^5$
11. $(k - m)^7$
12. $(a - 3)^4$
13. $(x - 2)^5$
14. $(b - z)^5$

Written Expand each binomial.

1. $(x + m)^4$
2. $(r + s)^6$
3. $(y + p)^7$
4. $(x - y)^3$
5. $(b - z)^5$
6. $(r - m)^6$

7. $(2m + y)^5$

8. $(3r + y)^4$

9. $(2b + x)^6$

10. $(2x + 3y)^4$

11. $(3x - 2y)^5$

12. $(2m - 3)^6$

13. $(2y + 1)^5$

14. $\left(2 + \dfrac{x}{2}\right)^6$

15. $\left(\dfrac{y}{3} + 3\right)^6$

Find the requested term of each of the following.

16. Fifth term of $(x + y)^7$

17. Fourth term of $(2x + 3y)^9$

18. Seventh term of $(x - y)^{15}$

19. Fifth term of $(x - 2)^{10}$

20. Sixth term of $(2m + 3n)^{12}$

21. Eighth term of $(3a + 5b)^{11}$

Solve each problem.

22. Jorma Johnson invested $5000 at 8% annual interest for 3 years. The interest is compounded semiannually. Find the value of Jorma's investment after 3 years. Use $A = 5000(1 + 0.04)^6$.

23. Joanne Mauch owns a tree plantation. The value of her trees increases about 10% each year. The trees are now worth $10,000. What will be their value 6 years from now? Use $V = 10,000(1 + 0.10)^6$.

Challenge Simplify each of the following.

1. $\dfrac{k!}{(k-1)!}$

2. $\dfrac{(k+3)!}{(k+2)!}$

3. $(k + 1)!(k + 2)$

4. $\dfrac{3!4(k-3)!}{(k-2)!}$

Pascal's Triangle
excursions in algebra

Blaise Pascal (1623–1662) was a French mathematician. At age nineteen he invented a computing machine, a forerunner of today's computers and calculators. He also devised a quick method for finding the coefficients of the expansion for $(a + b)^n$.

You can make the following observations in the triangle of coefficients.

1. Each row begins and ends with 1.

2. Each coefficient is the sum of the two coefficients to the left and right in the row directly above.

Power	Coefficients of the Expansion
$(a + b)^0$	1
$(a + b)^1$	1 1
$(a + b)^2$	1 2 1 $1 + 1 = 2$
$(a + b)^3$	1 3 3 1
$(a + b)^4$	1 4 6 4 1
$(a + b)^5$	1 5 10 10 5 1 $6 + 4 = 10$

Exercises Use Pascal's triangle to find the coefficients of the expansion of each expression.

1. $(a + b)^4$

2. $(a + b)^5$

3. $(a + b)^6$

4. $(a + b)^7$

Use Pascal's triangle to expand each of the following.

5. $(a + b)^4$

6. $(a + b)^6$

7. $(a + b)^8$

8. $(a + b)^9$

9. $(x + y)^6$

10. $(x - y)^6$

11. $(2a + b)^4$

12. $(x - 3y)^4$

Chapter Summary

1. **Definition of an Arithmetic Sequence:** An arithmetic sequence is a sequence in which the difference between any two consecutive terms is the same. (385)
2. **Definition of the nth term of an Arithmetic Sequence:** The nth term, a_n, of an arithmetic sequence with first term, a_1, and common difference, d, is given by $a_n = a_1 + (n - 1)d$. (386)
3. **Definition of Series:** The indicated sum of the terms of a sequence is called a series. (389)
4. **The Sum of an Arithmetic Series:** The sum, S_n, of the first n terms of an arithmetic series is given by $S_n = \frac{n}{2}(a_1 + a_n)$. (390)
5. **Definition of Geometric Sequence:** In a geometric sequence, each term after the first is found by multiplying the previous term by a constant. (394)
6. **Definition of the nth term of a Geometric Sequence:** The nth term, a_n, of a geometric sequence with first term, a_1, and common ratio, r, is given by either $a_n = a_1 r^{n-1}$ or $a_n = a_{n-1} r$. (394)
7. **Sum of a Geometric Series:** The sum, S_n, of the first n terms of a geometric series is given by $S_n = \frac{a_1 - a_1 r^n}{1 - r}$ where $r \neq 1$. (398)
8. **Sum of an Infinite Geometric Series:** The sum, S, of an infinite geometric series where $^-1 < r < 1$ is given by $S = \frac{a_1}{1 - r}$. (401)
9. **The Binomial Theorem:** If n is a positive integer, then $(a + b)^n = 1 \cdot a^n b^0 + \frac{n}{1} a^{n-1} b^1 + \frac{n(n - 1)}{1 \cdot 2} a^{n-2} b^2 + \ldots + \frac{n}{1} a^1 b^{n-1} + 1 \cdot a^0 b^n$. (416)
10. **Definition of n Factorial:** $n! = n(n - 1)(n - 2) \ldots (1)$. (416)
11. The following equivalent form of the Binomial Theorem uses both sigma and factorial notation.

$$(a + b)^n = \sum_{k=0}^{n} \frac{n!}{k!(n - k)!} a^{n-k} b^k \quad (417)$$

13–1 **1.** Find the first 5 terms of the arithmetic sequence when $a_1 = 6$, $d = 8$.

2. Find the next 4 terms of the arithmetic sequence 9, 12, 15, ...

Find the nth term of each arithmetic sequence described below.

3. $a_1 = 3$, $d = 7$, $n = 34$ **4.** $a_1 = {}^-9$, $d = {}^-2$, $n = 21$

5. Which term of $^-5$, 2, 9, . . . is 142?

6. Find the missing terms for the arithmetic sequence $^-7$, ____, ____, ____, 9.

13–2 **Find S_n for each arithmetic series described below.**

7. $a_1 = 12$, $a_n = 117$, $n = 36$ **8.** $a_1 = 4$, $d = 6$, $n = 18$

9. Find the sum of the series $7 + 10 + 13 + \ldots + 97$.

13–3 **10.** Find the common ratio of the sequence $\dfrac{2}{3}, \dfrac{4}{3}, \dfrac{8}{3}, \dfrac{16}{3}, \ldots$.

11. Find the next 2 terms for the geometric sequence $\dfrac{15}{2}$, 15, 30, ____, ____.

12. Find the 5th term of the geometric sequence in which $a_1 = 7$ and $r = 3$.

13. Find the geometric means of 4, ____, ____, ____, 324.

13–4 **Find the sum of each geometric series described below.**

14. $a_1 = 6$, $r = 3$, $n = 5$ **15.** $a_1 = 625$, $a_n = 16$, $r = \dfrac{2}{5}$

16. A ball dropped from a height of 21 feet rebounds $\dfrac{2}{3}$ of the distance from which it was dropped on each bounce. How far has the ball traveled after 6 bounces (rebounds)?

17. For a geometric series, find a_1 given that $S_n = 1441$, $r = \dfrac{3}{5}$, and $n = 5$.

13–5 **18.** Find the sum of the series $\dfrac{1}{2} + \dfrac{1}{3} + \dfrac{2}{9} + \dfrac{4}{27} + \ldots$.

Find a common fraction equivalent to the repeating decimals.

19. $0.\overline{4}$ **20.** $0.1\overline{7}$

13–6 **21.** Write the sum $\displaystyle\sum_{k=8}^{11} (3k - 4)$ in expanded form.

22. Evaluate $\displaystyle\sum_{r=0}^{10} (5 + 8r)$.

13–7 **23.** Find the first 5 terms of this sequence: $a_1 = 1$, $a_2 = 3$, $a_{n+2} = a_{n+1} + 2 \cdot a_n$.

24. Express the following series using sigma notation: $2 + 6 + 12 + 20 + 30 + 42$.

13–8 **25.** Find the pattern and complete the sequence for 3, 7, 12, 18, 25, ____, ____, ____, ____.

13–9 **26.** Find the fourth term of $(x + 2y)^6$.

27. Expand $(3a + b)^5$.

Find S_n for each arithmetic series.

1. $a_1 = 7$, $n = 31$, $a_n = 127$

2. $a_1 = 13$, $d = {}^-2$, $n = 17$

Find the sum of each geometric series.

3. $a_1 = 125$, $r = \dfrac{2}{5}$, $n = 4$

4. $a_1 = 16$, $a_n = -\dfrac{1}{2}$, $r = -\dfrac{1}{2}$

Solve each problem.

5. Find the next 4 terms of the arithmetic sequence 42, 37, 32, ...

6. Find the 27th term of an arithmetic sequence when $a_1 = 2$, $d = 6$.

7. Which term of the arithmetic sequence 7, 13, 19, . . . is 193?

8. How many integers between 26 and 415 are multiples of 9?

9. Find the first 3 terms of this arithmetic series: $a_1 = 7$, $n = 13$, $S_n = 1027$.

10. Find the sum of the series $91 + 85 + 79 + \ldots + ({}^-29)$.

11. Find the next 2 terms of the geometric sequence $\dfrac{1}{81}, \dfrac{1}{27}, \dfrac{1}{9}$, ——, ——.

12. Find the sixth term of a geometric sequence if $a_1 = 5$ and $r = {}^-2$.

13. Find the geometric means of 7, ——, ——, 189.

14. A vacuum pump removes $\dfrac{1}{7}$ of the air from a jar on each stroke of its piston. What percent of the air remains after 4 strokes of the piston?

15. Find the sum of the series $12 - 6 + 3 - \dfrac{3}{2} + \ldots$.

16. Find common fractions equivalent to the repeating decimals $0.\overline{7}$ and $0.3\overline{2}$.

17. Describe the sequence 2, 6, 18, 54, 162, . . . in terms of n.

18. Write $\displaystyle\sum_{k=2}^{6} (3k^2 - 1)$ in expanded form.

19. Find the sum of $\displaystyle\sum_{k=3}^{15} (14 - 2k)$.

20. Describe this sequence recursively: 2, 6, 18, 54, 162, . . .

21. Find the first 5 terms of this sequence: $a_1 = 3$, $a_2 = 1$, $a_{n+2} = a_{n+1} + 2 \cdot a_n$.

22. Find the pattern and complete the sequence 3, 3, 6, 18, 72, ——, ——, ——.

23. Find the third term of $(x + y)^8$.

24. Expand $(2s + 3t)^5$.

chapter
14
Probability

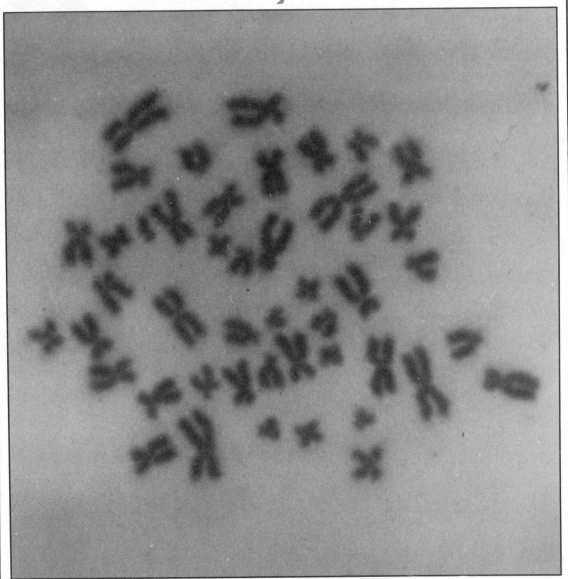

In studying plants and animals, biologists often gather extensive data. Sometimes they can discover genetic patterns and use probability to predict characteristics of future generations.

14–1   Counting

Jana Lee is ordering a new automobile. She still has **three choices** to make.

1. 4-cylinder or 6-cylinder engine?
2. Standard or automatic transmission?
3. Blue, white, or orange?

These three choices are called **independent events.** That is, the choice of one of them does *not* affect the others. Jana's possible choices can be shown in a diagram.

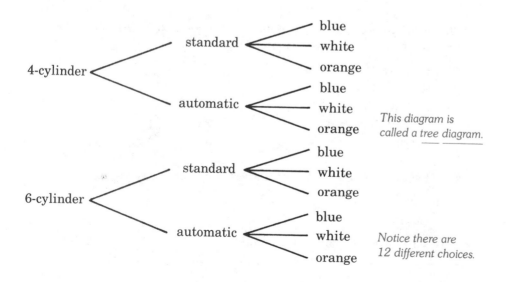

This diagram is called a tree diagram.

Notice there are 12 different choices.

You can find the total number of choices that Jana has without drawing a diagram.

Choices: 4-cyl. or 6-cyl.   standard or automatic   blue or white or orange
Number of choices: 2   2   3

Multiplication can be used to find the total number of choices that Jana has.

$$2 \cdot 2 \cdot 3 = 12$$

Suppose an event can occur in p different ways. Another independent event can occur in q different ways. Then the total number of ways both events can occur is $p \cdot q$ ways.

Basic Counting Principle

This principle can be extended to any number of independent events.

1 **How many different three-letter patterns can be formed using the letters a, b, and c?**

Letters: 1st   2nd   3rd
Ways to choose: 3   3   3

A pattern is a selection of three letters. Each one must be a or b or c.

There are $3 \cdot 3 \cdot 3$ or 27 possible patterns.

2 **How many different three-letter patterns can be formed using the letters a, b, and c if each letter is used exactly once?**

Letters: 1st   2nd   3rd
Ways to choose: 3   2   1

Note that after the first letter is chosen, it may not be chosen again. That leaves only 2 ways.

There are $3 \cdot 2 \cdot 1 = 3!$ or 6 patterns.

3 **How many seven-digit phone numbers can begin with the prefix 457?**

Digit in phone number: 4th   5th   6th   7th
Ways to choose: 10   10   10   10

There are $10 \cdot 10 \cdot 10 \cdot 10 = 10^4$ or 10,000 numbers.

exercises

Exploratory Tell whether each choice is independent or not.

1. Choose color and size to order an item of clothing.

2. Choose a president, secretary, and treasurer for a club.

3. Choose five numbers in a bingo game.

4. Choose the winner and loser of a chess game.

5. Each of five people guess the total number of runs in a baseball game. They write down the guess, without telling what it is.

6. The numerals 0 through 9 are written on pieces of paper and placed in a jar. Three of them are selected one after the other, without replacement.

Written Solve each of the following.

1. The letters g, h, j, k, and l are to be used to form five-letter patterns. How many patterns can be formed if repetitions are allowed?

2. A license plate must have two letters (not I or O) followed by three digits. The last digit cannot be zero. How many possible plates are there?

3. There are five roads from Albany to Briscoe, six from Briscoe to Chadwick, three from Chadwick to Dover. How many different routes are there from Albany to Dover?

4. A store has 15 sofas, 12 lamps, and 10 tables at half-price. How many different combinations of a sofa, a lamp, and a table can be bought at the sale?

5. A restaurant serves 5 main dishes, 3 salads, and 4 desserts. How many different meals could be ordered if each has a main dish, a salad, and a dessert?

6. A car dealer offers a choice of 6 vinyl top colors, 18 body colors, and 7 upholstery colors. How many color combinations are there?

7. Four ferry boats make the crossing between Harrod and Lafayette. How many different ways can a traveler make a round trip?

8. Using the ferry boats in problem 7, how many different ways can a traveler make a round trip, but return on a different ferry boat from the one she went on?

9. How many ways can six different books be placed on a shelf?

10. How many ways can six books be placed on a shelf if the only dictionary must be on an end?

11. How many different 4-letter patterns can be formed from the letters, a, e, i, o, r, s, and t if no letter occurs more than once?

12. How many of the patterns in exercise 11 begin with a vowel and end with a consonant?

13. How many 4-digit patterns are there in which all the digits are different?

14. In how many ways can 3 dice of different colors be thrown at the same time?

15. Using the letters from the word *equation,* how many 5-letter patterns can be formed in which q is followed immediately by u?

16. How many five-digit numbers between and including 65,000 and 69,999 can be made if no digit is repeated?

17. Draw a tree diagram to show the possibilities for boys and girls in a family with 2 children.

18. Draw a tree diagram to show the possibilities for boys and girls in a family with 3 children.

14-2   Linear Permutations

Suppose a group of objects are placed in an arrangement. The arrangement of things in a certain order is called a **permutation.** In a permutation, the *order* of the objects is very important.

Suppose 5 students enter a room in which there are 8 chairs in a row. How many different ways are there for the students to be seated? The first student chooses a chair from the eight chairs. The second student has seven chairs to choose from, and so on.

Students:	1st	2nd	3rd	4th	5th
Choices:	8	7	6	5	4

There are $8 \cdot 7 \cdot 6 \cdot 5 \cdot 4$ or 6720 possible seating arrangements.

In mathematics, this number of ways to arrange 8 things, taking them 5 at a time, is written $P(8, 5)$. Mathematicians speak of taking n objects, r at a time.

Note that $8 \cdot 7 \cdot 6 \cdot 5 \cdot 4 = \dfrac{8!}{(8-5)!}$ or $\dfrac{8!}{3!}$.

> **The number of permutations of n objects, taken r at a time, is defined as follows.**
>
> $$P(n, r) = \frac{n!}{(n-r)!}$$

Definition of $P(n, r)$

If all the objects are taken at once, you write $P(n, n)$.

$$P(n, n) = \frac{n!}{(n-n)!} \text{ or } \frac{n!}{1} \qquad 0! = 1$$

---

example

1 **Sally has 7 candles, each of a different color. How many ways can she arrange the candles in a candelabra that holds 3 candles?**

Find the number of permutations of 7 objects, taken 3 at a time.

$$P(n, r) = \frac{n!}{(n-r)!}$$

$$P(7, 3) = \frac{7!}{(7-3)!} \qquad \textit{Substitute 7 for n and 3 for r.}$$

$$= \frac{7 \cdot 6 \cdot 5 \cdot 4 \cdot 3 \cdot 2 \cdot 1}{4 \cdot 3 \cdot 2 \cdot 1} \text{ or } 210$$

There are 210 ways to arrange the candles in the candelabra.

2 **How many ways can 4 algebra, 3 chemistry, and 5 history books be placed on a shelf if the books are arranged according to subject?**

Think of the books as being in 3 groups. There are $P(3, 3)$ or 3! ways of arranging these groups.

Also, there are $P(4, 4)$ or 4! ways of arranging the books in the algebra group, $P(3, 3)$ or 3! ways of arranging the books in the chemistry group, and $P(5, 5)$ or 5! ways of arranging the books in the history group. Thus, there are $3! \cdot 4! \cdot 3! \cdot 5!$ or 103,680 ways of arranging the books according to subject.

How many different arrangements can be made from the letters of the word *free*? The four letters can be arranged in $P(4, 4)$ ways. $P(4, 4) = 4!$ or $4 \cdot 3 \cdot 2 \cdot 1$ or 24. There are 24 ways. However, some of these arrangements look the same. The two *e*'s are not distinguishable. If we call them e_1 and e_2, then e_1fre_2 and e_2fre_1 are different. Drop the subscripts and the two appear the same: *efre*. The two *e*'s can be arranged in $P(2, 2)$ ways. $P(2, 2) = 2!$ or 2.

$\dfrac{P(4, 4)}{P(2, 2)} = \dfrac{4!}{2!}$ *To find the number of arrangements, divide by 2!.*

$\qquad\quad = \dfrac{4 \cdot 3 \cdot 2 \cdot 1}{2 \cdot 1}$ or 12

There are 12 ways to arrange the letters.

When some objects are alike, use the following rule to find the number of permutations of those objects.

> **The number of permutations of *n* objects of which *p* are alike and *q* are alike is found by evaluating the following expression.**
> $$\frac{n!}{p!\,q!}$$

Permutations with Repetitions

3 **How many seven-letter patterns can be formed from the letters of *benzene*?**

Find the number of permutations of 7 objects of which 3 are *e*'s and 2 are *n*'s.

$\dfrac{7!}{3!2!} = \dfrac{7 \cdot 6 \cdot 5 \cdot 4 \cdot 3 \cdot 2 \cdot 1}{3 \cdot 2 \cdot 1 \cdot 2 \cdot 1}$

$\qquad\ = 420$

There are 420 seven-letter patterns.

exercises

Exploratory Tell whether each statement below is true or false.

1. $5! - 3! = 2!$

2. $6 \cdot 5! = 6!$

3. $\dfrac{6!}{3!} = 2!$

4. $(6 - 3)! = 6! - 3!$

5. $\dfrac{6!}{30} = 4!$

6. $\dfrac{6!}{8!} \cdot \dfrac{8!}{6!} = 1$

7. $3! + 4! = 5 \cdot 3!$

8. $1!2!3!2! = 4!$

9. $\dfrac{P(9, 9)}{9!} = 1$

10. $\dfrac{3!}{3} = \dfrac{2!}{2}$

Written How many different ways can the letters of the following words be arranged?

1. FLOWER
2. STUDY
3. POP
4. SEE
5. PEGGY
6. LEVEL
7. MISSISSIPPI
8. ALASKA
9. ALGEBRA
10. PARALLEL
11. ESSENTIAL
12. PERPENDICULAR

Find the value of each of the following.

13. $\dfrac{P(6, 4)}{P(5, 3)}$

14. $\dfrac{P(10, 3)}{P(5, 3)}$

15. $\dfrac{P(6, 3) \cdot P(4, 2)}{P(5, 2)}$

16. $\dfrac{P(5, 3)}{P(8, 5)P(5, 5)}$

Find n in each of the following equations.

17. $n[P(5, 3)] = P(7, 5)$

18. $P(n, 4) = 3[P(n, 3)]$

19. $P(n, 4) = 40[P(n - 1, 2)]$

20. $7[P(n, 5)] = P(n, 3) \cdot P(9, 3)$

Solve each problem.

21. Don has 5 pennies, 3 nickels, and 4 dimes. The coins of each denomination are indistinguishable. How many ways can he arrange the coins in a row?

22. Estelle has 8 quarters, 5 dimes, 3 nickels, and a penny. The coins of each denomination are indistinguishable. How many ways can she place the coins in a straight line?

23. Ten scores received on a test were 82, 91, 75, 83, 91, 64, 83, 77, 91, and 75. In how many different orders might they be recorded?

24. How many 6-digit numbers can be made using the digits from 833,284?

25. There are 3 identical red flags and 5 identical white flags that are used to send signals. All 8 flags must be used. How many signals can be given?

26. Five algebra and four geometry books are to be placed on a shelf. How many ways can they be arranged if all the algebra books are together?

27. How many ways can 4 nickels and 5 dimes be distributed among 9 children if each is to receive one coin?

28. There are 4 green, 1 red, and 1 blue books on a shelf. How many ways can they be arranged if the red book and the blue book are separated?

14-3   Circular Permutations

A food vending machine has 6 items on each of the revolving trays. One such tray has an orange, an apple, a can of juice, a salad, a cup of yogurt, and a boiled egg. How many ways can these items be arranged on the tray?

Think of each tray as a circle. Let the letters, o, a, j, s, y, and e stand for the various items on the tray. Three possible arrangements are shown below.

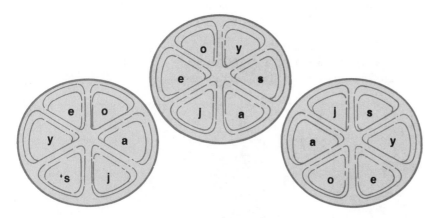

How does the first arrangement change as the tray is turned? Which arrangement is *really* different from the other two?

When 6 objects are placed in a line, there are 6! or 720 arrangements of the 6 objects taken 6 at a time. However, when they are arranged in a circle, some of the arrangements are alike. These arrangements fall into groups of six, each of which can be found from one another by turning the circle. Thus, the number of really different arrangements around a circle is $\frac{1}{6}$ of the total number of arrangements in a line.

$$\frac{1}{6} \cdot 6! = \frac{6 \cdot 5 \cdot 4 \cdot 3 \cdot 2 \cdot 1}{6}$$
$$= 5 \cdot 4 \cdot 3 \cdot 2 \cdot 1$$
$$= 5! \text{ or } (6 - 1)!$$

There are $(6 - 1)!$ arrangements of 6 objects in a circle.

> If n objects are arranged in a circle, then there are $\frac{n!}{n}$ or $(n - 1)!$ permutations of the n objects around the circle.

example

1 **Five people are to be seated at a round table. How many seating arrangements are possible?**

$(5 - 1)! = 4!$
$\quad\quad\quad = 4 \cdot 3 \cdot 2 \cdot 1 \text{ or } 24$

Suppose the people are seated around the table. Everyone moves one chair to the left. Each person is still sitting next to the same two people as before.

If n objects on a circle are arranged in relation to a fixed point, then there are $n!$ permutations. Even though the objects are on a circle, the permutations are linear since a reference point has been established.

Suppose now that five people are to be seated at a round table. One of them is seated close to the door as shown. How many arrangements are possible?

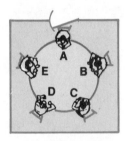 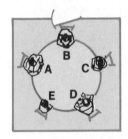 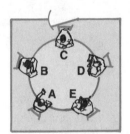

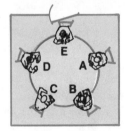 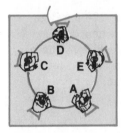

These arrangements are different. In each one, a different person sits closest to the door. Thus, there are $P(5, 5)$ or $5!$ arrangements relative to a fixed point which is the door.

$$5! = 5 \cdot 4 \cdot 3 \cdot 2 \cdot 1 \text{ or } 120$$

Suppose three keys are placed on a key ring. Then it appears that there are at most $(3 - 1)!$ or 2 different arrangements of keys on the ring.

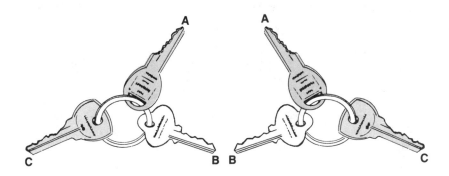

But what happens if the key ring with the first arrangement is turned over? The second arrangement appears. Then there is really only one arrangement of the three keys. These two arrangements are **reflections** of one another. There are only half as many arrangements when reflections are possible.

$$\frac{(3 - 1)!}{2} = \frac{2}{2} \text{ or } 1$$

examples

2 **How many different ways can 5 charms be placed on a bracelet that has no clasp?**

This is a circular permutation. Because the bracelet can be turned over, it is also reflective.

$$\frac{(5 - 1)!}{2} = \frac{4!}{2}$$

$$= \frac{4 \cdot 3 \cdot 2 \cdot 1}{2} \text{ or } 12$$

There are 12 different ways to arrange the charms.

3 **How many different ways can 5 charms be placed on a bracelet that has a clasp?**

This is no longer a circular permutation since objects are arranged with respect to a fixed point, the clasp. However, it is still reflective.

$$\frac{5!}{2} = \frac{5 \cdot 4 \cdot 3 \cdot 2 \cdot 1}{2}$$

$$= \frac{5 \cdot 4 \cdot 3 \cdot 2 \cdot 1}{2} \text{ or } 60$$

There are 60 different ways to arrange the charms.

Exploratory State whether arrangements of the following objects are reflective or not reflective. Then, state whether their permutations are linear or circular.

1. charms on a charm bracelet, having no clasp
2. a football huddle of 11 players
3. chairs arranged in a circle
4. beads on a necklace with no clasp
5. chairs in a row
6. a pearl necklace that is open
7. people seated around a square table relative to each other
8. people seated around a square table relative to one chair
9. a baseball team's batting order
10. a list of students in a given class
11. placing 6 coins in a circular pattern on a table

Written Evaluate each of the following.

1. $8! - 6!$
2. $5!3!$
3. $\dfrac{6!}{4!}$
4. $3 \cdot 5!$
5. $6! + 5!$
6. $\dfrac{8! + 6!}{8! - 6!}$
7. $P(8, 5)$
8. $P(10, 4)$
9. $3!P(6, 5) \cdot P(9, 2)$
10. $4!3!P(7, 3)$
11. $\dfrac{P(6, 4) \cdot P(5, 2)}{5!}$
12. $\dfrac{P(8, 3) \cdot P(5, 4)}{P(6, 6)}$
13. $\dfrac{P(12, 6)}{P(12, 3) \cdot P(8, 2)}$
14. $\dfrac{P(10, 8)}{5!P(8, 5)}$

Solve each of the following.

15. How many ways can 6 keys be arranged on a key ring?
16. How many ways can 6 people be seated around a campfire?
17. How many ways can 8 charms be arranged on a charm bracelet that has no clasp?
18. How many ways can 4 men and 4 women be seated alternately at a round table?
19. How many ways can 5 people be seated at a round table relative to each other?
20. How many ways can 6 people be seated at a round table relative to the door in the room?
21. How many ways can 5 people be seated around a circular table if 2 of the people must be seated next to each other?
22. Twenty beads are strung in a circle. Fourteen are brown and 6 are red. How many ways can the beads be strung in the circle if a clasp is used?
23. There are 8 chairs around a table. One of the chairs is reserved for the President. How many seating arrangements are possible for the President and his 7 advisors?
24. A charm bracelet has 20 links and no clasp. How many ways can 6 charms be arranged on the bracelet if each charm requires one link?

14–4   Combinations

Suppose that from a group of nine boys, five are chosen to start the basketball game. In this case, the order in which the boys are chosen is not important. Such a selection is called a **combination.**

The combination of nine things taken five at a time is written $C(9, 5)$.

You know that five things can be arranged in 5! ways. These arrangements are eliminated when finding the number of combinations.

$$C(9, 5) = \frac{P(9, 5)}{5!}$$

$$= \frac{9!}{(9 - 5)! \cdot 5!} \qquad P(9, 5) = \frac{9!}{(9 - 5)!}$$

$$= \frac{9!}{4! \cdot 5!} \text{ or } 126$$

The number of combinations of n objects, taken r at a time, is written $C(n, r)$.

$$C(n, r) = \frac{n!}{(n - r)!r!}$$

Definition of $C(n, r)$

The main difference between a permutation and a combination is whether order is considered (permutation) or not (combination).

---

example

1 **From a group of 6 men and 4 women, how many committees of 2 men and 3 women can be formed?**

Order is not considered. The questions are: How many ways can 2 men be chosen from 6? How many ways can 3 women be chosen from 4?

$$C(6, 2) \cdot C(4, 3) = \frac{6!}{(6 - 2)!2!} \cdot \frac{4!}{(4 - 3)!3!}$$

$$= \frac{6!}{4!2!} \cdot \frac{4!}{1!3!} \qquad \text{\textit{Write out the factorials to see how to get the next line.}}$$

$$= \frac{6 \cdot 5}{2 \cdot 1} \cdot \frac{4}{1}$$

$$= 15 \cdot 4 \text{ or } 60$$

There are 60 possible committees.

2 **From a deck of 52 cards, how many ways can 5 cards be drawn so that 3 are of 1 suit and 2 are of another?**

$C(4, 2)$ First, select 2 suits from the 4 suits.

$C(13, 3)$ Then, select 3 cards from 1 suit of 13 cards.

$C(13, 2)$ Next, select 2 cards from the other suit.

Thus, the number of ways is as follows.

$$C(4, 2) \cdot C(13, 3) \cdot C(13, 2) = \frac{4!}{2!2!} \cdot \frac{13!}{10!3!} \cdot \frac{13!}{11!2!}$$

$$= \frac{4 \cdot 3}{2 \cdot 1} \cdot \frac{13 \cdot 12 \cdot 11}{3 \cdot 2 \cdot 1} \cdot \frac{13 \cdot 12}{2 \cdot 1}$$

$$= 6 \cdot 286 \cdot 78$$

$$= 133,848$$

There are 133,848 ways to draw the cards.

3 **In an urn, there are 17 numbered discs. Eight are red, 5 are white, and 4 are blue. How many ways can 2 red, 1 white, and 2 blue discs be chosen?**

$C(8, 2)$ Select 2 of the 8 red discs.

$C(5, 1)$ Select 1 of the 5 white discs.

$C(4, 2)$ Select 2 of the 4 blue discs.

$$C(8, 2) \cdot C(5, 1) \cdot C(4, 2) = \frac{8 \cdot 7}{2 \cdot 1} \cdot 5 \cdot \frac{4 \cdot 3}{2 \cdot 1}$$

$$= 28 \cdot 5 \cdot 6$$

$$= 840$$

There are 840 ways to choose the discs.

4 **Find the total number of diagonals that can be drawn in a decagon.**

Each diagonal has two endpoints. Suppose one has endpoints A and B. Then segment AB and segment BA are the same. Thus, order is not considered, and the combination of 10 points, taken two at a time, is desired. This gives the total number of line segments. But 10 of them are sides, so the number of diagonals is as follows.

$$C(10, 2) - 10 = \frac{10!}{(10 - 2)!2!} - 10$$

$$= \frac{10!}{8!2!} - 10$$

$$= \frac{10 \cdot 9 \cdot 8!}{8!2!} - 10 \qquad \textit{Note } 10! = 10 \cdot 9 \cdot 8 \cdot 7 \cdot 6 \cdot 5 \cdot 4 \cdot 3 \cdot 2 \cdot 1$$
$$\qquad\qquad\qquad\qquad\qquad\qquad = 10 \cdot 9 \cdot 8!$$

$$= \frac{10 \cdot 9}{2 \cdot 1} - 10$$

$$= 35$$

There are 35 diagonals.

exercises

Exploratory State whether arrangements of the following represent a combination or a permutation.

1. a team of 5 people chosen from a group of 12 people
2. three-letter patterns chosen from the letters of the word *algebra*
3. a hand of 5 cards
4. a batting order in baseball
5. seating students in a row
6. the answers on a true-false test
7. a committee of 4 men and 5 women chosen from 8 men and 7 women
8. people seated around a table

Written Evaluate.

1. $C(8, 3)$
2. $C(8, 5) \cdot C(7, 3)$
3. $C(7, 2)$
4. $C(24, 21)$

Find the value of n in each of the following.

5. $C(n, 3) = C(n, 8)$
6. $C(n, 5) = C(n, 7)$
7. $C(n, 12) = C(30, 18)$
8. $C(14, 3) = C(n, 11)$

Solve each of the following.

9. From a list of 12 books, how many groups of 5 books can be selected?
10. How many baseball teams of 9 members can be formed from 14 players?
11. Suppose there are 9 points on a circle. How many different 4-sided closed figures can be formed by joining any 4 of these points?
12. There are 85 telephones at Kennedy High School. How many 2-way connections can be made among the school telephones?
13. How many different groups of 25 people can be formed from 27 people?
14. Suppose there are 8 points in a plane, no 3 of which are collinear. How many distinct triangles could be formed with these points as vertices?
15. From a deck of 52 playing cards, how many different 5-card hands can have 5 cards of the same suit?
16. From a deck of 52 playing cards, how many different 4-card hands can have each card from a different suit?

A bag contains 4 red, 6 white, and 9 blue marbles. How many ways can 5 marbles be selected to meet the following conditions?

17. All the marbles are white.
18. All the marbles are blue.
19. All the marbles are red.
20. Two are red, 2 are white, and 1 is blue.
21. Two must be blue.
22. Two are 1 color and 3 are another color.

From a group of 8 men and 10 women, a committee of 5 is to be formed. How many committees can be formed if the committee is to be comprised as follows?

23. All are men.
24. There are 3 men and 2 women.
25. There is 1 man and 4 women.
26. All are women.

14–5   Probability

When a coin is tossed, only two outcomes are possible. Either the coin will show a *head* or a *tail*. The desired outcome is called a **success.** Any other outcome is called a **failure.**

> **If an event can succeed in s ways and fail in f ways, then the probabilities of success $P(s)$ and of failure $P(f)$ are as follows.**
>
> $$P(s) = \frac{s}{s + f} \qquad P(f) = \frac{f}{s + f}$$

Probability of Success and of Failure

If the event cannot succeed, $P(s) = 0$. If the event cannot fail, $P(s) = 1$.

$$P(s) + P(f) = \frac{s}{s + f} + \frac{f}{s + f}$$

$$= \frac{s + f}{s + f} \text{ or } 1$$

This is an important property of probabilities.

Because their sum is one, $P(s)$ and $P(f)$ are called complements. For example, if $P(s)$ is $\frac{1}{3}$, then $P(f)$ is $1 - \frac{1}{3}$ or $\frac{2}{3}$.

examples

1 **A bag contains 5 blue marbles and 4 white marbles. If one marble is chosen at random, what is the probability that it is blue?**

$P(blue\ marble) = \dfrac{s}{s + f}$ *P(blue marble) is read the probability of selecting a blue marble.*

$\qquad\qquad\quad = \dfrac{5}{5 + 4} \text{ or } \dfrac{5}{9}$ *A blue marble is a success.*
A white marble is a failure.

The probability of selecting a blue marble is $\dfrac{5}{9}$.

2 **A committee of 2 is to be selected from a group of 6 men and 3 women. What is the probability that the 2 selected are women?**

$P(two\ women) = \dfrac{C(3,\ 2)}{C(9,\ 2)}$ *There are C(3, 2) ways to select 2 of 3 women.*
There are C(9, 2) ways to select 2 of 9 people.

$\qquad\qquad\quad = \dfrac{\frac{3!}{1!2!}}{\frac{9!}{7!2!}}$

$\qquad\qquad\quad = \dfrac{3}{36} \text{ or } \dfrac{1}{12}$

The probability that the 2 selected are women is $\dfrac{1}{12}$.

The odds of the successful outcome of an event is expressed as the ratio of the number of ways it can succeed to the number of ways it can fail.

$$\text{Odds} = \text{the ratio of } s \text{ to } f \quad \text{or} \quad \frac{s}{f}$$

Definition of Odds

examples

3 **What are the odds of tossing a die and getting a 3?**

The number 3 is on only one face of the die. The other five faces have a number other than 3.

$$\text{Odds} = \frac{1}{5}$$ *A 3 can appear only 1 way.*
Other numbers can appear 5 ways.

The odds of getting a 3 are 1 to 5.

4 **Suppose Michael draws 5 cards from a deck of 52 cards. What are the odds that 4 of the cards will be of one suit and the fifth of another suit?**

$C(4, 2)$ Select 2 suits among 4.
$C(13, 4)$ Select 4 cards from a suit containing 13 cards.
$C(13, 1)$ Select 1 card from the other suit.

The number of ways to select 4 cards from one suit and 1 card from another is found as follows.

$$\begin{aligned}
C(4, 2) \cdot C(13, 4) \cdot C(13, 1) &= \frac{4!}{2! \, 2!} \cdot \frac{13!}{4! \, 9!} \cdot \frac{13!}{1! \, 12!} \\
&= \frac{4 \cdot 3}{2 \cdot 1} \cdot \frac{13 \cdot 12 \cdot 11 \cdot 10}{4 \cdot 3 \cdot 2 \cdot 1} \cdot \frac{13}{1} \\
&= 6 \cdot 715 \cdot 13 \\
&= 55,770
\end{aligned}$$

Thus, the number of outcomes that can be considered successful is 55,770. The total number of outcomes is the combination of 52 cards taken 5 at a time.

$$\begin{aligned}
C(52, 5) &= \frac{52!}{47! \, 5!} \\
&= \frac{52 \cdot 51 \cdot 50 \cdot 49 \cdot 48}{5 \cdot 4 \cdot 3 \cdot 2 \cdot 1} \\
&= \frac{311,875,200}{120} \\
&= 2,598,960
\end{aligned}$$

The total number of outcomes, including successful outcomes and failures, is 2,598,960. Thus, the number of failures is 2,598,960 − 55,770 or 2,543,190. The odds of selecting 4 cards from one suit and 1 card from another suit are $\frac{55,770}{2,543,190}$ or $\frac{143}{6521}$.

exercises

Exploratory State the odds of an event occurring given the probability that it occurs as follows.

1. $\frac{1}{2}$ 2. $\frac{3}{4}$ 3. $\frac{1}{7}$ 4. $\frac{5}{8}$

5. $\frac{7}{15}$ 6. $\frac{8}{9}$ 7. $\frac{4}{9}$ 8. $\frac{3}{20}$

State the probability of an event occurring given the following odds.

9. $\frac{3}{4}$ 10. $\frac{5}{1}$ 11. $\frac{6}{5}$ 12. $\frac{3}{7}$

13. $\frac{7}{3}$ 14. $\frac{4}{9}$ 15. $\frac{5}{11}$ 16. $\frac{1}{1}$

Solve each of the following.

17. The odds are 6-to-1 *against* an event occurring. What is the probability that it will occur?

18. The probability of an event occurring is $\frac{3}{4}$. What are the odds that it will not occur?

Written In a bag are 7 pennies, 4 nickels, and 5 dimes. Three coins are selected at random. Find the probability of each of the following selections.

1. all 3 pennies
2. all 3 nickels
3. all 3 dimes
4. 2 pennies, 1 dime
5. 1 penny, 1 dime, 1 nickel
6. 1 dime, 2 nickels

In a bag are 5 red, 9 blue, and 6 white marbles. Two are selected at random. Find the probability of each of the following selections.

7. 2 red
8. 2 blue
9. 1 red and 1 blue
10. 1 red and 1 white

There are 5 fudgesicles and 8 popsicles in the freezer. If 2 are selected at random, find the probability that the following occurs.

11. 2 fudgesicles
12. 2 popsicles

Suppose you select 2 letters from the word *algebra*. What is the probability of selecting 2 letters and having the following occur?

13. 1 vowel and 1 consonant
14. 2 vowels
15. 2 consonants

Sharon has 8 mystery books and 9 science-fiction books. Four are selected. Find the probability that the following occurs.

16. 4 mystery books
17. 4 science-fiction books
18. 2 mysteries and 2 science-fiction
19. 3 mysteries and 1 science-fiction

From a deck of 52 cards, 5 cards are dealt. What are the odds of the following?

20. 5 aces
21. 5 face cards
22. 5 from one suit
23. 2 of one suit and 3 of another

14–6   Multiplying Probabilities

The Basic Counting Principle can be used to help find probabilities. Suppose you toss a white die and then toss a green die. The probability that the white die shows a 2 is $\frac{1}{6}$. The probability that the green die shows a 2 is $\frac{1}{6}$. The probability that both dice show a 2 is $\frac{1}{6} \cdot \frac{1}{6}$ or $\frac{1}{36}$. Since the outcome of tossing the white die does *not* affect the outcome of tossing the green die, the events are independent.

> **If two events, *A* and *B*, are independent, then the probability of both events occurring is found as follows.**
>
> $$P(A \text{ and } B) = P(A) \cdot P(B)$$

Probability of Two Independent Events

example

1 **A bag contains 5 red marbles and 4 white marbles. A marble is to be selected, and replaced in the bag. A second selection is then made. What is the probability of selecting 2 red marbles?**

These events are independent because the first marble selected is replaced. The outcome of the second selection is not affected by the results of the first selection.

$$P(\text{both red}) = P(\text{red}) \cdot P(\text{red})$$
$$= \frac{5}{9} \cdot \frac{5}{9} \text{ or } \frac{25}{81}$$

What is the probability of selecting 2 red marbles from 5 red ones and 4 white ones if the first selection is *not* replaced? These events are dependent because the outcome of the first selection affects the outcome of the second selection. Suppose the first selection is red.

$$\begin{array}{cc} \text{first selection} & \text{second selection} \\ P(\text{red}) = \frac{5}{9} & P(\text{red}) = \frac{4}{8} \end{array}$$

$$P(\text{both red}) = P(\text{red}) \cdot P(\text{red following red})$$
$$= \frac{5}{9} \cdot \frac{4}{8} \text{ or } \frac{5}{18}$$

> **Suppose two events, *A* and *B*, are dependent. Then the probability of both occurring is found as follows.**
>
> $$P(A \text{ and } B) = P(A) \cdot P(B \text{ following } A)$$

Probability of Two Dependent Events

2 There are 5 nickels, 7 dimes and 9 pennies in a coin purse. Suppose two coins are to be selected, without replacing the first one. What is the probability of selecting a penny and then a dime?

$P(penny\ and\ dime) = P(penny) \cdot P(dime\ following\ penny)$

$$= \frac{9}{21} \cdot \frac{7}{20} \qquad P(A\ and\ B) = P(A) \cdot P(B\ following\ A)$$

$$= \frac{3}{20}$$

The probability is $\frac{3}{20}$.

3 What is the probability of selecting an eight followed by a nine from a deck of 52 cards if the first card is replaced before the second card is drawn? What is the probability if the first card is not replaced?

If the first card is replaced before the second card is drawn, then the events are independent.

$P(eight\ and\ nine) = P(eight) \cdot P(nine) \qquad P(eight) = \frac{4}{52}\ or\ \frac{1}{13}$

$$= \frac{1}{13} \cdot \frac{1}{13} \qquad\qquad P(nine) = \frac{4}{52}\ or\ \frac{1}{13}$$

$$= \frac{1}{169}$$

If the first card is not replaced before the second card is drawn, then the events are dependent.

$P(eight\ and\ nine) = P(eight) \cdot P(nine\ after\ eight\ is\ drawn)$

$$= \frac{1}{13} \cdot \frac{4}{51}$$

$$= \frac{4}{663}$$

exercises

Exploratory Identify the events in each of the following problems as *independent* or *dependent*.

1. In a bag are 5 red, 3 green, and 8 blue marbles. Three are selected in sequence without replacement. What is the probability of selecting a red, green, and blue in that order?

2. There are 4 glasses of root beer and 3 glasses of ice tea on the counter. Bill drinks two of them. What is the probability that he drank 2 root beers?

3. In a bag are 5 apricots and 4 plums. Marie selects one, replaces it and selects another. What is the probability that both selections were apricots?

4. When James plays Ted in cribbage, the odds are 3 to 2 that he will win. What is the probability that he will win the next 4 games?

Written

1–4. Solve each problem in Exploratory Exercises 1–4.

A bag contains 5 red, 3 white, and 7 blue marbles. If 3 marbles are selected in succession, what is the probability that they are red, white, and blue in that order?

5. Suppose no marbles are replaced.

6. Suppose each marble is replaced.

In a bag are 5 red, 3 blue, and 7 black marbles. Three marbles are chosen, one after the other. What is the probability that there is one of each under the following conditions?

7. No replacement occurs

8. Replacement occurs each time

One hundred tickets, numbered consecutively 1 to 100, are placed in a box. What is the probability that in 5 separate drawings, the following selections occur?

9. 5 odd numbers, if replacement occurs

10. 5 odd numbers, if no replacement occurs

11. 5 consecutive numbers if no replacement occurs

The letters _A, B, E, I, J, K,_ and _M_ are written on cards that are placed in a box. Two letters are selected. What is the probability that the following occurs?

12. both vowels, if no replacement occurs

13. both vowels, if replacement occurs

14. both the same letter, if no replacement occurs

There are 6 plates, 5 saucers, and 5 cups on the counter. Charlie accidentally knocks off two and breaks them. What is the probability that he broke the following?

15. 2 plates

16. 2 cups

17. a cup and a saucer, in that order

18. a cup and a saucer, in any order

A red and a green die are tossed. What is the probability that the following occurs?

19. both show 3

20. neither show 3

21. the red shows a 3 and the green shows a 4

22. the red shows a 3 and the green shows any other number

23. both show the same number

24. both show different numbers

History

excursions in algebra

Maria Agnesi (ahn ya ze) was an Italian mathematician who lived from 1718 to 1799. At one time, she was a professor of mathematics at Bologna, Italy. In 1748, she wrote about a special set of curves that she called _versiera_. The general equation for those curves is $yx^2 = a^2(a - y)$.

The popular name for this type of curve is the _Witch of Agnesi,_ because the curve resembles the outline of a witch's hat.

Exercises Graph each of the following _versiera_. State the value of _a_.

1. $yx^2 = 4(2 - y)$

2. $yx^2 = {}^-64 - 16y$

14-7   Adding Probabilities

Suppose a card is to be drawn from a standard deck of 52 cards. What is the probability of drawing an ace or a king? Since no card is both an ace and a king, the events are said to be **mutually exclusive.** That is, the two events cannot occur simultaneously.

ways to draw an ace

There are 4 aces in a deck. $\frac{4}{52}$ or $\frac{1}{13}$

ways to draw a king

$\frac{4}{52}$ or $\frac{1}{13}$ There are 4 kings in a deck.

ways to draw an ace or a king

ace   king   ace or king

$$\frac{1}{13} + \frac{1}{13} = \frac{2}{13}$$

The probability of one of two mutually exclusive events occurring is the sum of their probabilities.

$$P(A \ or \ B) = P(A) + P(B)$$

Probability of Mutually Exclusive Events

This rule can be extended to any number of mutually exclusive events. **Inclusive events** are *not* mutually exclusive.

What is the probability of drawing an ace or a red card? Since there are two red aces, the events are inclusive.

ways to select an ace

There is an ace in each suit, hearts, diamonds, spades, and clubs.

$\frac{4}{52}$

ways to select a red card

$\frac{26}{52}$ Hearts and diamonds are red.

ways to select a red ace

$\frac{2}{52}$ There are two red aces.

Now the ways to select a red ace are counted twice, once in the ways to select an ace and once in the ways to select a red card.

ways to select an ace or a red card

ace   red   red ace   ace or red

$$\frac{4}{52} + \frac{26}{52} - \frac{2}{52} = \frac{28}{52}$$
$$= \frac{7}{13}$$

The probability of one of two inclusive events, A and B, occurring is the sum of the individual probabilities decreased by the probability of both occurring.

$$P(A \text{ or } B) = P(A) + P(B) - P(A \text{ and } B)$$

Probability of Inclusive Events

examples

1 Vivian has 6 nickels, 4 pennies, and 3 dimes in her purse. She selects one. What is the probability it is a penny or a nickel?

$$P(penny \text{ or } nickel) = P(penny) + P(nickel)$$
$$= \frac{4}{13} + \frac{6}{13}$$
$$= \frac{10}{13}$$

There is no coin that is both a penny and a nickel. These events are mutually exclusive.

The probability of selecting a penny or a nickel is $\frac{10}{13}$.

2 A card is to be selected from a deck of 52 cards. What is the probability that it is a red card or a face card?

$$P(red \text{ or } face \text{ } card) = P(red) + P(face \text{ } card) - P(red \text{ } face \text{ } card)$$
$$= \frac{26}{52} + \frac{12}{52} - \frac{6}{52}$$
$$= \frac{32}{52}$$
$$= \frac{8}{13}$$

There are 6 face cards that are red. Thus, the events are inclusive.

The probability of selecting a red card or a face card is $\frac{8}{13}$.

3 A committee of 5 people is to be formed from a group of 7 men and 6 women. What is the probability that the committee will have at least 3 women?

At least 3 women means that the committee may have 3, or 4, or 5 women. It is not possible to select a group of 3, a group of 4, and a group of 5 women all to be on the same 5-member committee. The events are mutually exclusive.

$$P(at \text{ } least \text{ } 3 \text{ } women) = P(3 \text{ } women) + P(4 \text{ } women) + P(5 \text{ } women)$$
$$= \frac{C(6,3) \cdot C(7,2)}{C(13,5)} + \frac{C(6,4) \cdot C(7,1)}{C(13,5)} + \frac{C(6,5) \cdot C(7,0)}{C(13,5)}$$
$$= \frac{140}{429} + \frac{35}{429} + \frac{2}{429}$$
$$= \frac{177}{429} \text{ or } \frac{59}{143}$$

The probability of at least 3 women on the committee is $\frac{59}{143}$.

exercises

Exploratory Identify each of the following events as inclusive or exclusive.

1. In a box are slips of paper numbered from 1 to 10. A slip of paper is drawn and a die is tossed. What is the probability of getting a 2 on one of them?

2. Two cards are drawn from a standard deck of playing cards. What is the probability that the 2 cards are both kings or both queens?

3. In her pocket, Linda has 5 nickels, 3 dimes, and 7 pennies. She selects 3 coins. What is the probability that she has selected 3 nickels or 3 pennies?

4. From a standard deck of playing cards, 2 cards are drawn. What is the probability of having drawn a black card or an ace?

5. The Dodger pitching staff has 4 left-handers and 7 right-handers. If 2 are selected, what is the probability that at least one of them is a left-hander?

6. Five coins are dropped. What is the probability of having at least 3 heads?

7. In one class, 3 of the 12 girls are redheads and 2 of the 15 boys are redheads. What is the probability of selecting a boy or a redhead?

8. There are 8 red, 3 blue, and 12 black marbles in a bag. If 3 are selected, what is the probability that all are red or all are blue?

Written

1–8. Solve each problem in Exploratory Exercises 1–8.

In a bag are 6 red and 5 white marbles. Three are selected. What is the probability that the following occurs?

9. all 3 red or all 3 white

10. at least 2 red

11. at least 2 white

12. exactly 2 white

Two cards are drawn from a standard deck of cards. What is the probability that the following occurs?

13. both aces or both face cards

14. both black or both face cards

15. both aces or both red

16. both either red or an ace

Seven coins are tossed. What is the probability that the following occurs?

17. 3 heads or 2 tails

18. at least 5 heads

19. 3 heads or 3 tails

20. all tails or all heads

From a group of 6 men and 8 women, a committee of 6 is to be selected. What is the probability of the following?

21. all men or all women

22. 5 men or 5 women

23. 3 men and 3 women

24. 4 men or 4 women

The numerals 1 through 25 are written on slips of paper and placed in a bag. The numerals 20 through 40 are written on slips of paper and placed in a different bag. One slip of paper is selected at random from each bag. What is the probability that the following occurs?

25. Both numerals are 20.

26. Neither numeral is 20.

27. Both numerals are greater than 10.

28. At least one of the numerals is 22.

The binomial expansion of $(a + b)^n$ can be written as follows, if n is a positive integer.

$$(a + b)^n = 1 \cdot a^n + \left(\frac{n}{1}\right)a^{n-1}b + \left(\frac{n}{1}\right)\left(\frac{n-1}{2}\right)a^{n-2}b^2 + \left(\frac{n}{1}\right)\left(\frac{n-1}{2}\right)\left(\frac{n-2}{3}\right)a^{n-3}b^3 + \cdots + 1 \cdot b^n$$

The coefficients and some equivalent expressions are listed below.

Term	Coefficient	Equivalent expressions	
1st	1	$C(n, 0)$	
2nd	$\dfrac{n}{1}$	$C(n, 1)$	*Recall that C(n, r) also is written* $\dfrac{n!}{(n-r)!r!}$ *or* $\dfrac{n(n-1)\cdots(n-r+1)}{1 \cdot 2 \cdots r}$
3rd	$\dfrac{n}{1} \cdot \dfrac{n-1}{2}$	$C(n, 2)$	

Notice, for example, that the coefficient of the 3rd term is $C(n, 2)$. The power of b in the 3rd term is 2. Thus, the coefficient of the rth term is $C(n,(r - 1))$. The power of b in the rth term is $(r - 1)$ and that of a is $[n - (r - 1)]$ or $n - r + 1$.

> In the binomial expansion of $(a + b)^n$, the rth term is as follows.
>
> $$C[n,(r - 1)]a^{n-(r-1)}b^{r-1}$$
>
> or
>
> $$\frac{n!}{(n - (r - 1))!(r - 1)!}a^{n-r+1}b^{r-1}$$

Finding the rth Term in the Binomial Expansion

Example   Find the fifth term of $(2x - 3y)^6$.

$$\frac{n!}{(n - r + 1)!(r - 1)!}a^{n-r+1}b^{r-1} = \frac{6!}{(6 - 5 + 1)!(4!)}a^{6-5+1}b^{5-1}$$

Substitute 6 for n and 5 for r.

$$= \frac{6 \cdot 5}{1 \cdot 2}(2x)^2(-3y)^4$$

Substitute 2x for a and -3y for b.

$$= 15(4x^2)(81y^4) \text{ or } 4860x^2y^4$$

The fifth term is $4860x^2y^4$.

Exercises   **Find the indicated term of the given binomial expansion.**

1. 4th, $(a + b)^9$

2. 3rd, $(2x + y)^5$

3. 5th, $(x - y)^8$

4. 2nd, $(4x + 3y)^6$

5. $(n + 1)$st, $(5x - 2y)^9$

6. 4th, $(x + 2y)^6$

14–8   Binomial Trials

Arthur normally wins 1 out of every 3 backgammon games he plays. In other words, the probability that Arthur wins when he plays backgammon is $\frac{1}{3}$.

Suppose Arthur plays 4 games. What is the probability that he will win 3 and lose only one?

The possible ways of winning 3 games and losing one are shown at the right. The illustration shows the combinations of four things, namely games, taken three at a time, namely wins. That is, $C(4, 3)$.

W	W	W	L		W	W	L	W
W	L	W	W		L	W	W	W

The terms of the binomial expansion of $(W + L)^4$ can be used to express the probabilities.

$$(W + L)^4 = W^4 + 4W^3L + 6W^2L^2 + 4WL^3 + L^4$$

coefficient	term	meaning
$C(4, 4)$	W^4	1 way to win all 4 games
$C(4, 3)$	$4W^3L$	4 ways to win 3 games and lose 1 game
$C(4, 2)$	$6W^2L^2$	6 ways to win 2 games and lose 2 games
$C(4, 1)$	$4WL^3$	4 ways to win 1 game and lose 3 games
$C(4, 0)$	L^4	1 way to lose all 4 games

The probability that Arthur wins when he plays is $\frac{1}{3}$. And, thus, the probability that he loses is $\frac{2}{3}$. Substitute $\frac{1}{3}$ for W and $\frac{2}{3}$ for L in the term $4W^3L$. For example, the probability of winning 3 out of 4 games is $4\left(\frac{1}{3}\right)^3\left(\frac{2}{3}\right)$ or $\frac{8}{81}$.

What is the probability of winning 2 games and losing 2 games?

Problems that can be solved using a binomial expansion are called **binomial trials.**

A binomial trial exists if and only if the following conditions occur.

1. There are only two possible outcomes.
2. The events are independent.

Conditions of Binomial Trials

1 **What is the probability that 3 coins show heads and 2 show tails when 5 coins are tossed?**

There are only 2 possible outcomes: heads (H) or tails (T). The tosses of 5 coins are independent events. When $(H + T)^5$ is expanded, the term containing H^3T^2 will give the desired probability.

$$C(5, 3)H^3T^2 = \frac{5 \cdot 4}{2 \cdot 1}\left(\frac{1}{2}\right)^3\left(\frac{1}{2}\right)^2 \text{ or } \frac{5}{16}$$
Replace H by P(H) which is $\frac{1}{2}$ and T by P(T) or $\frac{1}{2}$.

The probability of 3 heads and 2 tails is $\frac{5}{16}$.

2 **The probability that Amy wins a game with Marla is $\frac{1}{5}$; that Marla wins is $\frac{4}{5}$. Suppose they play 7 games. What is the probability that Amy will win at least 3 of the games?**

There are only two outcomes of each game: Amy wins (A) or Marla wins (M). The binomial expansion of $(A + M)^7$ follows.

$$(A + M)^7 = A^7 + 7A^6M + 21A^5M^2 + 35A^4M^3 + 35A^3M^4 + 21A^2M^5 + 7AM^6 + M^7$$

Amy must win 7, 6, 5, 4, or 3 games.

$$A^7 + 7A^6M + 21A^5M^2 + 35A^4M^3 + 35A^3M^4$$

$$= \left(\frac{1}{5}\right)^7 + 7 \cdot \left(\frac{1}{5}\right)^6\left(\frac{4}{5}\right) + 21\left(\frac{1}{5}\right)^5\left(\frac{4}{5}\right)^2 + 35\left(\frac{1}{5}\right)^4\left(\frac{4}{5}\right)^3 + 35\left(\frac{1}{5}\right)^3\left(\frac{4}{5}\right)^4$$
Substitute $\frac{1}{5}$ for A and $\frac{4}{5}$ for M.

$$= \frac{1}{78125} + 7\left(\frac{1}{15625}\right)\left(\frac{4}{5}\right) + 21\left(\frac{1}{3125}\right)\left(\frac{16}{25}\right) + 35\left(\frac{1}{625}\right)\left(\frac{64}{125}\right) + 35\left(\frac{1}{125}\right)\left(\frac{256}{625}\right)$$

$$= \frac{1 + 28 + 336 + 2240 + 8960}{78,125}$$

$$= \frac{11,565}{78,125} \text{ or } \frac{2313}{15,625}$$

The probability that Amy will win at least 3 games is $\frac{2313}{15,625}$.

exercises

Exploratory Tell whether each of the following in exercises 2–9 represents a binomial trial or not. State how to solve those that represent a binomial trial.

1. Ann tosses a coin 3 times. What is the probability of 2 heads and 1 tail?

Jess draws 4 cards from a deck of 52 playing cards. What is the probability of drawing 4 aces if the following occurs?

2. He replaces the card.

3. He does not replace the card.

There are 8 algebra books, 4 geometry books, and 6 trigonometry books on a shelf. If 2 are selected, with replacement after the first selection, what is the probability of the following?

4. both algebra
5. both geometry
6. both trigonometry
7. one algebra, one geometry
8. one algebra, one trigonometry
9. one geometry, one trigonometry

Written   A coin is tossed 4 times. What is the probability of the following?

1. exactly 1 head
2. no heads
3. 2 heads and 2 tails
4. 3 or more tails

A die is tossed 5 times. What is the probability of the following?

5. only one 4
6. at least three 4's
7. no more than two 4's
8. exactly five 4's

Cathy Black has a bent coin. The probability of heads is $\frac{2}{3}$ with this coin. She flips the coin 4 times. What is the probability of the following?

9. no heads
10. 4 heads
11. at least 3 heads
12. no more than 2 heads

Joey Diller guesses on all 10 questions on a true-false test. What is the probability of the following?

13. 7 correct
14. at least 6 correct
15. all incorrect
16. at least half incorrect

A batter is now batting 0.200 (meaning 200 hits in 1000 times at bat). In the next 5 at-bats, what is the probability of having the following?

17. exactly 1 hit
18. exactly 3 hits
19. at least 4 hits
20. at least 2 hits

Three coins are tossed. What is the probability of the following?

21. 3 heads
22. 3 tails
23. at least 2 heads
24. exactly 2 tails

If a tack is dropped, the probability that it will land point up is $\frac{2}{5}$. Ten tacks are dropped. What is the probability of the following?

25. all point up
26. exactly 3 point up
27. exactly 5 point up
28. at least 6 point up

Harold is a skeet shooter. He will hit the clay pigeon 9 of 10 times. If he shoots 12 times, what is the probability of the following?

29. all misses
30. exactly 7 hits
31. all hits
32. at least 10 hits

Chapter Summary

1. Two events are independent if the result of the first event has no effect on the second.   (423)

2. Basic Counting Principle: Suppose an event can be chosen in p different ways. Another independent event can be chosen in q different ways. Then the two events can be chosen successively in $p \cdot q$ ways. (424)

3. Definition of $P(n, r)$:   The number of permutations of n objects, taken r at a time is defined as follows.

$$P(n, r) = \frac{n!}{(n - r)!} \quad (426)$$

4. Permutations with Repetition: The number of permutations of n objects of which p are alike and q are alike is found by evaluating the following expression.

$$\frac{n!}{p!q!} \quad (427)$$

5. Circular Permutations: If n objects are arranged in a circle, then there are $\frac{n!}{n}$ or $(n - 1)!$ arrangements.   (430)

6. Definition of $C(n, r)$:   The number of combinations of n objects, taken r at a time, is written $C(n, r)$.

$$C(n, r) = \frac{n!}{(n - r)!r!} \quad (433)$$

7. Probability of Success and of Failure: If an event can succeed in s ways and fail in f ways, then the probabilities of success $P(s)$ and of failure $P(f)$ are as follows.

$$P(s) = \frac{s}{s + f} \qquad P(f) = \frac{f}{s + f} \quad (436)$$

8. Definition of Odds: The odds of the successful outcome of an event is expressed as the ratio of the number of ways it can succeed to the number of ways it can fail.

$$\text{Odds} = \text{the ratio of } s \text{ to } f \text{ or } \frac{s}{f} \quad (437)$$

9. **Probability of Two Independent Events:** If two events, A and B, are independent, then the probability of both events occurring is found as follows.

$$P(A \text{ and } B) = P(A) \cdot P(B). \quad (439)$$

10. **Probability of Two Dependent Events:** Suppose two events, A and B, are dependent. Then the probability of both occurring is found as follows.

$$P(A \text{ and } B) = P(A) \cdot P(B \text{ following } A). \quad (439)$$

11. **Probability of Mutually Exclusive Events:** The probability of one of two mutually exclusive events occurring is the sum of their probabilities.

$$P(A \text{ or } B) = P(A) + P(B) \quad (442)$$

12. **Probability of Inclusive Events:** The probability of one of two inclusive events, A and B, is the sum of the individual probabilities decreased by the probability of both occurring.

$$P(A \text{ or } B) = P(A) + P(B) - P(A \text{ and } B) \quad (443)$$

13. **Conditions of Binomial Trials:** A binomial trial problem exists if the following conditions hold.
    1. There are only two possible outcomes.
    2. The events are independent. (446)

Chapter Review

14–1 **Using only the digits 0, 1, 2, 3, and 4, how many 3-digit patterns can be formed under the following conditions?**

    1. Repetitions are allowed.

    2. No repetitions are allowed.

14–2 **On a shelf are 8 mystery and 7 romance novels. How many ways can they be arranged as follows?**

    3. all mysteries together

    4. all mysteries together, romances together.

    5. Evaluate $\dfrac{C(8, 5)}{C(5, 3)}$

    6. Evaluate $\dfrac{P(7, 3)}{P(5, 2)}$

14–3 **Solve each problem.**

    7. How many ways can 8 people be seated at a round table?

    8. How many ways can 10 charms be placed on a bracelet that has a clasp?

14–4   **9.** How many baseball teams can be formed from 15 players if only 3 pitch while the others play the remaining 8 positions?

    10. From a deck of 52 cards, how many different 4-card hands exist?

14–5 **11.** A card is selected from a deck of 52 cards. What is the probability that it is a queen?

12. In a bag are 6 red and 2 white marbles. If two marbles are selected, what is the probability that one is red and the other is white?

14–6 **13.** In his pocket, Jose has 5 dimes, 7 nickels, and 4 pennies. He selects 4 coins. What is the probability that he has 2 dimes and 2 pennies?

14. Ben has 6 navy blue socks and 4 black socks in a drawer. One dark morning he pulls out 2 socks. What is the probability that he has 2 black socks?

14–7 **15.** From a deck of 52 cards, one card is selected. What is the probability that it is an ace or a face card?

16. If a letter is selected at random from the alphabet, what is the probability that it is a letter from the words CAT or SKATE?

14–8 **17.** Four coins are tossed. What is the probability that they show 3 heads and 1 tail?

18. A die is tossed 5 times. What is the probability of at least two 3's?

Chapter Test

Solve each of the following.

1. From 8 shirts, 6 pair of slacks, and 4 jackets, how many different outfits can be made?

2. In a row are 8 chairs. How many ways can 5 people be seated?

3. How many ways can 11 books be arranged on a shelf?

4. How many ways can the letters from the word *television* be arranged?

5. How many ways can 6 keys be placed on a key ring?

6. How many different basketball teams could be formed from a group of 12 girls?

7. Nine points are placed on a circle. How many triangles can be formed using these points, three at a time, as vertices?

8. From a group of 4 men and 5 women, a committee of 3 is to be formed. What is the probability that it will have 2 men and 1 woman?

9. A red die and a green die are tossed. What is the probability that the red will show even and the green will show a number greater than four?

10. From a deck of cards, what is the probability of selecting a 4 followed by a 7 if no replacement occurs?

11. While shooting arrows, William Tell can hit an apple 9 out of 10 times. What is the probability that he will hit it exactly 4 out of the next 7 times?

12. Five bent coins are tossed. The probability of heads is $\frac{2}{3}$ for each of them. What is the probability that no more than 2 will show heads?

Find the value of each of the following.

13. $P(8, 3)$ **14.** $P(6, 4)$ **15.** $C(8, 3)$ **16.** $C(6, 4)$

Solve the following expression for *n*.

17. $7C(6, 4) = 5C(n, 2)$

chapter
15 statistics

Insurance companies use statistics extensively in calculating rates. For example, an automobile insurance company compiles data such as number of accidents, amount of damages, road conditions, age of drivers, and so on.

15–1   Organizing Data

Statistics provide techniques for collecting, organizing, analyzing, and interpreting numerical information called **data.** Organized data is easier to read and interpret. One way to organize data is by using tables. The following table shows the normal monthly precipitation for selected cities in the United States.

Normal Monthly Precipitation in Inches

City	Jan.	Feb.	Mar.	Apr.	May	Jun.	July	Aug.	Sep.	Oct.	Nov.	Dec.	Total
Albuquerque, NM	0.30	0.39	0.47	0.48	0.53	0.50	1.39	1.34	0.77	0.79	0.29	0.52	7.77
Boston, MA	3.69	3.54	4.01	3.49	3.47	3.19	2.74	3.46	3.16	3.02	4.51	4.24	42.52
Chicago, IL	1.85	1.59	2.73	3.75	3.41	3.95	4.09	3.14	3.00	2.62	2.20	2.11	34.44
Houston, TX	3.57	3.54	2.68	3.54	5.10	4.52	4.12	4.35	4.65	4.05	4.03	4.04	48.19
Mobile, AL	4.71	4.76	7.07	5.59	4.52	6.09	8.86	6.93	6.59	2.55	3.39	5.92	66.98
San Francisco, CA	4.37	3.04	2.54	1.59	0.41	0.13	0.01	0.03	0.16	0.98	2.29	3.98	19.53

The table organizes the data so that you can quickly answer questions like the following.

What city has the most precipitation in January?

What is the driest month in Houston?

The totals provided help you answer questions like the following.

Which city has the most precipitation in one year?

How many of the cities have more than 30 inches of precipitation in one year?

Some tables group data together. For example, you could make a table which provides the normal precipitation in selected cities by seasons.

example

1 **Make a table which provides the normal precipitation in selected cities, by seasons. Use the data from the table shown above.**

City	Winter Jan.–Mar.	Spring Apr.–Jun.	Summer Jul.–Sep.	Fall Oct.–Dec.
Albuquerque	1.16	1.51	3.50	1.60
Boston	11.24	10.15	9.36	11.77
Chicago	6.17	11.11	10.23	6.93
Houston	9.79	13.16	13.12	12.12
Mobile	16.54	16.20	22.38	11.86
San Francisco	9.95	2.13	0.20	7.25

Notice that once data has been grouped, individual measurements lose their identities.

2 **Use the table shown below to answer the following questions.**

1. How many master's degrees were earned in 1960?
2. How many degrees were earned in 1970?
3. Did the total number of degrees earned increase from 1940 to 1978?

Earned Degrees (in thousands)

Year	Bachelor's	Master's	Doctorate	Total
1940	187	27	3.4	217.4
1950	434	58	1.6	498.6
1960	395	75	9.8	479.8
1970	833	209	29.9	1071.9
1978	998	311	32.2	1341.2

1. There were 75 thousand or 75,000 master's degrees earned in 1960.
2. There were a total of 1071.9 thousand or 1,071,900 degrees earned in 1970.
3. There were a total of 1341.2 thousand degrees earned in 1978 and 217.4 thousand degrees earned in 1940. The total number of degrees earned did increase from 1940 to 1978.

exercises

Exploratory Use the table below to solve each of the following problems.

U.S. Imports and Exports in Billions of Dollars, 1978

Source: Statistical Abstracts of the United States, 1979

Region	Imports	Exports
Africa	16,898	5,886
Asia	58,300	39,628
Oceania	2,350	3,462
Europe	37,987	43,615
North America	46,173	38,448
South America	10,308	10,860

1. In 1978, how much were U.S. exports to North America?
2. In 1978, how much were U.S. imports from South America?
3. In 1978, how much were U.S. imports from Oceania?
4. In 1978, how much were U.S. exports to Africa?
5. In 1978, how much were U.S. exports to Europe?
6. In 1978, how much were U.S. imports from Asia?

7. Find each entry for a new column on the table with the heading, **Difference.**

8. Find each entry for a new column on the table with the heading, **Imports as a Percent of Exports.**

Written Two dice were tossed 64 times with the following results.

5	8	11	10	8	8	7	10	3	9	10	8	2	9	12	3
11	5	2	3	5	7	11	7	11	10	11	10	6	7	8	7
9	5	6	4	4	5	10	8	6	7	4	8	5	10	5	5
8	5	11	9	12	4	7	2	7	4	3	9	2	11	7	6

1. Organize the data into a table with the headings *Number of Dots,* and *Frequency of Occurrences.*

2. Which number or numbers of dots occurred most frequently?

3. Which number or numbers of dots occurred least frequently?

Percent of Households Owning Motor Vehicles, by Income, 1977
Source: U.S. Bureau of Census

Annual Income	One Vehicle	Two or More Vehicles
Under $3000	37.3	9.2
$3000–$6999	52.8	9.8
$7000–$9999	62.7	17.8
$10,000–$14,999	57.9	28.0
$15,000–$24,999	45.7	41.3
$25,000 and over	27.3	48.5

4. What percent of households with an annual income from $10,000–$14,999 had one vehicle in 1977?

5. What percent of households with an annual income from $10,000–$14,999 had two or more vehicles in 1977?

6. What percent of households with an annual income under $3000 had one vehicle in 1977?

7. What percent of households with an annual income of $25,000 or over had one vehicle in 1977?

Passenger Car Production by Makes (in thousands)
Source: *Automotive News,* Jan. 12, 1981

Company	1965	1970	1975	1980
American Motors Corporation	346.4	276.1	323.7	167.8
Chrysler Corporation	1,467.6	1,273.5	902.9	639.0
Ford Motor Company	2,565.8	2,017.2	1,808.0	1,306.9
General Motors Corporation	4,949.4	2,979.2	3,679.1	4,063.6
Other	6.1	4.1	3.2	200.3

8. What company produced the most cars in 1980?

9. What company produced the most cars in 1970?

10. In what year did Ford Motor Company produce the most cars?

11. In what year did General Motors Corporation produce the least cars?

12. How many cars were produced in 1965?

13. How many cars were produced in 1980?

The following represent the total precipitation in inches for certain cities in 1980.

31	26	35	20	38	30	41	21	23	25	24	27	30	19	27
38	30	31	33	20	22	30	33	27	25	33	25	27	31	27
17	38	46	33	22	27	22	19	25	33	36	30	45	31	45
35	23	25	40	36	20	30	22	26	41	35	25	30	30	27
33	25	28	27	24	45	26	21	41	26	22	31	37	38	26
20	22	26	25	20	27	25	23	27	31	35	27	25	40	24
41	30	17	22	26	19	33	36	30	28					

14. Organize the data into a table with the headings *Precipitation* and *Number of Cities*. Under *Precipitation* include each number from 17 through 46.

15. Which number of inches occurred most frequently?

16. How many cities had 38 inches of precipitation?

17. What is the greatest number of inches of precipitation for any of the cities?

18. What is the least number of inches of precipitation for any of the cities?

19. Organize the data into a table with the headings *Precipitation* and *Number of Cities*. Under *Precipitation* group the data by threes. For example, the first entry under *Precipitation* is 17–19.

20. How many cities had from 32–34 inches of precipitation?

21. How many cities had from 23–25 inches of precipitation?

History

excursions in algebra

Edmund Halley

Jacob Bernoulli

Statistical methods have been developed in the last 300 years. This has happened as researchers in other fields needed better methods for analyzing data.

In 1661, **John Graunt** collected and studied records of births and deaths in London. Graunt, a merchant, was one of the first to study population in this way. A pamphlet he wrote told about the life expectancy of different people at different ages.

Edmund Halley, an astronomer, made a similar study in 1693 in Breslau, Germany. He had promised to provide some "filler" for a scientific publication. This study led to improvements in public record keeping. He also showed how to make calculations for life insurance purposes. He used his tables of life expectancy in this study.

A book by **Jacob Bernoulli,** who is considered the founder of probability theory, was published in 1713. This book showed how probability theory can be applied to a great number of collected statistical data.

15–2   Graphs

Graphs often are used to present data and show relationships. There are several ways of presenting the data in the following table.

Average Motor Fuel Consumption in U.S.

gallons per vehicle

Year	1950	1955	1960	1965	1970	1975
Consumption	603	644	661	656	722	676

This graph is called a **picto-graph.** Like a bar graph, it shows how specific quantities compare.

This graph is called a **bar graph.** It shows how specific quantities compare. *Which is easier to draw, a bar graph or a picto-graph?*

This graph is called a **line graph.** It is helpful for showing trends or changes.

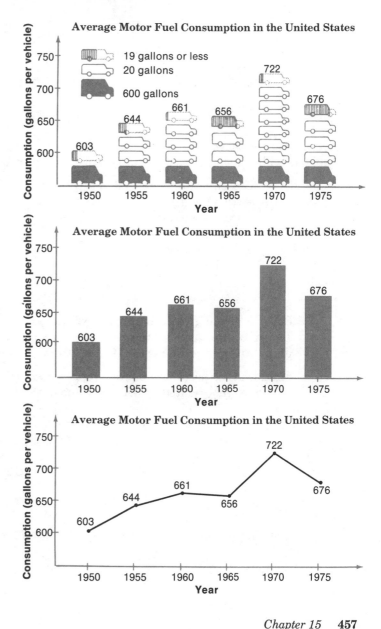

1 **Draw a bar graph and a line graph to present the following data.**

Percent of 18 Year Olds with High School Diplomas

Year	1940	1950	1955	1960	1965	1970	1975
Percent	49.3	60.0	62.5	70.0	73.9	75.6	74.3

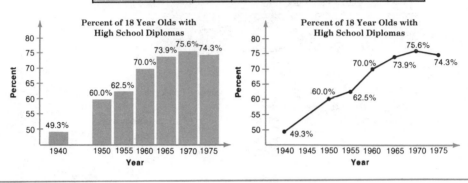

Circle graphs show how parts are related to the whole. For example, the following graph shows the cost of a $4 paperback book.

The circle is separated into pro-portional parts. For example, 25% of the book's cost goes to royalties and profit. Thus, 25% of the circle, 90°, is used to show this part of the book's cost.

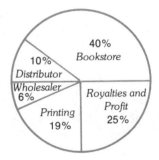

2 **Draw a circle graph to show how the cost of a $5.98 record is broken down. The manufacturer's cost is $1.83. The manufacturer's income is $0.68. The distributor's income is $0.41. And the retailer's income is $3.06.**

First, find the percent of a circle represented by each cost. Then, figure the number of degrees represented by each cost and draw the graph.

Cost	Percent of Circle	Approximate Degrees
Manufacturer's cost	$\frac{1.83}{5.98}$ or 31%	$360 \times 31\%$ or 111.6
Manufacturer's income	$\frac{0.68}{5.98}$ or 11%	$360 \times 11\%$ or 39.6
Distributor's income	$\frac{0.41}{5.98}$ or 7%	$360 \times 7\%$ or 25.2
Retailer's income	$\frac{3.06}{5.98}$ or 51%	$360 \times 51\%$ or 183.6

exercises

Exploratory Use the bar graph below to solve each of the following.

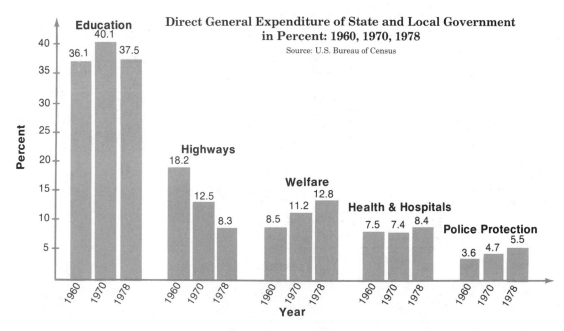

Direct General Expenditure of State and Local Government
in Percent: 1960, 1970, 1978

Source: U.S. Bureau of Census

1. In 1960, what percent of expenditures was for highways?
2. In 1960, what percent of expenditures was for police protection?
3. In 1970, what percent of expenditures was for health and hospitals?
4. In 1978, what percent of expenditures was for education?
5. In which year, 1960, 1970, or 1978 was the percent of expenditures for education greatest?
6. In which year, 1960, 1970, or 1978 was the percent of expenditures for welfare least?
7. In 1970 was a greater percent spent on health and hospitals or on police protection?
8. In 1960 was a greater percent spent on highways or on welfare?

Written Draw bar graphs for the data in each of the following tables.

1. *Record Album Shipments (in millions)*

Year	1974	1976	1978	1980
Units	276	273	341	308

2. *Home Runs Scored by NL Home Run Champions*

Year	1960	1965	1970	1975	1980
Home Runs	41	52	45	38	48

3. *Indianapolis 500-Winner's Speed*

Year	1960	1965	1970	1975	1980
Speed/mph	138.7	150.6	155.7	149.2	142.8

4. *Postal Rates for First Class Mail*

Years	1966	1969	1972	1975	1978	1981
Cost/ounce	5¢	6¢	8¢	13¢	15¢	20¢

5. Consumer Spending on Food (in billions)

Year	1930	1940	1950	1960	1970	1980
Dollars	18.0	16.6	46.0	70.5	119.6	302.9

6. World Population by Regions (in millions), 1978

Continent	Africa	N. America	Latin America	Asia	Europe	Oceania
Population	442	242	349	2,461	480	22

7. School Days Missed Due to Illness or Injury, Ages 6–16

Year	1970	1972	1974	1976	1978
Days in Millions	222	236	242	193	201

8. World and U.S. Populations (in millions)

Year	1900	1925	1950	1975	2000 (estimated)
World	1,600	1,900	2,510	4,100	6,353
U.S.	76	116	152	214	260

9. U.S. Energy Consumption

Year	Coal	Refined Petroleum	Natural Gas	Other
1965	22%	44%	30%	4%
1970	19%	44%	33%	4%
1975	18%	46%	28%	8%
1980	20%	45%	27%	8%

10–18. Draw line graphs for the data in problems **1–9**.

The following table gives the population distribution by age in the U.S. for 1880 and 1980.

Year	Under 5	5–19	20–44	45–64	65 and over
1880	13.8%	34.3%	35.9%	12.6%	3.4%
1980	7.2%	24.8%	37.1%	19.6%	11.3%

19. Draw a circle graph to show the population distribution by age in 1880.

20. Draw a circle graph to show the population distribution by age in 1980.

The data in the following table gives a breakdown of the civilian labor force in the United States for various years, in millions of persons.

Employment Status	1970	1975	1978	1979	1980
Employed in nonagricultural industries	75.2	81.4	91.0	93.6	94.0
Employed in agriculture	3.5	3.4	3.3	3.3	3.3
Unemployed	4.1	7.8	6.0	6.0	7.4
Total civilian labor force	82.8	92.6	100.3	102.9	104.7

21–25. For each year, draw a circle graph to show the breakdown of the civilian labor force.

15-3   Central Tendency

During a cold spell lasting 43 days, the following high temperatures (in degrees Fahrenheit) were recorded in Chicago. What temperature is most representative of the high temperatures for that period?

26	17	12	5	4	25	17	23	13
6	25	19	27	22	26	20	31	16
12	27	16	27	16	30	7	31	24
5	29	18	16	22	29	8	31	
13	24	5	$^-7$	20	29	18	12	

The most representative temperature, the average temperature, is neither the greatest nor the least temperature. It is a value somewhere in the middle of the group.

The most commonly used averages are the **median, mode,** and **mean.** They are defined in the following way.

> **The median of a set of data is the middle value. If there are two middle values, it is the value halfway between.**
>
> **The mode of a set of data is the most frequent value. Some sets of data have multiple modes.**
>
> **The mean of a set of data is the sum of all the values divided by the number of values.**

Definition of Median, Mode, and Mean

temperatures

31	24	16
31	24	16
31	23	13
30	22	13
29	22	12
29	20	12
29	20	12
27	19	8
27	18	7
27	18	6
26	17	5
26	17	5
25	16	5
25	16	4
		$^-7$

To find the median of the Chicago temperatures, arrange the values in descending order, as shown in the margin. Then, find the middle value. In this case, the median temperature is 19.

To find the mode, determine how many times each particular high temperature occurred. Then find the most frequently occurring value. In this case, the mode is 16.

To find the mean, add all the values. Then divide by 43, the number of values. In this case, the mean temperature to the nearest tenth is 18.5.

This example shows that median, mode, and mean are not always the same value.

The value of every item in a set of data affects the value of the mean. Thus, when extreme values are included, the mean may become less representative of the set. The values of the median and the mode are *not* affected by extreme values.

1 **Find the mean of {1, 2, 4, 93} and {24, 25, 25, 26}.**

$$\{1, 2, 4, 93\}$$

$$\text{mean} = \frac{1 + 2 + 4 + 93}{4}$$

$$= \frac{100}{4} \text{ or } 25$$

The mean is not close to any one of the four values in this set. In this case, it *is not* a particularly representative value.

$$\{24, 25, 25, 26\}$$

$$\text{mean} = \frac{24 + 25 + 25 + 26}{4}$$

$$= \frac{100}{4} \text{ or } 25$$

There are *no* extreme values in this set. In this case, the mean is a representative value.

The mean for both sets is 25.

2 **Find the median, mode, and mean of the hourly wages of 80 workers. Five workers make $4.60 per hour, fifteen make $4.40 per hour, thirty make $5.70 per hour, ten make $6.60 per hour, and twenty make $4.50 per hour.**

Arrange the wages in descending order. Then find the middle value.

$6.60	10 workers
5.70	30 workers
4.60	5 workers
4.50	20 workers
4.40	15 workers

There are two middle values, the 40th value $5.70, and the 41st value $4.60. The median is the value halfway between, $\frac{5.70 + 4.60}{2}$ or $5.15.

More workers make $5.70 per hour than any other wage. So it is the most frequently occurring value. The mode is $5.70.

Add all 80 values. There are 10 values of $6.60, 30 values of $5.70, 5 values of $4.60, and so on. You can use multiplication to shorten the additions.

$$\text{mean} = \frac{10(6.60) + 30(5.70) + 5(4.60) + 20(4.50) + 15(4.40)}{80}$$

$$= \frac{66.00 + 171.00 + 23.00 + 90.00 + 66.00}{80}$$

$$= \frac{416}{80} \text{ or } 5.20$$

The median is $5.15, the mode is $5.70, and the mean is $5.20.

exercises

Exploratory **Find the median for each set of data.**

1. {1, 2, 3, 4, 5}
2. {2, 4, 6, 8, 10}
3. {1, 1, 2, 4, 1}
4. {7, 7, 7, 7, 7, 7, 7}
5. {8, 43, 2, 56, 44}
6. {7.1, 5.0, 2.7, 9.1, 8.1, 6.3, 8.5}
7. {2.1, 4.8, 2.1, 5.7, 2.1, 4.8, 2.1}
8. {1, 7, 7, 0, 2, 0, 4, 1, 3, 7, 7, 5, 4, 1, 8}
9. {11, 10, 13, 12, 12, 13, 15}
10. {50, 75, 65, 70, 55, 65, 50, 80}

11–20. Find the mode for each set of data in Exercises 1–10.

21–30. Find the mean for each set of data in Exercises 1–10.

Written **A die was tossed 25 times with the following results.**

5	3	1	6	5	2	1	5	4	1	6	6	4
6	5	6	3	6	4	4	4	1	1	2	2	

1. Find the median, mode, and mean for the tosses.

2. Two dice were tossed 64 times. Find the median, mode and mean for the following results.

8	11	10	8	8	7	10	3	9	10	8	2	9
5	2	3	5	7	11	7	11	10	11	10	6	7
5	6	4	4	5	10	8	6	7	4	8	5	10
5	11	9	12	4	7	2	7	4	3	9	2	11
5	11	9	8	12	3	7	8	5	5	7	6	

3. The heights in feet of the 20 highest mountains in the world are given below. Find the median, mode, and mean for the heights.

29,002	14,255	18,700	28,146	22,835
13,653	14,431	28,250	13,202	14,408
25,263	19,344	19,565	19,887	14,701
15,781	18,481	14,495	14,110	20,270

4. Find the median, mode, and mean of the hourly wages of 200 workers. One hundred workers make $4.00 per hour, ten make $5.50 per hour, ten make $6.75 per hour, twenty make $3.80 per hour, and sixty make $5.25 per hour.

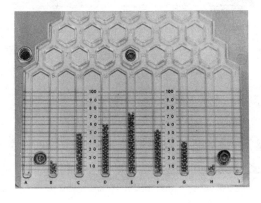

The picture on the left shows a device filled with small steel marbles. The marbles roll past a series of hexagonal obstacles, collecting at the bottom in each of nine columns. The horizontal lines help you estimate the number of marbles in each column.

5. Estimate the number of marbles in each column.

6. Find the median, mode, and mean for the number of marbles in a column.

Statistics can be misleading. Graphs for a set of data can look very different from one another. Compare the following graphs for the data below.

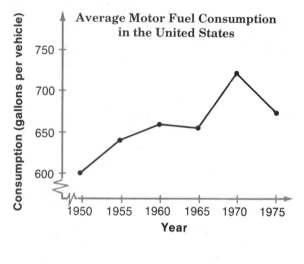

Notice how the vertical and horizontal scales of the two graphs differ. Scales can be "cramped" or "spread out" to make a graph that gives a certain impression. Which graph would you use to give the impression that motor fuel consumption increased a great deal from 1950 to 1970?

Advertisements often use graphs that have no scales, or only one scale. These graphs *seem* to show statistics, but actually give no information.

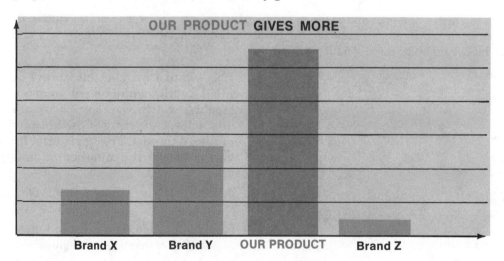

If a sample is small, conclusions drawn from the set of data are *not* always reliable. How many cars should be tested before an advertiser can make the following claim?

Suppose four people were asked which car used less oil. If 75% agreed, how many people thought that *Our Car* used less oil?

The advertisement above is misleading in other ways. For example, what was the condition of the cars tested? Suppose *Car Z* was old and out of tune, and used more oil than *Our Car,* which was brand new. Is it reasonable to assume that a brand new *Car Z* would use more oil than a brand new *Our Car*?

Exercises   Solve each problem.

1–9. Draw two line graphs for each set of data in problems **1–9** on pages 459 and 460. Use different scales.

10. List additional ways the advertisement about *Our Car* is misleading.

Suppose an advertiser claims that 90% of all of one brand of cars sold in the last 10 years are still on the road.

11. If 10,000 cars were sold, how many are still on the road?

12. If 1000 cars were sold, how many are still on the road?

13. If 100 cars were sold, how many are still on the road?

14. If 10 cars were sold, how many are still on the road?

15. Find an example to show how you think averages could be used in a misleading way.

15–4   Dispersion

If 10,000 family incomes in a city were all the same, you would know all there is to know about the incomes. However, values in a set of data usually vary. The variation is called **dispersion**.

There are several kinds of measures of dispersion. The simplest measure is called the **range**.

The range of a set of data is the difference between the greatest and least values in the set.	*Definition of Range*

example 1 **The heights of a group of young pine trees in a reforestation plot are 58 cm, 56 cm, 51 cm, 54 cm, 49 cm, 61 cm, 54 cm, and 49 cm. Find the range.**

The greatest value is 61 centimeters.
The least value is 49 centimeters.

range = 61 − 49   *The range is the difference between the greatest and least values.*
      = 12

Because the range is the difference between the greatest and least values in a set of data, it is affected by unusually extreme values. In such cases, it is not a good measure of dispersion.

The most commonly used measure of dispersion is called the **standard deviation**. The standard deviation for a set of data is an average measure of how much each value differs from the mean.

From a set of data, the standard deviation is calculated by following these steps.

1. Find the mean.
2. Find the difference between each measurement and the mean.
3. Square each difference.
4. Find the mean of the squares.
5. Take the positive square root of this mean.

From a set of data with n values, x_i represents a value such that $1 \leq i \leq n$, and $\bar{x}$ represents the mean, then the standard deviation can be found as follows. $$\text{standard deviation} = \sqrt{\frac{\sum_{i=1}^{n} (x_i - \bar{x})^2}{n}}$$	*Definition of Standard Deviation*

example

2 The heights of a group of young pine trees in a reforestation plot are 58 cm, 56 cm, 51 cm, 54 cm, 49 cm, 61 cm, 54 cm, and 49 cm. Find the standard deviation.

mean height $= \dfrac{58 + 56 + 51 + 54 + 49 + 61 + 54 + 49}{8}$ or 54 $\bar{x} = 54$

standard deviation $= \sqrt{\dfrac{\sum\limits_{i=1}^{n} (x_i - \bar{x})^2}{n}}$

n is 8
$x_1 - \bar{x}$ is $58 - 54$ or 4
$x_2 - \bar{x}$ is $56 - 54$ or 2 and so on.

$= \sqrt{\dfrac{(4)^2 + (2)^2 + (^-3)^2 + (0)^2 + (^-5)^2 + (7)^2 + (0)^2 + (^-5)^2}{8}}$

$= \sqrt{\dfrac{16 + 4 + 9 + 0 + 25 + 49 + 0 + 25}{8}}$

$= \sqrt{\dfrac{128}{8}}$

$= \sqrt{16}$ or 4

The standard deviation is 4.

When studying standard deviation of a set of data, it is important to keep the mean in mind. For example, suppose a firm manufactures televisions and the standard deviation of the average monthly prices for televisions sold in the last two years is $50.

If the mean price over the last two years was $200, the standard deviation indicates a great deal of variation. If the mean price over the last two years was $600, the standard deviation indicates very little variation.

exercises

Exploratory Find the range for each set of data.

1. {1, 4, 11, 7, 2}
2. {2, 2, 8, 14, 6, 4}
3. {39, 47, 51, 38, 45, 29, 37, 40, 36, 48}
4. {70, 86, 81, 86, 81, 84, 89, 77, 80, 87, 83, 87, 90, 92, 87}
5. {50, 92, 79, 61, 76, 83, 65, 98, 82, 64, 76, 63, 57, 96, 75, 53, 66, 88, 59, 85, 95, 65, 81, 71}
6. {14.1, 15.8, 15.2, 14.0, 14.8, 14.1, 12.9, 14.4, 16.8, 16.2, 13.2, 15.9, 13.9, 15.4, 13.6, 15.1, 14.7, 13.2}
7. {250, 275, 325, 300, 200, 225, 175}
8. {132, 150, 138, 160, 133, 143, 148, 148, 151, 148, 141}
9. {81, 80, 87, 97, 82, 86, 85, 82, 72, 80, 85, 84, 84, 63, 90, 82, 85, 79, 95, 81}
10. {1050, 1175, 1075, 1025, 1100, 1125, 975, 1125, 1075, 1055}

Written

1–10. Find the standard deviation for each set of data in Exploratory Exercises 1–10.

The weights in pounds of the 11 players in each of two college football teams is as follows.

How College: 160, 180, 190, 200, 210, 170, 250, 220, 180, 200, 240

Now College: 160, 190, 210, 230, 240, 220, 150, 190, 210, 160, 240

11. Find the range in weights for the How College team.

12. Find the range in weights for the Now College team.

13. Find the mean weight for the How College team.

14. Find the mean weight for the Now College team.

15. Find the standard deviation in weights for the How College team.

16. Find the standard deviation in weights for the Now College team.

The mileage in miles per gallon obtained by the Electric Company and Gas Company cars is as follows.

Electric Company: 25, 13, 24, 18, 29, 12, 30, 16, 25, 21, 28, 25, 33, 11, 22, 12, 30, 16, 28, 23

Gas Company: 32, 16, 22, 24, 23, 13, 23, 31, 15, 21, 24, 27, 30, 21, 12, 24

17. Find the range in mileage for the Electric Company cars.

18. Find the range in mileage for the Gas Company cars.

19. Find the mean mileage in miles per gallon for the Electric Company cars.

20. Find the mean mileage in miles per gallon for the Gas Company cars.

21. Find the standard deviation in mileage for the Electric Company cars.

22. Find the standard deviation in mileage for the Gas Company cars.

The following tables give two frequency distributions for items. Bar graphs for these distributions are shown.

Item	1	2	3	4	5	6	7	8	9
Frequency	1	0	1	7	9	4	1	1	1

Item	1	2	3	4	5	6	7	8	9
Frequency	4	2	2	3	4	1	2	4	3

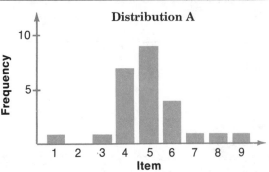

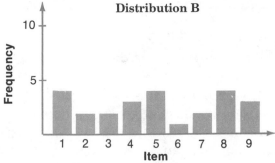

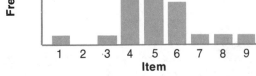

23. Find the range for distribution A.

24. Find the range for distribution B.

25. Find the mean for distribution A.

26. Find the mean for distribution B.

27. Find the standard deviation for distribution A.

28. Find the standard deviation for distribution B.

29. Look at the two graphs. Which distribution has its values clustered more around its mean?

30. Write a computer program to find the standard deviation for n data items.

15–5　The Normal Distribution

Score	Number of People
40–49	5
50–59	0
60–69	0
70–79	2
80–89	8
90–99	35
100–109	50
110–119	40
120–129	15
130–139	5
140–149	9
150–159	1
160–169	0
170–179	3
180–189	0
190–199	2

One way of analyzing data is to consider the frequency with which each value occurs. The table on the right gives the frequencies of certain scores on a mechanical aptitude test taken by 175 people.

The following bar graph shows the frequencies of the scores in the table.

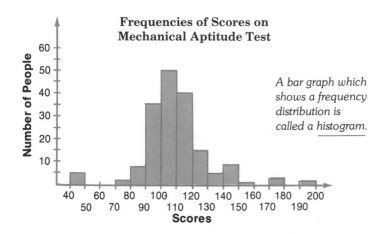

A bar graph which shows a frequency distribution is called a histogram.

The bar graph shows the **frequency distribution** of the scores. In other words, they show how the scores are spread out.

Frequency distributions are often shown by curves rather than histograms, especially when the distribution contains a great number of values. These curves may be of many different shapes. Many distributions have graphs like the following. Distributions with such a graph are called **normal distributions.**

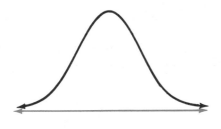

The curve is bell-shaped and symmetric. The shape of the curve indicates that frequencies in a normal distribution are concentrated in the center portion of the distribution. What does this tell you about the mean?

Normal distributions occur very frequently. For example, the diameter of a hole made by a drill press, the number of errors made by a typist, the tosses in a dart game if the player aims at the bull's-eye, the scores on tests, the grain yield on a farm, and the length of a newborn child can all be approximated by a normal distribution provided the number of data is sufficiently great.

Suppose a set of data consists of weights for 600 young people. Also, suppose the mean weight is 100 pounds and the standard deviation is 20 pounds. If the frequency distribution of these weights is a normal distribution, then the graph approximates the curve on the right.

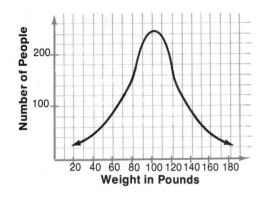

Normal distributions have these properties.

1. The graph is maximized at the mean.

2. About 68% of the items are within one standard deviation from the mean.

   Of the 68%, by symmetry, 34% are greater than the mean, and 34% are less.

3. About 95% of the items are within two standard deviations from the mean.

   Of the 95%, by symmetry, 47.5% are greater than the mean, and 47.5% are less.

4. About 99% of the items are within three standard deviations from the mean.

   Of the 99%, by symmetry, 49.5% are greater than the mean, and 49.5% are less.

As the graph of the distribution above shows, the mean, 100 pounds, is the most frequent weight. Out of 600 young people, about 408 have weights between 80 pounds and 120 pounds. About 570 have weights between 60 pounds and 140 pounds. And about 594 have weights between 40 pounds and 160 pounds.

1 **The approximate number of hours worked per week for 100 people is normally distributed. The mean is 40 hours per week and the standard deviation is 2 hours per week. About how many people work more than 42 hours per week?**

This frequency distribution is shown by the following curve. The percentages represent the percentage of 100 people working the number of hours within the given interval.

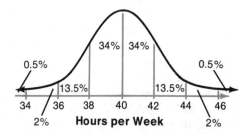

The percentage of people working more than 42 hours per week is 13.5% + 2% + 0.5% or 16%.

$$100 \times 16\% = 16$$

Thus, 16 people work more than 42 hours per week.

exercises

Exploratory Suppose 500 items are normally distributed. Solve each problem.

1. How many items are within one standard deviation from the mean?

2. How many items are within two standard deviations from the mean?

3. How many items are within three standard deviations from the mean?

4. How many items are within one standard deviation less than the mean?

5. How many items are within one standard deviation greater than the mean?

6. How many items are within two standard deviations greater than the mean?

7–12. Answer Exercises 1–6 for a normal distribution of 2000 items.

13–18. Answer Exercises 1–6 for a normal distribution of 16,000 items.

Written The lifetimes of 10,000 light bulbs is normally distributed. The mean lifetime is 300 days and the standard deviation is 40 days.

1. How many light bulbs will last between 260 and 340 days?

2. How many light bulbs will last between 220 and 380 days?

3. How many light bulbs will last less than 300 days?

4. How many light bulbs will last more than 300 days?

5. How many light bulbs will last more than 380 days?

6. How many light bulbs will last less than 180 days?

The diameters of metal fittings produced by a machine is normally distributed. The mean diameter is 7.5 centimeters and the standard deviation is 0.5 centimeters.

7. What percentage of the fittings have diameters between 7.0 centimeters and 8.0 centimeters?

8. What percentage of the fittings have diameters between 7.5 centimeters and 8.0 centimeters?

9. What percentage of the fittings have diameters between 6.5 centimeters and 7.5 centimeters?

10. What percentage of the fittings have diameters between 6.5 centimeters and 8.0 centimeters?

If you toss a fair coin 100 times, the least number of heads possible is 0, and the most is 100. If this experiment is repeated many times, the number of heads obtained for every 100 tosses is distributed about normally. There would be a mean of 50 and a standard deviation of 5.

11. What percentage of the experiments will show less than 50 heads?

12. What percentage of the experiments will show more than 50 heads?

13. What percentage of the experiments will show more than 65 heads?

14. What percentage of the experiments will show between 40 and 60 heads?

The number of hours of TV watched weekly by families in Westerville is normally distributed. The mean number of hours is 22 and the standard deviation is 7.5 hours.

15. What percentage of the families watch TV at least 22 hours per week?

16. What percentage of the families watch TV more than 14.5 hours per week?

17. What percentage of the families watch TV more than 37 hours per week?

18. What percentage of the families watch TV between 7 and 29.5 hours per week?

15–6   Predictions

The first step in determining how quantities are related often is making a **scatter diagram.** Such a diagram shows visually the nature of a relationship, both shape and closeness.

Suppose, for example, you wish to predict the quantity of a food product sold based on its weekly selling price. The following table shows the quantity sold for each of the last ten weeks, and its selling price.

Quantity Sold (dozens)	30	47	38	28	49	23	47	46	39	42
Price (cents per dozen)	28	22	29	32	20	35	21	20	24	29

The graph on the left is a scatter diagram for the data. The scatter of dots suggests a straight line that slopes downward from the upper left corner to the lower right corner.

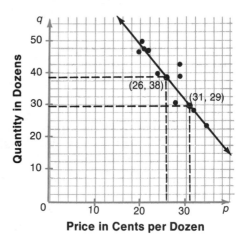

You can draw the line that is suggested by the dots. It represents the relationship between quantity and price. By choosing several points on the line, you can find the equation of the line. This equation is called the **prediction equation** for the relationship.

$$\text{slope} = \frac{38 - 29}{26 - 31} \text{ or } {}^-1.8$$

$q = {}^-1.8p + b$ *q stands for quantity and p stands for price*

$38 = {}^-1.8(26) + b$

$84.8 = b$ The equation is $q = {}^-1.8p + 84.8$.

Now, suppose that next week, the price of the food product will be 30 cents. Using the *prediction equation,* you can estimate that 30.8 dozen items will be sold.

$$q = {}^-1.8p + 84.8$$
$$= {}^-1.8(30) + 84.8 \text{ or } 30.8$$

1 **Draw a scatter diagram and find a prediction equation to show how typing speed and experience are related. Use the data in the following table.**

Typing speed (wpm)	33	45	46	20	40	30	38	22	52	44	42	55
Experience (years)	4	7	8	1	6	3	5	2	9	6	7	10

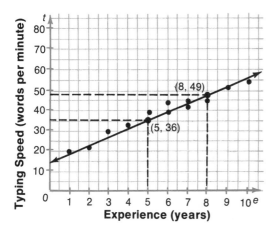

The black line is suggested by the pattern of dots. Two points with coordinates (5, 36) and (8, 49) lie on the line.

$$\text{slope} = \frac{49 - 36}{8 - 5}$$

$$= \frac{13}{3} \text{ or about } 4.3$$

Let e stand for experience.
Let t stand for typing speed.

$$t = 4.3e + b \qquad y = mx + b$$
$$36 = 4.3(5) + b$$
$$36 = 21.5 + b$$
$$14.5 = b$$

The prediction equation is $t = 4.3e + 14.5$.

The procedure for determining a prediction equation is dependent on your judgment. Such an equation is satisfactory only when rough prediction is desired. Statisticians normally use other, more precise procedures to determine prediction equations.

exercises

Exploratory The prediction equation in a study of the relationship between plant height in centimeters, h, and number of times watered per month, t, is $h = 0.5t + 0.5$. Predict the plant height for each of the following numbers of waterings.

1. 1 **2.** 3 **3.** 5 **4.** 8
5. 9 **6.** 10 **7.** 12 **8.** 15

A study of the relationship between cost for a unit of living space, c, and the number of square feet per unit, a, of living space resulted in the prediction equation $c = {}^-0.2a + 200$. Predict the cost of units of living space for each of the following areas.

9. 200 **10.** 300 **11.** 350 **12.** 400
13. 450 **14.** 550 **15.** 600 **16.** 800

Written   According to a certain prediction equation, if Acme Soap spends $20,000 on advertising, sales will be $10,000,000. If Acme Soap spends $50,000 on advertising, sales will be $22,000,000. Let x stand for advertising expenditure and y stand for sales revenue.

1. Find the slope of the prediction equation.

2. Find the y-intercept of the prediction equation.

3. Find the prediction equation.

4. Predict sales revenue if $10,000 is spent on advertising.

5. Predict sales revenue if $15,000 is spent on advertising.

6. Predict sales revenue if $35,000 is spent on advertising.

A certain study claims that the number of yearly visits to a public health clinic is related to a family's weekly income. According to the study's prediction equation, a family that earns $170 a week will visit the clinic 11 times a year. And a family that earns $220 a week will visit the clinic 6 times a year. Let x stand for family income and y stand for number of visits.

7. Find the slope of the prediction equation.

8. Find the y-intercept of the prediction equation.

9. Find the prediction equation.

10. Predict the number of yearly visits if a family earns $140 a week.

11. Predict the number of yearly visits if a family earns $250 a week.

12. Predict the number of yearly visits if a family earns $200 a week.

The following table shows the amount of sales for each of eight sales representatives during a given period, and the years of sales experience for each representative.

Amount of Sales	$9,000	$6,000	$4,000	$3,000	$3,000	$5,000	$8,000	$2,000
Years of Experience	6	5	3	1	4	3	6	2

13. Draw a scatter diagram to show how amount of sales and years of experience are related.

14. Find a prediction equation to show how amount of sales and years of experience are related.

15. Predict the amount of sales for a representative with 8 years of experience.

16. Predict the amount of sales for a representative with no experience.

The following table shows the statistics grades and the economics grades for a group of college students at the end of a given semester.

Statistics Grades	95	51	49	27	42	52	67	48	46
Economics Grades	88	70	65	50	60	80	68	49	40

17. Draw a scatter diagram to show how statistics grades and economics grades are related.

18. Find a prediction equation to show how statistics grades and economics grades are related.

19. Predict the economics grades of a student who receives a 75 in statistics.

20. Predict the statistics grade of a student who receives an 85 in economics.

Chapter Summary

1. Graphs are used to show relationships among data. Bar graphs and pictographs compare specific quantities. Line graphs show trends. Circle graphs compare parts to the whole. (457)

2. The median of a set of data is the middle value. If there are two middle values, it is the value halfway between. (461)

3. The mode of a set of data is the most frequent value. (461)

4. The mean of a set of data is the sum of all the values divided by the number of values. (461)

5. Definition of Range: The range of a set of data is the difference between the greatest and least values in the set. (466)

6. Definition of Standard Deviation: From a set of data with n values, x_i represents a value such that $1 \le i \le n$, and $\bar{x}$ represents the mean, then the standard deviation is

$$\sqrt{\frac{\sum_{i=1}^{n}(x_i - \bar{x})^2}{n}}.$$ (466)

7. Frequency distributions show how data are spread out. A histogram is a bar graph that shows a frequency distribution. The normal distribution commonly occurs. (469)

8. Normal distributions have the following properties.
   The graph is maximized at the mean.
   About 68% of the items are within one standard deviation from the mean.
   About 95% of the items are within two standard deviations from the mean.
   About 99% of the items are within three standard deviations from the mean. (470)

9. Scatter diagrams picture how quantities are related. Prediction equations give an approximate description of the relationship. (472)

15–1 **The following table gives the median family income for the years 1973 to 1979.**

Year	1973	1974	1975	1976	1977	1978	1979
Median Income	$12,051	$12,902	$13,719	$14,958	$16,009	$17,640	$19,661

1. What was the median family income in 1975?

2. Did the median family income increase or decrease from 1976 to 1977?

3–8. Find all the entries for a new row to the table with the heading, *Amount of Gain or Loss*.

15–2 **The following table gives the frequency of the number of diseased plants in garden plots from a certain nursery.**

Number of Diseased Plants per Plot	8	9	10	11	12	13	14	15	16	17	18	19	20	21	22	23	24	25
Number of Plots	1	0	3	5	0	8	0	7	13	16	15	10	9	12	10	18	17	19

9. Draw a line graph to present the data in the table above.

15–3 **10.** Find the median for the distribution in the table above.

11. Find the mode for the distribution in the table above.

12. Find the mean for the distribution in the table above.

15–4 **13.** Find the range for the distribution in the table above.

14. Find the standard deviation for the distribution in the table above.

15–5 **The monthly incomes of 10,000 workers in King City are distributed normally. Suppose the mean monthly income is $1250 and the standard deviation is $250.**

15. How many workers earn more than $1500 a month?

16. How many workers earn less than $750 a month?

15–6 **According to a certain prediction equation, if a person is 180 centimeters tall, that person weighs about 76 kilograms. A person 160 centimeters tall weighs about 57 kilograms. Let x stand for height in centimeters, and y stand for weight in kilograms.**

17. Find the slope of the prediction equation.

18. Find the y-intercept of the prediction equation.

19. Find the prediction equation.

20. Predict the weight of a person who is 174 centimeters tall.

The following high temperatures in degrees Fahrenheit were recorded during a cold spell in Cleveland lasting 40 days.

26	17	12	5	4	25	17	23
6	25	20	27	22	26	30	31
12	27	16	27	16	30	6	16
5	29	18	16	22	29	8	23
13	24	5	⁻7	20	29	18	2

1. Use the data to make a table with headings *Temperature in Degrees Fahrenheit,* and *Frequency.*
2. How many days was the high temperature 13 degrees?
3. How many days was the high temperature less than 20 degrees?
4. Draw a line graph to show the frequency distribution of the temperature.
5. Find the median of the distribution.
6. Find the mode of the distribution.
7. Find the mean of the distribution.
8. Find the range of the distribution.
9. Find the standard deviation of the distribution.

The frequencies of the scores on a college entrance examination are normally distributed. Suppose the mean score is 510 and the standard deviation is 80. And suppose 50,000 people took the examination.

10. What percentage of the scores is above 750?

11. How many people scored between 430 and 590?

According to a certain prediction equation, if a person is 50 years old, that person's systolic blood pressure is 135 millimeters. The blood pressure of a person 35 years old is 127.5 millimeters. Let x stand for age in years, and y stand for blood pressure in millimeters.

12. Find the slope of the prediction equation.

13. Find the y-intercept of the prediction equation.

14. Find the prediction equation.

15. Predict the systolic blood pressure of a person who is 45 years old.

chapter 16
Trigonometric Functions and Identities

It has been found that musical sounds are made of precise patterns of waves. These vibrational waves can be described by trigonometric functions.

16–1 Angles and the Unit Circle

Consider a circle, centered at the origin, with two rays extending from the center as shown. One ray is fixed along the positive x-axis. The other ray can rotate about the center.

These rays form an angle. The fixed ray is called the initial side of the angle. The other is called the terminal side of the angle.

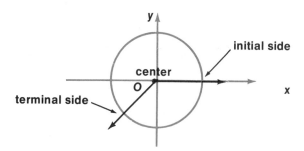

An angle with its vertex at the origin and its initial side along the positive x-axis is said to be in standard position.

Start with both sides along the positive x-axis. As the terminal side is rotated counterclockwise, the measure of the angle formed increases.

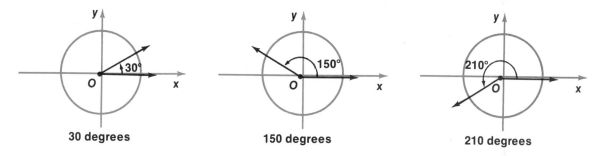

The rotation of the terminal side of the angle may include one or more complete revolutions about the center. The measurement of an angle representing one complete revolution of the circle is 360 degrees, usually written 360°.

The most widely used unit of angle measure is the degree.

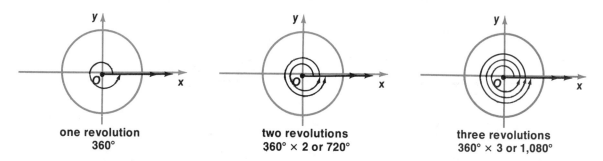

Angles that differ by one or more complete rotations of the circle are called **coterminal angles.** For example, 74°, 434°, and 794° are coterminal angles.

The terminal side of an angle can also rotate in a clockwise direction. A negative number is used to denote the measure of an angle formed in such a way.

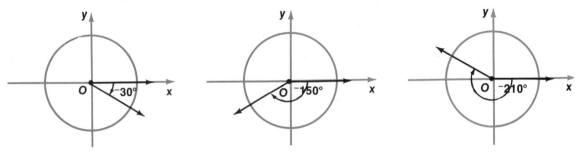

A unit other than the degree may be used in angle measurements.

Suppose a circle with a radius of 1 unit is centered at the origin. This circle is called a **unit circle**. Form an angle in standard position so that it intercepts an arc whose length is 1 unit. This angle is given the measurement 1 **radian**.

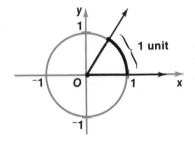

The circumference of a circle with a radius of 1 unit is $2\pi(1)$ or 2π units. Thus, an angle representing one complete revolution of the circle is 2π radians or 360 degrees. To convert radian measure to degree measure, or vice versa, use the following equations.

$$1 \text{ radian is } \frac{360}{2\pi} \text{ or } \frac{180}{\pi} \text{ degrees}$$

$$1 \text{ degree is } \frac{2\pi}{360} \text{ or } \frac{\pi}{180} \text{ radians}$$

When no unit of measure is written, it is assumed the unit is the radian. For example, 2π means 2π radians.

To convert radian measure to degree measure, multiply the number of radians by $\frac{180}{\pi}$.

To convert degree measure to radian measure, multiply the number of degrees by $\frac{\pi}{180}$.

1 Convert 45°, 240°, and ⁻150° to radians.

$$45 \cdot \frac{\pi}{180} = \frac{45\pi}{180} \text{ or } \frac{\pi}{4}$$

$$240 \cdot \frac{\pi}{180} = \frac{240\pi}{180} \text{ or } \frac{4\pi}{3}$$

$$^{-}150 \cdot \frac{\pi}{180} = -\frac{150\pi}{180} \text{ or } -\frac{5\pi}{6}$$

2 Convert $\dfrac{5\pi}{3}$, $-\dfrac{4\pi}{3}$, and $\dfrac{3}{4}$ to degrees.

$$\dfrac{5\pi}{3} \cdot \dfrac{180}{\pi} = \left(\dfrac{900\pi}{3\pi}\right)^{\circ} \text{ or } 300°$$

$$-\dfrac{4\pi}{3} \cdot \dfrac{180}{\pi} = \left(-\dfrac{720\pi}{3\pi}\right)^{\circ} \text{ or } ^{-}240°$$

$$\dfrac{3}{4} \cdot \dfrac{180}{\pi} = \left(\dfrac{540}{4\pi}\right)^{\circ} \text{ or } \dfrac{135°}{\pi}$$

exercises

Exploratory   Suppose angles with the following measurements are in standard position. For each angle, name the quadrant which contains the terminal side.

1. 245°
2. 397°
3. 800°
4. 275°
5. $\dfrac{\pi}{3}$
6. $\dfrac{3}{5}\pi$
7. $\dfrac{11}{3}\pi$
8. $2\dfrac{1}{3}\pi$
9. $^{-}240°$
10. $^{-}32°$
11. 440°
12. 300°
13. $\dfrac{5}{3}\pi$
14. $-\dfrac{12}{5}\pi$
15. $-\dfrac{4}{7}\pi$
16. $\dfrac{5}{9}\pi$
17. 945°
18. $^{-}210°$
19. 198°
20. $^{-}94°$
21. $-\dfrac{9}{4}\pi$
22. 4
23. $\dfrac{2}{3}\pi$
24. 7

Written   Convert each of the following to radians.

1. 90°
2. 120°
3. $^{-}45°$
4. 60°
5. 450°
6. $^{-}300°$
7. 150°
8. $^{-}600°$
9. 45°
10. $^{-}120°$
11. 330°
12. $^{-}240°$
13. 270°
14. $^{-}135°$
15. 180°
16. $^{-}210°$
17. 405°
18. 810°
19. $^{-}315°$
20. $^{-}270°$

Convert each of the following to degrees.

21. π
22. $-\dfrac{\pi}{2}$
23. $\dfrac{\pi}{4}$
24. $-\dfrac{\pi}{6}$
25. 3π
26. $-\dfrac{5}{4}\pi$
27. $-\dfrac{8}{3}\pi$
28. $-\dfrac{7}{4}\pi$
29. $\dfrac{\pi}{6}$
30. $\dfrac{5}{6}\pi$
31. $-\dfrac{\pi}{4}$
32. $\dfrac{3}{4}\pi$
33. $\dfrac{11\pi}{6}$
34. $\dfrac{7\pi}{4}$
35. 5
36. 2
37. $5\dfrac{1}{2}\pi$
38. $4\dfrac{1}{3}\pi$
39. $6\dfrac{1}{2}$
40. $3\dfrac{1}{3}$

16–2   Sine and Cosine

The photograph below is an oscilloscope display. The curve represents a single pure musical tone.

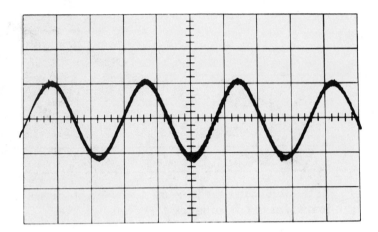

Both the **sine** function and the **cosine** function are used to describe phenomena like musical tones. These functions can be defined in terms of the unit circle.

Consider an angle in standard position. Let θ stand for the measurement of the angle. The terminal side of this angle intersects the circle at a particular point. The x-coordinate of the point is called cosine θ. The y-coordinate of the point is called sine θ.

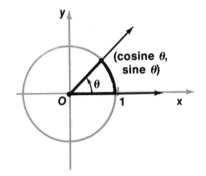

(cosine θ, sine θ)

Let θ stand for the measurement of an angle in standard position. Let (x, y) represent the coordinates of the point where the terminal side intersects the unit circle. Then the following equations hold.

$$\text{sine } \theta = y \text{ and cosine } \theta = x$$

Definition of Sine and Cosine

Sine is abbreviated *sin*. Cosine is abbreviated *cos*.

You can use geometry to find values of the sine and cosine functions for certain angles.

1 **Find sin 45°.**

Consider the right triangle formed by two sides and a diagonal of a square. One side and the hypotenuse of this right triangle are part of the initial and terminal sides of a 45° angle.

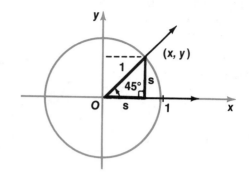

$$s^2 + s^2 = 1^2 \qquad \textit{Use the Pythagorean}$$
$$2s^2 = 1 \qquad \textit{Theorem to find s.}$$
$$s^2 = \frac{1}{2}$$

$$s = \sqrt{\frac{1}{2}} \text{ or } \frac{\sqrt{2}}{2}$$

The length of each side is $\frac{\sqrt{2}}{2}$ units. Thus, the coordinates of the point labeled (x, y) are $\left(\frac{\sqrt{2}}{2}, \frac{\sqrt{2}}{2}\right)$. Therefore, sin 45° = $\frac{\sqrt{2}}{2}$.

2 **Find cos 60°.**

Look at the graph on the right. The dashed line segment cuts the x-axis and the terminal side of the angle to form a 30°–60° right triangle. The lengths of the sides of the triangle are 1 unit, $\frac{1}{2}$ unit, and $\frac{\sqrt{3}}{2}$ units. Thus, the x-coordinate of the point labeled (x, y) is $\frac{1}{2}$.

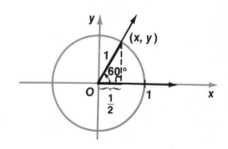

$$\cos 60° = \frac{1}{2}$$

3 **Find sin 120°.**

Notice that the dashed line segment cuts the x-axis and the terminal side of the angle to form a 30°–60° right triangle.

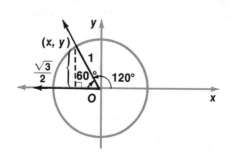

$$x^2 + y^2 = 1 \qquad \textit{Use the Pythagorean}$$
$$\left(\frac{1}{2}\right)^2 + y^2 = 1 \qquad \textit{Theorem to find y.}$$

$$y^2 = 1 - \left(\frac{1}{2}\right)^2$$

$$y = \sqrt{1 - \left(\frac{1}{4}\right)} \text{ or } \frac{\sqrt{3}}{2}$$

$$\sin 120° = \frac{\sqrt{3}}{2}$$

Using the technique shown in the examples, you should be able to complete a chart like the following.

degrees	0	30	45	60	90	120	135	150	180	210	225	240	270	300	315	330	360
radians	0	$\frac{\pi}{6}$	$\frac{\pi}{4}$	$\frac{\pi}{3}$	$\frac{\pi}{2}$	$\frac{2\pi}{3}$	$\frac{3\pi}{4}$	$\frac{5\pi}{6}$	π	$\frac{7\pi}{6}$	$\frac{5\pi}{4}$	$\frac{4\pi}{3}$	$\frac{3\pi}{2}$	$\frac{5\pi}{3}$	$\frac{7\pi}{4}$	$\frac{11\pi}{6}$	2π
sin θ	0	$\frac{1}{2}$	$\frac{\sqrt{2}}{2}$	$\frac{\sqrt{3}}{2}$	1	$\frac{\sqrt{3}}{2}$	$\frac{\sqrt{2}}{2}$	$\frac{1}{2}$	0	$-\frac{1}{2}$	$-\frac{\sqrt{2}}{2}$	$-\frac{\sqrt{3}}{2}$	-1	$-\frac{\sqrt{3}}{2}$	$-\frac{\sqrt{2}}{2}$	$-\frac{1}{2}$	0
cos θ	1	$\frac{\sqrt{3}}{2}$	$\frac{\sqrt{2}}{2}$	$\frac{1}{2}$	0	$-\frac{1}{2}$	$-\frac{\sqrt{2}}{2}$	$-\frac{\sqrt{3}}{2}$	-1	$-\frac{\sqrt{3}}{2}$	$-\frac{\sqrt{2}}{2}$	$-\frac{1}{2}$	0	$\frac{1}{2}$	$\frac{\sqrt{2}}{2}$	$\frac{\sqrt{3}}{2}$	1

Suppose you made a similar chart for angles from 360° to 720°. Are the values for sin θ and cos θ identical to those in the first chart?

degrees	360	390	405	420	450	480	495	510	540	570	585	600	630	660	675	690	720
radians	2π	$\frac{13\pi}{6}$	$\frac{9\pi}{4}$	$\frac{7\pi}{3}$	$\frac{5\pi}{2}$	$\frac{8\pi}{3}$	$\frac{11\pi}{4}$	$\frac{17\pi}{6}$	3π	$\frac{19\pi}{6}$	$\frac{13\pi}{4}$	$\frac{10\pi}{3}$	$\frac{7\pi}{2}$	$\frac{11\pi}{3}$	$\frac{15\pi}{4}$	$\frac{23\pi}{6}$	4π
sin θ	0	$\frac{1}{2}$	$\frac{\sqrt{2}}{2}$	$\frac{\sqrt{3}}{2}$	1	$\frac{\sqrt{3}}{2}$	$\frac{\sqrt{2}}{2}$	$\frac{1}{2}$	0	$-\frac{1}{2}$	$-\frac{\sqrt{2}}{2}$	$-\frac{\sqrt{3}}{2}$	-1	$-\frac{\sqrt{3}}{2}$	$-\frac{\sqrt{2}}{2}$	$-\frac{1}{2}$	0
cos θ	1	$\frac{\sqrt{3}}{2}$	$\frac{\sqrt{2}}{2}$	$\frac{1}{2}$	0	$-\frac{1}{2}$	$-\frac{\sqrt{2}}{2}$	$-\frac{\sqrt{3}}{2}$	-1	$-\frac{\sqrt{3}}{2}$	$-\frac{\sqrt{2}}{2}$	$-\frac{1}{2}$	0	$\frac{1}{2}$	$\frac{\sqrt{2}}{2}$	$\frac{\sqrt{3}}{2}$	1

Every 360°, or 2π radians, represents one complete revolution of a circle. Every 360°, or 2π radians, the sine and cosine functions repeat their values. Because of this, we say that the sine and cosine functions are periodic and have a **period** of 360°, or 2π radians.

A function f is called periodic if there is a number a such that $f(x) = f(x + a)$. The least positive value of a for which $f(x) = f(x + a)$ is the period of the function.

Definition of Periodic Function

example

4 **Find sin 930°.**

$$\sin 930° = \sin (570 + 360)° \qquad 930° = 570° + 360°$$
$$= \sin 570° \qquad \textit{Sine has a period of 360°.}$$
$$= \sin (210 + 360)° \qquad 570° = 210° + 360°$$
$$= \sin 210°$$
$$= -\frac{1}{2}$$

The table at the right lists the sign of the sine and cosine functions in each of the four quadrants.

Quadrant II		Quadrant I	
$\sin \theta$	$+$	$\sin \theta$	$+$
$\cos \theta$	$-$	$\cos \theta$	$+$

Quadrant III		Quadrant IV	
$\sin \theta$	$-$	$\sin \theta$	$-$
$\cos \theta$	$-$	$\cos \theta$	$+$

exercises

Exploratory   State whether the value of each is positive or negative.

1. $\sin 300°$
2. $\sin 240°$
3. $\cos (^-210°)$
4. $\cos (^-45°)$
5. $\sin 225°$
6. $\cos (^-135°)$
7. $\sin (^-270°)$
8. $\sin 315°$
9. $\sin \frac{\pi}{3}$
10. $\cos \frac{7\pi}{3}$
11. $\cos \frac{5}{3}\pi$
12. $\sin \left(-\frac{3}{4}\pi\right)$

Written   For each of the following, find the least positive angle that is coterminal.

1. $420°$
2. $^-40°$
3. $1020°$
4. $^-450°$
5. 3π
6. $^-120°$
7. $\frac{9}{2}\pi$
8. $\frac{11}{5}\pi$
9. $-\frac{\pi}{4}$
10. $600°$
11. $1200°$
12. $1400°$
13. $\frac{13}{3}\pi$
14. $\frac{27}{4}\pi$
15. $\frac{11}{4}\pi$
16. $680°$
17. $^-600°$
18. $1240°$
19. $-\frac{8}{9}\pi$
20. $^-240°$
21. $-\frac{7}{4}\pi$
22. $\frac{31}{6}\pi$
23. $-\frac{2}{3}\pi$
24. $\frac{21}{4}\pi$
25. $960°$
26. $^-300°$
27. $^-760°$
28. $240°$

Find each of the following.

29. $\cos 150°$
30. $\cos {}^-150°$
31. $\cos \frac{11}{3}\pi$
32. $\sin \frac{17}{4}\pi$
33. $\cos \left(-\frac{3}{4}\pi\right)$
34. $\sin \left(-\frac{5}{3}\pi\right)$
35. $\sin \frac{3\pi}{2}$
36. $\cos \frac{7}{4}\pi$
37. $\cos 390°$
38. $\sin {}^-240°$
39. $\cos \left(-\frac{7}{4}\pi\right)$
40. $\sin 660°$
41. $\sin 300°$
42. $\cos 900°$
43. $\cos 330°$
44. $\sin {}^-180°$
45. $\cos {}^-60°$
46. $\sin \left(-\frac{\pi}{6}\right)$
47. $\sin \frac{4}{3}\pi$
48. $\cos 1560°$

Evaluate each expression.

49. $\dfrac{\sin 30° + \cos 60°}{2}$
50. $\dfrac{4 \sin 300° + 2 \cos 30°}{3}$
51. $4(\sin 30°)(\cos 60°)$
52. $\sin 30° + \sin 60°$
53. $(\sin 60°)^2 + (\cos 60°)^2$
54. $8(\sin 120°)(\cos 120°)$
55. $\sin 240° + \cos 240°$
56. $(\sin 240°)(\cos 120°)$

16–3   Graphing Sine and Cosine

To graph the sine function, use the horizontal axis for the values of θ in either degrees or radians. Use the vertical axis for values of $\sin \theta$.

degrees	0	30	45	60	90	120	135	150	180	210	225	240	270	300	315	330	360
$\sin \theta$	0	$\frac{1}{2}$	$\frac{\sqrt{2}}{2}$	$\frac{\sqrt{3}}{2}$	1	$\frac{\sqrt{3}}{2}$	$\frac{\sqrt{2}}{2}$	$\frac{1}{2}$	0	$-\frac{1}{2}$	$-\frac{\sqrt{2}}{2}$	$-\frac{\sqrt{3}}{2}$	-1	$-\frac{\sqrt{3}}{2}$	$-\frac{\sqrt{2}}{2}$	$-\frac{1}{2}$	0
nearest tenth	0	0.5	0.7	0.9	1	0.9	0.7	0.5	0	−0.5	−0.7	−0.9	−1	−0.9	−0.7	−0.5	0

After plotting several points, complete the graph by connecting the points with a smooth, continuous curve.

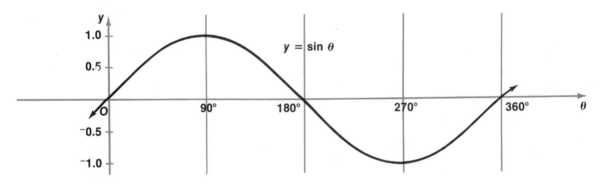

The graph of the cosine function is done in a similar manner.

degrees	0	30	45	60	90	120	135	150	180	210	225	240	270	300	315	330	360
$\cos \theta$	1	$\frac{\sqrt{3}}{2}$	$\frac{\sqrt{2}}{2}$	$\frac{1}{2}$	0	$-\frac{1}{2}$	$-\frac{\sqrt{2}}{2}$	$-\frac{\sqrt{3}}{2}$	-1	$-\frac{\sqrt{3}}{2}$	$-\frac{\sqrt{2}}{2}$	$-\frac{1}{2}$	0	$\frac{1}{2}$	$\frac{\sqrt{2}}{2}$	$\frac{\sqrt{3}}{2}$	1
nearest tenth	1	0.9	0.7	0.5	0	−0.5	−0.7	−0.9	−1	−0.9	−0.7	−0.5	0	0.5	0.7	0.9	1

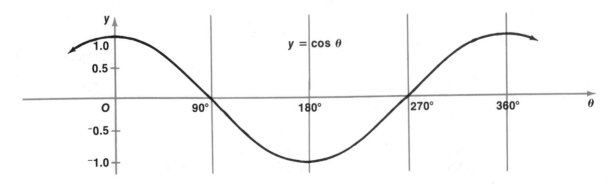

Recall that both the sine and cosine functions have a period of 360° or 2π radians. The graph of either function repeats itself every 360°. The following examples are variations of the sine function that have periods other than 360°.

1 **Graph $y = \sin 2\theta$. State the period.**

First, complete a table of values.

θ	0°	15°	30°	45°	60°	75°	90°	105°	120°	135°	150°	165°	180°
2θ	0°	30°	60°	90°	120°	150°	180°	210°	240°	270°	300°	330°	360°
$\sin 2\theta$	0	$\frac{1}{2}$	$\frac{\sqrt{3}}{2}$	1	$\frac{\sqrt{3}}{2}$	$\frac{1}{2}$	0	$-\frac{1}{2}$	$-\frac{\sqrt{3}}{2}$	-1	$-\frac{\sqrt{3}}{2}$	$-\frac{1}{2}$	0

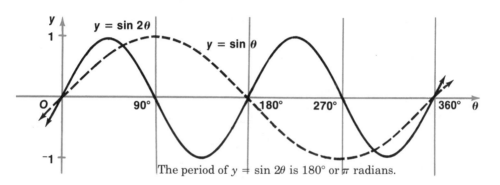

The period of $y = \sin 2\theta$ is 180° or π radians.

2 **Graph $y = \sin\frac{1}{2}\theta$. State the period.**

θ	0°	60°	90°	120°	180°	240°	270°	300°	360°
$\frac{1}{2}\theta$	0°	30°	45°	60°	90°	120°	135°	150°	180°
$\sin\frac{1}{2}\theta$	0	$\frac{1}{2}$	$\frac{\sqrt{2}}{2}$	$\frac{\sqrt{3}}{2}$	1	$\frac{\sqrt{3}}{2}$	$\frac{\sqrt{2}}{2}$	$\frac{1}{2}$	0

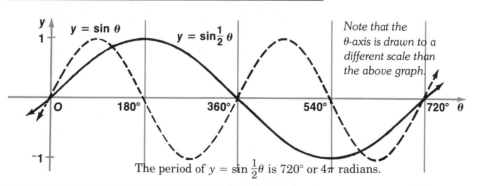

Note that the θ-axis is drawn to a different scale than the above graph.

The period of $y = \sin\frac{1}{2}\theta$ is 720° or 4π radians.

All the trigonometric functions you have graphed so far have a maximum value of 1 and a minimum value of ‾1. The amplitude of these graphs is 1. The graphs in the following examples have amplitudes other than 1.

3 Graph $y = 2 \cos \theta$. State the amplitude.

θ	0°	30°	60°	90°	120°	150°	180°	210°	240°	270°	300°	330°	360°
$\cos \theta$	1	$\dfrac{\sqrt{3}}{2}$	$\dfrac{1}{2}$	0	$-\dfrac{1}{2}$	$-\dfrac{\sqrt{3}}{2}$	‾1	$-\dfrac{\sqrt{3}}{2}$	$-\dfrac{1}{2}$	0	$\dfrac{1}{2}$	$\dfrac{\sqrt{3}}{2}$	1
$2 \cos \theta$	2	$\sqrt{3}$	1	0	‾1	‾$\sqrt{3}$	‾2	‾$\sqrt{3}$	‾1	0	1	$\sqrt{3}$	2

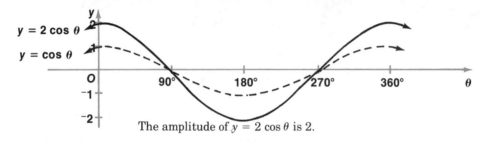

$y = 2 \cos \theta$

$y = \cos \theta$

The amplitude of $y = 2 \cos \theta$ is 2.

4 Graph $y = \dfrac{1}{2} \cos \theta$. State the amplitude.

θ	0°	30°	60°	90°	120°	150°	180°	210°	240°	270°	300°	330°	360°
$\cos \theta$	1	$\dfrac{\sqrt{3}}{2}$	$\dfrac{1}{2}$	0	$-\dfrac{1}{2}$	$-\dfrac{\sqrt{3}}{2}$	‾1	$-\dfrac{\sqrt{3}}{2}$	$-\dfrac{1}{2}$	0	$\dfrac{1}{2}$	$\dfrac{\sqrt{3}}{2}$	1
$\dfrac{1}{2} \cos \theta$	$\dfrac{1}{2}$	$\dfrac{\sqrt{3}}{4}$	$\dfrac{1}{4}$	0	$-\dfrac{1}{4}$	$-\dfrac{\sqrt{3}}{4}$	$-\dfrac{1}{2}$	$\dfrac{\sqrt{3}}{4}$	$-\dfrac{1}{4}$	0	$\dfrac{1}{4}$	$\dfrac{\sqrt{3}}{4}$	$\dfrac{1}{2}$

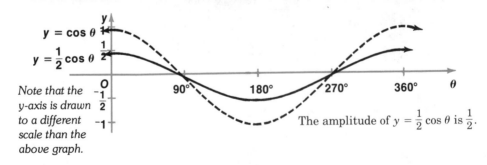

$y = \cos \theta$

$y = \dfrac{1}{2} \cos \theta$

Note that the y-axis is drawn to a different scale than the above graph.

The amplitude of $y = \dfrac{1}{2} \cos \theta$ is $\dfrac{1}{2}$.

From these examples the following generalizations can be made.

For functions of the form $y = a \sin b\theta$ and $y = a \cos b\theta$, the amplitude is $|a|$ and the period is $\dfrac{2\pi}{|b|}$.

Amplitudes and Periods

5   **Graph** $y = \frac{3}{2} \cos \frac{1}{2}\theta.$

The amplitude is $\left|\frac{3}{2}\right|$ or $\frac{3}{2}$. The period is $\frac{2\pi}{\left|\frac{1}{2}\right|}$ or 4π.

The graph has a shape like $y = \cos \theta$.

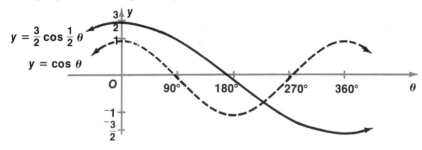

$y = \frac{3}{2} \cos \frac{1}{2}\theta$

$y = \cos \theta$

exercises

Exploratory   State the amplitude and period for each of the following.

1. $y = \sin \theta$

2. $y = \frac{1}{2} \cos \theta$

3. $y = \frac{2}{3} \cos \theta$

4. $y = 3 \sin \theta$

5. $y = 6 \sin \frac{2}{3}\theta$

6. $y = 3 \cos \frac{1}{2}\theta$

7. $y = 4 \cos \frac{3}{4}\theta$

8. $y = 2 \sin \frac{1}{5}\theta$

9. $y = 5 \sin \theta$

10. $y = \sin 4\theta$

11. $y = \cos 3\theta$

12. $y = \cos 2\theta$

13. $y = 4 \sin \frac{1}{2}\theta$

14. $y = {}^-2 \sin \theta$

15. $y = {}^-3 \sin \frac{2}{3}\theta$

16. $y = {}^-6 \sin 2\theta$

17. $y = -\frac{1}{2} \cos \frac{3}{4}\theta$

18. $3y = 2 \sin \frac{1}{2}\theta$

19. $\frac{1}{2}y = 3 \sin 2\theta$

20. $\frac{3}{4}y = \frac{2}{3} \sin \frac{3}{5}\theta$

Written   Graph each of the following.

1. $y = \sin \theta$

2. $y = \frac{1}{2} \cos \theta$

3. $y = \frac{2}{3} \cos \theta$

4. $y = 3 \sin \theta$

5. $y = 6 \sin \frac{2}{3}\theta$

6. $y = 3 \cos \frac{1}{2}\theta$

7. $y = 4 \cos \frac{3}{4}\theta$

8. $y = 2 \sin \frac{1}{5}\theta$

9. $y = 5 \sin \theta$

10. $y = \sin 4\theta$

11. $y = \cos 3\theta$

12. $y = \cos 2\theta$

13. $y = 4 \sin \frac{1}{2}\theta$

14. $y = {}^-2 \sin \theta$

15. $y = {}^-3 \sin \frac{2}{3}\theta$

16. $y = {}^-6 \sin 2\theta$

17. $y = -\frac{1}{2} \cos \frac{3}{4}\theta$

18. $3y = 2 \sin \frac{1}{2}\theta$

19. $\frac{1}{2}y = 3 \sin 2\theta$

20. $\frac{3}{4}y = \frac{2}{3} \sin \frac{3}{5}\theta$

Skills Review   Graph each function and its inverse.

1. $y = x$

2. $y = \frac{1}{2}x$

3. $y = {}^-x + 2$

4. $y = {}^-3x - 1$

5. $f(x) = x^2 - 2$

6. $f(x) = {}^-x^2 + 1$

7. $f(\theta) = (\theta + 1)^2$

8. $f(\theta) = (1 - \theta)^2$

16-4   Other Trigonometric Functions

Other trigonometric functions are defined using sine and cosine.

Let θ stand for the measurement of an angle in standard position on the unit circle. Then the following equations hold.

$$\left.\begin{array}{l} \tan \theta = \dfrac{\sin \theta}{\cos \theta} \\[2mm] \sec \theta = \dfrac{1}{\cos \theta} \end{array}\right\} \quad \text{for } \cos \theta \neq 0$$

$$\left.\begin{array}{l} \cot \theta = \dfrac{\cos \theta}{\sin \theta} \\[2mm] \csc \theta = \dfrac{1}{\sin \theta} \end{array}\right\} \quad \text{for } \sin \theta \neq 0$$

Definition of Tangent (tan), Cotangent (cot), Secant (sec), and Cosecant (csc)

example

1 Find each of the following.

a. $\tan 150°$

$$\tan 150° = \frac{\sin 150°}{\cos 150°}$$

$$= \frac{\frac{1}{2}}{-\frac{\sqrt{3}}{2}}$$

$$= -\frac{1}{\sqrt{3}} \text{ or } -\frac{\sqrt{3}}{3}$$

b. $\sec 45°$

$$\sec 45° = \frac{1}{\cos 45°}$$

$$= \frac{1}{\frac{\sqrt{2}}{2}}$$

$$= \frac{2}{\sqrt{2}} \text{ or } \sqrt{2}$$

After completing a table of values, you can graph $y = \tan \theta$.

θ	0°	30°	45°	60°	90°	120°	135°	150°	180°	210°	225°	240°	270°	300°	315°	330°	360°
$\tan \theta$	0	$\frac{\sqrt{3}}{3}$	1	$\sqrt{3}$	not defined	$-\sqrt{3}$	$^-1$	$-\frac{\sqrt{3}}{3}$	0	$\frac{\sqrt{3}}{3}$	1	$\sqrt{3}$	not defined	$^-\sqrt{3}$	$^-1$	$-\frac{\sqrt{3}}{3}$	0

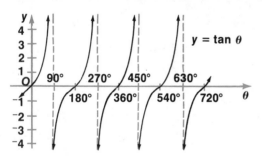

$y = \tan \theta$

The tangent function is not defined for 90° or 270°. The graph is separated by vertical asymptotes, indicated by dashed lines.

The period of the tangent function is 180° or π radians. What is the amplitude?

The following are graphs of the secant, cotangent, and cosecant functions. Compare them to the graphs of the cosine, tangent, and sine functions, shown as dashed curves.

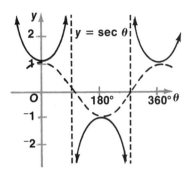 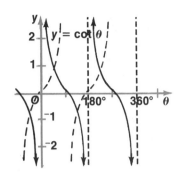 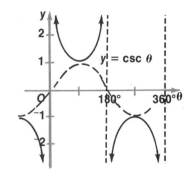

Note that the period of the secant and cosecant functions is 360° or 2π radians. The period of the cotangent function is 180° or π radians.

example

2 **Draw the graph of $y = -\frac{1}{2} \csc 2\theta$.**

θ	0°	15°	30°	45°	60°	75°	90°	105°	120°	135°	150°	165°	180°
2θ	0°	30°	60°	90°	120°	150°	180°	210°	240°	270°	300°	330°	360°
$-\frac{1}{2} \csc 2\theta$	not defined	-1	$-\frac{\sqrt{3}}{3}$	$-\frac{1}{2}$	$-\frac{\sqrt{3}}{3}$	-1	not defined	1	$\frac{\sqrt{3}}{3}$	$\frac{1}{2}$	$\frac{\sqrt{3}}{3}$	1	not defined

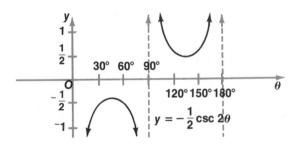

exercises

Exploratory State the values of θ between and including 0° and 360° for which each expression is not defined.

1. $\sin \theta$
2. $\cos \theta$
3. $\tan \theta$
4. $\cot \theta$
5. $\sec \theta$
6. $\csc \theta$

State the period of each function.

7. $y = \tan \frac{1}{2}\theta$

8. $y = \sec 3\theta$

9. $y = \csc 2\theta$

10. $y = \cot 5\theta$

11. $y = \tan 3\theta$

12. $y = 4 \sec \theta$

13. $y = \csc \frac{3}{4}\theta$

14. $y = \cot \frac{1}{3}\theta$

15. $y = 3 \tan \theta$

16. $y = \frac{1}{2} \sec \frac{1}{2}\theta$

17. $y = \frac{3}{4} \csc \frac{2}{3}\theta$

18. $y = 6 \cot 2\theta$

Written State whether values of the following functions are increasing or decreasing in each of the four quadrants.

1. $y = \sin \theta$

2. $y = \cos \theta$

3. $y = \tan \theta$

4. $y = \cot \theta$

5. $y = \sec \theta$

6. $y = \csc \theta$

Find each of the following.

7. $\sec 60°$

8. $\tan 120°$

9. $\cot 135°$

10. $\csc 45°$

11. $\tan \left(-\frac{\pi}{3}\right)$

12. $\csc (^-210°)$

13. $\sec 300°$

14. $\cot (^-60°)$

15. $\sec (^-120°)$

16. $\cot \left(-\frac{\pi}{6}\right)$

17. $\csc \left(-\frac{\pi}{6}\right)$

18. $\tan \frac{7}{6}\pi$

19. $\cot \frac{7}{4}\pi$

20. $\tan (^-300°)$

21. $\sec 240°$

22. $\cot 210°$

23. $\cot 540°$

24. $\csc 180°$

25. $\tan \frac{9}{4}\pi$

26. $\csc \frac{\pi}{2}$

27. $\tan \left(-\frac{5}{6}\pi\right)$

28. $\csc \frac{4}{3}\pi$

29. $\cot 270°$

30. $\sec 390°$

31. $\cot (^-600°)$

32. $\sec {}^-30°$

33. $\tan 405°$

34. $\csc \left(-\frac{7}{6}\pi\right)$

Graph each of the following.

35. $y = 3 \sec \theta$

36. $y = \csc \frac{1}{3}\theta$

37. $y = \frac{1}{3} \sec \theta$

38. $y = \cot \theta$

39. $y = \sec 3\theta$

40. $y = \csc 2\theta$

41. $y = 2 \sec \theta$

42. $y = 2 \tan \theta$

43. $y = \frac{1}{2} \tan \theta$

44. $y = -\frac{1}{2} \cot 2\theta$

45. $y = 3 \csc \frac{1}{2}\theta$

46. $y = {}^-\cot \theta$

Challenge Suppose a wheel is rolling along a straight line as shown below. A point at the center of the wheel follows a path which is a straight line.

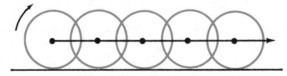

Find the paths followed by these other points.

1.

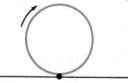

2.

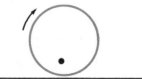

No algebra book would be complete without its share of figures and drawings. These figures and drawings are important aids in understanding the text material. Study a previous portion of this chapter given below.

Consider a circle, centered at the origin, with two rays extending from the center as shown. One ray is fixed along the positive *x*-axis. The other ray can rotate about the center.

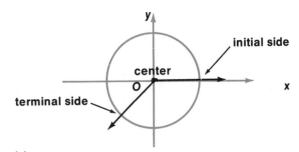

These rays form an angle. The fixed ray is called the initial side of the angle. The other is called the terminal side of the angle.

An angle with its vertex at the origin and its initial side along the positive x-axis is said to be in standard position.

As you read the text material, you should continuously refer to the drawing. The first sentence begins to describe in words what is illustrated in the drawing. You should read the first part of the first sentence, *Consider a circle, centered at the origin,* and then refer to the drawing. Notice the circle in the drawing has its center at the origin. Now, continue the first sentence, *with two rays extending from the center.* Notice the two rays in the drawing are extending from the center. You should continue reading the text in this manner. After each phrase or sentence, study the drawing. By reading the material in this manner, you will receive a better understanding of the ideas presented.

Exercises   Study the figures on pages 479, 480, 482 and 483. What ideas are illustrated in each figure?

16–5   Trigonometric Identities

Let θ be the measurement of an angle in standard position. Let (x, y) be the coordinates of the point of intersection of the terminal side and the circle. Then the following equations hold.

$$\cos \theta = x \text{ and } \sin \theta = y$$

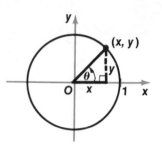

The equation for the unit circle is $x^2 + y^2 = 1$. By substituting $\cos \theta$ for x and $\sin \theta$ for y, you obtain the following equation.

$$(\cos \theta)^2 + (\sin \theta)^2 = 1$$

Normally, this equation is written in the following way.

$$\sin^2 \theta + \cos^2 \theta = 1$$

An equation like $\sin^2 \theta + \cos^2 \theta = 1$ is called an **identity** because it is true for all values of θ. Some trigonometric identities are given below.

Equations which are true for all values of the variables for which they are defined are called identities.

The following trigonometric identities hold for all values of θ except those for which either side of the equation is undefined.

$$\sin^2 \theta + \cos^2 \theta = 1$$

$$1 + \tan^2 \theta = \sec^2 \theta$$

$$1 + \cot^2 \theta = \csc^2 \theta$$

Basic Trigonometric Identities

examples

1 Show that $\cot \theta = \dfrac{1}{\tan \theta}$.

$$\cot \theta = \frac{\cos \theta}{\sin \theta} \qquad \textit{Definition of cot } \theta$$

$$= \frac{1}{\dfrac{\sin \theta}{\cos \theta}} \qquad \frac{\cos \theta}{\sin \theta} \cdot \frac{\frac{1}{\cos \theta}}{\frac{1}{\cos \theta}} = \frac{1}{\frac{\sin \theta}{\cos \theta}}$$

$$= \frac{1}{\tan \theta} \qquad \textit{Definition of tan } \theta$$

2 Show that $\sec^2 \theta + \csc^2 \theta = \dfrac{1}{\sin^2 \theta \cos^2 \theta}$.

$$\sec^2 \theta + \csc^2 \theta = \frac{1}{\cos^2 \theta} + \frac{1}{\sin^2 \theta} \qquad \textit{Definition of sec } \theta \textit{ and csc } \theta$$

$$= \frac{\sin^2 \theta + \cos^2 \theta}{\sin^2 \theta \cos^2 \theta} \qquad \frac{\sin^2 \theta}{\sin^2 \theta} \cdot \frac{1}{\cos^2 \theta} + \frac{\cos^2 \theta}{\cos^2 \theta} \cdot \frac{1}{\sin^2 \theta}$$

$$= \frac{1}{\sin^2 \theta \cos^2 \theta} \qquad \sin^2 \theta + \cos^2 \theta = 1$$

3 **Show that $1 + \tan^2 \theta = \sec^2 \theta$.**

$$1 + \tan^2 \theta = 1 + \left(\frac{\sin \theta}{\cos \theta}\right)^2 \qquad \textit{Definition of } \tan \theta$$

$$= 1 + \frac{\sin^2 \theta}{\cos^2 \theta}$$

$$= \frac{\cos^2 \theta}{\cos^2 \theta} + \frac{\sin^2 \theta}{\cos^2 \theta} \qquad 1 = \frac{\cos^2 \theta}{\cos^2 \theta}$$

$$= \frac{\cos^2 \theta + \sin^2 \theta}{\cos^2 \theta}$$

$$= \frac{1}{\cos^2 \theta} \qquad \sin^2 \theta + \cos^2 \theta = 1$$

$$= \sec^2 \theta$$

The trigonometric identities can be used to evaluate or simplify expressions containing trigonometric functions.

4 **Suppose $\cot \theta = \frac{3}{5}$. Find $\csc \theta$.**

$$\csc^2 \theta = 1 + \cot^2 \theta$$

$$= 1 + \left(\frac{3}{5}\right)^2$$

$$= \frac{34}{25}$$

$$\csc \theta = \pm\sqrt{\frac{34}{25}} \text{ or } \pm\frac{\sqrt{34}}{5}$$

5 **Simplify $\dfrac{1}{1 + \sin x} + \dfrac{1}{1 - \sin x}$.**

$$\frac{1}{1 + \sin x} + \frac{1}{1 - \sin x} = \frac{(1 - \sin x) + (1 + \sin x)}{(1 + \sin x)(1 - \sin x)}$$

$$= \frac{2}{1 - \sin^2 x}$$

$$= \frac{2}{\cos^2 x} \qquad \sin^2 x + \cos^2 x = 1$$

$$= 2\sec^2 x \qquad \sec x = \frac{1}{\cos x}$$

Exploratory   Which of the following are identities?

1. $\sin(-\theta) = -\sin\theta$

2. $\cos\theta\sec\theta = 1$

3. $\csc^2\theta = \cot^2\theta + 1$

4. $\sin^2\theta - \cos^2\theta = 1$

5. $\cot\theta\sin\theta = \cos\theta$

6. $\cos(-\theta) = \cos\theta$

Written   Solve each of the following for values of θ between $0°$ and $90°$.

1. If $\sin\theta = \frac{1}{2}$, find $\cos\theta$.

2. If $\cos\theta = \frac{2}{3}$, find $\sin\theta$.

3. If $\sin\theta = \frac{4}{5}$, find $\cos\theta$.

4. If $\sin\theta = \frac{3}{4}$, find $\sec\theta$.

5. If $\cos\theta = \frac{2}{3}$, find $\csc\theta$.

6. If $\cos\theta = \frac{4}{5}$, find $\tan\theta$.

7. If $\tan\theta = 4$, find $\sin\theta$.

8. If $\cot\theta = 2$, find $\tan\theta$.

Solve each of the following for values of θ between $90°$ and $180°$.

9. If $\sin\theta = \frac{3}{5}$, find $\cos\theta$.

10. If $\sin\theta = \frac{1}{2}$, find $\tan\theta$.

11. If $\cos\theta = -\frac{3}{5}$, find $\csc\theta$.

12. If $\tan\theta = -2$, find $\sec\theta$.

Solve each of the following for values of θ between $180°$ and $270°$.

13. If $\cot\theta = \frac{1}{4}$, find $\csc\theta$.

14. If $\sec\theta = -3$, find $\tan\theta$.

15. If $\sin\theta = -\frac{1}{2}$, find $\cos\theta$.

16. If $\cos\theta = -\frac{3}{5}$, find $\csc\theta$.

Solve each of the following for values of θ between $270°$ and $360°$.

17. If $\cos\theta = \frac{5}{13}$, find $\sin\theta$.

18. If $\tan\theta = -1$, find $\sec\theta$.

19. If $\sec\theta = \frac{5}{3}$, find $\cos\theta$.

20. If $\csc\theta = -\frac{5}{3}$, find $\cos\theta$.

Simplify each of the following.

21. $\tan\theta\cot\theta$

22. $\sec^2\theta - 1$

23. $\sin x + \cos x\tan x$

24. $\csc\theta\cos\theta\tan\theta$

25. $2(\csc^2\theta - \cot^2\theta)$

26. $\dfrac{\tan^2\theta - \sin^2\theta}{\tan^2\theta\sin^2\theta}$

Show that each of the following is an identity.

27. $1 + \cot^2\theta = \csc^2\theta$

28. $\dfrac{\sec\theta}{\csc\theta} = \tan\theta$

29. $\sin x\sec x = \tan x$

30. $\sec a - \cos a = \sin a\tan a$

Challenge   Solve each of the following.

1. If $\cos\theta = \frac{1}{4}$, find $\sin\theta$.

2. If $\sin\theta = \frac{1}{3}$, find $\tan\theta$.

3. If $\sin\theta = \frac{1}{3}$, find $\dfrac{\cos\theta\tan\theta}{\csc\theta}$.

4. If $\tan\theta = \frac{3}{4}$, find $\dfrac{\sin\theta\sec\theta}{\cot\theta}$.

16–6   Verifying Trigonometric Identities

You can use the basic trigonometric identities, along with the definitions of the trigonometric functions, to verify other identities. For example, suppose you wish to know if $\sin \theta \sec \theta \cot \theta = 1$ is an identity. To find out, simplify the expression on the left side of the equation by using the identities and definitions.

$$\sin \theta \sec \theta \cot \theta \overset{?}{=} 1$$

$$\sin \theta \cdot \frac{1}{\cos \theta} \cdot \frac{1}{\tan \theta} \overset{?}{=} 1 \qquad \sec \theta = \frac{1}{\cos \theta} \text{ and } \cot \theta = \frac{1}{\tan \theta}$$

$$\frac{\sin \theta}{\cos \theta} \cdot \frac{1}{\tan \theta} \overset{?}{=} 1 \qquad \textit{Multiply } \sin \theta \textit{ and } \frac{1}{\cos \theta}.$$

$$\tan \theta \cdot \frac{1}{\tan \theta} \overset{?}{=} 1 \qquad \tan \theta = \frac{\sin \theta}{\cos \theta}$$

$$1 = 1$$

Thus, $\sin \theta \sec \theta \cot \theta = 1$ is an identity.

In a way, verifying an identity is like checking the solution to an equation. You do not know if the expressions on each side are equal. That is what you are trying to verify. So, you must simplify one or both sides of the sentence *separately* until they are the same.

Often it is easiest to work with only one side of the sentence. You may choose either side.

examples

1 Verify $\tan^2 x - \sin^2 x = \tan^2 x \sin^2 x$.

$$\tan^2 x - \sin^2 x \overset{?}{=} \tan^2 x \sin^2 x$$

$$\left(\frac{\sin x}{\cos x}\right)^2 - \sin^2 x \overset{?}{=} \tan^2 x \sin^2 x$$

$$\sin^2 x \left(\frac{1}{\cos^2 x} - 1\right) \overset{?}{=} \tan^2 x \sin^2 x$$

$$\sin^2 x (\sec^2 x - 1) \overset{?}{=} \tan^2 x \sin^2 x$$
$$\tan^2 x \sin^2 x = \tan^2 x \sin^2 x$$

Thus, the identity has been verified.

2 Verify $\cot^2 x \sec^2 x = 1 + \cot^2 x$.

$$\cot^2 x \sec^2 x \overset{?}{=} 1 + \cot^2 x$$

$$\cot x = \frac{\cos x}{\sin x} \qquad \left(\frac{\cos x}{\sin x}\right)^2 \left(\frac{1}{\cos x}\right)^2 \overset{?}{=} \csc^2 x \qquad 1 + \cot^2 x = \csc^2 x$$

$$\sec x = \frac{1}{\cos x} \qquad \frac{\cos^2 x}{\sin^2 x} \cdot \frac{1}{\cos^2 x} \overset{?}{=} \left(\frac{1}{\sin x}\right)^2 \qquad \csc x = \frac{1}{\sin x}$$

$$\frac{1}{\sin^2 x} = \frac{1}{\sin^2 x}$$

Thus, the identity has been verified.

The following suggestions are helpful in verifying trigonometric identities. Study the examples to see how these suggestions can be used to verify an identity.

There is often more than one way to verify an identity. Remember that verifying an identity is not the same as solving an equation.

examples

3 **Verify that $1 - \cot^4 x = 2 \csc^2 x - \csc^4 x$.**

$$1 - \cot^4 x \stackrel{?}{=} 2 \csc^2 x - \csc^4 x$$

$$(1 - \cot^2 x)(1 + \cot^2 x) \stackrel{?}{=} 2 \csc^2 x - \csc^4 x \qquad \textit{Factor.}$$

$$[1 - (\csc^2 x - 1)][\csc^2 x] \stackrel{?}{=} 2 \csc^2 x - \csc^4 x \qquad \textit{1 + cot}^2\,x = \csc^2 x$$

$$[2 - \csc^2 x][\csc^2 x] \stackrel{?}{=} 2 \csc^2 x - \csc^4 x \qquad \textit{Simplify.}$$

$$2 \csc^2 x - \csc^4 x = 2 \csc^2 x - \csc^4 x$$

4 **Verify that $\dfrac{1 - \cos x}{\sin x} = \dfrac{\sin x}{1 + \cos x}$.**

$$\frac{1 - \cos x}{\sin x} \stackrel{?}{=} \frac{\sin x}{1 + \cos x}$$

$$\frac{1 - \cos x}{\sin x} \stackrel{?}{=} \frac{\sin x(1 - \cos x)}{(1 + \cos x)(1 - \cos x)} \qquad \textit{Multiply numerator and denominator by 1 - cos x.}$$

$$\frac{1 - \cos x}{\sin x} \stackrel{?}{=} \frac{\sin x(1 - \cos x)}{1 - \cos^2 x} \qquad \textit{Simplify the denominator.}$$

$$\frac{1 - \cos x}{\sin x} \stackrel{?}{=} \frac{\sin x(1 - \cos x)}{\sin^2 x} \qquad \textit{Substitute sin}^2\,x \textit{ for } 1 - \cos^2 x.$$

$$\frac{1 - \cos x}{\sin x} = \frac{1 - \cos x}{\sin x} \qquad \textit{Simplify.}$$

exercises

Exploratory Simplify each of the following.

1. $\csc^2 \theta - \cot^2 \theta$

2. $\tan \theta \cos^2 \theta$

3. $\dfrac{\sin^2 \theta + \cos^2 \theta}{\sin^2 \theta}$

4. $\dfrac{\tan x}{\sin x}$

5. $\csc^2 \gamma - \cot^2 \gamma$

6. $\cos \alpha \csc \alpha$

7. $\sin \theta \cot \theta$

8. $\tan x \csc x$

9. $\dfrac{\tan \theta}{\cot \theta}$

10. $\dfrac{\cos x \csc x}{\tan x}$

Written Verify each identity.

1. $\tan \beta (\cot \beta + \tan \beta) = \sec^2 \beta$

2. $\cos^2 \theta + \tan^2 \theta \cos^2 \theta = 1$

3. $\csc x \sec x = \cot x + \tan x.$

4. $\sec^2 x - \tan^2 x = \tan x \cot x$

5. $\dfrac{\sec \theta}{\sin \theta} - \dfrac{\sin \theta}{\cos \theta} = \cot \theta$

6. $\dfrac{1}{\sec^2 \theta} + \dfrac{1}{\csc^2 \theta} = 1$

7. $\dfrac{\sin \alpha}{1 - \cos \alpha} + \dfrac{1 - \cos \alpha}{\sin \alpha} = 2 \csc \alpha$

8. $\dfrac{\sec \alpha + \csc \alpha}{1 + \tan \alpha} = \csc \alpha$

9. $\dfrac{\cos^2 x}{1 - \sin x} = 1 + \sin x$

10. $\dfrac{1 - \cos \theta}{1 + \cos \theta} = (\csc \theta - \cot \theta)^2$

11. $\dfrac{\sin \theta}{\sec \theta} = \dfrac{1}{\tan \theta + \cot \theta}$

12. $\dfrac{\sec \theta + 1}{\tan \theta} = \dfrac{\tan \theta}{\sec \theta - 1}$

13. $\dfrac{\cot x + \csc x}{\sin x + \tan x} = \cot x \csc x$

14. $\dfrac{1 - 2 \cos^2 \theta}{\sin \theta \cos \theta} = \tan \theta - \cot \theta$

15. $\cos^2 x + \tan^2 x \cos^2 x = 1$

16. $\dfrac{\cos x}{1 + \sin x} + \dfrac{\cos x}{1 - \sin x} = 2 \sec x$

17. $\dfrac{1 + \tan^2 \theta}{\csc^2 \theta} = \tan^2 \theta$

18. $\tan x (\cot x + \tan x) = \sec^2 x$

19. $\dfrac{\sec x}{\sin x} - \dfrac{\sin x}{\cos x} = \cot x$

20. $\dfrac{1 + \tan \gamma}{1 + \cot \gamma} = \dfrac{\sin \gamma}{\cos \gamma}$

21. $\cos^4 x - \sin^4 x = \cos^2 x - \sin^2 x$

22. $1 + \sec^2 x \sin^2 x = \sec^2 x$

23. $\dfrac{\tan^2 x}{\sec x - 1} = 1 + \dfrac{1}{\cos x}$

24. $\sin \theta + \cos \theta = \dfrac{1 + \tan \theta}{\sec \theta}$

25. $\dfrac{1 + \sin x}{\sin x} = \dfrac{\cot^2 x}{\csc x - 1}$

26. $\dfrac{\sin x}{\sin x + \cos x} = \dfrac{\tan x}{1 + \tan x}$

Contest Problem   excursions in algebra

The following problem appeared in a high school mathematics contest sponsored by the Mathematical Association of America.

A tire on a car has an outside diameter of 25 inches. When the radius has been decreased a quarter of an inch, the number of revolutions per mile will be increased by about what percent?

16–7   Differences and Sums

It is often helpful to use formulas for the trigonometric values of the difference or sum of two angles. For example, you could find sin 15° by evaluating sin (45 − 30)°.

The following diagram shows two different angles in standard position on the unit circle.

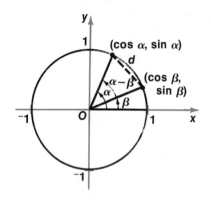

Use the distance formula to find d.

$$d = \sqrt{(\cos\alpha - \cos\beta)^2 + (\sin\alpha - \sin\beta)^2}$$

$$\begin{aligned}
d^2 &= (\cos\alpha - \cos\beta)^2 + (\sin\alpha - \sin\beta)^2 \\
&= (\cos^2\alpha - 2\cos\alpha\cos\beta + \cos^2\beta) \\
&\quad + (\sin^2\alpha - 2\sin\alpha\sin\beta + \sin^2\beta) \\
&= \cos^2\alpha + \sin^2\alpha + \cos^2\beta + \sin^2\beta \\
&\quad - 2\cos\alpha\cos\beta - 2\sin\alpha\sin\beta \\
&= 1 + 1 - 2\cos\alpha\cos\beta - 2\sin\alpha\sin\beta \\
&= 2 - 2\cos\alpha\cos\beta - 2\sin\alpha\sin\beta
\end{aligned}$$

The diagram below shows the angle having measure $\alpha - \beta$ in standard position on the unit circle.

$$d = \sqrt{[\cos(\alpha - \beta) - 1]^2 + [\sin(\alpha - \beta) - 0]^2}$$

$$\begin{aligned}
d^2 &= [\cos(\alpha - \beta) - 1]^2 + [\sin(\alpha - \beta) - 0]^2 \\
&= [\cos^2(\alpha - \beta) - 2\cos(\alpha - \beta) + 1] + [\sin^2(\alpha - \beta)] \\
&= \cos^2(\alpha - \beta) + \sin^2(\alpha - \beta) - 2\cos(\alpha - \beta) + 1 \\
&= \qquad 1 \qquad\qquad - 2\cos(\alpha - \beta) + 1 \\
&= 2 - 2\cos(\alpha - \beta)
\end{aligned}$$

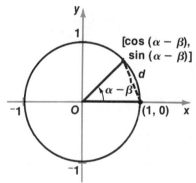

By equating the two expressions obtained for d^2, it is possible to find a formula for $\cos(\alpha - \beta)$.

$$2 - 2\cos(\alpha - \beta) = 2 - 2\cos\alpha\cos\beta - 2\sin\alpha\sin\beta$$

$$^-1 + \cos(\alpha - \beta) = {}^-1 + \cos\alpha\cos\beta + \sin\alpha\sin\beta \qquad \text{\textit{Divide both sides by} }^-2.$$

$$\cos(\alpha - \beta) = \cos\alpha\cos\beta + \sin\alpha\sin\beta \qquad \text{\textit{Add 1 to both sides.}}$$

Using the formula for $\cos(\alpha - \beta)$, you can find a formula for the expression $\cos(\alpha + \beta)$.

$$\begin{aligned}
\cos(\alpha + \beta) &= \cos(\alpha - {}^-\beta) \\
&= \cos\alpha\cos({}^-\beta) + \sin\alpha\sin({}^-\beta) \\
&= \cos\alpha\cos\beta - \sin\alpha\sin\beta
\end{aligned}$$

1 **Use the formula for cos ($\alpha - \beta$) to find cos (90° − θ).**

$$\cos (90° - \theta) = \cos 90° \cos \theta + \sin 90° \sin \theta$$
$$= 0 \cdot \cos \theta + 1 \cdot \sin \theta$$
$$= \sin \theta$$

2 **Use the formula cos (90° − θ) = sin θ to find sin (90° − γ).**

$$\sin (90° - \gamma) = \cos [90° - (90° - \gamma)]$$
$$= \cos (90° - 90° + \gamma)$$
$$= \cos \gamma$$

3 **Find sin ($\alpha - \beta$).**

$$\sin (\alpha - \beta) = \cos [90° - (\alpha - \beta)]$$
$$= \cos [(90° - \alpha) + \beta]$$
$$= \cos (90° - \alpha) \cos \beta - \sin (90° - \alpha) \sin \beta$$
$$= \sin \alpha \cos \beta - \cos \alpha \sin \beta$$

In a similar manner, you can derive two formulas for sin ($\alpha + \beta$).

The following identities hold for all values of α and β.

$$\cos (\alpha \pm \beta) = \cos \alpha \cos \beta \mp \sin \alpha \sin \beta$$
$$\sin (\alpha \pm \beta) = \sin \alpha \cos \beta \pm \cos \alpha \sin \beta$$

Difference and Sum Formulas

The examples below show how to evaluate expressions using the sum and difference formulas.

4 **Find sin 15°.**

$$\sin 15° = \sin (45° - 30°)$$
$$= \sin 45° \cos 30° - \cos 45° \sin 30°$$
$$= \frac{\sqrt{2}}{2} \cdot \frac{\sqrt{3}}{2} - \frac{\sqrt{2}}{2} \cdot \frac{1}{2}$$
$$= \frac{\sqrt{6} - \sqrt{2}}{4}$$

5 **Find cos 75°.**

$$\cos 75° = \cos (45° + 30°)$$
$$= \cos 45° \cos 30° - \sin 45° \sin 30°$$
$$= \frac{\sqrt{2}}{2} \cdot \frac{\sqrt{3}}{2} - \frac{\sqrt{2}}{2} \cdot \frac{1}{2}$$
$$= \frac{\sqrt{6} - \sqrt{2}}{4}$$

exercises

Exploratory Write each angle measure in terms of sums or differences of 30°, 45°, 60°, and 90° or their multiples.

1. 105°
2. ⁻15°
3. ⁻165°
4. 165°
5. 75°
6. ⁻75°
7. 285°
8. 255°

Written Evaluate each expression.

1. $\sin 75°$
2. $\sin 165°$
3. $\sin 285°$
4. $\cos 105°$
5. $\cos 195°$
6. $\cos 255°$
7. $\cos 15°$
8. $\sin 105°$
9. $\cos 165°$
10. $\cos 345°$

Verify each of the following.

11. $\sin (270° - \theta) = {}^{-}\cos \theta$
12. $\cos (270° - \theta) = {}^{-}\sin \theta$
13. $\sin (180° + \theta) = {}^{-}\sin \theta$
14. $\cos (180° + \theta) = {}^{-}\cos \theta$
15. $\sin (90° + \theta) = \cos \theta$
16. $\cos (90° + \theta) = {}^{-}\sin \theta$

Evaluate each expression.

17. $\cos 25° \cos 5° - \sin 25° \sin 5°$
18. $\sin 40° \cos 20° + \cos 40° \sin 20°$
19. $\cos 80° \cos 20° + \sin 80° \sin 20°$
20. $\sin 65° \cos 35° - \cos 65° \sin 35°$

Verify each of the following identities.

21. $\sin (x + y) \sin (x - y) = \sin^2 x - \sin^2 y$
22. $\sin \left(\theta + \dfrac{\pi}{3}\right) - \cos \left(\theta + \dfrac{\pi}{6}\right) = \sin \theta$
23. $\sin (60° + \theta) + \sin (60° - \theta) = \sqrt{3} \cos \theta$
24. $\cos (x + y) + \cos (x - y) = 2\cos x \cos y$
25. $\cos (x + y) \cos (x - y) = \cos^2 y - \sin^2 x$
26. $\sin (x + 30°) + \cos (x + 60°) = \cos x$
27. $\cos (30° + x) - \cos (30° - x) = {}^{-}\sin x$
28. $\sin \left(x + \dfrac{\pi}{4}\right) + \cos \left(x + \dfrac{\pi}{4}\right) = \sqrt{2} \cos x$

Use the identity $\tan (\alpha - \beta) = \dfrac{\tan \alpha - \tan \beta}{1 + \tan \alpha \tan \beta}$ to find the following.

29. $\tan (225° - 120°)$
30. $\tan (315° - 120°)$
31. $\tan (225° - 240°)$
32. $\tan (315° + 60°)$
33. $\tan (30° + 30°)$
34. $\tan (210° + 120°)$
35. $\tan 285°$
36. $\tan 195°$
37. $\tan 165°$
38. $\tan 75°$
39. $\tan (180° - \theta)$
40. $\tan (45° + \beta)$

Challenge Solve each of the following.

1. Use the formulas for sin $(\alpha - \beta)$ and cos $(\alpha - \beta)$ to derive the formula for tan $(\alpha - \beta)$.

   (*Hint:* Divide all terms of an expression by cos α cos β.)

2. Use the sum and difference formulas for sin and cos to verify the following identities.

   $\cos ({}^{-}\alpha) = \cos \alpha$
   $\sin ({}^{-}\alpha) = {}^{-}\sin \alpha$

Some problems may provide more information than what is actually necessary to solve the problem. Other problems may not provide enough information to solve the problems. And yet other problems may be misleading because they lead to unwarranted assumptions. Consider the following example.

Example Suppose two trains, each traveling uniformly, start towards each other at the same time along a straight track. One train is traveling at 60 mph and the other at 90 mph. At the start, with the trains 150 miles apart, a bee travels from one train to the other at the rate of 200 mph. When the bee reaches the second train, it immediately returns to the first train. This continues until the trains meet (and the bee is crushed by the impact). How many miles did the bee travel?

A first reaction may be to try to track the path of the bee. Instead, simply calculate the bee's distance by multiplying its rate of speed by the time it traveled.

To find the time it traveled, calculate the time it took the trains to meet.

Let t = the number of hours the trains traveled before meeting.

$$60t + 90t = 150$$
$$150t = 150$$
$$t = 1$$

The bee was traveling 200 mph. In one hour, the bee traveled a total distance of 200 miles.

Exercises Solve each problem.

1. Samuel went into a hardware store and asked the clerk how much 1 cost. The clerk said, "25¢." Then he asked how much 10 cost, and the clerk said, "50¢." "Good," he replied, "I'll take 1025," and then paid the clerk $1.00. What did he buy?

2. Kandy and Mark are both chess players. They have completed 7 games. Each has won the same number of games and there were no ties. How did this happen?

3. How much will it cost to cut a log into eight equal pieces, if cutting it into four equal pieces costs 90¢?

4. Find the digit that each letter represents so that the following equation is true.
$$(HE)^2 = THE$$

16-8   Double Angles and Half Angles

You can use the formula for $\sin(\alpha + \beta)$ to find $\sin 2\theta$.

$$\begin{aligned}
\sin 2\theta &= \sin(\theta + \theta) \\
&= \sin\theta\cos\theta + \cos\theta\sin\theta \\
&= 2\sin\theta\cos\theta
\end{aligned}$$

Similarly, a formula for $\cos 2\theta$ can be found.

$$\begin{aligned}
\cos 2\theta &= \cos(\theta + \theta) \\
&= \cos\theta\cos\theta - \sin\theta\sin\theta \\
&= \cos^2\theta - \sin^2\theta
\end{aligned}$$

Alternate forms can also be found by making substitutions.

$\cos^2\theta - \sin^2\theta = (1 - \sin^2\theta) - \sin^2\theta$ or $1 - 2\sin^2\theta$ *Substitute $1 - \sin^2\theta$ for $\cos^2\theta$.*
$\cos^2\theta - \sin^2\theta = \cos^2\theta - (1 - \cos^2\theta)$ or $2\cos^2\theta - 1$ *Substitute $1 - \cos^2\theta$ for $\sin^2\theta$.*

These formulas are known as the **double angle formulas.**

The following identities hold for all values of θ.

$$\sin 2\theta = 2\sin\theta\cos\theta \qquad \begin{aligned} \cos 2\theta &= \cos^2\theta - \sin^2\theta \\ &= 1 - 2\sin^2\theta \\ &= 2\cos^2\theta - 1 \end{aligned}$$

Double Angle Formulas

---

example

1   **Suppose x is between $0°$ and $90°$ and $\sin x = \frac{3}{5}$. Find $\sin 2x$.**

Since $\sin 2x = 2\sin x\cos x$, find $\cos x$ first. Use $\cos^2 x + \sin^2 x = 1$.

$$\cos^2 x + \sin^2 x = 1$$
$$\cos^2 x + \left(\frac{3}{5}\right)^2 = 1 \qquad \text{\textit{Substitute} } \tfrac{3}{5} \text{ \textit{for} } \sin x.$$
$$\cos^2 x = 1 - \left(\frac{3}{5}\right)^2$$
$$= \frac{16}{25}$$
$$\cos x = \pm\sqrt{\frac{16}{25}} \text{ or } \pm\frac{4}{5}$$

But x is between $0°$ and $90°$, so $\cos x$ must be positive.

$$\begin{aligned}
\sin 2x &= 2\sin x\cos x \\
&= 2\left(\frac{3}{5}\right)\left(\frac{4}{5}\right) \\
&= \frac{24}{25}
\end{aligned}$$

There also are formulas for $\cos\frac{\alpha}{2}$ and $\sin\frac{\alpha}{2}$.

$$2\cos^2\theta - 1 = \cos 2\theta$$

$$2\cos^2\frac{\alpha}{2} - 1 = \cos\alpha$$

$$\cos^2\frac{\alpha}{2} = \frac{1 + \cos\alpha}{2}$$

$$\cos\frac{\alpha}{2} = \pm\sqrt{\frac{1 + \cos\alpha}{2}}$$

Use double angle formulas.
Substitute α for 2θ
and $\frac{\alpha}{2}$ for θ.

Solve for the squared term.

Take the square root of both sides.

$$1 - 2\sin^2\theta = \cos 2\theta$$

$$1 - 2\sin^2\frac{\alpha}{2} = \cos\alpha$$

$$\sin^2\frac{\alpha}{2} = \frac{1 - \cos\alpha}{2}$$

$$\sin\frac{\alpha}{2} = \pm\sqrt{\frac{1 - \cos\alpha}{2}}$$

These formulas are known as the half angle formulas.

The following identities hold for all values of α.

$$\cos\frac{\alpha}{2} = \pm\sqrt{\frac{1 + \cos\alpha}{2}} \text{ and } \sin\frac{\alpha}{2} = \pm\sqrt{\frac{1 - \cos\alpha}{2}}$$

Half Angle Formulas

---

examples

2 Find cos 105°.

$$\cos 105° = \cos\frac{210°}{2}$$

$$= \pm\sqrt{\frac{1 + \cos 210°}{2}} \qquad \cos 210° = -\frac{\sqrt{3}}{2}$$

$$= \pm\sqrt{\frac{1 + \left(-\frac{\sqrt{3}}{2}\right)}{2}} \text{ or } \pm\frac{\sqrt{2 - \sqrt{3}}}{2}$$

Since 105° is between 90° and 180°, the value of cos 105° is negative.

The solution is $-\dfrac{\sqrt{2 - \sqrt{3}}}{2}$.

3 Find $\sin 67\frac{1}{2}°$.

$$\sin 67\frac{1}{2}° = \sin\frac{135°}{2}$$

$$= \pm\sqrt{\frac{1 - \cos 135°}{2}} \qquad \cos 135° = -\frac{\sqrt{2}}{2}$$

$$= \pm\sqrt{\frac{1 + \frac{\sqrt{2}}{2}}{2}} \text{ or } \pm\frac{\sqrt{2 + \sqrt{2}}}{2}$$

Since $67\frac{1}{2}°$ is between 0° and 90° the value of $\sin 67\frac{1}{2}°$ is positive.

The solution is $\dfrac{\sqrt{2 + \sqrt{2}}}{2}$.

exercises

Exploratory Answer each of the following.
1. x is a first quadrant angle. In which quadrant does the terminal side for $2x$ lie?
2. x is a second quadrant angle. In which quadrant does the terminal side for $2x$ lie?
3. x is a third quadrant angle. In which quadrant does the terminal side for $2x$ lie?
4. x is a fourth quadrant angle. In which quadrant does the terminal side for $2x$ lie?
5. $2x$ is a first quadrant angle. In which quadrant does the terminal side for x lie?
6. $2x$ is a second quadrant angle. In which quadrant does the terminal side for x lie?
7. $2x$ is a third quadrant angle. In which quadrant does the terminal side for x lie?
8. $2x$ is a fourth quadrant angle. In which quadrant does the terminal side for x lie?
9. $\frac{x}{2}$ is a first quadrant angle. In which quadrant does the terminal side for x lie?
10. $\frac{x}{2}$ is a second quadrant angle. In which quadrant does the terminal side for x lie?
11. $\frac{x}{2}$ is a third quadrant angle. In which quadrant does the terminal side for x lie?
12. $\frac{x}{2}$ is a fourth quadrant angle. In which quadrant does the terminal side for x lie?
13. x is a first quadrant angle. In which quadrant does the terminal side for $\frac{x}{2}$ lie?
14. x is a second quadrant angle. In which quadrant does the terminal side for $\frac{x}{2}$ lie?
15. x is a third quadrant angle. In which quadrant does the terminal side for $\frac{x}{2}$ lie?
16. x is a fourth quadrant angle. In which quadrant does the terminal side for $\frac{x}{2}$ lie?

Written Find $\sin 2x$, $\cos 2x$, $\sin \frac{x}{2}$, and $\cos \frac{x}{2}$ for each of the following.
1. $\sin x = \frac{1}{2}$, x is in the first quadrant
2. $\cos x = \frac{3}{5}$, x is in the first quadrant
3. $\cos x = -\frac{2}{3}$, x is in the third quadrant
4. $\sin x = \frac{4}{5}$, x is in the second quadrant
5. $\sin x = \frac{5}{13}$, x is in the second quadrant
6. $\cos x = \frac{1}{5}$, x is in the fourth quadrant
7. $\sin x = -\frac{3}{4}$, x is in the fourth quadrant
8. $\cos x = -\frac{1}{3}$, x is in the third quadrant
9. $\cos x = -\frac{1}{4}$, x is in the second quadrant
10. $\sin x = -\frac{3}{5}$, x is in the third quadrant
11. $\sin x = -\frac{3}{8}$, x is in the fourth quadrant
12. $\cos x = \frac{1}{6}$, x is in the first quadrant
13. $\sin x = -\frac{1}{4}$, x is in the third quadrant
14. $\cos x = -\frac{1}{3}$, x is in the second quadrant

Verify each identity.
15. $\cos^2 2x + 4 \sin^2 x \cos^2 x = 1$
16. $(\sin x + \cos x)^2 = 1 + \sin 2x$
17. $\sin^4 x - \cos^4 x = 2 \sin^2 x - 1$
18. $\sin 2x = 2 \cot x \sin^2 x$
19. $\sin^2 \theta = \frac{1}{2}(1 - \cos 2\theta)$
20. $\dfrac{1}{\sin x \cos x} - \dfrac{\cos x}{\sin x} = \tan x$
21. $\tan^2 \frac{x}{2} = \dfrac{1 - \cos x}{1 + \cos x}$
22. $2 \cos^2 \frac{x}{2} = 1 + \cos x$

16–9 Solving Trigonometric Equations

Trigonometric identities are true for *all* values of the variable involved. Most trigonometric equations are true for *some* but *not all* values of the variable.

1 Solve sin 2 θ + sin θ = 0 if 0° ≤ θ < 360°.

$$\sin 2\theta + \sin \theta = 0$$

$$2 \sin \theta \cos \theta + \sin \theta = 0 \qquad \textit{sin } 2\theta = 2 \textit{ sin } \theta \cos \theta$$

$$\sin \theta \,(2 \cos \theta + 1) = 0 \qquad \textit{Factor.}$$

$$\sin \theta = 0 \quad \text{or} \quad 2 \cos \theta + 1 = 0$$

$$\theta = 0°, 180° \qquad\qquad \cos \theta = -\frac{1}{2}$$

$$\theta = 120°, 240° \qquad \textit{The graphs often help you}$$
$$\textit{find the values of } \theta.$$

The solutions are 0°, 120°, 180°, and 240°.

Usually trigonometric equations are solved for values of the variable between 0° and 360° or 0 radians and 2π radians. There are solutions outside that interval. These other solutions differ by integral multiples of the period of the function.

2 Solve cos θ + 1 = 0 for all values of θ if θ is measured in radians.

The equation can be written in the form cos θ = $^-$1. By looking at the graph, the solutions are π, 3π, 5π, and so on and $^-\pi$, $^-$3π, $^-$5π, and so on.

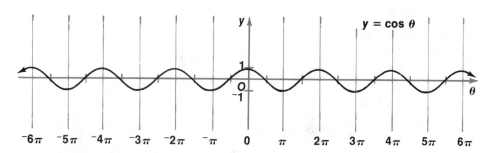

The only solution in the interval 0 radians to 2π radians is π. The period of cosine is 2π radians. So the solutions can be written as $\pi + 2n\pi$ where n is an integer.

If an equation cannot be easily solved by factoring, try writing the expressions in terms of only one trigonometric function.

example

3   **Solve $4 \sin x \cos x = {}^{-}\sqrt{3}$.**

$$4 \sin x \cos x = {}^{-}\sqrt{3}$$

$$2(2 \sin x \cos x) = {}^{-}\sqrt{3}$$

$$2 \sin x \cos x = -\frac{\sqrt{3}}{2}$$

$$\sin 2x = -\frac{\sqrt{3}}{2} \qquad \textit{2 sin x cos x = sin 2x}$$

$$2x = \frac{4\pi}{3} + 2n\pi, \frac{5\pi}{3} + 2n\pi \text{ for } n \text{ an integer}$$

$$x = \frac{2}{3}\pi + n\pi, \frac{5}{6}\pi + n\pi$$

The solutions are $\frac{2}{3}\pi + n\pi$ and $\frac{5}{6}\pi + n\pi$, where n is an integer.

Some trigonometric equations have *no solutions*. In other words, there is no replacement for the variable that will make the sentence true. For example, the equation $\cos x = 2$ has no solution. The solution set is $\emptyset$.

In the following examples, the solutions are found for values of the variable between 0 radians or 0° and 2π radians or 360°. The other solutions differ by integral multiples of the period of the function.

example

4   **Solve $2 \cos^2 \theta - 3 \cos \theta - 2 = 0$ if $0 \le \theta < 2\pi$.**

$$2 \cos^2 \theta - 3 \cos \theta - 2 = 0$$

$$(\cos \theta - 2)(2 \cos \theta + 1) = 0$$

$\cos \theta - 2 = 0 \qquad \text{or} \qquad 2 \cos \theta + 1 = 0$

$\quad\cos \theta = 2 \qquad\qquad\qquad 2 \cos \theta = {}^{-}1$

There is no solution $\qquad\qquad\qquad \cos \theta = -\frac{1}{2}$
to $\cos \theta = 2$ because
all values of $\cos \theta$ $\qquad\qquad\qquad \theta = \frac{2\pi}{3} \text{ or } \frac{4\pi}{3}$
are between ${}^{-}1$
and 1 inclusive.

The solutions are $\frac{2\pi}{3}$ and $\frac{4\pi}{3}$.

It is important to check your solutions. Some algebraic operations may introduce answers that are *not* solutions to the original equation.

5 Solve $\sin x = 1 - \cos x$ if $0° \leq x < 360°$.

$$\sin x = 1 - \cos x$$
$$\sin^2 x = 1 - 2 \cos x + \cos^2 x \qquad \textit{Square both sides.}$$
$$1 - \cos^2 x = 1 - 2 \cos x + \cos^2 x \qquad \sin^2 x = 1 - \cos^2 x$$
$$0 = 2 \cos^2 x - 2 \cos x$$
$$0 = 2 \cos x (\cos x - 1)$$

$$2 \cos x = 0 \qquad \text{or} \qquad \cos x - 1 = 0$$
$$\cos x = 0 \qquad\qquad\qquad \cos x = 1$$
$$x = 90°, 270° \qquad\qquad\qquad x = 0°$$

The solutions appear to be 90°, 270°, 0°. But, 270° does *not* satisfy the original equation. Thus, the solutions are 0° and 90°.

exercises

Exploratory How many solutions does each equation have if $0° \leq \theta < 360°$?

1. $\sin \theta = 1$

2. $\sin \theta = \frac{1}{2}$

3. $\cos \theta = -\frac{\sqrt{3}}{2}$

4. $\tan \theta = 1$

5. $\tan \theta = {}^-3$

6. $\tan^2 \theta = 1$

7. $\sin 2\theta = \frac{1}{2}$

8. $\cos 2\theta = \frac{3}{2}$

9. $\sin 2\theta = -\frac{\sqrt{3}}{2}$

10. $\cos^2 \theta = 1$

11. $\sin 3\theta = {}^-2$

12. $\cos 8\theta = 1$

Written Find all solutions if $0° \leq x < 360°$.

1. $2 \sin^2 x - 1 = 0$

2. $4 \cos^2 x = 1$

3. $2 \sin^2 x + \sin x = 0$

4. $2 \cos^2 x = \sin x + 1$

5. $\sin^2 x + \cos 2x - \cos x = 0$

6. $\cos x = 3 \cos x - 2$

7. $\sin 2x = \cos x$

8. $\sin 2x = 2 \cos x$

9. $4 \sin^2 x - 4 \sin x + 1 = 0$

10. $\sin^2 x = \cos^2 x - 1$

Solve each equation for all values of x.

11. $\cos 2x = \cos x$

12. $\sin^2 x - 2 \sin x - 3 = 0$

13. $\sin x = \cos x$

14. $\tan x = \sin x$

15. $3 \cos 2x - 5 \cos x = 1$

16. $\tan^2 x - \sqrt{3} \tan x = 0$

17. $\sin x = 1 + \cos x$

18. $\cos 2x + \cos x + 1 = 0$

19. $\sin \frac{x}{2} + \cos x = 1$

20. $\sin \frac{x}{2} + \cos \frac{x}{2} = \sqrt{2}$

Skills Review Determine whether the given functions are inverses of one another.

1. $y = 3x + 4$
   $x = 3y + 4$

2. $y = \frac{3}{2}x - 1$
   $3y = 2x + 2$

3. $f(x) = x + 1$
   $f(x) = 1 - x$

4. $f(x) = \sin x$
   $f(x) = \cos x$

16–10 Inverse Trigonometric Functions

The inverse of a function can be found by reversing the order of each ordered pair in the given function.

Since $(0, 1)$ is on the graph of the cosine function, $(1, 0)$ is on the graph of its inverse.

Since $(2\pi, 1)$ is on the graph of the cosine function, $(1, 2\pi)$ is on the graph of its inverse.

The inverse of the cosine function is *not* a function. Why?

Consider only a part of the domain of the cosine function, namely any x so that $0 \leq x \leq \pi$. It is possible to define a new function, called Cosine, whose inverse is a function.

$$y = \text{Cos } x \text{ if and only if } y = \cos x \text{ and } 0 \leq x \leq \pi$$

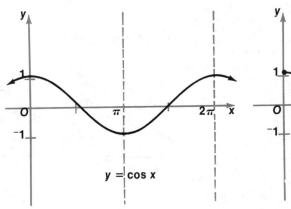
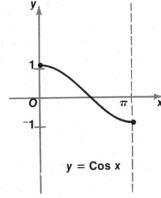

$$y = \cos x$$

The domain is
$\{x \mid x \text{ is an angle measurement}\}$.
The range is $\{y \mid {}^-1 \leq y \leq 1\}$.
The inverse is *not* a function.

$$y = \text{Cos } x$$

The domain is $\{x \mid 0 \leq x \leq \pi\}$.
The range is $\{y \mid {}^-1 \leq y \leq 1\}$.
The inverse is a function.

The values in the domain of Cosine are called **principal values.** Other new functions that have inverses can be defined.

$$y = \text{Sin } x \text{ if and only if } y = \sin x \text{ and } -\frac{\pi}{2} \leq x \leq \frac{\pi}{2}.$$

$$y = \text{Tan } x \text{ if and only if } y = \tan x \text{ and } -\frac{\pi}{2} < x < \frac{\pi}{2}.$$

The principal values of x in $y = \text{Sin } x$ are $\left\{ x \mid -\frac{\pi}{2} \leq x \leq \frac{\pi}{2} \right\}$.

The principal values of x in $y = \text{Tan } x$ are $\left\{ x \mid -\frac{\pi}{2} < x < \frac{\pi}{2} \right\}$.

The inverse cosine function is also called the Arccosine function and is symbolized by **Cos⁻¹** or **Arccos**.

> **Given $y = \text{Cos } x$, the inverse cosine function is defined by the following equation.**
>
> $$x = \text{Cos}^{-1} y$$

Definition of Inverse Cosine

The Arccosine function has the following characteristics.

1. Its domain is the set of real numbers from ⁻1 to 1.
2. Its range is the set of angle measurements from 0 to π.
3. $\text{Cos } x = y$ if and only if $\text{Cos}^{-1} y = x$.
4. $(\text{Cos}^{-1} \circ \text{Cos})(x) = (\text{Cos} \circ \text{Cos}^{-1})(x) = x$
5. Its graph is shown at the right.

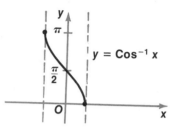

example

1 **Find $\text{Cos}^{-1}\left(-\dfrac{\sqrt{3}}{2}\right)$.**

$$\theta = \text{Cos}^{-1}\left(-\frac{\sqrt{3}}{2}\right)$$

$$\text{Cos } \theta = -\frac{\sqrt{3}}{2}$$

$$\theta = 150° \qquad \textit{Why is } \theta \textit{ not } 210°?$$

The Arcsine and Arctangent functions are defined similarly.

> **Given $y = \text{Sin } x$, the inverse sine function is defined by the following equation.**
>
> $$x = \text{Sin}^{-1} y$$

Definition of Inverse Sine

> **Given $y = \text{Tan } x$, the inverse tangent function is defined by the following equation.**
>
> $$x = \text{Tan}^{-1} y$$

Definition of Inverse Tangent

The graphs of the inverse sine and inverse tangent functions are shown at the right.

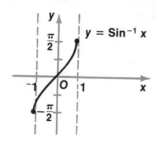

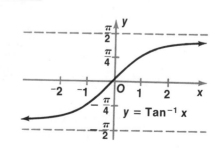

2 **Find $\cos\left(\text{Sin}^{-1}\frac{1}{2}\right)$.**

$$\text{Let } \theta = \text{Sin}^{-1}\frac{1}{2}$$

$$\text{then } \text{Sin }\theta = \frac{1}{2} \text{ so } \theta = 30°$$

$$\text{Cos}\left(\text{Sin}^{-1}\frac{1}{2}\right) = \text{Cos } 30°$$

$$= \frac{\sqrt{3}}{2}$$

In the examples thus far, the principal value of each inverse trigonometric function was known to be the value of a trigonometric function for some angle. Sometimes it is *not* known which angle the principal value corresponds to. In such a case, a diagram may be helpful.

3 **Find $\sin\left(\text{Cos}^{-1}\frac{2}{3}\right)$.**

Let $\theta = \text{Cos}^{-1}\frac{2}{3}$.

From the diagram, we see

that $\left(\frac{2}{3}\right)^2 + \sin^2\theta = 1$.

$\sin^2\theta = 1 - \frac{4}{9}$　　*Solve for sin θ.*

$\sin^2\theta = \frac{5}{9}$

$\sin\theta = \frac{\sqrt{5}}{3}$

Therefore, $\sin\left(\text{Cos}^{-1}\frac{2}{3}\right) = \frac{\sqrt{5}}{3}$.

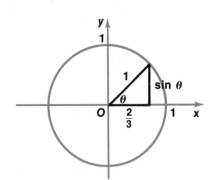

4 **Find $\sin\left[\text{Cos}^{-1}\left(-\frac{1}{2}\right) + \text{Tan}^{-1} 1\right]$.**

Let $\alpha = \text{Cos}^{-1}\left(-\frac{1}{2}\right)$ and let $\beta = \text{Tan}^{-1} 1$

$$\text{Cos }\alpha = -\frac{1}{2} \qquad\qquad \text{Tan }\beta = 1$$

$$\alpha = 120° \qquad\qquad\qquad \beta = 45°$$

$$\sin\left[\text{Cos}^{-1}\left(-\frac{1}{2}\right) + \text{Tan}^{-1} 1\right] = \sin(\alpha + \beta)$$

$$= \sin(120° + 45°)$$

$$= \sin 120° \cos 45° + \cos 120° \sin 45°$$

$$= \frac{\sqrt{3}}{2} \cdot \frac{\sqrt{2}}{2} + \left(-\frac{1}{2}\right) \cdot \frac{\sqrt{2}}{2} \text{ or } \frac{\sqrt{6} - \sqrt{2}}{4}$$

exercises

Exploratory   Find each of the following.

1. $\text{Sin } \dfrac{\pi}{6}$

2. $\text{Cos}^{-1} \dfrac{1}{2}$

3. $\text{Sin}^{-1}\left(-\dfrac{\sqrt{3}}{2}\right)$

4. $\text{Cos } 300°$

5. $\text{Tan } \pi$

6. $\text{Arctan } 1$

7. $\text{Tan } \dfrac{\pi}{4}$

8. $\text{Sin}^{-1}\left(-\dfrac{1}{2}\right)$

9. $\text{Cos}^{-1}\left(-\dfrac{\sqrt{3}}{2}\right)$

10. $\text{Sin } 270°$

11. $\text{Tan}^{-1}(1)$

12. $\text{Sin}^{-1} 0$

13. $\text{Cos}\left(-\dfrac{3}{4}\pi\right)$

14. $\text{Arcsin } \dfrac{\sqrt{3}}{2}$

15. $\text{Sin}^{-1} \dfrac{\sqrt{3}}{2}$

16. $\text{Tan}^{-1}\left(\dfrac{\sqrt{3}}{3}\right)$

17. $\text{Cos } 45°$

18. $\text{Sin}^{-1} 1$

19. $\text{Sin}^{-1}(^-1)$

20. $\text{Sin } \dfrac{5}{6}\pi$

21. $\text{Cos}^{-1} 0$

22. $\text{Sin}^{-1} \dfrac{1}{2}$

23. $\text{Sin } 0°$

24. $\text{Tan}\left(-\dfrac{\pi}{4}\right)$

Written   Find each of the following.

1. $\text{Sin } \dfrac{\pi}{6}$

2. $\text{Tan}^{-1}(^-1)$

3. $\text{Sin}^{-1} 1$

4. $\text{Cos}^{-1}\left(-\dfrac{1}{2}\right)$

5. $\sin\left(\text{Sin}^{-1} \dfrac{1}{2}\right)$

6. $\text{Sin}^{-1}\left(\cos \dfrac{\pi}{2}\right)$

7. $\cos\left(\text{Cos}^{-1} \dfrac{1}{2}\right)$

8. $\cos\left(\text{Cos}^{-1} \dfrac{4}{5}\right)$

9. $\tan\left(\text{Sin}^{-1} \dfrac{5}{13}\right)$

10. $\text{Arccos } \dfrac{\sqrt{3}}{2}$

11. $\sin\left(2 \text{ Cos}^{-1} \dfrac{3}{5}\right)$

12. $\text{Arctan } \sqrt{3}$

13. $\sin\left(2 \text{ Sin}^{-1} \dfrac{1}{2}\right)$

14. $\text{Sin}^{-1}\left(\tan \dfrac{\pi}{4}\right)$

15. $\cos\left[\text{Cos}^{-1}\left(-\dfrac{\sqrt{2}}{2}\right) - \dfrac{\pi}{2}\right]$

16. $\sin\left(\text{Sin}^{-1} \dfrac{\sqrt{3}}{2}\right)$

17. $\tan\left[\text{Cos}^{-1}\left(-\dfrac{3}{5}\right)\right]$

18. $\sin[\text{Arctan}(^-\sqrt{3})]$

19. $\cos(\text{Tan}^{-1} \sqrt{3})$

20. $\cos\left[\text{Arcsin}\left(-\dfrac{1}{2}\right)\right]$

21. $\cos(\text{Tan}^{-1} 1)$

22. $\sin\left[\dfrac{\pi}{2} - \text{Tan}^{-1}(1)\right]$

23. $\cos\left[\dfrac{4}{3}\pi - \text{Cos}^{-1}\left(-\dfrac{1}{2}\right)\right]$

24. $\sin\left[\dfrac{\pi}{2} - \text{Cos}^{-1}\left(\dfrac{1}{2}\right)\right]$

25. $\sin\left(\text{Sin}^{-1} 1 - \text{Cos}^{-1} \dfrac{1}{2}\right)$

26. $\cos\left(\text{Cos}^{-1} 0 + \text{Sin}^{-1} \dfrac{1}{2}\right)$

27. $\cos\left(\text{Tan}^{-1} \sqrt{3} - \text{Sin}^{-1} \dfrac{1}{2}\right)$

28. $\sin\left(2 \text{ Sin}^{-1} \dfrac{\sqrt{3}}{2}\right)$

29. $\sin(\text{Tan}^{-1} 1 + \text{Sin}^{-1} 1)$

30. $\cos\left[\text{Cos}^{-1}\left(-\dfrac{1}{2}\right) - \text{Sin}^{-1} 1\right]$

Chapter Summary

1. **Definition of Sine and Cosine:** Let θ stand for the measurement of an angle in standard position. Let (x, y) represent the coordinates of the point where the terminal side intersects the unit circle. Then sine $\theta = y$ and cosine $\theta = x$. (482)

2. **Definition of Periodic Function:** A function f is called periodic if there is a number a such that $f(x) = f(x + a)$. The least positive value of a for which $f(x) = f(x + a)$ is the period of the function. (484)

3. **Amplitudes and Periods:** For functions of the form $y = a \sin b\theta$ and $y = a \cos b\theta$, the amplitude is $|a|$ and the period is $\dfrac{2\pi}{|b|}$. (488)

4. **Definition of Tangent, Cotangent, Secant, and Cosecant:** Let θ stand for the measurement of an angle in standard position. Then the following equations hold wherever they are defined. (490)

$$\tan \theta = \frac{\sin \theta}{\cos \theta} \qquad \cot \theta = \frac{\cos \theta}{\sin \theta} \qquad \sec \theta = \frac{1}{\cos \theta} \qquad \csc \theta = \frac{1}{\sin \theta}$$

5. **Basic Trigonometric Identities:** The following trigonometric identities hold for all values of θ except those for which either side of the equation is undefined. (494)

$$\sin^2 \theta + \cos^2 \theta = 1$$
$$1 + \tan^2 \theta = \sec^2 \theta$$
$$1 + \cot^2 \theta = \csc^2 \theta$$

6. **Difference and Sum Formulas:** The following identities hold for all values of α and β. (501)

$$\cos (\alpha \pm \beta) = \cos \alpha \cos \beta \mp \sin \alpha \sin \beta$$
$$\sin (\alpha \pm \beta) = \sin \alpha \cos \beta \pm \cos \alpha \sin \beta$$

7. Double Angle Formulas: The following identities hold for all values of θ. (504)

$$\sin 2\theta = 2 \sin \theta \cos \theta$$

$$\cos 2\theta = \cos^2 \theta - \sin^2 \theta$$
$$= 1 - 2 \sin^2 \theta$$
$$= 2 \cos^2 \theta - 1$$

8. Half Angle Formulas: The following identities hold for all values of α. (505)

$$\cos \frac{\alpha}{2} = \pm \sqrt{\frac{1 + \cos \alpha}{2}} \text{ and } \sin \frac{\alpha}{2} = \pm \sqrt{\frac{1 - \cos \alpha}{2}}$$

9. Definition of Inverse Cosine: Given $y = \text{Cos } x$, the inverse cosine function is defined by the following equation. $x = \text{Cos}^{-1} y$. (511)

10. Definition of Inverse Sine: Given $y = \text{Sin } x$, the inverse sine function is defined by the following equation. $x = \text{Sin}^{-1} y$. (511)

11. Definition of Inverse Tangent: Given $y = \text{Tan } x$, the inverse tangent function is defined by the following equation.
$$x = \text{Tan}^{-1} y. \quad (511)$$

Chapter Review

16–1 Convert each of the following to radians.

   1. 120°   **2.** ⁻315°   **3.** 270°   **4.** 225°

Convert each of the following to degrees.

   5. $\frac{\pi}{3}$ **6.** $-\frac{5}{12}\pi$ **7.** $\frac{4}{3}$ **8.** $\frac{7}{4}\pi$

16–2 For each of the following, find the least positive angle that is coterminal.

   9. ⁻155°   **10.** 830°   **11.** 540°   **12.** 945°

   13. $\frac{20}{3}\pi$ **14.** $-\frac{4}{3}\pi$ **15.** $-\frac{2}{9}\pi$ **16.** $-\frac{11}{6}\pi$

Find each of the following.

   17. sin 120°   **18.** cos 210°   **19.** cos 3π **20.** sin (⁻150°)

   21. sin ⁻30°   **22.** sin $\frac{5}{4}\pi$ **23.** cos (⁻135°)   **24.** cos (300°)

   25. $(\sin 30°)^2 + (\cos 30°)^2$ **26.** $(\sin 45°)(\sin 225°)$

16–3 Graph each of the following. Then state the amplitude and period for each graph.

   27. $y = \sin x$ **28.** $y = -\frac{1}{2} \cos \theta$ **29.** $y = 4 \sin 2\theta$

16–4 **Find each of the following.**

30. $\csc \pi$ **31.** $\sec (^-30°)$ **32.** $\csc 135°$ **33.** $\cos 600°$

34. $\sin \frac{4}{3}\pi$ **35.** $\cot \frac{7}{6}\pi$ **36.** $\tan 120°$ **37.** $\sec (^-60°)$

16–5 **Solve each of the following for values of θ between 90° and 180°.**

38. If $\sin \theta = \frac{1}{2}$, find $\cos \theta$.   **39.** If $\csc \theta = \frac{5}{3}$, find $\cos \theta$.

40. If $\sec \theta = ^-3$, find $\tan \theta$.   **41.** If $\cot \theta = -\frac{1}{4}$, find $\csc \theta$.

Solve each of the following for values of θ between 270° and 360°.

42. If $\sin \theta = -\frac{4}{5}$, find $\cos \theta$.   **43.** If $\sec \theta = 1$, find $\tan \theta$.

44. If $\csc \theta = -\frac{5}{3}$, find $\cot \theta$.   **45.** If $\sin \theta = -\frac{1}{2}$, find $\sec \theta$.

16–6 **Verify each identity.**

46. $\sin^4 x - \cos^4 x = \sin^2 x - \cos^2 x$ **47.** $\dfrac{\sin \theta}{\tan \theta} + \dfrac{\cos \theta}{\cot \theta} = \cos \theta + \sin \theta$

48. $\dfrac{\sin \theta}{1 - \cos \theta} = \csc \theta + \cot \theta$ **49.** $\tan x + \cot x = \sec x \csc x$

16–7 **Find each of the following.**

50. $\sin 105°$ **51.** $\cos 240°$ **52.** $\cos 15°$ **53.** $\sin (^-255°)$

Verify each of the following identities.

54. $\cos (90° - \theta) = \sin \theta$ **55.** $\cos (60° + \theta) + \cos (60° - \theta) = \cos \theta$

16–8 **56.** If $\sin x = -\frac{3}{5}$ and x is in the third quadrant, find $\sin 2x$.

57. If $\sin x = \frac{1}{4}$ and x is in the first quadrant, find $\cos 2x$.

58. If $\cos 2x = -\frac{17}{25}$ and $\cos x = \frac{2}{5}$, find $\sin x$.

16–9 **Find all solutions if $0° \le x < 360°$.**

59. $2 \cos^2 x + \sin^2 x = 2 \cos x$ **60.** $\cos 2x = \cos x$ **61.** $\cos 2x \sin x = 1$

62. $\cos x = 1 - \sin x$ **63.** $2 \sin 2x = 1$ **64.** $\tan^2 x + \tan x = 0$

16–10 **Find each of the following.**

65. $\text{Cos}^{-1} \left(\dfrac{\sqrt{3}}{2} \right)$ **66.** $\text{Sin}^{-1} (^-1)$ **67.** $\text{Tan}^{-1} \sqrt{3}$

68. $\text{Sin}^{-1} \left(\tan \dfrac{\pi}{4} \right)$ **69.** $\cos (\text{Sin}^{-1} 1)$ **70.** $\sin \left(2 \, \text{Sin}^{-1} \dfrac{1}{2} \right)$

Convert each of the following to radians.
1. $135°$ 2. $275°$ 3. $^-150°$ 4. $^-4°$

Convert each of the following to degrees.
5. $\frac{4}{5}\pi$ 6. $\frac{12}{5}\pi$ 7. $-\frac{7}{4}\pi$ 8. 7

For each of the following, find the least positive angle that is coterminal.
9. $620°$ 10. $^-260°$ 11. $595°$ 12. $^-1270°$

Find each value.
13. $\sin 225°$ 14. $\cos (^-120°)$ 15. $\cos \frac{3}{4}\pi$ 16. $\sin \frac{7}{4}\pi$

Graph each of the following. Then state the amplitude and period.
17. $y = 2 \sin 2x$ 18. $y = \frac{3}{4} \cos \frac{2}{3}x$

Find each of the following.
19. $\tan 225°$ 20. $\csc {}^-120°$ 21. $\cos \frac{2}{3}\pi$ 22. $\sec 150°$

Solve each of the following for values of θ between 180° and 270°.
23. If $\sin \theta = -\frac{1}{2}$, find $\tan \theta$. 24. If $\cot \theta = \frac{3}{4}$, find $\sec \theta$.

Verify each identity.
25. $\dfrac{\cos x}{1 - \sin^2 x} = \sec x$ 26. $\dfrac{\sec x}{\sin x} - \dfrac{\sin x}{\cos x} = \cot x$ 27. $\dfrac{1 + \tan^2 \theta}{\cos^2 \theta} = \sec^4 \theta$

Evaluate each of the following.
28. $\sin 255°$ 29. $\cos 165°$

30. If x is in the first quadrant and $\cos x = \frac{3}{4}$, find $\sin \frac{1}{2}x$.

31. If $\cos 2x = \frac{2}{9}$ and $\sin x = \frac{1}{3}$, find $\cos x$.

Find all solutions if $0° \le x < 360°$.
32. $2 \sin x \cos x - \sin x = 0$ 33. $\cos 2x + \sin x = 1$
34. $\sec x = 1 + \tan x$ 35. $2 \cos^2 2x + \cos 2x - 1 = 0$

Find each of the following.
36. $\text{Tan}^{-1} \dfrac{\sqrt{3}}{3}$ 37. $\text{Sin}^{-1}\left(-\dfrac{1}{2}\right)$ 38. $\text{Cos}^{-1}(\sin 30°)$ 39. $\sin 2\left(\text{Cos}^{-1} \dfrac{1}{2}\right)$

chapter
17 Right Triangle Trigonometry

For maximum strength, structures must be constructed as designed. Civil engineers often use surveying equipment and trigonometry to check building construction.

17–1 Right Triangles

Trigonometry can be used to find the missing measures of triangles. Consider the right triangle below.

The **hypotenuse** of the triangle is side AB. Its length is c units.

The side opposite angle A is side BC. Its length is a units.

The side adjacent to angle A is side AC. Its length is b units.

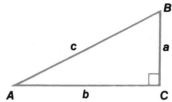

For convenience of notation, we refer to the angle with vertex at A as angle A and use A to stand for its measurement. Similarly, we refer to angle B and its measurement, B. And we refer to angle C and its measurement, C.

Suppose a unit circle is drawn with its center at vertex A as shown below.

The triangle in the interior of the unit circle is similar to triangle ABC. Hence, the measures of the corresponding sides of the triangles are proportional.

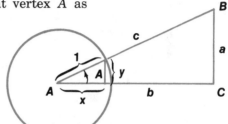

SOH-CAH-TOA is a helpful mnemonic device for remembering the first 3 equations.

$$sin = \frac{opposite}{hypotenuse}$$
$$cos = \frac{adjacent}{hypotenuse}$$
$$tan = \frac{opposite}{adjacent}$$

In this figure, $\sin A = y$. Since the two triangles are similar, $\frac{y}{a} = \frac{1}{c}$. Hence, $y = \frac{a}{c}$ and $\sin A = \frac{a}{c}$. Using the figure, trigonometric values can be defined in the following way.

$$\sin A = \frac{a}{c} \qquad \cos A = \frac{b}{c} \qquad \tan A = \frac{a}{b}$$

$$\csc A = \frac{c}{a} \qquad \sec A = \frac{c}{b} \qquad \cot A = \frac{b}{a}$$

example **1** Find the sine, cosine, tangent, cosecant, secant, and cotangent of angle A to the nearest four decimal places.

$$\sin A = \frac{6}{10} \text{ or } 0.6000$$

$$\cos A = \frac{8}{10} \text{ or } 0.8000$$

$$\tan A = \frac{6}{8} \text{ or } 0.7500$$

$$\csc A = \frac{10}{6} \text{ or } 1.6667$$

$$\sec A = \frac{10}{8} \text{ or } 1.2500$$

$$\cot A = \frac{8}{6} \text{ or } 1.3333$$

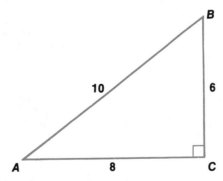

2 **Find sin A to the nearest four decimal places.**

First, use the Pythagorean Theorem to find the value of a.

$$a^2 + 7^2 = 11^2$$
$$a^2 = 72$$
$$a = \sqrt{72}$$

Then, find the value of $\frac{a}{c}$.

$$\sin A = \frac{\sqrt{72}}{11}$$

$$\sin A = 0.7714 \qquad \text{The sine of angle } A \text{ is about } 0.7714.$$

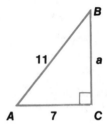

Consider two special right triangles. Triangle ABC is an isosceles right triangle. Assume the congruent sides are each 1 unit long. Use the Pythagorean Theorem to find the length of the hypotenuse.

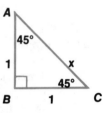

$$1^2 + 1^2 = x^2$$
$$2 = x^2$$
$$\sqrt{2} = x \qquad \text{The hypotenuse is } \sqrt{2} \text{ units long.}$$

Now, write the values of the trigonometric functions.

$$\sin 45° = \frac{1}{\sqrt{2}} \text{ or } \frac{\sqrt{2}}{2} \qquad \cos 45° = \frac{1}{\sqrt{2}} \text{ or } \frac{\sqrt{2}}{2} \qquad \tan 45° = \frac{1}{1} \text{ or } 1$$

$$\csc 45° = \frac{\sqrt{2}}{1} \text{ or } \sqrt{2} \qquad \sec 45° = \frac{\sqrt{2}}{1} \text{ or } \sqrt{2} \qquad \cot 45° = \frac{1}{1} \text{ or } 1$$

Triangle DEG is an equilateral triangle. Assume each side is 2 units long. The altitude EF forms a triangle whose angle measurements are 30°, 60°, and 90°. Since altitude EF is the perpendicular bisector of side DG, the length of side DF is 1. Find the length of side EF.

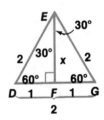

$$x^2 + 1^2 = 2^2$$
$$x^2 = 3$$
$$x = \sqrt{3} \qquad \text{Side } EF \text{ is } \sqrt{3} \text{ units long.}$$

Now, write the trigonometric values.

$$\sin 30° = \frac{1}{2} \qquad\qquad \cos 30° = \frac{\sqrt{3}}{2} \qquad\qquad \tan 30° = \frac{1}{\sqrt{3}} \text{ or } \frac{\sqrt{3}}{3}$$

$$\csc 30° = \frac{2}{1} \text{ or } 2 \qquad \sec 30° = \frac{2}{\sqrt{3}} \text{ or } \frac{2\sqrt{3}}{3} \qquad \cot 30° = \frac{\sqrt{3}}{1} \text{ or } \sqrt{3}$$

$$\sin 60° = \frac{\sqrt{3}}{2} \qquad\qquad \cos 60° = \frac{1}{2} \qquad\qquad \tan 60° = \frac{\sqrt{3}}{1} \text{ or } \sqrt{3}$$

$$\csc 60° = \frac{2}{\sqrt{3}} \text{ or } \frac{2\sqrt{3}}{3} \qquad \sec 60° = \frac{2}{1} \text{ or } 2 \qquad \cot 60° = \frac{1}{\sqrt{3}} \text{ or } \frac{\sqrt{3}}{3}$$

exercises

Exploratory For each triangle, give the sine of each acute angle. State each answer in fraction form.

1.

2.

3.

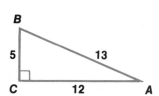
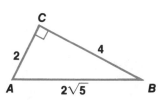
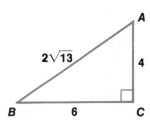

4–6. Give the cosine of each acute angle in problems **1–3.**

7–9. Give the tangent of each acute angle in problems **1–3.**

Written Find each value to the nearest four decimal places.

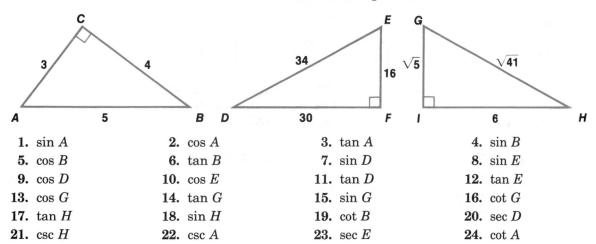

1. sin A	**2.** cos A	**3.** tan A	**4.** sin B
5. cos B	**6.** tan B	**7.** sin D	**8.** sin E
9. cos D	**10.** cos E	**11.** tan D	**12.** tan E
13. cos G	**14.** tan G	**15.** sin G	**16.** cot G
17. tan H	**18.** sin H	**19.** cot B	**20.** sec D
21. csc H	**22.** csc A	**23.** sec E	**24.** cot A

For each triangle, find sin A, cos A, and tan A to the nearest four decimal places.

25.

26.

27.

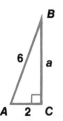
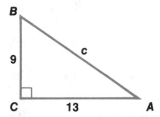
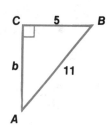

Find the value of each expression. Write each answer in fraction form.

28. $2 \cos 30°$

29. $^-\sin 60°$

30. $\sin^2 45° + \cos^2 45°$

31. $2 \sin 60° \cos 60°$

32. $\cos^2 30° - \sin^2 30°$

33. $\sin 30° \cos 60° - \sin 60° \cos 30°$

34. $\csc 45° - \sec 30°$

35. $\sec 60° + \cot 30°$

17-2   Trigonometric Tables

Decimal approximations for values of trigonometric functions are given in the back of this book. Angles with measurements from 0° to 90° at intervals of ten minutes are provided. Part of the table of values is shown below.

Values of Trigonometric Functions

Angle	Sin	Cos	Tan	Cot	Sec	Csc	
27°00′	0.4540	0.8910	0.5095	1.963	1.122	2.203	63°00′
10′	0.4566	0.8897	0.5132	1.949	1.124	2.190	50′
20′	0.4592	0.8884	0.5169	1.935	1.126	2.178	40′
30′	0.4617	0.8870	0.5206	1.921	1.127	2.166	30′
40′	0.4643	0.8857	0.5243	1.907	1.129	2.154	20′
50′	0.4669	0.8843	0.5280	1.894	1.131	2.142	10′
28°00′	0.4695	0.8829					
35°00′	0.5736	0.8192	0.7002	1.428	1.221	1.743	55°00′
10′	0.5760	0.8175	0.7046	1.419	1.223	1.736	50′
20′	0.5783	0.8158	0.7089	1.411	1.226	1.729	40′
30′	0.5807	0.8141	0.7133	1.402	1.228	1.722	30′
40′	0.5831	0.8124	0.7177	1.393	1.231	1.715	20′
50′	0.5854	0.8107	0.7221	1.385	1.233	1.708	10′
36°00′	0.5878	0.8090	0.7265	1.376	1.236	1.701	54°00′
	Cos	Sin	Cot	Tan	Csc	Sec	Angle

Degrees are separated into minutes. Sixty minutes are equivalent to one degree. Thus, for example, $1\frac{1}{2}$ degrees can be expressed as 1 degree 30 minutes, and is abbreviated 1°30′.

Angle measurements from 0°00′ to 45°00′ are listed on the left-hand side of the table. Use the column headings at the top along with angle measurements by reading *down* the left-hand side. For example, cos 27°10′ = 0.8897.

Angle measurements from 45°00′ to 90°00′ are listed on the right-hand side of the table. Use the column headings at the bottom along with angle measurements by reading *up* the right-hand side. For example, tan 54°30′ = 1.402.

examples

1 Find tan 31°40′.

Since 31°40′ is found on the left side of the table, use tan on the top of the table. Look below tan and to the right of 31°40′.

tan 31°40′ = 0.6168   Therefore, tan 31°40′ is about 0.6168.

2 Round 55°12′ to the nearest 10 minutes. Then find an approximate value for sin 55°12′.

12 rounded to the nearest tens place is 10. Thus, 55°12′ rounded to the nearest 10 minutes is 55°10′. Since 55°10′ is on the right side of the table, use sin on the bottom of the table. Look above sin and to the left of 55°10′.

$$\text{sin } 55°10′ = 0.8208$$

Therefore, sin 55°12′ is about 0.8208.

A more accurate approximation of trigonometric values can be found by using **interpolation.** For example, suppose you wish to find sin 28°23'. Use the table to find sin 28°20' and sin 28°30'.

$$
10'\begin{cases} 3'\begin{cases} \text{sin } 28°20' = 0.4746 \\ \text{sin } 28°23' = \text{unknown} \end{cases} d \\ \text{sin } 28°30' = 0.4772 \end{cases} 0.0026
$$

d stands for the difference between 0.4746 and the unknown value.

Then set up a proportion and solve for *d*.

$$\frac{3}{10} = \frac{d}{0.0026}$$
$$10d = 3(0.0026)$$
$$10d = 0.0078$$
$$d = 0.00078$$
$$\text{or } 0.0008$$

The table gives the values to the nearest four decimal places. Therefore, round the value for d to four decimal places.

Add 0.0008 to the value of sin 28°20'.

sin 28°23' = 0.4746 + 0.0008 or 0.4754

The value of sin 28°23' is about 0.4754.

examples

3   **Find cot 31°47'.**

$$
10'\begin{cases} 7'\begin{cases} \text{cot } 31°40' = 1.621 \\ \text{cot } 31°47' = \text{unknown} \end{cases} d \\ \text{cot } 31°50' = 1.611 \end{cases} {}^-0.010
$$

$$\frac{7}{10} = \frac{d}{{}^-0.010}$$
$$10d = 7({}^-0.010)$$
$$10d = {}^-0.070$$
$$d = {}^-0.007$$

cot 31°47' = 1.621 − 0.007 or 1.614

The value of cot 31°47' is about 1.614.

4   **Suppose sin x = 0.7820. Find the measure of x to the nearest minute.**

$$
10'\begin{cases} d\begin{cases} \text{sin } 51°20' = 0.7808 \\ \text{sin } x \quad\; = 0.7820 \end{cases} 0.0012 \\ \text{sin } 51°30' = 0.7826 \end{cases} 0.0018
$$

Use the table to find those values which the given value is between.

$$\frac{d}{10} = \frac{0.0012}{0.0018}$$

$$0.0018d = 0.0120$$

$$d = 6.66$$

$$\approx 7 \qquad \textit{Round to the nearest whole number.}$$

$$x \approx 51°20' + 7' \text{ or } 51°27'$$

The value of x is about $51°27'$.

The sum and difference formulas for sine and cosine can be used to find the trigonometric values of angles whose measures are not listed in the table.

$$\cos (a \pm b) = \cos a \cos b \mp \sin a \sin b$$
$$\sin (a \pm b) = \sin a \cos b \pm \cos a \sin b$$

5 **Find sin 153°.**

$$\sin 153° = \sin (180° - 27°) \qquad \textit{153° is not listed in the table.}$$
$$= \sin 180° \cos 27° - \cos 180° \sin 27° \qquad \textit{sin (a − b) = sin a cos b − cos a sin b}$$
$$= 0 \cdot \cos 27° - (^-1) \sin 27°$$
$$= \sin 27°$$
$$= 0.4540$$

The value of $\sin 153°$ is about 0.4540.

6 **Find tan 160°.**

$$\tan 160° = \frac{\sin 160°}{\cos 160°} \qquad \tan \theta = \frac{\sin \theta}{\cos \theta}$$

$$= \frac{\sin (180° - 20°)}{\cos (180° - 20°)}$$

$$= \frac{\sin 180° \cos 20° - \cos 180° \sin 20°}{\cos 180° \cos 20° + \sin 180° \sin 20°} \qquad \begin{array}{l}\textit{sin (a − b) = sin a cos b − cos a sin b}\\ \textit{cos (a − b) = cos a cos b + sin a sin b}\end{array}$$

$$= \frac{0 \cdot \cos 20° - (^-1) \sin 20°}{^-1 \cdot \cos 20° + 0 \cdot \sin 20°}$$

$$= \frac{\sin 20°}{^-\cos 20°}$$

$$= -\frac{0.3420}{0.9397}$$

$$= ^-0.3639$$

The value of $\tan 160°$ is about $^-0.3639$.

exercises

Exploratory Use the table to find each trigonometric value.

1. sin 42°
2. cos 81°
3. sin 68°
4. tan 5°
5. tan 89°50′
6. cos 42°20′
7. tan 49°30′
8. sin 3°10′

Round each angle measurement to the nearest 10 minutes. Then approximate each value.

9. cos 63°18′
10. tan 77°14′
11. sin 73°46′
12. cos 73°58′
13. cos 18°2′
14. tan 43°51′
15. sin 27°18′
16. sin 53°43′

Written Approximate each trigonometric value. Use interpolation when necessary.

1. cos 38°
2. tan 12°
3. sin 68°
4. tan 88°
5. sin 16°20′
6. tan 85°16′
7. tan 77°30′
8. sin 38°15′
9. cos 59°10′
10. sin 127°40′
11. tan 88°52′
12. sec 47°10′
13. csc 33°33′
14. cot 44°44′
15. tan 110°55′
16. sec 11°11′
17. sin 194°35′
18. cot 47°18′
19. tan 42°42′
20. csc 273°18′

Find the measure of x to the nearest minute.

21. cos x = 0.5132
22. tan x = 1.705
23. sin x = 0.3291
24. tan x = 0.3147
25. cos x = 0.7193
26. sin x = 0.1111
27. tan x = 0.2222
28. cos x = 0.3333
29. sin x = 0.8081
30. tan x = 42.71
31. csc x = 1.412
32. cot x = 0.1234
33. sec x = 1.319
34. csc x = 1.319
35. cot x = 1.384

Challenge Use the sum and difference formulas to prove each of the following.

1. sin (180° − a) = sin a
2. cos (180° − a) = ⁻cos a

Test Problem   excursions in algebra

How well are students learning mathematics? To answer this question, the National Assessment of Educational Progress recently tested a nationwide sample of students. One of the exercises from the test is given below.

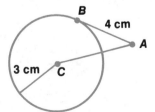

The tangent segment AB is 4 cm long. If the radius of the circle is 3 cm, how far is point A from the center of the circle?

17–3   Solving Right Triangles

Trigonometric functions can be used to solve problems involving right triangles.

1 **Find the values of a and b in the right triangle.**

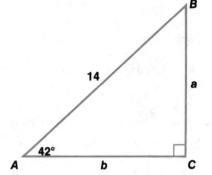

$$\frac{a}{14} = \sin 42°$$

$$\frac{a}{14} = 0.6691$$

$a = 9.4$ *Round to the nearest tenth.*

$$\frac{b}{14} = \cos 42°$$

$$\frac{b}{14} = 0.7431$$

$b = 10.4$ *Round to the nearest tenth.*

Therefore, $a = 9.4$ and $b = 10.4$.

2 **Solve the right triangle.**   *To solve a right triangle means to find all the measures of the sides and angles.*

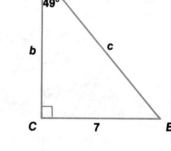

$49° + B = 90°$ *Angles A and B are complementary.*

$B = 41°$

$$\frac{7}{c} = \sin 49°$$

$$\frac{7}{c} = 0.7547$$

$7 = 0.7547c$

$c = 9.3$ *Round to the nearest tenth.*

$$\frac{7}{b} = \tan 49°$$

$7 = 1.150b$

$b = 6.1$ *Round to the nearest tenth.*

Therefore $B = 41°$, $c = 9.3$, and $b = 6.1$.

3 **Solve the right triangle shown below.**

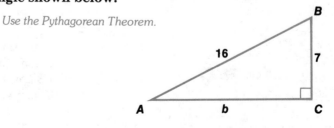

$7^2 + b^2 = 16^2$ *Use the Pythagorean Theorem.*

$49 + b^2 = 256$

$b^2 = 207$

$b \approx 14.4$

$$\sin A = \frac{7}{16}$$

$$\sin A = 0.4375$$

$$A = 25°57'$$

$$\cos B = \frac{7}{16}$$

$$\cos B = 0.4375$$

$$B = 64°3'$$

Therefore, $b = 14.4$, $A = 25°57'$, and $B = 64°3'$.

exercises

Exploratory State equations that would enable you to solve each problem. Use the triangle below.

1. If $A = 15°$ and $c = 37$, find a.
2. If $A = 76°$ and $a = 13$, find b.
3. If $A = 49°13'$ and $a = 10$, find c.
4. If $a = 21.2$ and $A = 71°13'$, find b.
5. If $a = 13$ and $B = 16°$, find c.
6. If $A = 19°07'$ and $b = 11$, find c.
7. If $c = 16$ and $a = 7$, find b.
8. If $b = 10$ and $c = 20$, find a.
9. If $a = 7$ and $b = 12$, find A.
10. If $a = b$ and $c = 12$, find B.

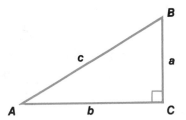

Written Suppose triangle ABC is a right triangle. Let A and B be the acute angles, and a and b be the measures of the sides opposite these angles. The measure of the hypotenuse is c. Solve each triangle. Round to two decimal places or the nearest minute.

1. $a = 2$, $b = 7$
2. $c = 10$, $a = 8$
3. $c = 13$, $a = 12$
4. $a = 11$, $b = 21$
5. $b = 6$, $c = 13$
6. $c = 21$, $b = 18$
7. $A = 16°$, $c = 14$
8. $A = 63°$, $a = 9.7$
9. $A = 37°15'$, $b = 11$
10. $B = 64°$, $c = 19.2$
11. $B = 42°10'$, $a = 9$
12. $B = 83°$, $b = \sqrt{31}$
13. $c = 6$, $B = 13°$
14. $a = 9$, $B = 49°$
15. $b = 42$, $A = 77°$
16. $b = 22$, $A = 22°22'$
17. $a = 33$, $B = 33°$
18. $a = 44$, $B = 44°44'$
19. $A = 55°55'$, $c = 16$
20. $B = 18°$, $a = \sqrt{15}$
21. $A = 45°$, $c = 7\sqrt{2}$
22. $B = 30°$, $b = 11$
23. $c = 25$, $A = 15°$
24. $a = 7$, $A = 27°$

Skills Review Solve each of the following equations.

1. $x^2 - 6x - 12 = 0$
2. $x^2 + 12x - 13 = 0$
3. $3x^2 - 14x + 8 = 0$
4. $6x^2 + 7x + 2 = 0$
5. $x - 9\sqrt{x} + 8 = 0$
6. $x - 13\sqrt{x} + 36 = 0$

17-4   Using Right Triangles

Right triangles and the trigonometric functions can be used to solve a number of problems.

1 A ladder 14 meters long rests against the wall of a house. The foot of the ladder rests on level ground 2 meters from the wall. What angle does the ladder form with the ground?

$$\cos x = \frac{2}{14}$$

$$\cos x = 0.1429$$

$$x = 81°47'$$

The measurement of the angle is 81°47′ to the nearest minute.

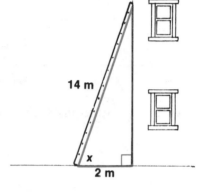

14 m

x

2 m

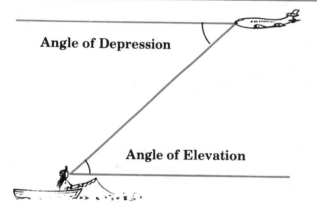

Angle of Depression

Angle of Elevation

A person fishing on a lake sees a small plane flying overhead. The angle formed by her line of sight to the plane and a horizontal is called the **angle of elevation.** The angle formed by the line of sight from the pilot to the boat and a horizontal is called the **angle of depression.** The angles of elevation and depression are alternate interior angles and have equal measures.

2 Two hikers are 300 meters from the base of a radio tower. The measurement of the angle of elevation to the top of the tower is 40°. How high is the tower?

$$\frac{x}{300} = \tan 40°$$

$$\frac{x}{300} = 0.8391$$

$$x = 0.8391(300) \text{ or } 251.73$$

The height of the tower is about 252 meters.

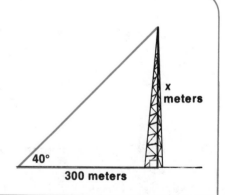

x meters

40°

300 meters

3 The base of a television antenna and two points on the ground are in a straight line. The two points are 100 feet apart. From the two points, the measurements of the angles of elevation to the top of the antenna are 30° and 20°. Find the height of the antenna.

$$\tan 30° = \frac{y}{x}$$

$$x \tan 30° = y$$

$$x \tan 30° = (x + 100) \tan 20°$$

$$x \tan 30° = x \tan 20° + 100 \tan 20°$$

$$x \tan 30° - x \tan 20° = 100 \tan 20°$$

$$x (\tan 30° - \tan 20°) = 100 \tan 20°$$

$$x = \frac{100 \tan 20°}{\tan 30° - \tan 20°}$$

$$= \frac{100(0.3640)}{0.5774 - 0.3640}$$

$$= 170.6$$

$$\tan 20° = \frac{y}{x + 100}$$

$$y = (x + 100) \tan 20°$$

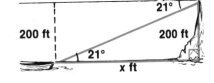

$$y = 170.6 \tan 30°$$

$$= 170.6(0.5774)$$

$$= 98.5$$

The height is 99 feet to the nearest foot.

4 Robert is standing on top of a cliff 200 feet above a lake. The measurement of the angle of depression to a boat on the lake is 21°. How far is the boat from the base of the cliff?

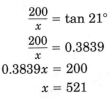

$$\frac{200}{x} = \tan 21°$$

$$\frac{200}{x} = 0.3839$$

$$0.3839x = 200$$

$$x = 521$$

The boat is about 521 feet from the base of the cliff.

exercises

Written Solve each problem. Round all answers to two decimal places.

1. At a point on the ground that is 30 meters from the base of a tree, the measurement of the angle of elevation to the top of the tree is 65°. How tall is the tree?

2. A flagpole casts a shadow 40 feet long when the measurement of the angle of elevation to the sun is 31°20′. How tall is the flagpole?

3. The measurement of the angle of depression of an aircraft carrier from a plane 1000 feet above the water is 63°18′. How far is the plane from the carrier?

4. At the point from which it is being flown, the measurement of the angle of elevation of a kite is 70°. It is held by a string 65 meters long. How far is the kite above the ground?

5. A 24 foot ladder leans against a building. It forms an angle with the building measuring 18°. How far is the foot of the ladder from the base of the building?

6. The top of a lighthouse is 120 meters above sea level. From the top of the lighthouse, the measurement of the angle of depression of a boat at sea is 43°. Find the distance of the boat from the foot of the lighthouse.

7. A tree is broken by the wind. The top touches the ground 13 meters from the base. It makes an angle with the ground measuring 29°. How tall was the tree before it was broken?

8. The pilot of a plane flying 5000 feet above sea level observes two ships in line due east. The measurements of the angles of depression are 30° and 39°. How far apart are the ships?

9. In a parking garage, each floor is 20 feet apart. The ramp to each floor is 120 feet long. What is the measurement of the angle of elevation of the ramp?

10. A railroad track rises 10 feet for every 400 feet along the track. What is the measurement of the angle the track forms with the horizontal?

11. The Washington Monument is 555 feet high. What is the measurement of the angle of elevation of the top when observed from a point $\frac{1}{4}$ mile from the base? (1 mile = 5280 feet)

12. A train travels 5000 meters along a track whose angle of elevation has a measurement of 3°. How much did it rise during this distance?

13. The diagram shows square ABCD. The midpoint of side AD is E. Find the values of x, y, and z to the nearest minute.

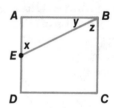

14. The measurement of the angle of elevation to the top of a building from a point on the ground is 38°20′. From a point 50 feet closer to the building, the measurement of the angle of elevation is 45°. What is the height of the building?

15. Two observers 200 feet apart are in line with the base of a flagpole. The measurement of the angle of elevation of the top from one observer is 30° and from the other 60°. How far is the flagpole from each observer?

16. To find the height of a mountain peak two points, A and B, were located on a plain in line with the peak. The angles of elevation were measured from each point. The angle at A was 36°40′ and the angle at B was 21°10′. The distance from A to B was 720 feet. How high is the peak above the level of the plain?

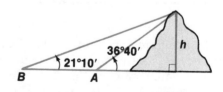

17. Two buildings are separated by an alley. Joe is looking out a window 60 feet above the ground in one building. He observes the measurement of the angle of depression of the base of the second building to be 50°, and that of the angle of elevation of the top to be 40°. How high is the second building?

18. A television antenna sits atop a building. From a point 200 feet from the base of the building, the measurement of the angle of elevation of the top of the antenna is 80°. That of the angle of elevation of the bottom of the antenna from the same point is 75°. How tall is the antenna?

19. The isosceles triangle *RST* at the right has base *TS* measuring 10 centimeters and base angles each measuring 39°. Find the length of the altitude *QR*.

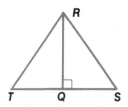

20. A pendulum 50 centimeters long is moved 40° from the vertical. How far did the tip of the pendulum rise?

21. A ship sails due north from port for 90 kilometers, then 40 kilometers east, and then 70 kilometers north. How far is the ship from port?

History   excursions in algebra

Eratosthenes *(air uh TAHS thun nees),* an astronomer who lived in Greece in the 3rd century B.C., is credited with providing the first accurate measure of the earth's circumference. To do this, Erathosthenes reasoned as follows.

At noon on the day of the summer solstice, the sun is directly over the city of Syene. At the same time, in Alexandria, which is north of Syene, the sun is 7°12′ south of being directly overhead. Since the distance between the two cities is 5,000 stadia. The following proportion can be written.

$$\frac{360°}{7°12′} = \frac{c}{5,000}$$

Solving the proportion gives the value of *c*, the earth's circumference, as 250,000 stadia, or 24,661 miles. This is only 158 miles less than the currently accepted value.

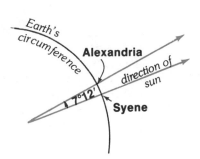

The stadium (singular form of stadia) is an ancient unit of measurement.

Jon Thomas is a civil engineer. Part of his job is to determine if machinery is being overloaded. Overloading can ruin equipment or make it wear out sooner. Sometimes, it is a potential danger to human safety.

The boom hoist shown below carries a load of 900 pounds. Jon needs to find the tension, *t*, in the cable and the compression, *c,* in the boom. To do this, he uses the following method.

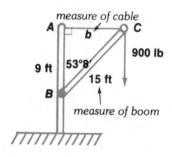

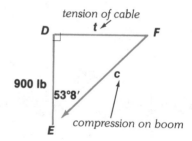

First, assume triangle *ABC* is a right triangle, and find *b*.
Use the Pythagorean Theorem.

$$b^2 = 15^2 - 9^2$$
$$= 225 - 81$$
$$= 144$$
$$b = 12 \quad \textit{the measure of the cable}$$

Since triangle *ABC* is similar to triangle *DEF,* the following proportions can be used.

$$\frac{t}{900} = \frac{12}{9} \quad \textit{since } \frac{DF}{DE} = \frac{AC}{AB} \qquad\qquad \frac{c}{900} = \frac{15}{9} \quad \textit{since } \frac{EF}{DE} = \frac{BC}{AB}$$
$$9t = 10{,}800 \qquad\qquad\qquad\qquad\qquad 9c = 13{,}500$$
$$t = 1200 \qquad\qquad\qquad\qquad\qquad\quad c = 1500$$

The tension is 1200 pounds.   The compression is 1500 pounds.

Exercises   Find the tension and compression for each of the following weights.

1. 500 pounds
2. 1000 pounds
3. 1200 pounds
4. 1500 pounds

17–5   Law of Sines

The trigonometric functions also can be used to solve problems involving triangles that are *not* right triangles.

Consider triangle *ABC* with height *h* units and sides with lengths *a* units, *b* units, and *c* units. The area of this triangle is given by area = $\frac{1}{2}bh$. Also, $\sin A = \frac{h}{c}$. By combining these equations, you can find a new formula for the area of the triangle.

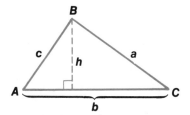

$$\text{area} = \frac{1}{2}bh$$

$$= \frac{1}{2}b(c \sin A) \qquad \sin A = \frac{h}{c}, \text{ so } h = c \sin A$$

In a similar way, you can find two other formulas for the area of a triangle.

$$\text{area} = \frac{1}{2}ac \sin B \qquad\qquad \text{area} = \frac{1}{2}ab \sin C$$

All of these formulas represent the area of the same triangle. Thus, the following must be true.

$$\frac{1}{2}bc \sin A = \frac{1}{2}ac \sin B = \frac{1}{2}ab \sin C$$

The **Law of Sines** is obtained by dividing each of the above expressions by $\frac{1}{2}abc$.

$$\frac{\sin A}{a} = \frac{\sin B}{b} = \frac{\sin C}{c}$$

> Let triangle *ABC* be any triangle with *a*, *b*, and *c* representing the measures of sides opposite angles with measurements *A*, *B*, and *C* respectively. Then,
>
> $$\frac{\sin A}{a} = \frac{\sin B}{b} = \frac{\sin C}{c}.$$

Law of Sines

1 **Find the area of triangle *ABC* if *a* = 6, *b* = 10, and *C* = 40°.**

$$\text{area} = \frac{1}{2}(6)(10) \sin 40°.$$

$$= \frac{1}{2}(6)(10)(0.6428)$$

$$= 19.284 \qquad \text{To the nearest whole unit, the area is 19 square units.}$$

2 **Solve the triangle on the right.**

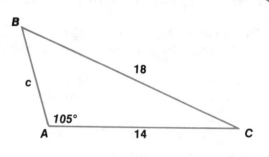

$$\frac{\sin B}{14} = \frac{\sin 105°}{18}$$

$$\sin B = \frac{14 \sin 105°}{18}$$

$$= \frac{14(0.9659)}{18}$$

$$= 0.7513$$

$$B = 48°42'$$

$$48°42' + 105° + C = 180°$$

$$C = 26°18'$$

$$\frac{\sin 26°18'}{c} = \frac{\sin 105°}{18}$$

$$c = \frac{18 \sin 26°18'}{\sin 105°}$$

$$= \frac{18(0.4431)}{0.9659}$$

$$= 8.26$$

Therefore, $B = 48°42'$, $C = 26°18'$, and $C = 8.26$.

3 **A surveyor measures a fence 440 meters long. She takes bearings of a land-mark C from A and B and finds that $A = 48°$ and $B = 75°$. Find the distance from A to C.**

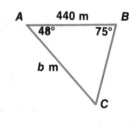

$$48° + 75° + C = 180°$$

$$C = 57°$$

$$\frac{\sin 75°}{b} = \frac{\sin 57°}{440}$$

$$b = \frac{440 \sin 75°}{\sin 57°}$$

$$= 506.7$$

To the nearest meter, the distance is 507 meters.

Exploratory State an equation that would enable you to find the area of each triangle.

1. $a = 10$, $b = 17$, $C = 46°$
2. $b = 15$, $c = 20$, $A = 63°$
3. $a = 15$, $b = 30$, $C = 90°$
4. $a = 6$, $c = 4$, $B = 52°$

State an equation that would enable you to solve each triangle described below.

5. If $b = 10$, $a = 14$, and $A = 50°$, find B.
6. If $A = 40°$, $B = 60°$, and $a = 20$, find b.
7. If $b = 2.8$, $A = 53°$, and $B = 61°$, find a.
8. If $b = 16$, $c = 12$, and $B = 42°$, find C.

Written Find the area of each triangle described below.

1. $a = 12$, $b = 12$, $C = 50°$
2. $a = 15$, $b = 22$, $C = 90°$
3. $b = 11.5$, $c = 14$, $A = 20°$
4. $a = 11$, $c = 5$, $B = 50°6'$
5. $a = 11$, $b = 13$, $C = 31°10'$
6. $b = 4$, $c = 19$, $A = 73°24'$
7. $a = 9.4$, $c = 13.5$, $B = 95°$
8. $b = 17.3$, $c = 12.4$, $A = 110°$

Solve each triangle described below.

9. $a = 8$, $A = 49°$, $B = 57°$
10. $A = 45°$, $a = 83$, $b = 79$
11. $A = 83°10'$, $a = 80$, $b = 70$
12. $A = 40°$, $B = 60°$, $c = 20$
13. $B = 70°$, $C = 58°$, $a = 84$
14. $A = 30°$, $C = 70°$, $c = 8$
15. $b = 15$, $c = 17$, $C = 64°40'$
16. $a = 23$, $A = 73°25'$, $C = 24°30'$
17. $B = 36°36'$, $C = 119°$, $b = 8$
18. $a = 14$, $b = 7.5$, $A = 103°$

Solve each problem. Round all answers to two decimal places.

19. An isosceles triangle has a base of 22 centimeters and a vertex angle measuring 36°. Find its perimeter.

20. A triangular lot faces two streets that meet at an angle measuring 85°. The sides of the lot facing the streets are each 160 feet in length. Find the perimeter of the lot.

21. Two planes leave an airport at the same time. Each flies at a speed of 110 miles per hour. One flies in the direction 60° east of north. The other flies in the direction 40° east of south. How far apart are the planes after 3 hours?

22. A building 60 feet tall is on top of a hill. A surveyor is at a point on the hill and observes that the angle of elevation to the top of the building has measurement 42° and to the bottom of the building has measurement 18°. How far is the surveyor from the building?

Challenge Use the Law of Sines to show that each statement is true.

1. $\dfrac{a}{b} = \dfrac{\sin A}{\sin B}$

2. $\dfrac{b}{a + b} = \dfrac{\sin B}{\sin A + \sin B}$

3. $\dfrac{a - b}{b} = \dfrac{\sin A - \sin B}{\sin B}$

4. $\dfrac{a + b}{a - b} = \dfrac{\sin A + \sin B}{\sin A - \sin B}$

Solve the following equations.

5. $\dfrac{\cos x}{\sin x} = \sin x \cos x$

6. $\sin x = \cos 2x$

17-6 Law of Cosines

If two sides and the included angle, or three sides of a triangle, are given, the Law of Sines cannot be used to solve the triangle. Another formula is needed.

Consider triangle ABC with height measuring h units and sides with lengths a units, b units, and c units. Suppose segment AD is x units long. Then segment DC is $(b - x)$ units long.

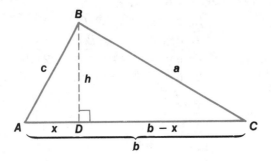

Use the Pythagorean Theorem and the definition of the cosine function to find how A, a, b, and c are related.

$$a^2 = (b - x)^2 + h^2 \qquad \text{\textit{Use the Pythagorean Theorem.}}$$
$$= b^2 - 2bx + x^2 + h^2 \qquad \text{\textit{Expand } } (b - x)^2.$$
$$= b^2 - 2bx + c^2 \qquad \text{\textit{} } c^2 = x^2 + h^2.$$
$$= b^2 - 2b(c \cos A) + c^2 \qquad \cos A = \frac{x}{c} \text{ \textit{so} } x = c \cos A.$$
$$= b^2 + c^2 - 2bc \cos A$$

In a similar way, two other formulas can be found relating the lengths of sides to the cosine of B and C. All three formulas, the *Law of Cosines,* can be summarized as follows.

> Let triangle ABC be any triangle with a, b, and c representing the measures of sides opposite angles with measurements A, B, and C respectively. Then, the following equations are true.
>
> $$a^2 = b^2 + c^2 - 2bc \cos A$$
> $$b^2 = a^2 + c^2 - 2ac \cos B$$
> $$c^2 = a^2 + b^2 - 2ab \cos C$$

Law of Cosines

Use the Law of Cosines to solve a triangle in the following cases.
1. To find the length of the third side of any triangle if the lengths of two sides and the measurement of the included angle are given.
2. To find the measurement of an angle of a triangle if the lengths of three sides are given.

1 **Solve the triangle where $A = 35°$, $b = 16$, and $c = 19$.**

$a^2 = 16^2 + 19^2 - 2(16)(19) \cos 35°$ *Use the Law of Cosines.*

$\quad = 16^2 + 19^2 - 2(16)(19)(0.8192)$

$\quad = 118.93$

$a = 10.9$

$\dfrac{\sin 35°}{10.9} = \dfrac{\sin B}{16}$ *Use the Law of Sines.*

$\sin B = \dfrac{16 \sin 35°}{10.9}$

$\quad = \dfrac{16(0.5736)}{10.9}$

$\quad = 0.8420$

$B = 57°21'$

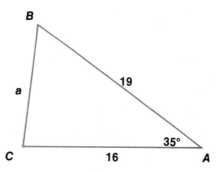

$35° + 57°21' + C = 180°$

$\quad\quad\quad C = 180° - 35° - 57°21'$

$\quad\quad\quad\quad = 87°39'$

Therefore, $a = 10.9$, $B = 57°21'$, and $C = 87°39'$.

2 **Solve the triangle where $a = 11$, $b = 13$, and $c = 15$.**

$11^2 = 13^2 + 15^2 - 2(13)(15) \cos A$ *Use the Law of Cosines.*

$2(13)(15) \cos A = 13^2 + 15^2 - 11^2$

$\cos A = \dfrac{13^2 + 15^2 - 11^2}{2(13)(15)}$

$\quad = 0.7000$

$A = 45°34'$

$\dfrac{\sin 45°34'}{11} = \dfrac{\sin B}{13}$ *Use the Law of Sines.*

$\sin B = \dfrac{13 \sin 45°34'}{11}$

$\quad = \dfrac{13(0.7141)}{11}$

$\quad = 0.8439$

$B = 57°33'$

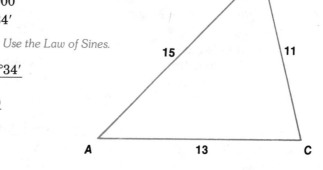

$45°34' + 57°33' + C = 180°$

$\quad\quad\quad C = 180° - 45°34' - 57°33'$

$\quad\quad\quad\quad = 76°53'$

Therefore, $A = 45°34'$, $B = 57°33'$, and $C = 76°53'$.

Exploratory In each of the following, three parts of a triangle are given. Determine whether the Law of Sines or the Law of Cosines would be used first to solve the triangle.

1. $A = 40°$, $b = 6$, $c = 7$
2. $a = 10$, $A = 40°$, $c = 8$
3. $a = 14$, $b = 15$, $c = 16$
4. $A = 40°$, $C = 70°$, $c = 14$
5. $C = 35°$, $a = 11$, $b = 10.5$
6. $c = 21$, $a = 14$, $B = 60°$
7. $c = 10.3$, $a = 21\frac{1}{2}$, $b = 16.71$
8. $b = 17$, $B = 42°58'$, $a = 11$
9. $c = 14.1$, $A = 29°$, $b = 7.6$
10. $A = 28°50'$, $b = 5$, $c = 4.9$

Written Solve each triangle.

1. $a = 140$, $b = 185$, $c = 166$
2. $A = 51°$, $b = 40$, $c = 45$
3. $a = 5$, $b = 6$, $c = 7$
4. $a = 5$, $b = 12$, $c = 13$
5. $a = 20$, $c = 24$, $B = 47°$
6. $b = 13$, $a = 21.5$, $C = 39°20'$
7. $A = 40°$, $B = 59°$, $c = 14$
8. $B = 19°$, $a = 51$, $c = 61$
9. $a = 345$, $b = 648$, $c = 442$
10. $A = 25°26'$, $a = 13.7$, $B = 78°$

Solve each problem.

11. A triangular plot of land has two sides which have length 400 feet and 600 feet. The measurement of the angle between those sides is $46°20'$. Find its perimeter and area.

12. The sides of a triangular city lot have length 50 meters, 70 meters, and 85 meters. Find the measurement of the angle opposite the short side.

13. A pilot is flying from Chicago to Columbus, a distance of 300 miles. He starts his flight 15° off course and flies on this course for 75 miles. How far is he from Columbus and by how much must he correct his error?

14. Two ships leave San Francisco at the same time. One travels 40° west of north at a speed of 20 knots. The other travels 10° west of south at a speed of 15 knots. How far apart are they after 11 hours? (1 knot = 1 nautical mile per hour)

15. A ship at sea is 70 miles from one radio transmitter and 130 miles from another. The measurement of the angle between the signals is 130°. How far apart are the transmitters?

16. A 40 foot television antenna stands on top of a building. From a point on the ground, the angles of elevation of the top and bottom of the antenna, respectively have measurements of 56° and 42°. How tall is the building?

17. The sides of a triangle are 6.8 cm, 8.4 cm, and 4.9 cm. Find the measure of the smallest angle.

18. The sides of a parallelogram are 55 cm and 71 cm. Find the length of each diagonal if the larger angle is 106°.

Show that each statement is true.

19. $c^2 = a^2 + b^2 - 2ab \cos C$

20. $b^2 = a^2 + c^2 - 2ac \cos B$

21. $1 - \cos A = \dfrac{(a - b + c)(a + b - c)}{2bc}$

22. $1 + \cos A = \dfrac{(a + b + c)(b + c - a)}{2bc}$

17-7   Examining Solutions

When the lengths of two sides of a triangle and the measurement of the angle opposite one of them are given, one solution does not always exist. In such a case, one of the following will be true.

1. No triangle exists.
2. Exactly one triangle exists.
3. Two triangles exist.

In other words, the triangle may have no solution, one solution, or two solutions.

Suppose you are given a, b, and A. First, consider the case where $A < 90°$.

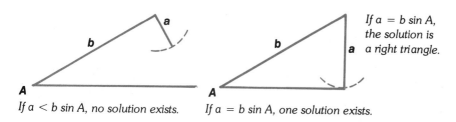

If $a < b \sin A$, no solution exists.   If $a = b \sin A$, one solution exists.

If $a = b \sin A$, the solution is a right triangle.

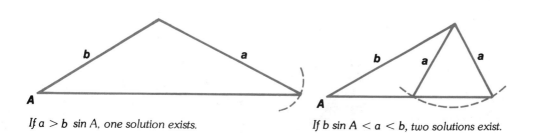

If $a > b$ sin A, one solution exists.   If $b \sin A < a < b$, two solutions exist.

Consider the case where $A \geq 90°$.

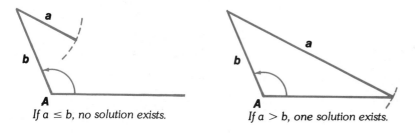

If $a \leq b$, no solution exists.   If $a > b$, one solution exists.

1 **Solve the triangle where** $A = 50°$**,** $b = 10$**, and** $a = 2$**.**

$$b \sin A = 10 \sin 50°$$
$$= 10(0.7660)$$
$$= 7.66$$

Since $50° < 90°$ and $2 < 7.66$, no solution exists.

2 **Solve the triangle where** $A = 40°$**,** $b = 10$**, and** $a = 8$**.**

$$b \sin A = 10 \sin 40°$$
$$= 10(0.6428)$$
$$= 6.428$$

Since $40° < 90°$ and $6.428 < 8 < 10$, two solutions exist.

$$\frac{\sin 40°}{8} = \frac{\sin B}{10}$$
$$\sin B = \frac{10 \sin 40°}{8}$$
$$= \frac{10(0.6428)}{8}$$
$$= 0.8035$$

$B = 53°28'$ or $126°32'$ *Since two solutions exist, there must be two values for B.*
The equation sin $(180° - a) = \sin a$ is used to find the second value.

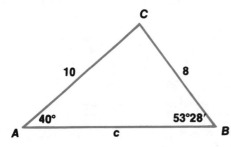

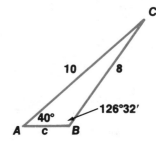

$$40° + 53°28' + C = 180°$$
$$C = 180° - 40° - 53°28'$$
$$C = 86°32'$$

$$c = \frac{8 \sin 86°32'}{\sin 40°}$$
$$= \frac{8(0.9981)}{(0.6428)} \text{ or } 12.4$$

One solution is $B = 53°28'$, $C = 86°32'$, and $c = 12.4$.

$$40° + 126°32' + C = 180°$$
$$C = 180° - 40 - 126°32'$$
$$C = 13°28'$$

$$c = \frac{8 \sin 13°28'}{\sin 40°}$$
$$= \frac{8(0.2328)}{(0.6428)} \text{ or } 2.9$$

Another solution is $B = 126°32'$, $C = 13°28'$, and $c = 2.9$.

3 Solve the triangle where $A = 40°$, $b = 10$, and $a = 14$.

Since $40° < 90°$ and $14 > 10$, one solution exists.

$$\frac{\sin 40°}{14} = \frac{\sin B}{10}$$

$$\sin B = \frac{10 \sin 40°}{14}$$

$$= \frac{10(0.6428)}{14}$$

$$= 0.4591$$

$$B = 27°20'$$

$$40° + 27°20' + C = 180°$$

$$C = 180° - 40° - 27°20'$$

$$C = 112°40'$$

$$\frac{\sin 40°}{14} = \frac{\sin 112°40'}{c}$$

$$c = \frac{14 \sin 112°40'}{\sin 40°}$$

$$= \frac{14(0.9228)}{0.6428}$$

$$= 20.1$$

Therefore, $B = 27°20'$, $C = 112°40'$, and $c = 20.1$.

exercises

Exploratory State if the given information determines one triangle, two triangles, or no triangle.

1. $A = 140°$, $b = 10$, $a = 3$

2. $A = 118°$, $b = 11$, $a = 17$

3. $A = 30°$, $a = 4$, $b = 8$

4. $A = 43°$, $b = 20$, $a = 11$

5. $A = 58°$, $a = 17$, $b = 13$

6. $A = 38°$, $b = 10$, $a = 8$

Written Determine the number of possible solutions. If a solution exists, solve the triangle.

1. $a = 6$, $b = 10$, $A = 36°52'$

2. $a = 6$, $b = 8$, $A = 150°$

3. $a = 12$, $b = 19$, $A = 57°$

4. $a = 7$, $b = 6$, $A = 30°$

5. $a = 64$, $c = 90$, $C = 98°$

6. $a = 26$, $b = 29$, $A = 58°$

7. $b = 40$, $a = 32$, $A = 125°20'$

8. $a = 9$, $b = 20$, $A = 31°$

9. $a = 12$, $b = 14$, $A = 90°$

10. $A = 25°$, $a = 125$, $b = 150$

11. $A = 40°$, $b = 16$, $a = 10$

12. $A = 76°$, $a = 5$, $b = 20$

13. $B = 34°20'$, $b = 5$, $a = 11$

14. $A = 120°$, $b = 20$, $a = 18$

15. $a = 3$, $b = 4$, $c = 8$

16. $a = 16$, $b = 17$, $c = 24$

hypotenuse (519)
opposite side (519)
adjacent side (519)
sine (519)
cosine (519)
tangent (519)
cosecant (519)

secant (519)
cotangent (519)
interpolation (523)
angle of elevation (528)
angle of depression (528)
Law of Sines (533)
Law of Cosines (536)

Chapter Summary

1. The trigonometric functions relate the sides and acute angles of a right triangle as follows. (519)

$$\sin A = \frac{a}{c}$$

$$\cos A = \frac{b}{c}$$

$$\tan A = \frac{a}{b}$$

$$\csc A = \frac{c}{a}$$

$$\sec A = \frac{c}{b}$$

$$\cot A = \frac{b}{a}$$

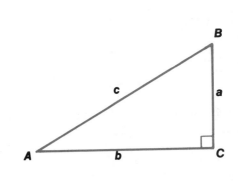

2. The special triangle with angle measurements of 45°, 45°, and 90° has sides whose lengths are in the ratio of 1 to 1 to $\sqrt{2}$. (520)

3. The special triangle with angle measurements of 30°, 60°, and 90° has sides whose lengths are in the ratio of 1 to $\sqrt{3}$ to 2. (520)

4. The values of trigonometric functions may be found in a table. Sometimes interpolation is needed to find a value which is between consecutive entries in the table. (522)

5. Trigonometric functions can be used to solve right triangles. (526)

6. Trigonometric functions may be used to solve many problems including those involving angles of elevation and depression. (528)

7. Law of Sines: Let triangle ABC be any triangle with a, b, and c representing the measures of sides opposite angles with measurements A, B, and C respectively. Then the following equations are true.

$$\frac{\sin A}{a} = \frac{\sin B}{b} = \frac{\sin C}{c} \quad (533)$$

8. Law of Cosines: Let triangle ABC be any triangle with a, b, and c representing the measures of sides opposite angles with measurements A, B, and C respectively. Then, the following equations are true.

$$a^2 = b^2 + c^2 - 2bc \cos A$$
$$b^2 = a^2 + c^2 - 2ac \cos B$$
$$c^2 = a^2 + b^2 - 2ab \cos C \quad (536)$$

9. When the lengths of two sides of a triangle and the measurement of the angle opposite one of them are given, one solution does not always exist. No triangle may exist, one triangle may exist, or two triangles may exist. (539)

Chapter Review

17–1 Find each value to the nearest four decimal places.

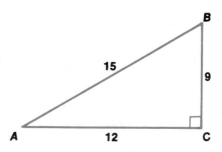

1. $\sin A$	**2.** $\sin B$	**3.** $\cos A$
4. $\cos B$	**5.** $\tan A$	**6.** $\tan B$
7. $\csc A$	**8.** $\sec A$	**9.** $\cot B$

Find the value of each expression. Write each answer in fraction form.

10. $\cos 30°$	**11.** $\tan 60°$	**12.** $\sin 45°$

17–2 Use a table to approximate each trigonometric value. Use interpolation when necessary.

13. $\sin 70°$	**14.** $\sin 18°20'$	**15.** $\cos 35°$
16. $\cos 81°40'$	**17.** $\tan 47°$	**18.** $\tan 16°35'$

Find the measure of x to the nearest minute.

19. $\sin x = 0.9272$	**20.** $\sin x = 0.2164$	**21.** $\cos x = 0.9171$
22. $\cos x = 0.5150$	**23.** $\tan x = 0.3476$	**24.** $\tan x = 1.664$

17–3 Solve each right triangle.

25. $A = 25°$, $c = 6$	**26.** $A = 50°$, $a = 11$
27. $B = 85°$, $a = 6.21$	**28.** $B = 31°$, $c = 12$

29. $a = 1, b = 3$

31. $b = 7, c = 10$

30. $a = 15, c = 20$

32. $a = 10, b = 24$

17–4 **Solve each problem. Round all answers to two decimal places.**

33. From a point on the ground 50 meters from the base of a flagpole, the measurement of the angle of elevation of the top is 48°. How tall is the flagpole?

34. A pilot 3000 feet above the ocean notes the measurement of the angle of depression of a ship is 42°. How far is the plane from the ship?

35. A building is 80 feet tall. Find the measurement of the angle of elevation to the top of the building from a point on the ground 100 feet from the base of the building.

36. The base of a monument and two points on the ground are in a straight line. The two points are 50 meters apart. The measurements of the angles of elevation to the top of the monument are 45° and 25°. Find the height of the monument.

17–5 **Use the Law of Sines to solve each triangle.**

37. $A = 50°, b = 12, a = 10$

39. $B = 46°, C = 83°, b = 65$

38. $A = 83°10', a = 80, b = 70$

40. $A = 45°, B = 30°, b = 20$

17–6 **Use the Law of Cosines to solve each triangle.**

41. $A = 60°, b = 2, c = 5$

43. $C = 40°, a = 6, b = 7$

42. $C = 65°, a = 4, b = 7$

44. $B = 24°, a = 42, c = 6.5$

17–7 **Determine the number of possible solutions. If a solution exists, solve the triangle.**

45. $A = 36°, a = 2, b = 14$

47. $A = 46°, a = 10, b = 8$

46. $A = 40°, a = 8, b = 10$

48. $A = 130°, a = 25, b = 16$

Find each value to the nearest four decimal places.

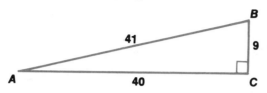

1. sin A
2. cos A
3. tan A
4. cos B

Find the value of each expression. Write each answer in fraction form.

5. cos 60°
6. tan 45°

Use a table to approximate each trigonometric value. Use interpolation when necessary.

7. sin 67°
8. cos 38°10′
9. tan 59°38′
10. sin 13°3′

Find the measure of x to the nearest minute.

11. cos $x = 0.4384$
12. tan $x = 0.4734$
13. sin $x = 0.4423$
14. tan $x = 1.635$

Solve each right triangle.

15. $A = 36°$, $b = 14$
16. $B = 75°$, $b = 6$
17. $A = 22°$, $c = 8$
18. $a = 7$, $c = 12$

Solve each problem.

19. A 32-foot ladder leans against a building. The top touches the building 26 feet above the ground. What is the measurement of the angle formed by the ladder with the ground?

20. From the top of a cliff, a camper sees a deer. The measurement of the angle of depression to the deer is 70°. The cliff is 50 meters high. How far is the deer from the base of the cliff?

Determine the number of possible solutions. If a solution exists, solve each triangle.

21. $a = 13$, $b = 11$, $c = 17$
22. $A = 46°$, $B = 77°$, $a = 6$
23. $A = 75°$, $b = 21$, $a = 30$
24. $A = 65°$, $b = 21$, $a = 6$
25. $A = 70°$, $B = 31°$, $c = 17$
26. $A = 44°$, $a = 12$, $b = 14$
27. $A = 140°$, $b = 10$, $a = 7$
28. $C = 48°$, $a = 7$, $b = 9$

Appendix:
BASIC

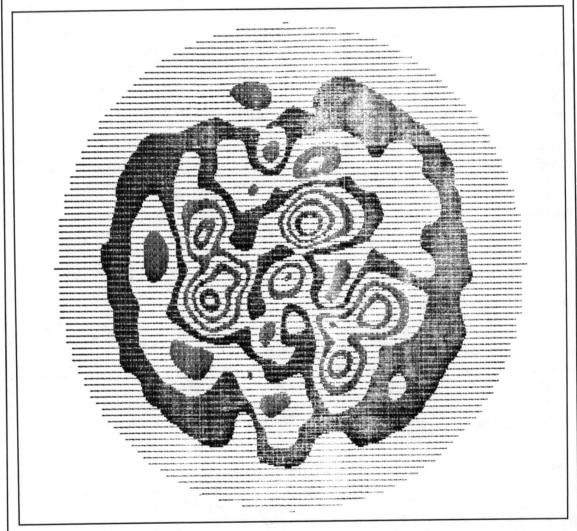

A computer can be programmed with equations that attempt to explain atmospheric phenomena. The shaded contours on this map show simulated atmospheric pressure at sea level during one study. This computer pattern is compared with actual conditions over a period of time. The pattern consists of densely packed numbers and letters.

The Language of BASIC

BASIC is a computer language. It has many similarities to algebra. Some of the similarities are shown below.

Algebra	BASIC		Algebra	BASIC
$+$	$+$		$\leq$	$<=$
$-$	$-$		$>$	$>$
$\times$	$*$		$\geq$	$>=$
$\div$	$/$		$\neq$	$<>$
$=$	$=$		3^2	$3\uparrow2$
$<$	$<$		a	A

In BASIC, raising to a power is indicated by ↑.

A variable is represented by a letter or by a letter and a numeral.

A, B, M, Z1, R3, A6   *Notice that a letter precedes a numeral.*

In BASIC, an operation symbol can never be left out. To write A times B, write A*B, not *ab* as in algebra.

A computer program is a series of statements that give directions to the computer. A program is used to put information into the computer (*input*), have the calculations done, and get the results out of the computer (*output*). A sample program follows.

line numbers → 5   PRINT 6.731 + 8.213 + 3.726 ←
→ 10   END ←   *statements*

Some computer terminals type only capital letters.

In a BASIC program each statement has a line number. Usually, integers from 1 to 9999 can be used as line numbers. The computer performs the instructions in numerical order by line number. The last statement in any BASIC program must be an **END statement.**

Most programs use only a few statements. In the sample program above each statement begins with a word. One begins with PRINT, the other with END. Other words that are often used are READ and DATA. Each **READ statement** must be accompanied by a **DATA statement.**

---

example

1   **Write a program to compute the sum and product of three numbers.**

```
10   READ A, B, C
20   PRINT A+B+C
30   PRINT A*B*C
40   DATA 71, 16, 84
50   END
```

The computer assigns the numbers from the DATA statement to the variables A, B, and C in order.
$A = 71$ $B = 16$ $C = 84$

The sum and product of any three numbers can be found simply by changing the numbers in the DATA statement in line 40.

Before the computer will do a program it must be given the RUN command. Commands do *not* have line numbers.

10	READ A, B, C	*The computer assigns 16 to A, 13 to B, and*
20	PRINT A+B+C	*7 to C from the data in line 40.*
30	PRINT A*B*C	
40	DATA 16, 13, 7	
50	END	
	RUN	*The RUN command tells the computer to execute the program.*
	36	$A+B+C = 16+13+7$ *or 36*
	1456	$A*B*C = 16*13*7$ *or 1456*

There is a specific order of operations used by the computer.

1. **Do all operations in parentheses, from the innermost parentheses outward.**
2. **Evaluate all powers from left to right.**
3. **Do all multiplications and/or divisions from left to right.**
4. **Do all additions and/or subtractions from left to right.**

Order of Operations in BASIC

The order of operations is illustrated in the next example.

example

2   Evaluate 12/2 − (5 + 3) * 4 ↑ 2 + 3.

$$12/2 - (5 + 3) * 4 \uparrow 2 + 3 = 12/2 - 8*4 \uparrow 2 + 3$$
$$= 12/2 - 8*16 + 3$$
$$= 6 - 128 + 3$$
$$= {}^-119$$

Do operations in parentheses.
Evaluate powers.
Do the division and multiplication.
Do the addition and subtraction.

The value of the expression is ⁻119.

When the results of computations exceed six significant digits the computer will use **E notation.** This is the computer equivalent of scientific notation. The E means *times 10 to the given power.*

Result of Computation	E Notation	Meaning
37867275	3.78673E+07	3.78673×10^7
0.003629	3.629E−03	3.629×10^{-3}

exercises

Written Write an expression in BASIC for each of the following.

1. $3x + 5y - 7$

2. $a \cdot b \cdot c - 3$

3. $5m - 3b + 8$

4. $17 \div a$

5. 8^2

6. $^-4(a + b)^2$

Evaluate each of the following.

7. 6+8*2

8. (3+2)↑2

9. (2*(5+8))/13

10. ((14+10)/4)/2

11. 3*(5↑2)

12. (6+8)/2+5

Evaluate each of the following. Let A = 5, B = 6, C = 15.

13. A*B+3

14. A+3*B

15. C−B+5

16. C/A

17. A*(B+3)

18. (A+3)*B

Write an expression in BASIC for each of the following.

19. $3x^2 + 2x + 5$

20. a^{x+2}

21. $\dfrac{x + 5}{2y}$

22. $\dfrac{5x + 3}{2x + 4}$

23. $\dfrac{a}{b} + n$

24. $\dfrac{(x^3 + 7x^2 + 5)^3}{x + 1}$

Write each of the following in scientific notation.

25. 6.17324E+04

26. 7.9E+08

27. 2.176E+17

28. 1.325E−06

29. 4.0005E+03

30. 7.304E−11

Write each of the following in E notation.

31. 16,500,000

32. 0.0000127

33. 9.0087×10^5

Write the printout for each statement. Let A = 3, B = 4, and R6 = 8.

34. 130   PRINT 7*B

35. 710   PRINT 121+19

36. 75   PRINT A*R6+7

37. 30   PRINT A+B+R6

38. 40   PRINT 4*B+R6*2

39. 90   PRINT (2*R6)/4

Write a BASIC program to compute and print each of the following. Use only PRINT and END statements.

40. The sum and product of 31, 14, 62, and 29.

41. The difference of 673 and 49 and the quotient of 673 ÷ 49.

42. The perimeter and area of a rectangle with length 4.7 cm and width 2.8 cm.

43. The circumference and area of a circle with radius 6.37 cm. Use 3.1416 for π.

Write a BASIC program to compute and print each of the following. Use READ and DATA statements.

44. The sum and product of 31, 14, 62, and 29.

45. The difference of 673 and 49 and the quotient of 673 ÷ 49.

46. The perimeter and area of a rectangle with length 4.7 cm and width 2.8 cm.

47. The circumference and area of a circle with radius 6.37 cm. Use 3.1416 for π.

Assignment of Variables

In BASIC the equals sign, =, has a slightly different use than in algebra. Unlike algebra, the left side of an equation in BASIC can have exactly one variable and nothing else. Compare the equations below.

<table>
<tr><th>Algebra</th><th>BASIC</th></tr>
<tr><td>$2x + 15y = 27 + 36y$</td><td>X=16*Y+37*Z−5</td></tr>
</table>

In this equation both right and left members have two terms. This algebraic sentence is *not* acceptable in BASIC.

In this statement the value of the expression on the right is computed and assigned to the variable on the left.

In BASIC the equals sign tells the computer to assign the value of the expression on the right to the variable on the left. Assignment statements are called **LET statements.**

The word LET may be omitted on many computers.

```
10   LET X=6
20   LET Y=3
30   PRINT X↑Y
40   END
     RUN
     216
```

In this program, 6 is assigned to X, and 3 is assigned to Y. The value of X↑Y, or 6³, is computed and printed. The printout is 216, the value of 6³.

```
10   READ Y,Z
20   LET X=16*Y+37*Z−5
30   PRINT X
40   DATA 47, 38
50   END
     RUN
     2153
```

In this program, the data are assigned to the variables as follows: Y = 47, Z = 38. The computation is $16 \cdot 47 + 37 \cdot 38 - 5$ which is $752 + 1406 - 5$ or 2153. This value is assigned to X, and then printed.

Consider the following program.

```
10   LET K=0
20   PRINT 2↑3
30   LET K=K+1
40   PRINT 2↑4
50   LET K=K+1
60   PRINT 2↑5
70   LET K=K+1
80   PRINT K
90   END
```

In algebra, line 30 is nonsense. But in BASIC it means that 1 is added to the old value of K to obtain a new value for K.

This program will count how many numbers are printed. What does the value of K in line 80 tell you? It tells you that three "compute and print" operations were performed.

The two programs below accomplish the same task. Which do you prefer?

```
10   LET A=3
11   LET B=4
12   LET C=5
13   LET D=6
14   LET X=2
20   LET Y=A*X↑3+B*X−(C*D)
30   PRINT Y
40   END
```

```
10   DATA 3, 4, 5, 6, 2
15   READ A, B, C, D, X

20   LET Y=A*X↑3+B*X−(C*D)
30   PRINT Y
40   END
```

exercises

Written   Let A = 3, B = 4, and M1 = 16. Find the value of X.

1. 190   LET X=6*A   **2.** 30   LET X=M1/B   **3.** 25   LET X=A*B+5

4. 170   LET X=A↑4   **5.** 20   LET X=B+M1*3   **6.** 40   LET X=M1−B+3*A

Each mathematical expression below is followed by an incorrect BASIC expression. Correct the BASIC expression.

7. $\dfrac{m+2}{r+4}$ M+2/R+4

8. $\dfrac{ab}{y+3}$ AB/(Y+3)

9. $\dfrac{(x+a)^2}{2z}$ (X+A)↑2/2*Z

10. $\left(\dfrac{x}{y}\right)^{n-3}$ (X/Y)↑N−3

Correct the error in each expression or statement below.

11. 7X+34   **12.** (7+8/2   **13.** 3*X↑2+4X

14. 20   LET Y=3A   **15.** 20   LET 2*X=5+13   **16.** 30   LET X+Y=27+12

Identify what each program does. Then determine the output for each program.

17.
```
 5   DATA 6, 8
10   READ L,W
15   LET P=2*L+2*W
20   PRINT P
25   END
```

18.
```
 5   DATA 7, 12
10   READ B,H
15   LET A=(1/2)*B*H
20   PRINT A
25   END
```

For each of the following, write a program that will have input, execution, and output. In each case the output will be the value of X.

19. A = 3, B = 7, C = 9, X=A+B(C−1)

20. A = 6, B = 18, C = 30, X=$\dfrac{3}{2}\left(\dfrac{B}{A}+C\right)$

21. M = 1, R = 2, Q = 6, X = $\dfrac{Q^R−M}{Q+M}$

22. P1 = 3.1416, R = 5, X = P1(R²)

23. A = 6, B = 7, C = 8, D = 9, E = 10, X = $\dfrac{A+B+C+D+E}{5}$

IF-THEN Statements and Loops

Operations in a program may be repeated by using a **GO TO statement** as in the following program.

10	READ S	*The computer returns to line 10*
20	DATA 3, 7, 15	*each time it executes line 50 and*
30	A=S↑2	*uses the next number on the data*
40	PRINT A,	*list. The comma in line 40 causes the*
50	GO TO 10	*output to be printed in one line.*
60	END	

The printout is as follows.

9   49   225   *When all the data have been used, the computer*
OUT OF DATA IN LINE 10   *prints OUT OF DATA and ends the program.*

The GO TO statement has the following form.

line number GO TO line number

Suppose you wish to find the area of each of ten different circles with radii of 1 unit, 2 units, 3 units, and so on to 10 units. Consider the following program.

10	LET R=1	
20	A=(3.1416)*R↑2	*The approximation 3.1416 is used for π.*
30	PRINT A	
40	LET R=R+1	
50	GO TO 20	*The computer goes back to 20.*
60	END	*Can line 60 ever be reached?*

In its present form this program will never stop. An IF-THEN statement is needed as a test line so that the program will stop when R > 10. Study the sequence of the revised program as shown below.

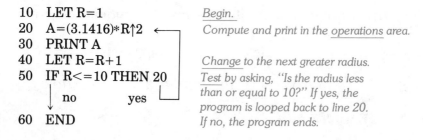

10	LET R=1	*Begin.*
20	A=(3.1416)*R↑2	*Compute and print in the operations area.*
30	PRINT A	
40	LET R=R+1	*Change to the next greater radius.*
50	IF R<=10 THEN 20	*Test by asking, "Is the radius less*
	no yes	*than or equal to 10?" If yes, the*
		program is looped back to line 20.
60	END	*If no, the program ends.*

The IF-THEN statement compares two numbers and tells the computer what to do based on the results of the comparison. The general form of the IF-THEN statement is as follows.

<u>line number</u> IF <u>algebraic sentence</u> THEN <u>line number</u>

If the algebraic sentence is true, then the computer proceeds to the line whose number follows THEN. If the algebraic sentence is false, the computer simply goes to the next line of the program.

The algebraic sentence uses one of the following symbols.

BASIC SYMBOL	EXAMPLE	
=	A=B	
<	A<B	
<=	A<=B	"A is less than or equal to B"
>	A>B	
>=	A>=B	"A is greater than or equal to B"
<>	A<>B	"A is not equal to B"

Consider the revised program on the preceding page again. Since lines 20 through 50 are repeated in the program, they form a **loop.** All loops must have a beginning (line 10), a set of operations to be performed (lines 20 and 30), a change in the input variable (line 40), and a test line to continue or break the loop (line 50).

In line 40 the value of R is increased by 1 each time through the loop. Suppose that the areas of circles are wanted whose radii are even integers from 2 to 10. How would lines 10 and 40 be changed?

Sometimes a programmer needs to count how many times an operation is performed. In the following program, line 15 keeps the count. Each time through the loop the count is increased by one.

example

1 **Write a program to count the multiples of 3 between 10 and 100.**

5	LET K=0	*Assign a zero starting value for K, the "counter."*
10	LET X=12	*Assign the first multiple of 3 greater than 10 to X.*
15	LET K=K+1	*Increase the counter by 1.*
20	LET X=X+3	*The next multiple of 3 is found.*
25	IF X<=100 THEN 15	*Test line. The computer loops back to line 15 until X>100.*
30	PRINT K	*Output*
35	END	

An IF-THEN statement may be used with READ and DATA statements to end a program. Consider the following example.

2 Write a program that finds the area of each of three squares with sides of 3 cm, 7 cm, and 15 cm. Use an IF-THEN statement to end the program.

```
10   READ S
20   DATA 3, 7, 15, ⁻1          The final number is not one of the side measures.
30   IF S=−1 THEN 70            What does line 30 do?
40   A=S↑2
50   PRINT "THE AREA IS" A "SQ CM."
60   GO TO 10
70   END
RUN
THE AREA IS 9 SQ CM.            Output
THE AREA IS 49 SQ CM.
THE AREA IS 225 SQ CM.          No OUT OF DATA statement is printed.
```

In a PRINT statement words and punctuation marks enclosed in quotation marks are printed exactly as they are typed. Line 50 in the program above is an example. This and other uses of the PRINT statement are listed below.

```
10   PRINT A               There is a single output.
20   PRINT X, Y, Z         There are three outputs on the same line.
30   PRINT A+B             There is one computation, one output.
40   PRINT 7+A, B−9        There are two computations, two outputs.
50   PRINT "EXAMPLE"       Prints text.
60   PRINT "SOLUTION IS" X  Prints text and numerical output.
70   PRINT                 The line is left blank.
```

3 Write two print statements. The first sets up headings for computing the area of triangles. The second prints the data and the results. Include a READ line for variables B and A.

```
10   READ B, A
20   PRINT "BASE", "ALTITUDE", "AREA OF TRIANGLE"
30   PRINT B, A, (B*A)/2
```

exercises

Written Let A = 5, B = 8, and X = 10. Tell the number of the statement that the computer will do next.

1. 10 IF A<20 THEN 75
    15 PRINT B

2. 15 IF A>=4 THEN 90
    20 PRINT 2*A

3. 10 IF A<>B THEN 50
    20 PRINT X

4. 10 IF (A+B)<X THEN 60
    20 PRINT 2*X

5. 50 IF (A−B)>X THEN 75
    60 PRINT B−A

6. 45 IF (B*X)<A↑3 THEN 10
    50 PRINT B*X

Use the program below to answer exercises 7–10. Tell whether A, B, or both A and B will be printed, and give the values of any variables printed.

```
10  IF A>B THEN 40
20  LET A=A+10
25  LET B=B+2
30  IF A>=B THEN 50
40  PRINT A
50  PRINT B
60  END
```

7. Let A = 12, B = 12
8. Let A = 14, B = 19
9. Let A = 9, B = 21
10. Let A = 21, B = 5

Describe what each program will do.

11.
```
10  LET M=0
20  PRINT M, M↑2
30  LET M=M+3
40  IF M<=30 THEN 20
50  END
```

12.
```
10  LET X=1
20  PRINT 4*X
30  LET X=X+1
40  IF X<21 THEN 20
50  END
```

Write a BASIC program to do each of the following. Use an IF-THEN statement.

13. Print the squares of the integers from 21 to 35 inclusive.

14. Print the cubes of the even integers from from 10 to 36 inclusive.

15. Print the multiples of 5 from 10 to 100.

16. Count the multiples of 4 from 4 through 125 inclusive, and print the count.

17. Count the multiples of 7 from 20 through 1000 inclusive, and print the count.

18. Print the integers from 10 to 1 in descending order.

19. Given two unequal numbers a and b, print them in ascending order.

20. Print a table showing the radii and volumes of spheres with radii of 7 cm, 3.2 cm, and 6.8 cm. Volume of sphere: $V = \frac{4}{3}\pi r^3$.

21. Compute and print the product $9 \cdot 8 \cdot 7 \cdot 6 \cdot 5 \cdot 4 \cdot 3 \cdot 2 \cdot 1$. (*Hint:* Let P represent the product and begin the program with P = 1. Use a loop.)

FOR-NEXT Loops

FOR-NEXT statements can increase the efficiency of a program. Compare the programs below.

Begin	10 LET R=1
	20 A=(3.1416)*R↑2
	30 PRINT A
Increment	40 LET R=R+1
Test	50 IF R<=10 THEN 20
	60 END

```
10   FOR R=1 TO 10 STEP 1
20   A=(3.1416)*R↑2
30   PRINT A
40   NEXT R
50   END
```

In a single line at the right, line 10, the value of R is started at 1 and is increased by 1 until it reaches 10.

10 FOR R=1	TO 10	STEP 1
begin	*test*	*increment*
LET R=1	Is R≤10?	LET R=R+1

The general form of a FOR statement is as follows.

line number FOR *variable* = ___ TO ___ STEP ___

The blanks may include numbers, variables, or expressions.

A FOR statement must always be paired with a NEXT statement. The steps may be positive, negative, or fractions as shown below.

```
240   FOR X=8 TO 3 STEP ⁻1
270   NEXT X

110   FOR J=⁻3 TO 12 STEP 1/2
200   NEXT J

120   FOR R5=(17+A↑2)/3 TO 3*B↑2 STEP .1
140   NEXT R5

330   FOR X=2 TO 10
380   NEXT X
```

No step size means increments of 1. Any other step size must be indicated.

---

example

1 **Write a program that prints the odd integers from 1 to 25, their squares, and their cubes.**

```
10   PRINT "N", "N↑2", "N↑3"     This line places headings on the table.
20   FOR N=1 TO 25 STEP 2
30   PRINT N, N↑2, N↑3
40   NEXT N
50   END
```

2 **Write a program that adds the even integers from 2 to 100 inclusive.**

10　LET S=0	*The variable S represents the sum, set at zero.*
20　FOR X=2 TO 100 STEP 2	
30　LET S=S+X	*In line 30, the sum of the even integers is*
40　NEXT X	*accumulated. When X = 2, S = 0 and S + X = 2.*
	When X = 4, S = 2 and S + X = 6, and so on.
50　PRINT "SUM OF EVEN INTEGERS IS" S	
60　END	

It is often useful to have loops within loops. These are called nested loops. There are only two ways these loops can appear in a program as shown.

Nested Loops	Independent Loops	Not Acceptable
FOR X	FOR X	FOR X
FOR Y	NEXT X	FOR Y
NEXT Y	FOR Y	NEXT X
NEXT X	NEXT Y	NEXT Y
The loops do not cross.	*The loops do not cross. They are not nested.*	*These loops cross.*

exercises

Written　**Use a FOR-NEXT loop to rewrite each program.**

1.
```
10   LET M=1
20   PRINT M, M↑2, M↑3
30   LET M=M+1
40   IF M<=5 THEN 20
50   END
```

2.
```
10   LET K=0
15   LET S=0
20   LET K=K+1
30   IF K>5 THEN 60
40   LET S=S+1
50   GO TO 20
60   PRINT "SUM IS" S
70   END
```

Correct the errors in the following programs. Then run your corrected program if possible.

3.
```
10   FOR X=1 TO 5
20   FOR Y=2 TO 4 STEP 2
30   PRINT X*Y
40   NEXT X
50   NEXT Y
60   END
```

4.
```
10   FOR X=7 TO 15 STEP 3
20   PRINT X, X↑3
30   FOR Y=2 TO 5
40   PRINT Y, Y+2↑Y
50   NEXT X
60   NEXT Y
70   END
```

Write a program to do each of the following. Use a FOR-NEXT statement.

5. For the integers from 10 to 20, print each integer, its third power, and its fifth power.

6. Use the expression $X\uparrow(1/2)$ to indicate square root and $X\uparrow(1/3)$ to indicate cube root. For the integers from 1 to 15, print the integer, its square root, and its cube root. Check these results with the table on pages 573 and 574.

7. The formula for converting Fahrenheit temperature to Celsius is $C = 5/9 \cdot (F - 32)$. Print the Fahrenheit temperatures and Celsius temperatures for $F = 0$ to 100 in steps of 5.

8. The lengths and widths of 3 rectangles are as follows: 8, 5; 9, 6; and 13, 17. Print a table that includes the lengths, widths, perimeters, and areas of the rectangles. (*Hint:* Use a FOR-NEXT loop that loops 3 times.)

9. The bases and heights of 4 triangles are as follows: 6, 8; 8, 12; 9, 10; 200, 300. Compute and print the areas of the triangles.

10. Compute and print the sum of the integers from 1 to 100 inclusive.

11. Compute and print the sum of the multiples of 3 from 3 to 99 inclusive.

12. Compute and print the sum of the squares of the integers from 1 to 20 inclusive. Have your program check its answer with the formula $S = \dfrac{n(n + 1)(n + 2)}{6}$ where $n = 20$.

13. Compute and print the sum of the cubes of the integers from 1 to 10 inclusive. Have your program check its answer with the formula $S = \left(\dfrac{n(n + 1)}{2}\right)^2$ where $n = 10$.

Challenge   Solve the following problem.

One hundred dollars is deposited in a bank that pays 9% interest compounded monthly. That is, the monthly interest is 0.75%. Compute and print the value of the account after 10 years. (Hint: To find the accumulated money, use the formula $A = A(1.0075)$ starting with the original deposit as the value of A, and 1.0075 as the interest factor. The formula is repeated 120 times.)

Flow Charts

Programmers often use diagrams called flow charts to organize their programs. Some shapes have special meanings in flow charts.

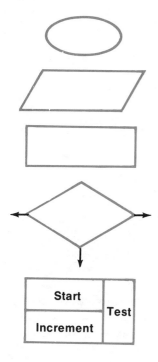

An oval is used to begin or end a program.

A parallelogram is used to show input or output. Use it with READ or PRINT statements.

A rectangle shows processing operations. Use it with a LET statement.

A diamond shows a decision. Arrows show how the flow continues. Use it with IF-THEN statements.

An iteration box shows all parts of a loop. *Iterate* means to do over and over. Use it with FOR-NEXT statements.

Below is a program and a flow chart to print the integers and their squares from 1 to 100.

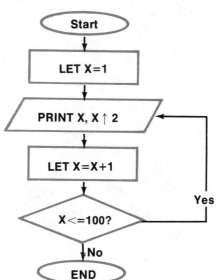

10   LET X=1

20   PRINT X, X↑2

30   LET X=X+1

40   IF X<=100 THEN 20

50   END

The following example uses an iteration box for a loop.

1 **Make a flow chart and write a program to sum the even integers from 2 to 100.**

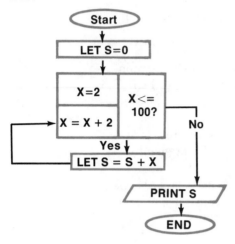

```
10   LET S=0
20   FOR X=2 TO 100 STEP 2
30   LET S=S+X
40   NEXT X
50   PRINT S
60   END
```

2 **Suppose you are given a set of 5 test scores for each of 25 students. Write a flow chart and a program to print the average for each student. Print "FAIL" if the average is less than 60. Print "PASS" if the average is 60 or more. The processing ends after the twenty-fifth average is printed.**

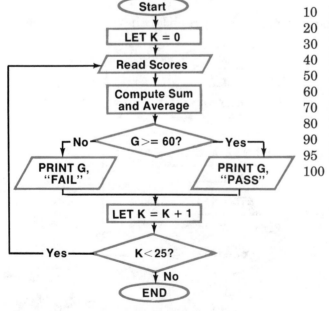

```
10    LET K=0
20    READ A,B,C,D,E
30    LET G=(A+B+C+D+E)/5
40    IF G>=60 THEN 70
50    PRINT G, "FAIL"
60    GO TO 80
70    PRINT G, "PASS"
80    LET K=K+1
90    IF K<25 THEN 20
95    DATA . . .    To use the program,
100   END             the twenty-five sets
                      of scores listed are
                      in the data line.
```

exercises

Written Make a flow chart for each of the following.

1. 10   LET Y=1
    20   PRINT Y, Y↑3
    30   LET Y=Y+1
    40   IF Y↑3<=1000 THEN 20
    50   END

2. 10   LET S=0
    20   FOR M=1 TO 20
    30   LET S=S+M
    40   NEXT M
    50   LET A=S↑(1/2)
    60   PRINT A
    70   END

Write a program from each flow chart below.

3.

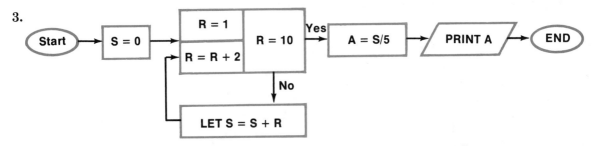

4.

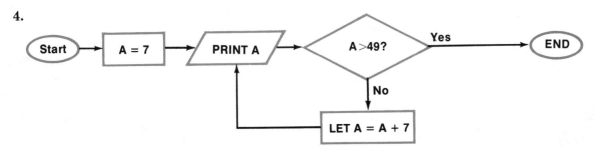

Write a flow chart and a program for each of the following.

5. Find the sum of the first n positive integers, where $n = 50$.

6. You are given three numbers the values of which are unknown to you beforehand. Print the three numbers in increasing order from least to greatest. Make comparisons by pairs and exhaust all possibilities.

7. You are given the coordinates of a point in the xy-plane. Decide in which quadrant the point lies. If the point lies on an axis, decide on which axis the point lies. Include the origin as a possibility.

Subscripted Variables

Sometimes it is difficult to provide enough labels for variables in a large amount of data. When this happens, subscripted variables may be used in BASIC.

Algebra	**BASIC**
$x_1, x_2, x_3, \ldots, x_n$	$X(1), X(2), X(3), \ldots, X(N)$

In BASIC, subscripted variables consist of a single letter and a pair of parentheses. Either a positive integer or an ordered pair of positive integers may appear within the parentheses. These integers may be represented by variables or BASIC expressions.

A(10)
Z(6)
B(3, 4)   *This variable refers to an item in the 3rd row, 4th column of an array of data.*

B(A)
Q(M)   *The computer finds the values of A and M and R from the program.*
N(4+R)

Z1(Q)   *This is not allowed. Z1 is a variable that may not be subscripted. Z1(Q) is not a single letter followed by parentheses.*

Consider the following program.

```
10   DATA 2,3,5,2.2,7,6,9,18,24,11
20   FOR R=1 TO 10
30   READ A(R)
40   PRINT A(R)*3.1416
50   NEXT R
60   END
```

*Data are diameters of circles. This loop yields A(1), A(2), A(3), . . . , A(10). What is the value of A(7)? of A(7)*3.1416? What does this program do?*

If the value of any of the subscripts is greater than 10, the size of the list must be given. A dimension statement, DIM, can do this.

10   DIM R(17)

The statement above tells the computer to reserve 17 memory spaces for subscripted variables.

The program on the next page shows the use of the DIM statement.

example

1   **Write a program to print the square root of the following numbers: 3, 9.2, 7, 11.6, 0, 254, 113, 73.9, 46, 19, 79, 101.**

10	DIM R(12)	*Reserve 12 memory spaces.*
20	FOR M=1 TO 12	*Set up FOR-NEXT loop.*
30	READ R(M)	
40	PRINT R(M)↑(1/2)	*Compute and print square root.*
50	NEXT M	
60	DATA 3,9.2,7,11.6,0,254,113,73.9,46,19,79,101	
70	END	

The program below enters into the computer hourly earnings of fifteen workers. It computes and prints the average wage.

10	DIM G(15)	*Reserve 15 memory spaces.*
20	LET S=0	*S is the sum of wages. It begins at zero.*
30	FOR I=1 TO 15	
40	READ G(I)	*Which entry in the data list is G(7)?*
50	LET S=S+G(I)	*Add the next wage to the*
60	NEXT I	*sum of the previous wages.*
70	LET A=S/15	*Why divide by 15?*
80	PRINT "AVERAGE WAGE IS", A	
90	PRINT "HOURLY WAGES"	
100	FOR X=1 TO 15	
105	PRINT G(X);	
110	NEXT X	
120	DATA 4.20,3.15,3.60,4.35,5.10,3.20,3.15,4.05	
130	DATA 4.65,3.40,5.50,6.05,4.75,3.80,4.90	
140	END	

Suppose the following array is to be read into the computer. The program on the right will do this.

Columns

	1	2	3	4	5
Rows 1	13	16	57	86	23
2	41	54	62	27	70
3	5	11	35	81	7

The 62 is in row 2, column 3. It can be represented by B(2, 3).

This loop changes rows. For each row, the inner loop goes through a full cycle.

10	DIM M(3, 5)
20	FOR R = 1 TO 3
30	FOR C = 1 TO 5
40	READ M(R, C)
50	NEXT C
60	NEXT R

This loop changes columns

Written   Refer to the array on page 563. Use the letter B and a set of parentheses to write a correct subscripted variable to refer to each of these entries in the array.

1. 13   **2.** 5   **3.** 86   **4.** 7

5. 35   **6.** 16   **7.** 41   **8.** 70

Write a BASIC subscripted variable for each of the following.

9. m_3 **10.** t_4 **11.** r_y **12.** z_{x+1}

13. q_{24} **14.** k_{m+n} **15.** $x_{(1,3)}$ **16.** $y_{(a,r)}$

The first four lines of a program are shown below. Use them to evaluate the following.

```
10   DATA 8, −4, 16, −12,2,17
20   FOR R=1 TO 6
30   READ A(R)
40   NEXT R
```

17. A(2)   **18.** A(5−1)

19. A(3)−1   **20.** 2*A(4)

21. A(1)/2   **22.** A(A(5))

23. 6+A(3)   **24.** A(6)−A(4)

Let K = 3 and J = 2. Evaluate the following. Use the same program lines as in exercises 17–24.

25. A(J)*A(K)   **26.** A(J*K)   **27.** 2*A(J)   **28.** A(2*J)

Write the necessary DIM statement.

29. $[a_1, a_2, \ldots , a_{40}]$ **30.** $[m_{41}, m_{42}, \ldots m_{79}]$

Write BASIC programs that will do the following.

31. Kristy has grades of 67, 72, 74, 63, and 81 in Algebra One. Anne Marie has grades of 91, 87, 81, 83, and 89. Find and print the average of each girl's grades.

32. Print each of the following numbers and its absolute value. Use 5, 3, 7, 0, −1, 15, −11, −12, −6, −22 in the DATA statement.

33. The table below shows the scores for one game in a bowling league. The program computes the average for each team. Copy and complete the program. Use S(M,T) as the variable for entries in the table. Print both the team number and its average.

```
 5   FOR M=1 TO 5
10   FOR T=_____
15   READ S(M,T)
20   NEXT _____
25   NEXT _____
30   FOR T=1 TO 6
35   LET S=_____
40   FOR M=1 TO 5
45   LET S=S+_____
50   NEXT _____
55   PRINT T,_____
60   NEXT _____
65   DATA . . .
70   END
```

Teams	1	2	3	4	5	6
Members 1	165	151	130	147	137	132
2	135	122	146	123	153	114
3	149	155	101	181	166	127
4	118	140	135	110	111	175
5	102	119	179	129	146	159

Matrices

Subscripted variables can be used to identify terms of a matrix. Two subscripts separated by a comma are written inside the parentheses following the variable. The first subscript indicates the row and the second subscript indicates the column.

Consider the matrix, $A = \begin{bmatrix} 9 & ^-1 & 6 \\ 4 & 7 & ^-8 \end{bmatrix}$. In BASIC, the values of $A(1,2)$ and $A(2,1)$ would be $^-1$ and 4, respectively. The DIM statement for this matrix would be 10 DIM A(2,3). The DIM statement is necessary only if either of the subscripts is greater than 10.

Suppose the above matrix is to be read and stored in the computer. This can be accomplished by using nested loops.

This loop changes rows. In each row, the inner loop goes through a full cycle.

```
10   DIM  A(2,3)
20   FOR  R=1 TO 2
30   FOR  C=1 TO 3
40   READ  A(R,C)
50   NEXT  C
60   NEXT  R
70   DATA  9,-1,6,4,7,-8
80   END
```

This loop changes columns.

Note that the terms are listed by rows.

A BASIC program may be used to find the value of the determinant of a matrix.

example

1 **Write a program to find the value of the determinant of the matrix, $Z = \begin{bmatrix} 2 & ^-8 \\ 9 & 3 \end{bmatrix}$.**

```
10   FOR  R=1 TO 2
20   FOR  C=1 TO 2
30   READ  Z(R,C)
40   NEXT  C
50   NEXT  R
60   PRINT "DETERMINANT IS" Z(1,1)*Z(2,2)-Z(1,2)*Z(2,1)
65   DATA  2,-8,9,3
70   END
```

A BASIC program may be used to add matrices or multiply a matrix by a scalar. Consider the following examples.

2 Write a program to add A and B if $A = \begin{bmatrix} 7 & -2 & 1 & -3 \\ 9 & 1 & 4 & -5 \\ 0 & -8 & -1 & 9 \end{bmatrix}$

and $B = \begin{bmatrix} 1 & -8 & 3 & 5 \\ -2 & 1 & -4 & 6 \\ 1 & 0 & -9 & 7 \end{bmatrix}$. Then show the output of the program.

```
10   DIM  A(3,4),B(3,4)          This statement may be omitted in this case.
20   FOR  R=1 TO 3
30   FOR  C=1 TO 4
40   READ A(R,C)                 These loops read and store the elements
50   NEXT C                      of matrix A.
60   NEXT R
70   FOR  R=1 TO 3
80   FOR  C=1 TO 4
90   READ B(R,C)                 These loops read and store the elements
100   PRINT  A(R,C)+B(R,C);      of matrix B. Then the sum of corresponding
110   NEXT C                     elements is computed and printed.
120   PRINT
130   NEXT R                     Line 120 causes the matrix to be printed row by row.
140   DATA 7,−2,1,−3,9,1,4,−5,0,−8,−1,9,1,−8,3,5,−2,1,−4,6,1,0,−9,7
150   END
RUN
8  −10   4    2
7   2    0    1
1  −8   −10  16
```

3 Write a program to multiply a 6 × 8 matrix, X, by a scalar, S.

```
10   DIM  X(6,8)
20   READ S
30   FOR  R=1 TO 16
40   FOR  C=1 TO 33
50   READ X(R,C)
60   PRINT  X(R,C)*S;
70   NEXT C
80   PRINT
90   NEXT R
100   DATA . . .    The first number in the DATA statement must be the value of S.
110   END           Then the terms of the matrix are listed row by row.
```

exercises

Written Write a BASIC subscripted variable to name each of the following terms in matrix A shown at the right.

1. 1
2. $^-1$
3. 4
4. 8
5. $^-2$
6. $^-6$
7. 3
8. $^-7$
9. 2

$$A = \begin{bmatrix} 1 & 2 & 8 \\ {}^-2 & {}^-1 & 3 \\ 4 & {}^-7 & {}^-6 \end{bmatrix}$$

Write the output when the following statements are added to the program shown at the right.

```
10  FOR R=1 TO 2
20  FOR C=1 TO 4
30  READ X(R,C)
50  NEXT C
60  NEXT R
70  DATA 1,9,5,1,-7,6,8,-3
```

10. 40 PRINT X(R,C);

11. 40 PRINT X(R,C);
    55 PRINT

12. 40 PRINT X(R,C)

Let $A = \begin{bmatrix} {}^-3 & 6 & {}^-9 \\ 4 & {}^-3 & 0 \\ 8 & {}^-2 & 7 \end{bmatrix}$, $B = \begin{bmatrix} 1 & 5 & 7 \\ {}^-11 & 13 & {}^-8 \\ 0 & {}^-2 & 4 \end{bmatrix}$, and $C = \begin{bmatrix} 4 & 6 & 4 \\ 11 & {}^-4 & 6 \\ {}^-2 & 2 & 8 \end{bmatrix}$. Write a program in BASIC to find each of the following.

13. A + C
14. B + C
15. A + ($^-$B)
16. C − A
17. 3C
18. 4B + A

Let $D = \begin{bmatrix} 1 & 3 \\ {}^-2 & 2 \end{bmatrix}$ and $E = \begin{bmatrix} 4 & 7 & 0 \\ 6 & {}^-1 & 9 \end{bmatrix}$. Write a program in BASIC to find each of the following.

19. det D
20. D × E
21. D^2

Write a program in BASIC to solve each of the following.

22. Find the sum of the numbers in each column of a 4 × 4 matrix. Have the sums printed in a 1 × 4 matrix.

23. Find the greatest term in a given matrix. Print the term and its row and column.

24. Given two matrices, find their sum if possible. If not possible, print "CANNOT BE ADDED."

25. Find the mean of the numbers in each row of 4 × 4 matrix. Have the means printed in a 4 × 1 matrix.

Computer Programming Exercises

The following section provides a variety of problems that are to be solved by computer programs. The BASIC programming techniques in the previous lessons are to be used when writing the computer programs. The problems are listed by chapter for easy reference.

Most of the problems do not have specific data. In these problems a blank DATA statement must be inserted in the program. Before the program is run, data must be inserted in the DATA statement(s). If specific data is given, the problem is to be solved using this data only.

All programs must label the output with appropriate headings.

Chapter 1   Equations and Inequalities

1. Find the interest on a sum of money given the principal, p, rate of interest, r, and time, t. Use the information given in Written Exercises 31–36 on page 3 as the data.

2. Find the area of a trapezoid, given the height, h, and both bases, b and B. Use the information given in Written Exercises 37–44 on page 3 as the data.

Chapter 2   Linear Relations and Functions

1. Given the coordinates of two points in the coordinate plane, find the slope of the line through the two points, if defined, or state that the slope is undefined.

2. Given the coordinates of two points on a line, find an equation of the line.

3. Generate a set of ordered pairs that satisfy the equation $y = x + |x|$. Then use these ordered pairs to graph the function $y = x + |x|$.

4. Generate a set of ordered pairs that satisfy the equation $y = [x] + x$. Then use these ordered pairs to graph the function $y = [x] + x$.

Chapter 3   Systems of Equations and Inequalities

1. Evaluate the determinant of a third order matrix.

2. Use Cramer's Rule to solve the following system of equations.
$$0.61x + 0.63y = 61$$
$$0.63x - 0.77y = 0.6$$

Refer also to the following exercises: Page 73—Written Exercises 34 and 35; Page 80—Written Exercise 40.

Chapter 4   Polynomials

1. Find the factors of any positive integer greater than 1, using the INT function. (*Hint:* 4 is a factor of 52 only if INT (52/4) = 52/4.)

2. Express an integer in terms of its prime factors. For example, $24 = 2 \times 2 \times 2 \times 3$. If the integer itself is prime, then the output of the program should print that fact.

Chapter 5   Roots

1. Use the divide-and-average method to find the square root of a number. You must input the radicand and two original estimates. Have the program stop when two successive estimates are identical to at least four decimal places.

2. Iteration formulas can be used to approximate numbers. To find square roots, the formula is $X(N + 1) = \frac{1}{2}(X(N) + A/X(N))$. You must input the radicand, A, and an estimate, X(0). The program should start with N = 0, N = 1, N = 2, . . ., and repeat the formula until two successive X(N)'s are identical to at least four decimal places.

3. The iteration formula for cube roots is $X(N + 1) = \frac{1}{3}(2 \cdot X(N) + A/X(N)^2)$. Use this formula to find the cube root of 89. The answer should be accurate to four decimal places.

4. The iteration formula for fourth roots is $X(N + 1) = \frac{1}{4}(3 \cdot X(N) + A/X(N)^3)$. Use this formula to find the fourth root of 49. The answer should be accurate to four decimal places.

Chapter 6   Quadratic Equations

1. Write a computer program that will solve any quadratic equation using the quadratic formula. Be sure to print out complex solutions if they exist.

2. Write a computer program to find the value of the discriminant for given quadratic equations. The program should print the value of the discriminant and describe the nature of the solutions for each equation.

Refer also to Written Exercise 49 on page 179.

Chapter 7   Quadratic Relations and Functions

1. Given any quadratic equation $f(x) = ax^2 + bx + c$, find the equation of the axis of symmetry, the coordinates of the vertex, and direction of opening of its graph. (*Hint:* rewrite the equation in the form $f(x) = a(x - h)^2 + k$. State an expression for h and k in terms of a, b, and c.)

2. If you hit a baseball up in the air with a velocity of v meters per second, its height after t seconds is given by the formula $h = vt - 4.9t^2$. Find and print the height of the baseball for any given input of velocity (meters) and time (seconds).

Chapter 8   Conics

1. Find the radius and coordinates of the center of a circle given by the equation $Ax^2 + Cy^2 + Dx + Ey + F = 0$.

Refer also to Written Exercise 33 on page 225.

2. Given the equation of an ellipse in the form $\dfrac{(x - h)^2}{2} + \dfrac{(y - k)^2}{b^2} = 1$, find the coordinates of its center, vertices, and foci.

Chapter 9   Polynomial Functions

1. Use the Factor Theorem to find factors of the polynomial $P(x) = ax^3 + bx^2 + cx + d$.

2. Use the Rational Zero Theorem to find all possible rational roots of the equation $ax^3 + bx^2 + cx + d = 0$ given that a, b, c, and d are integers.

Refer also to the following exercises: Page 261—Written Exercise 49; Page 265—Written Exercise 31; Page 276—Excursion Exercise 5; Page 282—Written Exercise 38.

Chapter 10   Rational Polynomial Expressions

1. Find the GCF of any two integers using the Euclidean Algorithm. See page 303.

2. Evaluate $f(x) = \dfrac{^-5x(x + 2)}{(x - 3)(x + 1)}$ for integer values of x between $^-10$ and 10 inclusive. Use these ordered pairs to graph $f(x)$.

Refer also to the following exercises: Page 298—Written Exercise 38; Page 310—Written Exercise 20.

Chapter 11   Exponents

1. Print a table of integers and their cube roots for the integers from 1 to 20. Use the exponent $\dfrac{1}{3}$ to find the roots. Compare your printout with the cube root table on page 574.

2. Print a table of integers and their cubes for the integers from 1 to 20. Compute the cubes as $\dfrac{1}{n^{-3}}$. Compare your printout with the table of cubes on page 574.

Chapter 12   Exponential and Logarithmic Functions

1. Print a table of logarithms base 2 for the integers from 1 through 16.

2. Native Americans were paid $24 for Manhattan Island in 1626. Suppose this money was put in a savings account at 4% interest compounded quarterly. Then in 1913 the total savings account was invested in IBM stock. Find the value of the investment in 1980. (Assume a $10 share purchased in 1913 is worth $260,000 in 1980.)

Chapter 13 Sequences and Series

1. Find the sum of an arithmetic series given the first term, a_1, the number of terms, n, and the common difference.

2. Find the sum of a geometric series given the first term, a_1, the common ratio, r, and the number of terms, n.

3. Find the value of e to four decimal places using the following formula.

$$e = 2 + \frac{1}{2!} + \frac{1}{3!} + \frac{1}{4!} + \frac{1}{5!} + \frac{1}{6!} + \frac{1}{7!}$$

Refer also to Challenge Exercises 1 and 2 on page 407.

Chapter 14 Probability

1. Evaluate the expression $P(n, r)$ for any values of n and r.

2. Evaluate the expression $C(n, r)$ for any values of n and r.

3. Simulate the tossing of 3 coins for 1000 times. Count the number of times each outcome (3 heads, 3 tails, 2 heads and 1 tail, or 2 tails and 1 head) occurs. Print the total for each outcome with appropriate labels.

Chapter 15 Statistics

Given the total precipitation for thirty cities in 1980, solve each problem.

1. Find the mean of the precipitations.

2. Arrange the data in order from least to greatest.

3. Find the median of the precipitations.

4. Find the mode of the precipitations.

Refer also to Written Exercise 30 on page 468.

Chapter 16 Trigonometric Functions and Identities

1. Make a table of the degree measures of angles given their radian measures in increments from 0.01 from 0 to 2.

2. Given the value of a sine function for an angle between 0° and 90°, find the angle. (*Note:* Most computers have the Arctan function only, given ATN(X).)

Chapter 17 Right Triangle Trigonometry

1. Given the lengths of three sides of a right triangle, find the measures of the two acute angles of the triangle.

2. Find the length of one side of any triangle, given the lengths of the other two sides and the measure of the angle included between them.

Symbols

a^n	the nth power of a
$\|a\|$	the absolute value of a
^-a	additive inverse of a or the opposite of a
Cos^{-1}	Arccosine
$C(n, r)$	combinations of n elements taken r at a time
$a + bi$	complex number
$^\circ$	degrees
det	determinant
e	base of natural logarithms
$\in$	is an element of
$\emptyset$	empty set
$=$	equals or is equal to
$\neq$	does not equal
$\approx$	approximately equal to
$f(x)$	f of x or the value of f at x
f^{-1}	inverse function of f
$!$	factorial
$f \circ g$	composition function f of g
$>$	is greater than
$<$	is less than
$\geq$	is greater than or equal to
$\leq$	is less than or equal to
$\log_b x$	the logarithm to the base b of x
$P(n, r)$	permutations of n things taken r at a time
$\pm$	positive or negative
$\{\ \}$	set
$\sqrt{\ \ }$	the principal square root of
$\sqrt[n]{\ \ }$	the nth root of
Σ	(sigma) summation symbol

Squares and Square Roots

n	n^2	$\sqrt{n}$	$\sqrt{10n}$	n	n^2	$\sqrt{n}$	$\sqrt{10n}$
1.0	1.00	1.000	3.162	5.5	30.25	2.345	7.416
1.1	1.21	1.049	3.317	5.6	31.36	2.366	7.483
1.2	1.44	1.095	3.464	5.7	32.49	2.387	7.550
1.3	1.69	1.140	3.606	5.8	33.64	2.408	7.616
1.4	1.96	1.183	3.742	5.9	34.81	2.429	7.681
1.5	2.25	1.225	3.873	6.0	36.00	2.449	7.746
1.6	2.56	1.265	4.000	6.1	37.21	2.470	7.810
1.7	2.89	1.304	4.123	6.2	38.44	2.490	7.874
1.8	3.24	1.342	4.243	6.3	39.69	2.510	7.937
1.9	3.61	1.378	4.359	6.4	40.96	2.530	8.000
2.0	4.00	1.414	4.472	6.5	42.25	2.550	8.062
2.1	4.41	1.449	4.583	6.6	43.56	2.569	8.124
2.2	4.84	1.483	4.690	6.7	44.89	2.588	8.185
2.3	5.29	1.517	4.796	6.8	46.24	2.608	8.246
2.4	5.76	1.549	4.899	6.9	47.61	2.627	8.307
2.5	6.25	1.581	5.000	7.0	49.00	2.646	8.367
2.6	6.76	1.612	5.099	7.1	50.41	2.665	8.426
2.7	7.29	1.643	5.196	7.2	51.84	2.683	8.485
2.8	7.84	1.673	5.292	7.3	53.29	2.702	8.544
2.9	8.41	1.703	5.385	7.4	54.76	2.720	8.602
3.0	9.00	1.732	5.477	7.5	56.25	2.739	8.660
3.1	9.61	1.761	5.568	7.6	57.76	2.757	8.718
3.2	10.24	1.789	5.657	7.7	59.29	2.775	8.775
3.3	10.89	1.817	5.745	7.8	60.84	2.793	8.832
3.4	11.56	1.844	5.831	7.9	62.41	2.811	8.888
3.5	12.25	1.871	5.916	8.0	64.00	2.828	8.944
3.6	12.96	1.897	6.000	8.1	65.61	2.846	9.000
3.7	13.69	1.924	6.083	8.2	67.24	2.864	9.055
3.8	14.44	1.949	6.164	8.3	68.89	2.881	9.110
3.9	15.21	1.975	6.245	8.4	70.56	2.898	9.165
4.0	16.00	2.000	6.325	8.5	72.25	2.915	9.220
4.1	16.81	2.025	6.403	8.6	73.96	2.933	9.274
4.2	17.64	2.049	6.481	8.7	75.69	2.950	9.327
4.3	18.49	2.074	6.557	8.8	77.44	2.966	9.381
4.4	19.36	2.098	6.633	8.9	79.21	2.983	9.434
4.5	20.25	2.121	6.708	9.0	81.00	3.000	9.487
4.6	21.16	2.145	6.782	9.1	82.81	3.017	9.539
4.7	22.09	2.168	6.856	9.2	84.64	3.033	9.592
4.8	23.04	2.191	6.928	9.3	86.49	3.050	9.644
4.9	24.01	2.214	7.000	9.4	88.36	3.066	9.695
5.0	25.00	2.236	7.071	9.5	90.25	3.082	9.747
5.1	26.01	2.258	7.141	9.6	92.16	3.098	9.798
5.2	27.04	2.280	7.211	9.7	94.09	3.114	9.849
5.3	28.09	2.302	7.280	9.8	96.04	3.130	9.899
5.4	29.16	2.324	7.348	9.9	98.01	3.146	9.950

Cubes and Cube Roots

n	n^3	$\sqrt[3]{n}$	$\sqrt[3]{10n}$	$\sqrt[3]{100n}$	n	n^3	$\sqrt[3]{n}$	$\sqrt[3]{10n}$	$\sqrt[3]{100n}$
1.0	1.000	1.000	2.154	4.642	5.5	166.375	1.765	3.803	8.193
1.1	1.331	1.032	2.224	4.791	5.6	175.616	1.776	3.826	8.243
1.2	1.728	1.063	2.289	4.932	5.7	185.193	1.786	3.849	8.291
1.3	2.197	1.091	2.351	5.066	5.8	195.112	1.797	3.871	8.340
1.4	2.744	1.119	2.410	5.192	5.9	205.379	1.807	3.893	8.387
1.5	3.375	1.145	2.466	5.313	6.0	216.000	1.817	3.915	8.434
1.6	4.096	1.170	2.520	5.429	6.1	226.981	1.827	3.936	8.481
1.7	4.913	1.193	2.571	5.540	6.2	238.328	1.837	3.958	8.527
1.8	5.832	1.216	2.621	5.646	6.3	250.047	1.847	3.979	8.573
1.9	6.859	1.239	2.668	5.749	6.4	262.144	1.857	4.000	8.618
2.0	8.000	1.260	2.714	5.848	6.5	274.625	1.866	4.021	8.662
2.1	9.261	1.281	2.759	5.944	6.6	287.496	1.876	4.041	8.707
2.2	10.648	1.301	2.802	6.037	6.7	300.763	1.885	4.062	8.750
2.3	12.167	1.320	2.844	6.127	6.8	314.432	1.895	4.082	8.794
2.4	13.824	1.339	2.884	6.214	6.9	328.509	1.904	4.102	8.837
2.5	15.625	1.357	2.924	6.300	7.0	343.000	1.913	4.121	8.879
2.6	17.576	1.375	2.962	6.383	7.1	357.911	1.922	4.141	8.921
2.7	19.683	1.392	3.000	6.463	7.2	373.248	1.931	4.160	8.963
2.8	21.952	1.409	3.037	6.542	7.3	389.017	1.940	4.179	9.004
2.9	24.389	1.426	3.072	6.619	7.4	405.224	1.949	4.198	9.045
3.0	27.000	1.442	3.107	6.694	7.5	421.875	1.957	4.217	9.086
3.1	29.791	1.458	3.141	6.768	7.6	438.976	1.966	4.236	9.126
3.2	32.768	1.474	3.175	6.840	7.7	456.533	1.975	4.254	9.166
3.3	35.937	1.489	3.208	6.910	7.8	474.552	1.983	4.273	9.205
3.4	39.304	1.504	3.240	6.980	7.9	493.039	1.992	4.291	9.244
3.5	42.875	1.518	3.271	7.047	8.0	512.000	2.000	4.309	9.283
3.6	46.656	1.533	3.302	7.114	8.1	531.441	2.008	4.327	9.322
3.7	50.653	1.547	3.332	7.179	8.2	551.368	2.017	4.344	9.360
3.8	54.872	1.560	3.362	7.243	8.3	571.787	2.025	4.362	9.398
3.9	59.319	1.574	3.391	7.306	8.4	592.704	2.033	4.380	9.435
4.0	64.000	1.587	3.420	7.368	8.5	614.125	2.041	4.397	9.473
4.1	68.921	1.601	3.448	7.429·	8.6	636.056	2.049	4.414	9.510
4.2	74.088	1.613	3.476	7.489	8.7	658.503	2.057	4.431	9.546
4.3	79.507	1.626	3.503	7.548	8.8	681.472	2.065	4.448	9.583
4.4	85.184	1.639	3.530	7.606	8.9	704.969	2.072	4.465	9.619
4.5	91.125	1.651	3.557	7.663	9.0	729.000	2.080	4.481	9.655
4.6	97.336	1.663	3.583	7.719	9.1	753.571	2.088	4.498	9.691
4.7	103.823	1.675	3.609	7.775	9.2	778.688	2.095	4.514	9.726
4.8	110.592	1.687	3.634	7.830	9.3	804.357	2.103	4.531	9.761
4.9	117.649	1.698	3.659	7.884	9.4	830.584	2.110	4.547	9.796
5.0	125.000	1.710	3.684	7.937	9.5	857.375	2.118	4.563	9.830
5.1	132.651	1.721	3.708	7.990	9.6	884.736	2.125	4.579	9.865
5.2	140.608	1.732	3.733	8.041	9.7	912.673	2.133	4.595	9.899
5.3	148.877	1.744	3.756	8.093	9.8	941.192	2.140	4.610	9.933
5.4	157.464	1.754	3.780	8.143	9.9	970.299	2.147	4.626	9.967

Common Logarithms of Numbers

n	0	1	2	3	4	5	6	7	8	9
10	0000	0043	0086	0128	0170	0212	0253	0294	0334	0374
11	0414	0453	0492	0531	0569	0607	0645	0682	0719	0755
12	0792	0828	0864	0899	0934	0969	1004	1038	1072	1106
13	1139	1173	1206	1239	1271	1303	1335	1367	1399	1430
14	1461	1492	1523	1553	1584	1614	1644	1673	1703	1732
15	1761	1790	1818	1847	1875	1903	1931	1959	1987	2014
16	2041	2068	2095	2122	2148	2175	2201	2227	2253	2279
17	2304	2330	2355	2380	2405	2430	2455	2480	2504	2529
18	2553	2577	2601	2625	2648	2672	2695	2718	2742	2765
19	2788	2810	2833	2856	2878	2900	2923	2945	2967	2989
20	3010	3032	3054	3075	3096	3118	3139	3160	3181	3201
21	3222	3243	3263	3284	3304	3324	3345	3365	3385	3404
22	3424	3444	3464	3483	3502	3522	3541	3560	3579	3598
23	3617	3636	3655	3674	3692	3711	3729	3747	3766	3784
24	3802	3820	3838	3856	3874	3892	3909	3927	3945	3962
25	3979	3997	4014	4031	4048	4065	4082	4099	4116	4133
26	4150	4166	4183	4200	4216	4232	4249	4265	4281	4298
27	4314	4330	4346	4362	4378	4393	4409	4425	4440	4456
28	4472	4487	4502	4518	4533	4548	4564	4579	4594	4609
29	4624	4639	4654	4669	4683	4698	4713	4728	4742	4757
30	4771	4786	4800	4814	4829	4843	4857	4871	4886	4900
31	4914	4928	4942	4955	4969	4983	4997	5011	5024	5038
32	5051	5065	5079	5092	5105	5119	5132	5145	5159	5172
33	5185	5198	5211	5224	5237	5250	5263	5276	5289	5302
34	5315	5328	5340	5353	5366	5378	5391	5403	5416	5428
35	5441	5453	5465	5478	5490	5502	5514	5527	5539	5551
36	5563	5575	5587	5599	5611	5623	5635	5647	5658	5670
37	5682	5694	5705	5717	5729	5740	5752	5763	5775	5786
38	5798	5809	5821	5832	5843	5855	5866	5877	5888	5899
39	5911	5922	5933	5944	5955	5966	5977	5988	5999	6010
40	6021	6031	6042	6053	6064	6075	6085	6096	6107	6117
41	6128	6138	6149	6160	6170	6180	6191	6201	6212	6222
42	6232	6243	6253	6263	6274	6284	6294	6304	6314	6325
43	6335	6345	6355	6365	6375	6385	6395	6405	6415	6425
44	6435	6444	6454	6464	6474	6484	6493	6503	6513	6522
45	6532	6542	6551	6561	6571	6580	6590	6599	6609	6618
46	6628	6637	6646	6656	6665	6675	6684	6693	6702	6712
47	6721	6730	6739	6749	6758	6767	6776	6785	6794	6803
48	6812	6821	6830	6839	6848	6857	6866	6875	6884	6893
49	6902	6911	6920	6928	6937	6946	6955	6964	6972	6981
50	6990	6998	7007	7016	7024	7033	7042	7050	7059	7067
51	7076	7084	7093	7101	7110	7118	7126	7135	7143	7152
52	7160	7168	7177	7185	7193	7202	7210	7218	7226	7235
53	7243	7251	7259	7267	7275	7284	7292	7300	7308	7316
54	7324	7332	7340	7348	7356	7364	7372	7380	7388	7396

The values given are mantissas correct to four decimal places. For example, log 5.42 = 0.7340.

Common Logarithms of Numbers

n	0	1	2	3	4	5	6	7	8	9
55	7404	7412	7419	7427	7435	7443	7451	7459	7466	7474
56	7482	7490	7497	7505	7513	7520	7528	7536	7543	7551
57	7559	7566	7574	7582	7589	7597	7604	7612	7619	7627
58	7634	7642	7649	7657	7664	7672	7679	7686	7694	7701
59	7709	7716	7723	7731	7738	7745	7752	7760	7767	7774
60	7782	7789	7796	7803	7810	7818	7825	7832	7839	7846
61	7853	7860	7868	7875	7882	7889	7896	7903	7910	7917
62	7924	7931	7938	7945	7952	7959	7966	7973	7980	7987
63	7993	8000	8007	8014	8021	8028	8035	8041	8048	8055
64	8062	8069	8075	8082	8089	8096	8102	8109	8116	8122
65	8129	8136	8142	8149	8156	8162	8169	8176	8182	8189
66	8195	8202	8209	8215	8222	8228	8235	8241	8248	8254
67	8261	8267	8274	8280	8287	8293	8299	8306	8312	8319
68	8325	8331	8338	8344	8351	8357	8363	8370	8376	8382
69	8388	8395	8401	8407	8414	8420	8426	8432	8439	8445
70	8451	8457	8463	8470	8476	8482	8488	8494	8500	8506
71	8513	8519	8525	8531	8537	8543	8549	8555	8561	8567
72	8573	8579	8585	8591	8597	8603	8609	8615	8621	8627
73	8633	8639	8645	8651	8657	8663	8669	8675	8681	8686
74	8692	8698	8704	8710	8716	8722	8727	8733	8739	8745
75	8751	8756	8762	8768	8774	8779	8785	8791	8797	8802
76	8808	8814	8820	8825	8831	8837	8842	8848	8854	8859
77	8865	8871	8876	8882	8887	8893	8899	8904	8910	8915
78	8921	8927	8932	8938	8943	8949	8954	8960	8965	8971
79	8976	8982	8987	8993	8998	9004	9009	9015	9020	9025
80	9031	9036	9042	9047	9053	9058	9063	9069	9074	9079
81	9085	9090	9096	9101	9106	9112	9117	9122	9128	9133
82	9138	9143	9149	9154	9159	9165	9170	9175	9180	9186
83	9191	9196	9201	9206	9212	9217	9222	9227	9232	9238
84	9243	9248	9253	9258	9263	9269	9274	9279	9284	9289
85	9294	9299	9304	9309	9315	9320	9325	9330	9335	9340
86	9345	9350	9355	9360	9365	9370	9375	9380	9385	9390
87	9395	9400	9405	9410	9415	9420	9425	9430	9435	9440
88	9445	9450	9455	9460	9465	9469	9474	9479	9484	9489
89	9494	9499	9504	9509	9513	9518	9523	9528	9533	9538
90	9542	9547	9552	9557	9562	9566	9571	9576	9581	9586
91	9590	9595	9600	9605	9609	9614	9619	9624	9628	9633
92	9638	9643	9647	9652	9657	9661	9666	9671	9675	9680
93	9685	9689	9694	9699	9703	9708	9713	9717	9722	9727
94	9731	9736	9741	9745	9750	9754	9759	9763	9768	9773
95	9777	9782	9786	9791	9795	9800	9805	9809	9814	9818
96	9823	9827	9832	9836	9841	9845	9850	9854	9859	9863
97	9868	9872	9877	9881	9886	9890	9894	9899	9903	9908
98	9912	9917	9921	9926	9930	9934	9939	9943	9948	9952
99	9956	9961	9965	9969	9974	9978	9983	9987	9991	9996

Values of Trigonometric Functions

Angle	Sin	Cos	Tan	Cot	Sec	Csc	
0°00′	0.0000	1.0000	0.0000	—	1.000	—	90°00′
10′	0.0029	1.0000	0.0029	343.8	1.000	343.8	50′
20′	0.0058	1.0000	0.0058	171.9	1.000	171.9	40′
30′	0.0087	1.0000	0.0087	114.6	1.000	114.6	30′
40′	0.0116	0.9999	0.0116	85.94	1.000	85.95	20′
50′	0.0145	0.9999	0.0145	68.75	1.000	68.76	10′
1°00′	0.0175	0.9998	0.0175	57.29	1.000	57.30	89°00′
10′	0.0204	0.9998	0.0204	49.10	1.000	49.11	50′
20′	0.0233	0.9997	0.0233	42.96	1.000	42.98	40′
30′	0.0262	0.9997	0.0262	38.19	1.000	38.20	30′
40′	0.0291	0.9996	0.0291	34.37	1.000	34.38	20′
50′	0.0320	0.9995	0.0320	31.24	1.001	31.26	10′
2°00′	0.0349	0.9994	0.0349	28.64	1.001	28.65	88°00′
10′	0.0378	0.9993	0.0378	26.43	1.001	26.45	50′
20′	0.0407	0.9992	0.0407	24.54	1.001	24.56	40′
30′	0.0436	0.9990	0.0437	22.90	1.001	22.93	30′
40′	0.0465	0.9989	0.0466	21.47	1.001	21.49	20′
50′	0.0494	0.9988	0.0495	20.21	1.001	20.23	10′
3°00′	0.0523	0.9986	0.0524	19.08	1.001	19.11	87°00′
10′	0.0552	0.9985	0.0553	18.07	1.002	18.10	50′
20′	0.0581	0.9983	0.0582	17.17	1.002	17.20	40′
30′	0.0610	0.9981	0.0612	16.35	1.002	16.38	30′
40′	0.0640	0.9980	0.0641	15.60	1.002	15.64	20′
50′	0.0669	0.9978	0.0670	14.92	1.002	14.96	10′
4°00′	0.0698	0.9976	0.0699	14.30	1.002	14.34	86°00′
10′	0.0727	0.9974	0.0729	13.73	1.003	13.76	50′
20′	0.0756	0.9971	0.0758	13.20	1.003	13.23	40′
30′	0.0785	0.9969	0.0787	12.71	1.003	12.75	30′
40′	0.0814	0.9967	0.0816	12.25	1.003	12.29	20′
50′	0.0843	0.9964	0.0846	11.83	1.004	11.87	10′
5°00′	0.0872	0.9962	0.0875	11.43	1.004	11.47	85°00′
10′	0.0901	0.9959	0.0904	11.06	1.004	11.10	50′
20′	0.0929	0.9957	0.0934	10.71	1.004	10.76	40′
30′	0.0958	0.9954	0.0963	10.39	1.005	10.43	30′
40′	0.0987	0.9951	0.0992	10.08	1.005	10.13	20′
50′	0.1016	0.9948	0.1022	9.788	1.005	9.839	10′
6°00′	0.1045	0.9945	0.1051	9.514	1.006	9.567	84°00′
10′	0.1074	0.9942	0.1080	9.255	1.006	9.309	50′
20′	0.1103	0.9939	0.1110	9.010	1.006	9.065	40′
30′	0.1132	0.9936	0.1139	8.777	1.006	8.834	30′
40′	0.1161	0.9932	0.1169	8.556	1.007	8.614	20′
50′	0.1190	0.9929	0.1198	8.345	1.007	8.405	10′
7°00′	0.1219	0.9925	0.1228	8.144	1.008	8.206	83°00′
10′	0.1248	0.9922	0.1257	7.953	1.008	8.016	50′
20′	0.1276	0.9918	0.1287	7.770	1.008	7.834	40′
30′	0.1305	0.9914	0.1317	7.596	1.009	7.661	30′
40′	0.1334	0.9911	0.1346	7.429	1.009	7.496	20′
50′	0.1363	0.9907	0.1376	7.269	1.009	7.337	10′
8°00′	0.1392	0.9903	0.1405	7.115	1.010	7.185	82°00′
10′	0.1421	0.9899	0.1435	6.968	1.010	7.040	50′
20′	0.1449	0.9894	0.1465	6.827	1.011	6.900	40′
30′	0.1478	0.9890	0.1495	6.691	1.011	6.765	30′
40′	0.1507	0.9886	0.1524	6.561	1.012	6.636	20′
50′	0.1536	0.9881	0.1554	6.435	1.012	6.512	10′
9°00′	0.1564	0.9877	0.1584	6.314	1.012	6.392	81°00′
	Cos	Sin	Cot	Tan	Csc	Sec	Angle

For the values of cos, sin, tan, and so on for angles
greater than 45°, use the angle measures listed on the
right and the functions on the bottom. For example, cos
81° = 0.1564.

Values of Trigonometric Functions

Angle	Sin	Cos	Tan	Cot	Sec	Csc	
9°00′	0.1564	0.9877	0.1584	6.314	1.012	6.392	81°00′
10′	0.1593	0.9872	0.1614	6.197	1.013	6.277	50′
20′	0.1622	0.9868	0.1644	6.084	1.013	6.166	40′
30′	0.1650	0.9863	0.1673	5.976	1.014	6.059	30′
40′	0.1679	0.9858	0.1703	5.871	1.014	5.955	20′
50′	0.1708	0.9853	0.1733	5.769	1.015	5.855	10′
10°00′	0.1736	0.9848	0.1763	5.671	1.015	5.759	80°00′
10′	0.1765	0.9843	0.1793	5.576	1.016	5.665	50′
20′	0.1794	0.9838	0.1823	5.485	1.016	5.575	40′
30′	0.1822	0.9833	0.1853	5.396	1.017	5.487	30′
40′	0.1851	0.9827	0.1883	5.309	1.018	5.403	20′
50′	0.1880	0.9822	0.1914	5.226	1.018	5.320	10′
11°00′	0.1908	0.9816	0.1944	5.145	1.019	5.241	79°00′
10′	0.1937	0.9811	0.1974	5.066	1.019	5.164	50′
20′	0.1965	0.9805	0.2004	4.989	1.020	5.089	40′
30′	0.1994	0.9799	0.2035	4.915	1.020	5.016	30′
40′	0.2022	0.9793	0.2065	4.843	1.021	4.945	20′
50′	0.2051	0.9787	0.2095	4.773	1.022	4.876	10′
12°00′	0.2079	0.9781	0.2126	4.705	1.022	4.810	78°00′
10′	0.2108	0.9775	0.2156	4.638	1.023	4.745	50′
20′	0.2136	0.9769	0.2186	4.574	1.024	4.682	40′
30′	0.2164	0.9763	0.2217	4.511	1.024	4.620	30′
40′	0.2193	0.9757	0.2247	4.449	1.025	4.560	20′
50′	0.2221	0.9750	0.2278	4.390	1.026	4.502	10′
13°00′	0.2250	0.9744	0.2309	4.331	1.026	4.445	77°00′
10′	0.2278	0.9737	0.2339	4.275	1.027	4.390	50′
20′	0.2306	0.9730	0.2370	4.219	1.028	4.336	40′
30′	0.2334	0.9724	0.2401	4.165	1.028	4.284	30′
40′	0.2363	0.9717	0.2432	4.113	1.029	4.232	20′
50′	0.2391	0.9710	0.2462	4.061	1.030	4.182	10′
14°00′	0.2419	0.9703	0.2493	4.011	1.031	4.134	76°00′
10′	0.2447	0.9696	0.2524	3.962	1.031	4.086	50′
20′	0.2476	0.9689	0.2555	3.914	1.032	4.039	40′
30′	0.2504	0.9681	0.2586	3.867	1.033	3.994	30′
40′	0.2532	0.9674	0.2617	3.821	1.034	3.950	20′
50′	0.2560	0.9667	0.2648	3.776	1.034	3.906	10′
15°00′	0.2588	0.9659	0.2679	3.732	1.035	3.864	75°00′
10′	0.2616	0.9652	0.2711	3.689	1.036	3.822	50′
20′	0.2644	0.9644	0.2742	3.647	1.037	3.782	40′
30′	0.2672	0.9636	0.2773	3.606	1.038	3.742	30′
40′	0.2700	0.9628	0.2805	3.566	1.039	3.703	20′
50′	0.2728	0.9621	0.2836	3.526	1.039	3.665	10′
16°00′	0.2756	0.9613	0.2867	3.487	1.040	3.628	74°00′
10′	0.2784	0.9605	0.2899	3.450	1.041	3.592	50′
20′	0.2812	0.9596	0.2931	3.412	1.042	3.556	40′
30′	0.2840	0.9588	0.2962	3.376	1.043	3.521	30′
40′	0.2868	0.9580	0.2994	3.340	1.044	3.487	20′
50′	0.2896	0.9572	0.3026	3.305	1.045	3.453	10′
17°00′	0.2924	0.9563	0.3057	3.271	1.046	3.420	73°00′
10′	0.2952	0.9555	0.3089	3.237	1.047	3.388	50′
20′	0.2979	0.9546	0.3121	3.204	1.048	3.356	40′
30′	0.3007	0.9537	0.3153	3.172	1.049	3.326	30′
40′	0.3035	0.9528	0.3185	3.140	1.049	3.295	20′
50′	0.3062	0.9520	0.3217	3.108	1.050	3.265	10′
18°00′	0.3090	0.9511	0.3249	3.078	1.051	3.236	72°00′
	Cos	Sin	Cot	Tan	Csc	Sec	Angle

Values of Trigonometric Functions

Angle	Sin	Cos	Tan	Cot	Sec	Csc	
18°00′	0.3090	0.9511	0.3249	3.078	1.051	3.236	72°00′
10′	0.3118	0.9502	0.3281	3.047	1.052	3.207	50′
20′	0.3145	0.9492	0.3314	3.018	1.053	3.179	40′
30′	0.3173	0.9483	0.3346	2.989	1.054	3.152	30′
40′	0.3201	0.9474	0.3378	2.960	1.056	3.124	20′
50′	0.3228	0.9465	0.3411	2.932	1.057	3.098	10′
19°00′	0.3256	0.9455	0.3443	2.904	1.058	3.072	71°00′
10′	0.3283	0.9446	0.3476	2.877	1.059	3.046	50′
20′	0.3311	0.9436	0.3508	2.850	1.060	3.021	40′
30′	0.3338	0.9426	0.3541	2.824	1.061	2.996	30′
40′	0.3365	0.9417	0.3574	2.798	1.062	2.971	20′
50′	0.3393	0.9407	0.3607	2.773	1.063	2.947	10′
20°00′	0.3420	0.9397	0.3640	2.747	1.064	2.924	70°00′
10′	0.3448	0.9387	0.3673	2.723	1.065	2.901	50′
20′	0.3475	0.9377	0.3706	2.699	1.066	2.878	40′
30′	0.3502	0.9367	0.3739	2.675	1.068	2.855	30′
40′	0.3529	0.9356	0.3772	2.651	1.069	2.833	20′
50′	0.3557	0.9346	0.3805	2.628	1.070	2.812	10′
21°00′	0.3584	0.9336	0.3839	2.605	1.071	2.790	69°00′
10′	0.3611	0.9325	0.3872	2.583	1.072	2.769	50′
20′	0.3638	0.9315	0.3906	2.560	1.074	2.749	40′
30′	0.3665	0.9304	0.3939	2.539	1.075	2.729	30′
40′	0.3692	0.9293	0.3973	2.517	1.076	2.709	20′
50′	0.3719	0.9283	0.4006	2.496	1.077	2.689	10′
22°00′	0.3746	0.9272	0.4040	2.475	1.079	2.669	68°00′
10′	0.3773	0.9261	0.4074	2.455	1.080	2.650	50′
20′	0.3800	0.9250	0.4108	2.434	1.081	2.632	40′
30′	0.3827	0.9239	0.4142	2.414	1.082	2.613	30′
40′	0.3854	0.9228	0.4176	2.394	1.084	2.595	20′
50′	0.3881	0.9216	0.4210	2.375	1.085	2.577	10′
23°00′	0.3907	0.9205	0.4245	2.356	1.086	2.559	67°00′
10′	0.3934	0.9194	0.4279	2.337	1.088	2.542	50′
20′	0.3961	0.9182	0.4314	2.318	1.089	2.525	40′
30′	0.3987	0.9171	0.4348	2.300	1.090	2.508	30′
40′	0.4014	0.9159	0.4383	2.282	1.092	2.491	20′
50′	0.4041	0.9147	0.4417	2.264	1.093	2.475	10′
24°00′	0.4067	0.9135	0.4452	2.246	1.095	2.459	66°00′
10′	0.4094	0.9124	0.4487	2.229	1.096	2.443	50′
20′	0.4120	0.9112	0.4522	2.211	1.097	2.427	40′
30′	0.4147	0.9100	0.4557	2.194	1.099	2.411	30′
40′	0.4173	0.9088	0.4592	2.177	1.100	2.396	20′
50′	0.4200	0.9075	0.4628	2.161	1.102	2.381	10′
25°00′	0.4226	0.9063	0.4663	2.145	1.103	2.366	65°00′
10′	0.4253	0.9051	0.4699	2.128	1.105	2.352	50′
20′	0.4279	0.9038	0.4734	2.112	1.106	2.337	40′
30′	0.4305	0.9026	0.4770	2.097	1.108	2.323	30′
40′	0.4331	0.9013	0.4806	2.081	1.109	2.309	20′
50′	0.4358	0.9001	0.4841	2.066	1.111	2.295	10′
26°00′	0.4384	0.8988	0.4877	2.050	1.113	2.281	64°00′
10′	0.4410	0.8975	0.4913	2.035	1.114	2.268	50′
20′	0.4436	0.8962	0.4950	2.020	1.116	2.254	40′
30′	0.4462	0.8949	0.4986	2.006	1.117	2.241	30′
40′	0.4488	0.8936	0.5022	1.991	1.119	2.228	20′
50′	0.4514	0.8923	0.5059	1.977	1.121	2.215	10′
27°00′	0.4540	0.8910	0.5095	1.963	1.122	2.203	63°00′
	Cos	Sin	Cot	Tan	Csc	Sec	Angle

Values of Trigonometric Functions

Angle	Sin	Cos	Tan	Cot	Sec	Csc	
27°00'	0.4540	0.8910	0.5095	1.963	1.122	2.203	63°00'
10'	0.4566	0.8897	0.5132	1.949	1.124	2.190	50'
20'	0.4592	0.8884	0.5169	1.935	1.126	2.178	40'
30'	0.4617	0.8870	0.5206	1.921	1.127	2.166	30'
40'	0.4643	0.8857	0.5243	1.907	1.129	2.154	20'
50'	0.4669	0.8843	0.5280	1.894	1.131	2.142	10'
28°00'	0.4695	0.8829	0.5317	1.881	1.133	2.130	62°00'
10'	0.4720	0.8816	0.5354	1.868	1.134	2.118	50'
20'	0.4746	0.8802	0.5392	1.855	1.136	2.107	40'
30'	0.4772	0.8788	0.5430	1.842	1.138	2.096	30'
40'	0.4797	0.8774	0.5467	1.829	1.140	2.085	20'
50'	0.4823	0.8760	0.5505	1.816	1.142	2.074	10'
29°00'	0.4848	0.8746	0.5543	1.804	1.143	2.063	61°00'
10'	0.4874	0.8732	0.5581	1.792	1.145	2.052	50'
20'	0.4899	0.8718	0.5619	1.780	1.147	2.041	40'
30'	0.4924	0.8704	0.5658	1.767	1.149	2.031	30'
40'	0.4950	0.8689	0.5696	1.756	1.151	2.020	20'
50'	0.4975	0.8675	0.5735	1.744	1.153	2.010	10'
30°00'	0.5000	0.8660	0.5774	1.732	1.155	2.000	60°00'
10'	0.5025	0.8646	0.5812	1.720	1.157	1.990	50'
20'	0.5050	0.8631	0.5851	1.709	1.159	1.980	40'
30'	0.5075	0.8616	0.5890	1.698	1.161	1.970	30'
40'	0.5100	0.8601	0.5930	1.686	1.163	1.961	20'
50'	0.5125	0.8587	0.5969	1.675	1.165	1.951	10'
31°00'	0.5150	0.8572	0.6009	1.664	1.167	1.942	59°00'
10'	0.5175	0.8557	0.6048	1.653	1.169	1.932	50'
20'	0.5200	0.8542	0.6088	1.643	1.171	1.923	40'
30'	0.5225	0.8526	0.6128	1.632	1.173	1.914	30'
40'	0.5250	0.8511	0.6168	1.621	1.175	1.905	20'
50'	0.5275	0.8496	0.6208	1.611	1.177	1.896	10'
32°00'	0.5299	0.8480	0.6249	1.600	1.179	1.887	58°00'
10'	0.5324	0.8465	0.6289	1.590	1.181	1.878	50'
20'	0.5348	0.8450	0.6330	1.580	1.184	1.870	40'
30'	0.5373	0.8434	0.6371	1.570	1.186	1.861	30'
40'	0.5398	0.8418	0.6412	1.560	1.188	1.853	20'
50'	0.5422	0.8403	0.6453	1.550	1.190	1.844	10'
33°00'	0.5446	0.8387	0.6494	1.540	1.192	1.836	57°00'
10'	0.5471	0.8371	0.6536	1.530	1.195	1.828	50'
20'	0.5495	0.8355	0.6577	1.520	1.197	1.820	40'
30'	0.5519	0.8339	0.6619	1.511	1.199	1.812	30'
40'	0.5544	0.8323	0.6661	1.501	1.202	1.804	20'
50'	0.5568	0.8307	0.6703	1.492	1.204	1.796	10'
34°00'	0.5592	0.8290	0.6745	1.483	1.206	1.788	56°00'
10'	0.5616	0.8274	0.6787	1.473	1.209	1.781	50'
20'	0.5640	0.8258	0.6830	1.464	1.211	1.773	40'
30'	0.5664	0.8241	0.6873	1.455	1.213	1.766	30'
40'	0.5688	0.8225	0.6916	1.446	1.216	1.758	20'
50'	0.5712	0.8208	0.6959	1.437	1.218	1.751	10'
35°00'	0.5736	0.8192	0.7002	1.428	1.221	1.743	55°00'
10'	0.5760	0.8175	0.7046	1.419	1.223	1.736	50'
20'	0.5783	0.8158	0.7089	1.411	1.226	1.729	40'
30'	0.5807	0.8141	0.7133	1.402	1.228	1.722	30'
40'	0.5831	0.8124	0.7177	1.393	1.231	1.715	20'
50'	0.5854	0.8107	0.7221	1.385	1.233	1.708	10'
36°00'	0.5878	0.8090	0.7265	1.376	1.236	1.701	54°00'
	Cos	Sin	Cot	Tan	Csc	Sec	Angle

Values of Trigonometric Functions

Angle	Sin	Cos	Tan	Cot	Sec	Csc	
36°00′	0.5878	0.8090	0.7265	1.376	1.236	1.701	54°00′
10′	0.5901	0.8073	0.7310	1.368	1.239	1.695	50′
20′	0.5925	0.8056	0.7355	1.360	1.241	1.688	40′
30′	0.5948	0.8039	0.7400	1.351	1.244	1.681	30′
40′	0.5972	0.8021	0.7445	1.343	1.247	1.675	20′
50′	0.5995	0.8004	0.7490	1.335	1.249	1.668	10′
37°00′	0.6018	0.7986	0.7536	1.327	1.252	1.662	53°00′
10′	0.6041	0.7969	0.7581	1.319	1.255	1.655	50′
20′	0.6065	0.7951	0.7627	1.311	1.258	1.649	40′
30′	0.6088	0.7934	0.7673	1.303	1.260	1.643	30′
40′	0.6111	0.7916	0.7720	1.295	1.263	1.636	20′
50′	0.6134	0.7898	0.7766	1.288	1.266	1.630	10′
38°00′	0.6157	0.7880	0.7813	1.280	1.269	1.624	52°00′
10′	0.6180	0.7862	0.7860	1.272	1.272	1.618	50′
20′	0.6202	0.7844	0.7907	1.265	1.275	1.612	40′
30′	0.6225	0.7826	0.7954	1.257	1.278	1.606	30′
40′	0.6248	0.7808	0.8002	1.250	1.281	1.601	20′
50′	0.6271	0.7790	0.8050	1.242	1.284	1.595	10′
39°00′	0.6293	0.7771	0.8098	1.235	1.287	1.589	51°00′
10′	0.6316	0.7753	0.8146	1.228	1.290	1.583	50′
20′	0.6338	0.7735	0.8195	1.220	1.293	1.578	40′
30′	0.6361	0.7716	0.8243	1.213	1.296	1.572	30′
40′	0.6383	0.7698	0.8292	1.206	1.299	1.567	20′
50′	0.6406	0.7679	0.8342	1.199	1.302	1.561	10′
40°00′	0.6428	0.7660	0.8391	1.192	1.305	1.556	50°00′
10′	0.6450	0.7642	0.8441	1.185	1.309	1.550	50′
20′	0.6472	0.7623	0.8491	1.178	1.312	1.545	40′
30′	0.6494	0.7604	0.8541	1.171	1.315	1.540	30′
40′	0.6517	0.7585	0.8591	1.164	1.318	1.535	20′
50′	0.6539	0.7566	0.8642	1.157	1.322	1.529	10′
41°00′	0.6561	0.7547	0.8693	1.150	1.325	1.524	49°00′
10′	0.6583	0.7528	0.8744	1.144	1.328	1.519	50′
20′	0.6604	0.7509	0.8796	1.137	1.332	1.514	40′
30′	0.6626	0.7490	0.8847	1.130	1.335	1.509	30′
40′	0.6648	0.7470	0.8899	1.124	1.339	1.504	20′
50′	0.6670	0.7451	0.8952	1.117	1.342	1.499	10′
42°00′	0.6691	0.7431	0.9004	1.111	1.346	1.494	48°00′
10′	0.6713	0.7412	0.9057	1.104	1.349	1.490	50′
20′	0.6734	0.7392	0.9110	1.098	1.353	1.485	40′
30′	0.6756	0.7373	0.9163	1.091	1.356	1.480	30′
40′	0.6777	0.7353	0.9217	1.085	1.360	1.476	20′
50′	0.6799	0.7333	0.9271	1.079	1.364	1.471	10′
43°00′	0.6820	0.7314	0.9325	1.072	1.367	1.466	47°00′
10′	0.6841	0.7294	0.9380	1.066	1.371	1.462	50′
20′	0.6862	0.7274	0.9435	1.060	1.375	1.457	40′
30′	0.6884	0.7254	0.9490	1.054	1.379	1.453	30′
40′	0.6905	0.7234	0.9545	1.048	1.382	1.448	20′
50′	0.6926	0.7214	0.9601	1.042	1.386	1.444	10′
44°00′	0.6947	0.7193	0.9657	1.036	1.390	1.440	46°00′
10′	0.6967	0.7173	0.9713	1.030	1.394	1.435	50′
20′	0.6988	0.7153	0.9770	1.024	1.398	1.431	40′
30′	0.7009	0.7133	0.9827	1.018	1.402	1.427	30′
40′	0.7030	0.7112	0.9884	1.012	1.406	1.423	20′
50′	0.7050	0.7092	0.9942	1.006	1.410	1.418	10′
45°00′	0.7071	0.7071	1.000	1.000	1.414	1.414	45°00′
	Cos	Sin	Cot	Tan	Csc	Sec	Angle

Glossary

absolute value The absolute value of a number is the number of units that it is from zero on the number line. For any number a:

If $a \geq 0$, then $|a| = a$.

If $a < 0$, then $|a| = {}^-a$. (16)

additive identity Zero is the additive identity. The sum of any number is identical to the original number. (5)

additive inverse If the sum of two numbers is 0, they are called additive inverses of each other. (5)

algebraic expressions Algebraic expressions are mathematical expressions having at least one variable. (2)

amplitude For functions of the form $y = a \sin b\theta$ and $y = a \cos b\theta$, the amplitude is $|a|$. (488)

angle of depression An angle of depression is the angle formed by a horizontal line and the line of sight to an object at a lower level. (528)

angle of elevation The angle of elevation is the angle formed by a horizontal line, and the line of sight to an object at a higher level. (528)

antilogarithm If $\log x = a$, then $x = $ antilog a. (363)

Arccosine Given $y = \text{Cos } x$, the inverse cosine function is defined by $x = \text{Cos}^{-1} y$. (511)

Arcsine Given $y = \text{Sin } x$, the inverse sine function is defined by $x = \text{Sin}^{-1} y$. (511)

Arctangent Given $y = \text{Tan } x$, the inverse tangent function is defined by $x = \text{Tan}^{-1} y$. (511)

arithmetic means The terms between any two nonconsecutive terms of an arithmetic sequence, are called arithmetic means. (387)

arithmetic sequence An arithmetic sequence is a sequence in which the difference between any two consecutive terms is the same. (385)

arithmetic series The indicated sum of the terms of an arithmetic sequence is called an arithmetic series. (389)

associativity The way you group, or associate, three or more numbers does not change their sum or their product. That is, for all numbers a, b, and c, $(a + b) + c = a + (b + c)$ and $(a \cdot b) \cdot c = a \cdot (b \cdot c)$. (4)

asymptote Asymptotes are lines that a curve approaches. (239)

axis of symmetry An axis of symmetry is the line about which a figure is symmetric. (200)

bar graph A bar graph shows how specific quantities compare to one another. (457)

BASIC The word BASIC is the name of a computer language. (547)

binomial A polynomial with two unlike terms is a binomial. (114)

Binomial Theorem If n is a positive integer, then the following is true.

$$(a + b)^n = 1a^n b^0 + \frac{n}{1} a^{n-1} b^1$$

$$+ \frac{n(n-1)}{1 \cdot 2} a^{n-2} b^2 + \ldots$$

$$+ \frac{n}{1} a^1 b^{n-1} + 1a^0 b^n \quad (415)$$

binomial trial A binomial trial exists if and and only if the following conditions occur.
1. There are only two possible outcomes.
2. The events are independent. (446)

center of circle See circle.

center of hyperbola The center of hyperbola is the midpoint of the segment connecting the foci of a hyperbola. (239)

characteristic The characteristic is the power of 10 by which that number is multiplied when the number is expressed in scientific notation. (362)

circle The definition of circle is a set of points in a plane each of which is the same distance from a given point. The given distance is the radius of the circle and the given point is the center of the circle. (230)

circle graph A circle graph shows how parts are related to the whole. (458)

circular permutations If n objects are arranged in a circle, then there are $\frac{n!}{n}$ or $(n - 1)!$ permutations of the n objects around the circle. (430)

coefficient The numerical factor of a monomial is the coefficient. (107)

combination The number of combinations of n objects, taken r at a time, is written $C(n, r)$.

$$C(n, r) = \frac{n!}{(n - r)! r!} \quad (433)$$

common difference The common difference of an arithmetic sequence is the constant that is the difference between successive terms. (386)

common logarithms Common logarithms are logarithms to base 10. (362)

common ratio The common ratio of a geometric sequence is the constant that is the ratio of successive terms. (394)

commutativity The order in which two numbers are added or multiplied does not change their sum or product. That is, for all numbers a and b, $a + b = b + a$ and $a \cdot b = b \cdot a$. (4)

complex conjugates Complex conjugates are complex numbers of the form $a + bi$ and $a - bi$. (16)

complex fraction A complex rational expression, also called a complex fraction, is an expression whose numerator and denominator, or both, contain rational expressions. (296)

complex number A complex number is any number that can be written in the form $a + bi$ where a and b are real numbers and i is the imaginary unit. (159)

composition of functions Given functions f and g, the composite function $f \circ g$ can be described by the following equation.
$$[f \circ g](x) = f[g(x)] \quad (280)$$

compound interest The compound interest formula is $A = P\left(1 + \frac{r}{n}\right)^{nt}$ where P is the investment, r is the interest rate, n is the number of times the interest is compounded yearly, t is the number of years of the investment and A is the amount of money accumulated. (369)

computer program A computer program is a series of statements that give directions to the computer. (547)

conic section A conic section is a curve formed by slicing a hollow double cone with a plane. The equation of a conic section can be written in the form $Ax^2 + Bxy + Cy^2 + Dx + Ey + F = 0$ where A, B, and C are not all zero. (243)

conjugate axis The conjugate axis of a hyperbola is the segment perpendicular to the transverse axis at its center. (239)

conjugates Binomials that are of the form $a + b\sqrt{c}$ and $a - b\sqrt{c}$ are conjugates of each other. (146)

consistent and dependent system A system of equations where the graphs of the equations are the same line is called a consistent and dependent system. There is an infinite number of solutions to this system of equations. (75)

consistent and independent system A system of equations that has one ordered pair as its solution is a consistent and independent system. (75)

constant A monomial that contains no variable is a constant. (107)

constant function A constant function is a function of the form $f(x) = b$ where the slope is zero. (56)

constant of variation The constant k in either of the equations $y = kx$ or $y = \dfrac{k}{x}$ is called the constant of variation. (314)

coordinate plane The plane determined by the perpendicular axes is called the coordinate plane. (37)

coordinates Each point in the coordinate plane corresponds an ordered pair of numbers called its coordinates. (38)

cosecant Let θ stand for the measurement of an angle in standard position on the unit circle. Then the following equation holds whenever it is defined.
$$\csc \theta = \frac{1}{\sin \theta} \quad (490)$$

cosine Let θ stand for the measurement of an angle in standard position on the unit circle. Let (x, y) represent the point where the terminal side intersects the unit circle. Then the following equation holds.
$$\cos \theta = x \quad (482)$$

cotangent Let θ stand for the measurement of an angle in standard position on the unit circle. Then the following equation

holds whenever it is defined.
$$\cot \theta = \frac{\cos \theta}{\sin \theta} \quad (490)$$

coterminal angles Coterminal angles differ by a complete rotation of the circle. (479)

Cramer's Rule The solution to the system of equations
$$\begin{matrix} ax + by = c \\ dx + ey = f \end{matrix} \text{ is } (x, y) \text{ where}$$
$$x = \frac{\begin{vmatrix} c & b \\ f & e \end{vmatrix}}{\begin{vmatrix} a & b \\ d & e \end{vmatrix}} \text{ and } \frac{\begin{vmatrix} a & c \\ d & f \end{vmatrix}}{\begin{vmatrix} a & b \\ d & e \end{vmatrix}} \text{ and } \begin{vmatrix} a & b \\ d & e \end{vmatrix} \neq 0.$$
(90)

data Numerical observations are called data. (453)

DATA statement A DATA statement is a BASIC statement that lists information to be used in a computer program. (547)

degree of monomial The degree of a monomial is the sum of the exponents of its variables. (107)

degree of polynomial The degree of a polynomial is the degree of the monomial of greatest degree. (114)

dependent events Two events are dependent when the outcome of the first event affects the outcome of the second event. If two events, A and B, are dependent, then the probability of both occurring is found as follows.
$$P(A \text{ and } B) = P(A) \cdot P(B \text{ following } A) \quad (439)$$

depressed polynomial A polynomial whose degree is less than the original polynomial is called a depressed polynomial. It is the result of factoring out a factor of the original polynomial. (264)

determinant A determinant is a square array of numbers having a numerical value. (87)

direct variation A direct variation is a linear function described by $y = mx$ or $f(x) = mx$ where $m \neq 0$. (56)

discriminant In the quadratic formula, the expression under the radical sign, $b^2 - 4ac$, is called the discriminant. (180)

dispersion Dispersion is the variation of values in a set of data. (466)

distributive property For all numbers a, b, and c, $a(b + c) = ab + ac$ and $(b + c)a = ba + ca$. (6)

domain The domain is the set of all first coordinates of the ordered pairs of a relation. (40)

ellipse An ellipse is the set of all points in the plane such that the sum of the distances from two given points, called the foci, is constant. The general equation of an ellipse that has center (h, k) and major axis of length $2a$ is as follows. The equation is $\dfrac{(x - h)^2}{a^2} + \dfrac{(y - k)^2}{b^2} = 1$ when the major axis is parallel to the x-axis. The equation is $\dfrac{(x - h)^2}{b^2} + \dfrac{(y - k)^2}{a^2} = 1$ when the major axis is parallel to the y-axis. For an ellipse, $b^2 = a^2 - c^2$. (233)

END statement An END statement indicates that a computer program is finished. It is the last statement in a BASIC program. (547)

E notation E notation is the computer equivalent of scientific notation. (548)

equation A statement of equality between two mathematical expressions is called an equation. (8)

expansion by minors Expansion by minors is a method that can be used to find the value of any third or higher order determinant. (88)

exponent An exponent is a numeral written to the right and above a number indicating how many times the number is used as a factor. (1)

exponential equation An equation in which the variables appear as exponents is called an exponential equation. (372)

Fibonacci sequence A fibonacci sequence is a special sequence often found in nature. It is named after its discoverer, Leonardo Fibonacci. (412)

flow chart A flow chart is a diagram used to organize and plan a computer program. (559)

FOIL FOIL is a method used to multiply binomials. The product of 2 binomials is the sum of the products of
F the first terms
O the outer terms
I the inner terms
L the last terms. (115)

formula A mathematical sentence about the relationships among certain quantities is called a formula. (2)

FOR-NEXT loop A FOR-NEXT loop instructs the computer to perform a certain task a prescribed number of times. (556)

frequency distribution A frequency distribution shows how data are spread out. (469)

function A function is a relation in which each element of the domain is paired with exactly one element of the range. (41)

geometric means The terms between any two nonconsecutive terms of a geometric sequence are called geometric means. (395)

geometric sequence A geometric sequence is a sequence in which each term after the first is the product of the preceding term and the common ratio. (394)

geometric series The indicated sum of the terms of a geometric sequence is called a geometric series. (398)

GO TO statement A GO TO statement is a BASIC statement that returns the computer to a particular step in a program. (552)

greatest integer The greatest integer of x is written $[x]$ and means the greatest integer *not* greater than x. (57)

histogram A histogram is a bar graph that shows a frequency distribution. (466)

hyperbola A hyperbola is the set of all points in the plane such that the absolute value of the difference of the distances from two given points, called the foci, is constant. The general equation of a hyperbola that has center (h, k) and a horizontal transverse axis of length $2a$ is $\frac{(x - h)^2}{a^2} - \frac{(y - k)^2}{b^2} = 1$. The equation is $\frac{(y - k)^2}{a^2} - \frac{(x - h)^2}{b^2} = 1$ when the transverse axis is vertical. For the hyperbola, $b^2 = c^2 - a^2$. (238)

identity function An identity function is a linear function described by $y = x$ or $f(x) = x$. (56)

IF-THEN statement An IF-THEN statement instructs a computer to make a comparison and tells the computer what to do next, based on the results of the comparison. (553)

imaginary number For any positive real number b, $\sqrt{-b^2} = bi$, where i is a number whose square is $^-1$. The number i is called the imaginary unit, and bi is called a pure imaginary number. (156)

inclusive events Two events are inclusive if the outcomes of the events may be the same. The probability of two inclusive events, A and B, occurring is found as follows.
$P(A \text{ or } B) - P(A) + P(B) - P(A \text{ and } B)$. (442)

inconsistent system An inconsistent system is a system of equations where the graph of the equations is parallel lines. There is no solution to this system of equations. (75)

independent events Two events are independent if the outcome of one event does not affect the outcome of the other event. The probability of two independent events, A and B, occurring is found as follows.
$P(A \text{ and } B) = P(A) \cdot P(B)$ (423)

index of summation An index of summation is a variable used with the summation symbol (Σ). (405)

infinite geometric series An infinite geometric series is the indicated sum of the terms of an infinite geometric sequence. (401)

internal functions in BASIC The internal functions in BASIC perform prescribed tasks. They are ABS(X), SQR(X), INT(X), RND(X), SIN(X), COS(X), and TAN(X). (565)

interpolation Interpolation is a method for approximating values that are between given consecutive entries in a table, such as a table of logarithms or a table of trigonometric values. (365, 523)

inverse functions Two polynomial functions f and g are inverse functions if and only if both their compositions are the identity function. That is,
$[f \circ g](x) = [g \circ f](x) = x$. (283)

inverse variation A rational equation in two variables of the form $y = \frac{k}{x}$, where k is a constant, is called an inverse variation. The constant k is called the constant of variation, and y is said to vary inversely as x. (314)

irrational numbers Irrational numbers are real numbers that cannot be written as terminating or repeating decimals. (141)

latus rectum A latus rectum is the line segment through the focus of a parabola perpendicular to its axis of symmetry with endpoints on the parabola. (227)

Laws of Cosines Let triangle ABC be any triangle with a, b, and c representing the measures of sides opposite angles with measurements A, B, and C, respectively. Then the following equations are true.

$$a^2 = b^2 + c^2 - 2bc \cos A$$
$$b^2 = a^2 + c^2 - 2ac \cos B$$
$$c^2 = a^2 + b^2 - 2ab \cos C \quad (536)$$

Law of Sines Let triangle ABC be any triangle with a, b, and c representing the measures of sides opposite angles with measurements A, B, and C, respectively. Then the following equations are true.

$$\frac{\sin A}{a} = \frac{\sin B}{b} = \frac{\sin C}{c} \quad (533)$$

LET statement A LET statement is a BASIC statement that assigns a value to a variable. (550)

like terms Two monomials that are the same or differ only by their coefficients are called like terms. (107)

linear equation A linear equation is an equation whose graph is a straight line. (46)

linear function A linear function can be defined by $f(x) = mx + b$ where m and b are real numbers. Any function whose ordered pairs satisfy a linear equation in two variables is a linear function. (48)

linear permutation The arrangement of n objects in a certain linear order is called a linear permutation. The number of linear permutations of n objects, taken r at a time, is defined as follows.

$$P(n, r) = \frac{n!}{(n - r)!} \quad (426)$$

linear programming Linear programming is a method for finding the maximum or the minimum value of a function in two variables subject to given conditions on the variables. (96)

line graph A line graph shows trends or changes. (457)

logarithm Suppose $b > 0$ and $b \neq 1$. Then for $n > 0$, there is a number p such that $\log_b n = p$ if and only if $b^p = n$. (351)

major axis The major axis of an ellipse is the segment with endpoints at the vertices of the ellipse. (234)

mantissa The mantissa is the logarithm of a number between 1 and 10. (362)

mapping A mapping illustrates how each element in the domain of a relation is paired with an element in the range. (40)

matrix A matrix is a rectangular arrangement of terms in rows and columns enclosed in brackets or large parentheses. (84)

mean The mean of a set of data is the sum of all the values divided by the number of values. (461)

median The median of a set of data is the middle value. If there are two middle values, it is the value halfway between. (461)

midpoint The midpoint of a line segment with endpoints (x_1, y_1) and (x_2, y_2) has coordinates $\left(\frac{x_1 + x_2}{2}, \frac{y_1 + y_2}{2}\right)$. (224)

minor A minor is the determinant formed when the row and column containing the element are deleted. (88)

mode The mode of a set of data is the most frequent value. (461)

monomial A monomial is an expression that is a number, a variable, or the product of a number and one or more variables. (107)

multiplicative identity One is the multiplicative identity. The product of any number and 1 is identical to the original number. (5)

multiplicative inverses If the product of two numbers is 1, they are called multiplicative inverses or reciprocals of each other. (5)

mutually exclusive events Two events are mutually exclusive if their outcomes can never be the same. The probability of two mutually exclusive events, A and B, occurring is found as follows.

$$P(A \text{ or } B) = P(A) + P(B) \quad (442)$$

negative integer exponents For any number a, except $a = 0$, and for any positive integer n, $a^{-n} = \dfrac{1}{a^n}$. (321)

n factorial If n is a positive integer, the expression $n!$ (n factorial) is defined as follows.

$$n! = n(n - 1)(n - 2) \cdots (1) \quad (416)$$

normal distribution Normal distributions have bell-shaped, symmetric graphs. About 68% of the items are within one standard deviation from the mean. About 95% of the items are within two standard deviations from the mean. About 99% of the items are within three standard deviations from the mean. (469)

nth root For any numbers a and b, and any positive integer n, if $a^n = b$, then a is an nth root of b. (139)

nth term The nth term of an arithmetic sequence with the first term a_1 and common difference d is given by the following equation.

$$a_n = a_1 + (n - 1)d \quad (386)$$

odds The odds of the successful outcome of an event are expressed as the ratio of the number of ways it can succeed to the number of ways it can fail.

$$\text{Odds} = \text{the ratio of } s \text{ to } f \text{ or } \dfrac{s}{f} \quad (437)$$

origin The origin is the point on the coordinate plane whose coordinates are $(0, 0)$. (37)

parabola **1.** The general shape of the graph of a quadratic function is called a parabola. (200) **2.** A parabola is the set of all points that are the same distance from a given point and a given line. The point is called the focus. The line is called the directrix. The general equation of a parabola with vertex at (h, k) is $y = a(x - h)^2 + k$ when the directrix is horizontal. The equation is $x = a(y - k)^2 + h$ when the directrix is vertical. (226)

parallel lines In a plane, lines with the same slope are called parallel lines. Also, vertical lines are parallel. (71)

period For a function f, the least positive value of a for which $f(x) = f(x + a)$ is the period of the function. For functions of the form $y = a \sin b\theta$ and $y = a \cos b\theta$, the period is $\dfrac{2\pi}{|b|}$. (484, 488)

periodic function A function f is called periodic if there is a number a such that $f(x) = f(x + a)$. (484)

permutation A permutation is the arrangement of things in a certain order. (426)

perpendicular lines Two nonvertical lines are perpendicular if and only if the product of their slopes is $^-1$. Any vertical line is perpendicular to any horizontal line. (72)

pictograph A pictograph shows how specific quantities compare to one another. (457)

polynomial A polynomial is a monomial or the sum or difference of monomials. (114)

polynomial function A polynomial equation in the form $p(x) = a_n x^n + a_{n-1}x^{n-1} + \cdots a_2 x + a_0$ is a polynomial function. The coefficients $a_0, a_1, a_2, \ldots, a_{n-1}, a_n$ are real numbers and n is a nonnegative integer. (260)

prediction equation The equation of the line suggested by the dots on a scatter diagram is a prediction equation. (472)

principal values The values in the domain of the functions like Cosine, Sine, and Tangent are the principal values. (510)

PRINT statement A PRINT statement is a BASIC statement that directs the computer to print out data or messages. (554)

probability If an event can succeed in s ways and fail in f ways, then the probability of success $P(s)$ and of failure $P(f)$ are as follows.

$$P(s) = \frac{s}{s + f} \qquad P(f) = \frac{f}{s + f} \quad (436)$$

pure imaginary number For any positive real number b, $\sqrt{+(b^2)} = \sqrt{b^2}\sqrt{-1}$ or bi where i is a number whose square is $^-1$. bi is called a pure imaginary number. (156)

quadrants Two perpendicular number lines separate the plane into four parts called quadrants. (37)

quadratic equation Any equation that can be written in the form $ax^2 + bx + c = 0$, where a, b, and c are complex numbers and $a \neq 0$, is a quadratic equation. (171)

quadratic form For any numbers a, b, and c, except $a = 0$, an equation that may be written as $a[f(x)]^2 + b[f(x)] + c = 0$, where $f(x)$ is some expression in x, is in quadratic form. (189, 336)

quadratic formula The solutions of a quadratic equation of the form $ax^2 + bx + c = 0$ with $a \neq 0$ are given by the quadratic formula.

$$x = \frac{^-b \pm \sqrt{b^2 - 4ac}}{2a} \quad (177)$$

quadratic function A quadratic function is a function described by an equation of the form $f(x) = ax^2 + bx + c$ where $a \neq 0$. (197)

radian A radian is an angle that intercepts an arc whose length is 1 unit. (480)

radical equations Radical equations are equations containing variables in the radicands. (153, 339)

radical sign A radical sign, $\sqrt{}$, indicates a square root. (139)

radius See circle.

range **1.** The range is a set of all second coordinates of the ordered pairs of a relation. (40) **2.** The range of a set of data is the difference between the greatest and least values in the set. (466)

rational algebraic expression A rational algebraic expression can be expressed as the quotient of two polynomials. (293)

rational equation A rational equation is an equation that contains one or more rational expressions. (304)

rational exponents For any nonzero number b, and any integers m and n, with $n > 1$

$$b^{\frac{m}{n}} = \sqrt[n]{b^m} = (\sqrt[n]{b})^m$$

except when $\sqrt[n]{b}$ does not represent a real number. (329)

rationalizing the denominator Rationalizing the denominator is changing the form of a rational expression to one without radicals in the denominator. (148, 332)

READ statement A READ statement is a BASIC statement that instructs the computer to input the indicated data. (547)

reciprocal See multiplicative inverse.

recursive formula A recursive formula depends on knowing one or more previous terms. (408)

relation A relation is a set of ordered pairs. (40)

relative maximum or minimum A relative maximum or minimum is a point that represents the maximum or minimum respectively for a certain interval. (279)

row operations on matrices The row operations on matrices are as follows.
1. Interchange any two rows.
2. Replace any row with a nonzero multiple of that row.
3. Replace any row with the sum of that row and another row. (85)

RUN RUN is a BASIC command that instructs the computer to execute the program. (548)

scatter diagram A scatter diagram shows visually the nature of a relationship, both shape and closeness. (472)

scientific notation A number is expressed in scientific notation when it is in the form $a \times 10^n$ where $1 \le a < 10$ and n is an integer. (325)

secant Let θ stand for the measurement of an angle in standard position on the unit circle. Then the following equation holds whenever it is defined.
$$\sec \theta = \frac{1}{\cos \theta} \quad (490)$$

sequence A sequence is a set of numbers in a specific order. (385)

series The indicated sum of the terms of a sequence is called a series. (389)

sigma notation The Σ symbol is used to indicate a sum of a series. (405)

simplified expression An expression is simplified when:
1. It has no negative exponents.
2. It has no fractional exponents in the denominator.
3. It is not a complex fraction.
4. The index of any remaining radical is as small as possible. (333)

sine Let θ stand for the measurement of an angle in standard position on the unit circle. Let (x, y) represent the point where the terminal side intersects the unit circle. Then the following equation holds.
$$\sin \theta = y \quad (482)$$

slope The slope of a line described by $f(x) = mx + b$ is m. Slope is also given by the following expression.
$$\frac{\text{change in } y\text{-coordinates}}{\text{change in corresponding } x\text{-coordinates}}$$
(49)

slope-intercept form The equation $y = mx + b$ is in slope-intercept form. The slope is m and the y-intercept is b. (53)

solution set A solution set is the set of all replacements for variables that make an open sentence true. (8)

solving a right triangle Solving a right triangle means finding all the measures of the sides and angles. (526)

square matrix A matrix that has the same number of rows as columns is called a square matrix. (87)

square root For any number a and b, if $a^2 = b$, then a is a square root of b. (139)

standard deviation From a set of data with n values, if x_i represents a value such that $1 \le i \le n$, and $\bar{x}$ represents the mean, then the standard deviation is

$$\sqrt{\frac{\sum_{i=1}^{m} (x_i - \bar{x})^2}{n}}. \quad (466)$$

standard form The standard form of a linear equation is $ax + by = c$ where a, b, and c are real numbers and a and b are not both zero. (46)

subscripted variables Subscripted variables are used where there is a great amount of data. The subscripts provide labels for the different variables. (562)

sum of a geometric series The sum, S_n, of the first n terms of a geometric series is given by the following formula.

$$S_n = \frac{a_1 - a_1 r^n}{1 - r} \text{ where } r \neq 1 \quad (398)$$

sum of an arithmetic series, S_n The sum, S_n, of the first n terms of an arithmetic series is given by the following formula.

$$S_n = \frac{n}{2}(a_1 + a_n) \quad (390)$$

sum of an infinite geometric series The sum of an infinite geometric series is given by the formula

$$S = \frac{a_1}{1 - r} \text{ where } ^-1 < r < 1. \quad (401)$$

synthetic division A shortcut method used to divide polynomials by binomials is called synthetic division. (131)

synthetic substitution Synthetic substitution is the process of using the Remainder Theorem and synthetic division to find the value of a function. (263)

tangent Let θ stand for the measurement of an angle in standard position on the unit circle. Then the following equation holds whenever it is defined.

$$\tan \theta = \frac{\sin \theta}{\cos \theta} \quad (490)$$

term **1.** Each monomial in a polynomial is called a term. (114) **2.** A term is each number in a sequence. (385)

transverse axis The line segment of a hyperbola of length $2a$ that has its endpoints at the vertices is called the transverse axis. (239)

trichotomy property For any two numbers a and b, one of the following statements is true.

$$a < b, a = b, a > b \quad (20)$$

trinomial A polynomial with three unlike terms is called a trinomial. (114)

unit circle A unit circle has a radius of 1 unit. (480)

variable A variable is a symbol that represents an unknown quantity. (1)

vertical line test If any vertical line drawn on the graph of a relation passes through no more than one point of that graph, then the relation is a function. (42)

x-axis The horizontal number line in a plane is called the x-axis. (37)

x-intercept An x-intercept is the value of x when the value of the function or y is zero. (51)

y-axis The vertical number line in a plane is called the y-axis. (37)

y-intercept A y-intercept is the value of a function when x is 0. (51)

zero exponent For any number a, except $a = 0$, $a^0 = 1$. (111)

zero of function For any polynomial function $f(x)$, if $f(a) = 0$, then a is a zero of the function. (266)

Index

Selected Answers

CHAPTER 1 EQUATIONS AND INEQUALITIES

Exploratory Exercises Page 3 **1.** 7 **3.** $^{-}44$
5. 13 **7.** 21 **9.** 27 **11.** 21 **13.** 0 **15.** 4

Written Exercises Page 3 **1.** 41 **3.** 14 **5.** 6

7. 60 **9.** 10 **11.** 22 **13.** 148 **15.** $-\dfrac{19}{2}$

17. $^{-}7.9$ **19.** $\dfrac{5}{4}$ **21.** 94 **23.** $^{-}72$ **25.** $^{-}7.2$

27. $\dfrac{3}{7}$ **29.** 272.16 **31.** \$180 **33.** \$300

35. \$17,400 **37.** 128 **39.** 100 **41.** 93.6

43. $53\dfrac{1}{4}$

Exploratory Exercises Page 7 **1.** associative
3. distributive **5.** commutative **7.** distributive
9. commutative **11.** multiplicative inverse
13. commutative

Written Exercises Page 7 **1.** commutative
3. distributive **5.** commutative
7. commutative **9.** distributive **11.** additive
identity **13.** multiplicative inverse
15. additive identity **17.** commutative·
19. multiplicative inverse **21.** 20 **23.** $2x + 17y$

25. $31a + 10b$ **27.** $12 + 20a$ **29.** $\dfrac{2}{3}a + 2\dfrac{1}{2}b$

31. $4.4m - 2.9n$ **33.** 0, additive identity
35. 1, multiplicative identity

Exploratory Exercises Page 10 **1.** reflexive
3. subtraction **5.** transitive **7.** symmetric
9. substitution **11.** symmetric **13.** reflexive

Written Exercises Page 11 **1.** symmetric
3. transitive **5.** reflexive **7.** substitution
9. distributive **11.** division **13. a.** distributive
b. substitution **c.** division **15.** 7.5 **17.** 14

19. $\dfrac{20}{21}$ **21.** $\dfrac{35}{8}$ **23.** 7 **25.** $^{-}12$ **27.** 12

29. $-\dfrac{1}{6}$ **31.** $\dfrac{3}{10}$ **33.** 8 **35.** $65.1\overline{6}$ **37.** 210

39. $-\dfrac{21}{8}$ **41.** 3 **43.** $\dfrac{1}{2}$ **45.** 11 **47.** $^{-}4$ **49.** 10
51. $^{-}3$ **53.** $^{-}4$ **55.** $^{-}46$ **57.** 31

Exploratory Exercises Page 14 **1.** $4x$
3. $2x + 11$ **5.** $2(x + 7)$ **7.** $2x + 7$ **9.** $8 + x^2$

11. $\dfrac{1}{5}(4 + x)$ **13.** $8(x + x^2)$ **15.** $(x + 11)^2$

Written Exercises Page 14 **1.** 118 **3.** 26
5. 85% **7.** 18 years **9.** 19 years, 43 years
11. June 11 **13.** 5 **15.** 8 adults, 12 students
17. length is 92 m, width is 51 m **19.** 3 hours
21. 43 mph

Exploratory Exercises Page 18 **1.** 5 **3.** 10
5. 36 **7.** 5 **9.** 0 **11.** 0 **13.** $^{-}2$ **15.** 11

Written Exercises Page 18 **1.** 31, $^{-}53$
3. 16, $^{-}6$ **5.** 5, $^{-}19$ **7.** 14, $^{-}8$ **9.** 6, $^{-}13$

11. $8\dfrac{1}{3}, -3\dfrac{2}{3}$ **13.** 5.5, $^{-}10.5$ **15.** 26, 11

17. $2\dfrac{2}{3}, ^{-}4\dfrac{1}{3}$ **19.** 3, $^{-}3.8$ **21.** 10.5, 3.5

23. $-\dfrac{10}{21}, -\dfrac{20}{7}$ **25.** no solutions **27.** $\dfrac{2}{3}, \dfrac{7}{3}$

29. no solutions **31.** 5, 1 **33.** no solutions
35. no solutions

Skills Review Page 18 **1.** $30y$ **3.** $8y$ **5.** $2x$
7. $^{-}6y$ **9.** $5 + 6y$ **11.** $2x - 5$ **13.** $x - 2y$
15. $14 - 23x$

Exploratory Exercises Page 22 **1.** $>$ **3.** $<$
5. $<$ **7.** $=$ **9.** $=$ **11.** $<$ **13.** $>$ **15.** $>$ **17.** $>$

Written Exercises Page 22 **1.** $\{x \mid x > 12\}$
3. $\{n \mid n \geq 7\}$ **5.** $\{r \mid r > 3.2\}$ **7.** $\{x \mid x > ^{-}12\}$
9. $\{y \mid y > 17.6\}$ **11.** $\{x \mid x \geq 6\}$ **13.** $\{x \mid x > 4.5\}$
15. $\{w \mid w \geq 5\}$ **17.** $\{z \mid z \leq 3\}$ **19.** $\{t \mid t < 3.25\}$

21. $\{x \mid x > 2.25\}$ **23.** $\left\{x \mid x \geq \dfrac{3}{7}\right\}$ **25.** $\{r \mid r \geq 5\}$
27. $\{x \mid x \leq 2\}$ **29.** $\{m \mid m \geq 1\}$ **31.** $\{b \mid b > 2\}$

33. $\{x \mid x \geq 232\}$ **35.** $\left\{x \mid x < \dfrac{2}{3}\right\}$

37. $\{x \mid x \leq ^{-}1.425\}$ **39.** $\left\{w \mid w \leq \dfrac{4}{3}\right\}$

41. $\left\{x \mid x > \dfrac{40}{7}\right\}$

Exploratory Exercises Page 26 **1.** true
3. false **5.** true **7.** $^{-}3 < x$ and $x < 2$
9. $1 < 3y$ and $3y \leq 13$ **11.** $5 \leq 3 - 2g$ and

$3 - 2g < 1$ **13.** $^-2 < x < 10$ **15.** $^-2 \leq x \leq 10$
17. $^-5 \leq m \leq 5$

Written Exercises   Page 27   1. $60.37 or less
3. 21.25   **5.** $6,500   **7.** 6 adult; 9 student
9. 4 more   **11.** at least   4 gallons   **13.** 40 mph
15. $^-2 < y < 7$ **17.** $x < 5$ or $x > ^-1$ (all reals)
19. $3 < x < 6$ **21.** $x < ^-2$ or $x \geq 1$

Exploratory Exercises   Page 30   1. $|x| < 3$
3. $|x| > 6$ **5.** $|x| > 3$ **7.** $|x| \leq 4$ **9.** $|x| < 6$
11. $|x| < 2$

Written Exercises   Page 30   1. $\{x \mid ^-9 < x < 9\}$
3. $\{x \mid x > 2$ or $x < ^-4\}$ **5.** $\{x \mid ^-4 \leq x \leq 12\}$
7. $\{x \mid x \leq ^-3$ or $x \geq 3\}$ **9.** $\{x \mid x > 7$ or $x < ^-7\}$
11. $\{x \mid ^-13 \leq x \leq 13\}$ **13.** $\emptyset$ **15.** $\{x \mid x < ^-20$ or
$x > 14\}$ **17.** $\{x \mid ^-30 < x < 54\}$

19. $\{x \mid ^-9 \leq x \leq 18\}$ **21.** $\left\{x \mid x \geq \frac{15}{4}$ or $x \leq -\frac{9}{4}\right\}$
23. $\{x \mid ^-17.6 < x < 14.8\}$ **25.** $\emptyset$
27. $\{x \mid ^-1 \leq x \leq 6\}$ **29.** $\{x \mid x > 0\}$ **31.** all
reals

Chapter Review   Page 33   1. 92

3. $70.\overline{33}$ **5.** $\frac{13}{12}$ **7.** commutative   **9.** additive
identity   **11.** 402   **13.** $^-3p + 13q$

15. substitution   **17.** symmetric   **19.** $-\frac{33}{13}$

21. $\frac{8}{3}$ **23.** $\frac{56}{5}$ **25.** length 21 m, width 11 m

27. 12 more days   **29.** 11, 26   **31.** $^-2.5, 5.5$

33. $\left\{x \mid x \geq -\frac{1}{5}\right\}$ **35.** 15 gallons   **37.** $\frac{5}{3} < y \leq 5$

39. all reals   **41.** $\left\{x \mid -\frac{9}{2} \leq x \leq -\frac{1}{2}\right\}$

CHAPTER 2   LINEAR RELATIONS AND FUNCTIONS

Exploratory Exercises   Page 38

1.

4.

7.

10.
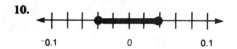

13.
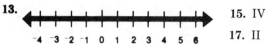

15. IV
17. II

19-26.
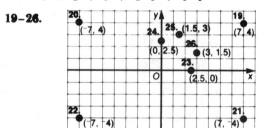

Written Exercises   Page 38

1.
39
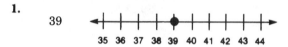

4.
23

7.
5

10.
10

13. $x < ^-6$

16. $y < 11$

19. $x \geq ^-3$

25. $x < ^-20$
or
$x \geq 12$

28. $-\frac{1}{3} \leq x \leq 2$

29. yes   **31.** no   **33.** yes   **35.** $(^-5, 1)$ **37.** $(1, 3)$
39. $(^-3, ^-3)$

Exploratory Exercises   Page 43
1. domain = {1, 3, 4}, range = {1, 3, 4}; yes
3. domain = {⁻17, 4, 8}, range = {⁻2, 3, 4, 8}; no
5. domain = {⁻3, ⁻2, 2, 4}, range = {⁻3, ⁻2, 2, 4};
yes   **7.** domain = {⁻3, 5}, range = {⁻3, 5}; yes
9. {(8, 3), (⁻1, 3), (2, 3)}; yes   **11.** {(15, 15),
(15, 30), (15, 45), (15, 60)}; no

Written Exercises   Page 43   1. {(⁻3, 3), (⁻2, 2),
(⁻1, 1), (0, 0), (1, 1), (2, 2), (3, 3)};
domain = {⁻3, ⁻2, ⁻1, 0, 1, 2, 3},
range = {3, 2, 1, 0}   **3.** {(2, y) such that y is any
real number}; domain = {2}, range = {all reals}

5. yes   **7.** no   **9.** no   **11.** no   **13.** $\frac{7}{10}$ **15.** $-\frac{7}{3}$

17. $-\frac{14}{3}$ **19.** $\frac{7}{a-2}$ **21.** ⁻7   **23.** 35   **25.** $-\frac{15}{2}$

27. $4t^3 + 2t^2 + t - 7$ **29.** $\frac{30}{7}$ **31.** 10   **33.** $-\frac{19}{15}$

35. $\frac{a(a+7)}{a+4}$

Exploratory Exercises   Page 48   1. no
3. yes   **5.** yes   **7.** yes   **9.** no   **11.** yes   **13.** no
15. yes

Written Exercises   Page 48   1. $2x - y = 6$
3. $x = 5$ **5.** $5x - 8y = ⁻8$ **7.** $3x - y = 0$

9.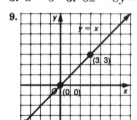

11.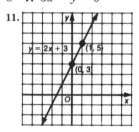

13.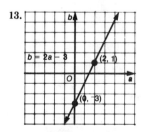

15.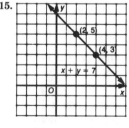

17.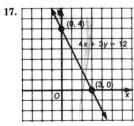

19.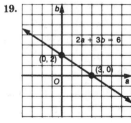

21.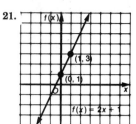

23.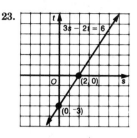

25.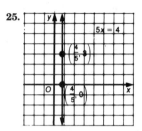

27.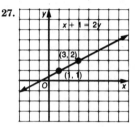

29.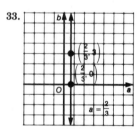

31.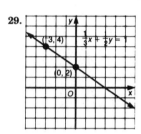

33.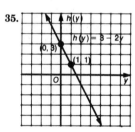

35.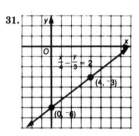

Exploratory Exercises   Page 52   1. 1, 2, ⁻2
3. ⁻4, 4, 1   **5.** 0, 2, none   **7.** 2, ⁻4, 2

Written Exercises   Page 52   1. 5, ⁻9, $\frac{9}{5}$

3. 7, 1, $-\frac{1}{7}$ **5.** $-\frac{2}{3}$, ⁻5, $-\frac{15}{2}$ **7.** 0, ⁻2, none

9. 1, ⁻2, 2   **11.** $-\frac{1}{2}$, $\frac{5}{2}$, 5   **13.** $\frac{3}{2}$, ⁻6, 4

15. $-\frac{1}{2}$, $\frac{7}{2}$, 7   **17.** $\frac{2}{3}$, ⁻4, 6   **19.** $-\frac{5}{2}$ **21.** $\frac{2}{11}$

23. $\frac{5}{2}$ **25.** 8   **27.** 0   **29.** 15   **31.** 2

33. $-\frac{1}{3}$

35.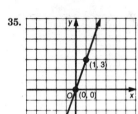

37.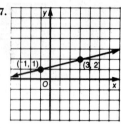

9.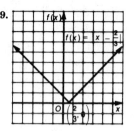

11.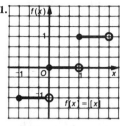

13.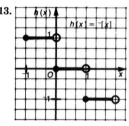

15.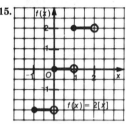

17.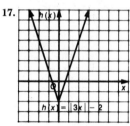

19.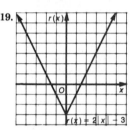

21.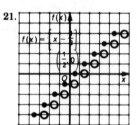

23.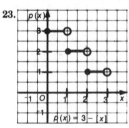

Exploratory Exercises   Page 54

1. $y = 5x - 3$ **3.** $y = {}^-x + 4$ **5.** $y = \frac{2}{3}x - 7$

7. $y = 2.5x$ **9.** $y = 0$ **11.** $^-4, 6$ **13.** $1, ^-8$

15. $\frac{1}{3}, 0$ **17.** $^-1, 0$ **19.** $y = -\frac{2}{5}x + 2$

21. $y = -\frac{2}{3}x + \frac{4}{3}$ **23.** $y = x - 2$

Written Exercises   Page 55   1. $2, 15$ **3.** $\frac{5}{3}$,

$^-0.2$ **5.** undefined, none   **7.** $2, ^-4$ **9.** $\frac{3}{5}, -\frac{3}{7}$

11. $y = \frac{3}{4}x - 7$ **13.** $y = -\frac{4}{5}x - \frac{7}{5}$ **15.** $y = 5x$

17. $y = -\frac{8}{3}x + 6$ **19.** $y = -\frac{5}{2}x + 16$

21. $y = \frac{2}{11}x + \frac{6}{11}$ **23.** $y = \frac{5}{2}x + 18$ **25.** $y = 3$

27. $y = -\frac{2}{3}x + 4$ **29.** $y = -\frac{6}{5}x + 6$

31. $y = \frac{3}{4}x - \frac{1}{4}$ **33.** $y = 0$ **35.** $2x - y = 2$

37. $3x + y = 11$ **39.** $2x + 3y = 9$
41. $x - y = {}^-3$ **43.** $5x + y = 5$ **45.** $x = {}^-1$
47. $x + 9y = 9$ **49.** $x - y = {}^-1$ **51.** $x = 0$

Exploratory Exercises   Page 58   1. A   **3.** D
5. A   **7.** A   **9.** G   **11.** D   **13.** G   **15.** A
17. A   **19.** G   **21.** C   **23.** A

Written Exercises   Page 58

1.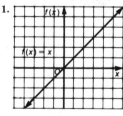

3.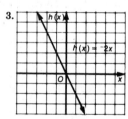

5.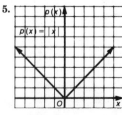

7.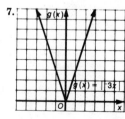

25. The graph of $y = [2x]$ jumps by ones at intervals of $\frac{1}{2}$ unit. The graph of $y = 2[x]$ jumps by twos at intervals of one unit.   **27.** The graph of $y = |x - 3|$ is like $y = |x|$ moved 3 units *to the right*. The graph of $y = |x| - 3$ is like $y = |x|$ moved 3 units *down*.   **29.** The graph of $y = |2x + 5|$ is like $y = |2x|$ moved 2.5 units *to the left*. The graph of $y = |2x| + 5$ is like $y = |2x|$ moved 2.5 units *up*.   **31.** The graphs of $y = |ax|$ and $y = a|x|$ are identical if $a \geq 0$. The graph of $y = a|x|$ opens down if $a < 0$.

Skills Review   Page 58   1. 3   **3.** 19   **5.** $^-7$
7. 8   **9.** $^-2$ **11.** $y \geq 5$ **13.** $y > 3$ **15.** $x \leq {}^-24$

Exploratory Exercises Page 61 1. $s = 10r$
3. 4.8 inches **5.** 45 inches **7.** $92 **9.** 1.75 hours

Written Exercises   Page 62
1. $p = 550y + 47,000$ **3.** $d = 6000 - 75x$
5. $c = 0.18t + 161$ **7.** $c = 1.25n$; $5.00, $6.25, $7.50 **9.** $c = 0.36 + 0.34m$; $2.40, $3.08, $3.76, $5.46, $7.16, $10.56, $15.66, $20.76

Exploratory Exercises   Page 65   1. all three
3. $(0, 0), (2, {}^-3)$ **5.** none **7.** $(2, {}^-3)$

Written Exercises   Page 65

1.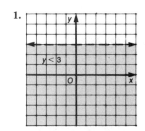

3.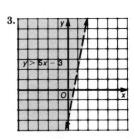

5.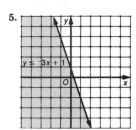

7.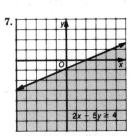

9.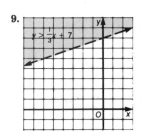

11.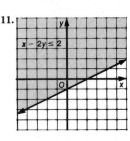

13.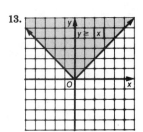

15.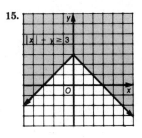

17.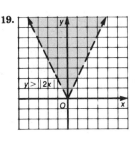

19.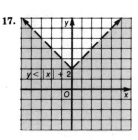

21.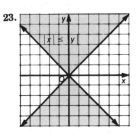

23.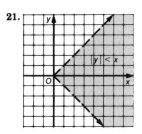

25.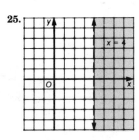

27.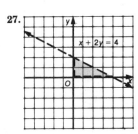

Chapter Review   Page 67
1.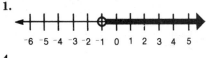

4.

7.

9–11.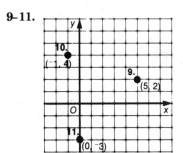

13. domain = $\{1, 2, 3, 4, 5\}$; range = $\{{}^-4.5, {}^-3.5, 4.5\}$; yes **15.** no **17.** no **19.** ${}^-29$ **21.** no **23.** yes

25.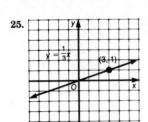

27.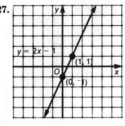

29. $-\dfrac{3}{7}, \dfrac{2}{7}, \dfrac{2}{3}$ **31.** $\dfrac{1}{2}, -\dfrac{15}{2}, 15$ **33.** $^-3$ **35.** 2

37. 6 **39.**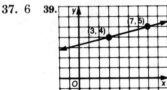

41. $y = 5x - 7$

43. $y = -\dfrac{6}{7}x - \dfrac{18}{7}$

45. $4x - y = 22$

47. $3x - y = 6$

49.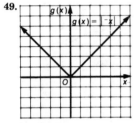

51.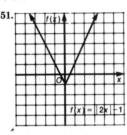

53.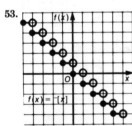

55. $c = 4.50 + p$

57.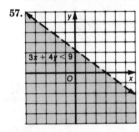

59.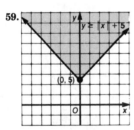

CHAPTER 3 SYSTEMS OF EQUATIONS AND INEQUALITIES

Exploratory Exercises Page 73 1. 4 **3.** $\dfrac{3}{2}$
5. $\dfrac{8}{9}$ **7.** $-\dfrac{1}{2}$ **9.** $-\dfrac{3}{8}$ **11.** $-\dfrac{8}{3}$

Written Exercises Page 73 1. parallel
3. parallel **5.** parallel **7.** neither **9.** neither

11. $y = \dfrac{1}{3}x$ **13.** $y = 3x$ **15.** $y = {}^-x + \dfrac{5}{6}$

17. $y = \dfrac{3}{2}x - \dfrac{23}{2}$ **19.** $y = \dfrac{1}{3}x + \dfrac{2}{3}$

21. $y = \dfrac{5}{3}x + \dfrac{5}{3}$ **23.** $y = -\dfrac{1}{2}x - 4$

25. $y = \dfrac{2}{3}x - 2$ **27.** $y = -\dfrac{1}{15}x - \dfrac{23}{5}$ **29.** $-\dfrac{3}{4}$

31. 4 **33.** A line connecting $(^-6, 5)$ and $(^-2, 7)$ has slope $\dfrac{1}{2}$. A line connecting $(5, 3)$ and $(1, 1)$ has slope $\dfrac{1}{2}$. These two lines are parallel since their slopes are the same. A line connecting $(^-6, 5)$ and $(1, 1)$ has slope $-\dfrac{4}{7}$. A line connecting $(^-2, 7)$ and $(5, 3)$ has slope $-\dfrac{4}{7}$. These two lines are parallel since their slopes are the same.

Exploratory Exercises Page 76 1. $(^-3, 6)$
3. $(5, 2)$ **5.** $(2, {}^-4)$ **7.** $(^-3, 6)$

Written Exercises Page 76 1. $(3, 1)$; consistent and independent **3.** no solutions; inconsistent **5.** $\{(x, y) / x + 2y = 5\}$; consistent and dependent **7.** $(2, {}^-6)$; consistent and independent **9.** $(8, 6)$; consistent and independent **11.** no solutions; inconsistent

13. $\left(-\dfrac{4}{3}, -\dfrac{14}{3}\right)$; consistent and independent
15. $\{(x, y) \mid 2x + 3y = 5\}$; consistent and dependent **17.** no solutions; inconsistent
19. $(1, {}^-2)$; consistent and independent
21. $\{(x, y) \mid 9x - 5 = 7y\}$; consistent and dependent **23.** $a = 3, b = 8$ **25.** $r = 3, s = 9$

Exploratory Exercises Page 79 Answers may vary.

Written Exercises Page 80 1. $(^-3, {}^-9)$

3. $\left(\dfrac{4}{3}, \dfrac{2}{3}\right)$ **5.** $(^-9, {}^-7)$ **7.** $(2, 1)$ **9.** $(^-1, 2)$
11. $(^-4, {}^-4)$ **13.** $(12, 2)$ **15.** $(5.25, 0.75)$

17. $\left(^-1, \dfrac{2}{3}\right)$ **19.** $(^-4, 6)$ **21.** $(^-1, 2)$
23. $\left(-\dfrac{64}{5}, \dfrac{31}{5}\right)$ **25.** $(10, 25)$ **27.** $(^-6, {}^-8)$
29. $(0.75, 0.5)$ **31.** $(^-3, 6)$ **33.** $(^-3, 4)$
35. $(2, {}^-3)$ **37.** 27, 15 **39.** width = 15 cm, length = 28 cm

Exploratory Exercises   Page 82   1. no
3. yes   **5.** yes

Written Exercises   Page 83   1. $(^-9, 2, 4)$
3. $(3, ^-1, 5)$ **5.** $(^-8, 13, ^-5)$ **7.** $(10, 1, ^-5)$

9. $(0, 2, ^-1)$ **11.** $(4, ^-8, 3)$ **13.** $\left(\dfrac{43}{14}, -\dfrac{1}{14}, -\dfrac{33}{14}\right)$
15. $(1, 2, 3)$ **17.** 8, 5, 3   **19.** 6, 7, 9

Skills Review   Page 83   1. $x > 6$ **3.** $a \geq 0$
5. $x > 3$ **7.** $x < 5$ **9.** $x \geq 4$ **11.** $x > 48$

Exploratory Exercises   Page 85   Answers
may vary.

Written Exercises   Page 85   1. $(2, ^-3)$

3. $(1, 1)$ **5.** $\left(\dfrac{1}{2}, \dfrac{1}{3}, \dfrac{1}{4}\right)$ **7.** $(7, 1, ^-2)$ **9.** $(5, 6, 7)$
11. $x = ^-1, y = 2, z = ^-2, w = 1$

Exploratory Exercises   Page 89   1. 14   **3.** 0
5. 1   **7.** 14   **9.** 72   **11.** $^-32$

Written Exercises   Page 89   1. $^-18$ **3.** 343
5. 6   **7.** $^-33$ **9.** 29   **11.** $^-111$ **13.** 47
15. 826,353

Exploratory Exercises   Page 92

1. $\dfrac{\begin{vmatrix} 5 & 2 \\ 3 & ^-1 \end{vmatrix}}{\begin{vmatrix} 3 & 2 \\ 4 & ^-1 \end{vmatrix}}, \dfrac{\begin{vmatrix} 3 & 5 \\ 4 & 3 \end{vmatrix}}{\begin{vmatrix} 3 & 2 \\ 4 & ^-1 \end{vmatrix}}$ **3.** $\dfrac{\begin{vmatrix} 16 & ^-4 \\ 21 & ^-5 \end{vmatrix}}{\begin{vmatrix} 2 & ^-4 \\ 3 & ^-5 \end{vmatrix}}, \dfrac{\begin{vmatrix} 2 & 16 \\ 3 & 21 \end{vmatrix}}{\begin{vmatrix} 2 & ^-4 \\ 3 & ^-5 \end{vmatrix}}$

5. $\dfrac{\begin{vmatrix} ^-8 & 1 \\ ^-14 & ^-2 \end{vmatrix}}{\begin{vmatrix} 3 & 1 \\ 4 & ^-2 \end{vmatrix}}, \dfrac{\begin{vmatrix} 3 & ^-8 \\ 4 & ^-14 \end{vmatrix}}{\begin{vmatrix} 3 & 1 \\ 4 & ^-2 \end{vmatrix}}$ **7.** $\dfrac{\begin{vmatrix} ^-11 & ^-8 \\ 3 & ^-8 \end{vmatrix}}{\begin{vmatrix} 1 & ^-8 \\ 8 & ^-8 \end{vmatrix}}, \dfrac{\begin{vmatrix} 1 & ^-11 \\ 8 & 3 \end{vmatrix}}{\begin{vmatrix} 1 & ^-8 \\ 8 & ^-8 \end{vmatrix}}$

11. $\dfrac{\begin{vmatrix} ^-6 & 4 & ^-1 \\ 2 & ^-2 & 3 \\ ^-10 & 2 & ^-4 \end{vmatrix}}{\begin{vmatrix} 2 & 4 & ^-1 \\ 1 & ^-2 & 3 \\ 1 & 2 & ^-4 \end{vmatrix}}, \dfrac{\begin{vmatrix} 2 & ^-6 & ^-1 \\ 1 & 2 & 3 \\ 1 & ^-10 & ^-4 \end{vmatrix}}{\begin{vmatrix} 2 & 4 & ^-1 \\ 1 & ^-2 & 3 \\ 1 & 2 & ^-4 \end{vmatrix}}, \dfrac{\begin{vmatrix} 2 & 4 & ^-6 \\ 1 & ^-2 & 2 \\ 1 & 2 & ^-10 \end{vmatrix}}{\begin{vmatrix} 2 & 4 & ^-1 \\ 1 & ^-2 & 3 \\ 1 & 2 & ^-4 \end{vmatrix}}$

Written Exercises   Page 92   1. $(1, 1)$

3. $(2, ^-3)$ **5.** $(^-3, 1)$ **7.** $\left(2, \dfrac{13}{8}\right)$ **9.** $\left(\dfrac{13}{7}, -\dfrac{2}{7}\right)$
11. $\left(^-3, \dfrac{1}{2}, 2\right)$ **13.** $\left(\dfrac{1}{2}, ^-2, \dfrac{1}{3}\right)$ **15.** 3 pennies,
5 nickels, 8 dimes

Exploratory Exercises   Page 94   1. yes
3. yes   **5.** yes   **7.** no

Written Exercises   Page 94

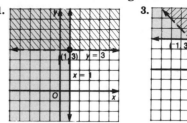

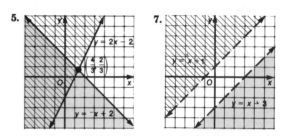

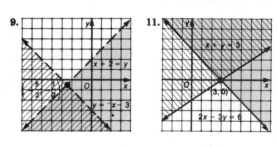

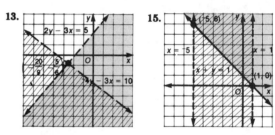

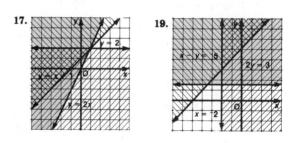

Exploratory Exercises   Page 98   1. $(0, 1)$,
$(1, 3)$ $(6, 3)$, $(10, 1)$ **3.** $(0, 1)$, $(6, 13)$, $(6, 1)$

Written Exercises   Page 98   1. vertices: (1, 2), (1, 4), (5, 8), (5, 2); max. 11, min. $^-5$ **3.** vertices: (1, 5), (3, 7), (5, 7), (5, 1); max. 7, min. $^-15$ **5.** vertices: (2, 2), (2, 8), (6, 12), (6, $^-6$); max. 30, min. 8   **7.** vertices: (0, 0), (0, 2), (2, 4), (5, 1), (5, 0); max. 25, min. $^-6$ **9a.** $x \geq 0$, $y \geq 0$, $4x + y \leq 32$, $x + 6y \leq 54$ **9c.** 14 gallons (6A, 8B)   **11a.** 30 dresses, 10 pantsuits   **13.** 4 rockers, 3 swivels   **15a.** $20

Chapter Review   Page 101   1. $y = 3x - 6$

3. $y = 6x + 5$ **5.** $y = -\frac{1}{2}x + \frac{13}{2}$ **7.** $y = \frac{2}{3}x - \frac{1}{3}$

9. $(^-2, ^-6)$, consistent and independent

11. (6, 5), consistent and independent   **13.** $\left(5\frac{1}{4}, \frac{3}{4}\right)$

15. $\left(\frac{14}{5}, \frac{4}{5}\right)$ **17.** (1, 2, 3)   **19.** (2, 1)   **21.** $^-2$

23. 26   **25.** $\left(\frac{1}{29}, -\frac{39}{29}\right)$ **27.** $\left(^-3, \frac{1}{3}, 1\right)$

29. 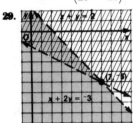   **31.**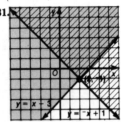

33. vertices: (0, 0), (0, 3), $\left(\frac{3}{2}, \frac{3}{2}\right)$, (2, 0); max. 12, min. 0   **35.** 30 acres of peanuts, 60 acres of corn

Cumulative Review   Page 104   1. 29   **3.** $\frac{1217}{3}$

5. $^-3x + 21y$ **7.** $^-3$ **9.** 1   **11.** $-\frac{9}{2}$

13. $x > \frac{16}{5}$ **15.** $y \geq \frac{3}{7}$ **17.** $\varnothing$ **23.** 89   **25.** $\frac{11}{4}$

19.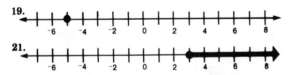

21.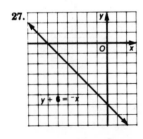

27. 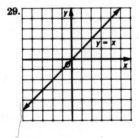   **29.**

31. 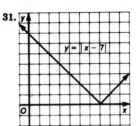   **33.**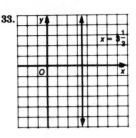

35. 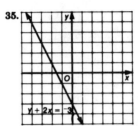   **37.**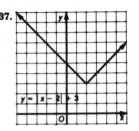

39. $y = -\frac{7}{10}x + \frac{26}{5}$ **41.** $8x - 3y = ^-24$

43. $2x + 3y = 13$ **45.** $\frac{3}{2}$ **47.** $(6, ^-2)$

49. $(^-3, ^-4)$ **51.** (4, 7)   **53.** $^-5$

55. 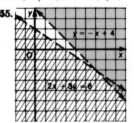   **57.** 4   **59.** $5.46   **61.** 12.5 lb at $5, 37.5 lb at $3

CHAPTER 4   POLYNOMIALS

Exploratory Exercises   Page 109   1. yes, 7

3. no   **5.** yes, $\frac{11}{7}$ **7.** no   **9.** 3   **11.** 9   **13.** 0

15. 5

Written Exercises   Page 109   1. $8m$ **3.** $5d^3$
5. $39x^2 - 3y^2$ **7.** y^{12} **9.** 2^7 **11.** 8^{14} **13.** y^{10}
15. $81a^4$ **17.** $20m^3k^5$ **19.** $5625x^8y^{10}z^4$

21. $\frac{16}{15}c^4d^2f$ **23.** $^-162r^8s^8t^{17}$ **25.** $2r^3k^2m^2$

27. $9m^4n^3p^2$ **29.** $^-a^7b^3$

Exploratory Exercises   Page 111   1. 1   **3.** 1
5. 1   **7.** r^3 **9.** x^4 **11.** a^2 **13.** 1   **15.** p^3x

Written Exercises   Page 112   1. 25   **3.** 9

5. $\frac{3}{2}$ **7.** $3n^5$ **9.** an **11.** $4a^7$ **13.** $\frac{x^2}{7}$ **15.** $-\frac{y^3}{2}$

17. $2ab$ **19.** $\frac{1}{2}$ **21.** $^-3s^6$ **23.** $-\frac{ab^4}{12}$ **25.** 1

27. $-2m^8p^{11}$ **29.** $-5st$ **31.** $4b^2c^3$ **33.** $\dfrac{r^4s^9}{-3}$

35. $x^3y^4z^5$

Skills Review **Page 112** **1.** 0 **3.** $-1\dfrac{3}{4}$
5. $c^2 + 2c - 3$ **7.** 6 **9.** -22
11. $2a^3 - a^2 + 4a + 6$

Exploratory Exercises **Page 116** **1.** 2 **3.** 8
5. 5 **7.** 3 **9.** 9

Written Exercises **Page 116** **1.** $16x + 2y$
3. $-6a + 4b$ **5.** $-9x - y - 2z$ **7.** $4m^2 + m + 1$
9. $5x^2 + 1$ **11.** $3a - b$ **13.** $r^2 - r + 6$
15. $-3x^2 - 3x + 14$
17. $7x^4 - 2x^3 + 7x^2 - 2x + 1$
19. $m^7 + 3m^5 - 3m^4 + m^3 - 2m^2 - 18$
21. $-3x^3y - xy^3 + 6$ **23.** $4gf^3 - 4bhf$
25. $15m^3n^3 - 30m^4n^3 + 15m^5n^6$
27. $-68b^5d^4 - 187b^6d^5 - 85b^4d^6$
29. $24x^4 + 2x^2 - 4x + 8$ **31.** $m^2 - 2m - 35$
33. $y^4 + y^3 + 5y^2 + 5y$ **35.** $6x^2 + 31x + 35$
37. $6x^2 - xy - 15y^2$ **39.** $m^2 + 8m + 16$
41. $y^2 - 4y + 4$ **43.** $y^2 - 25$
45. $x^2 - 6xy + 9y^2$ **47.** $16m^2 - 24mn + 9n^2$
49. $1 + 8r + 16r^2$ **51.** $16a^2 - 4b^2$ **53.** $x^6 - y^2$
55. $2x^3 - 9x^2 - 7x + 24$ **57.** $a^3 + b^3$
59. $2t^3 + 9t^2 - 19t - 40$ **61.** $p^3 + 4p^2 - 5p$
63. $6x^3 - 7x^2 - 7x + 6$
65. $2a^3 - 5a^2b - 4ab^2 + 12b^3$
67. $2k^3 - 11k^2 + 21k + 63$
69. $z^3 + z^3r + z^2r^2 + zr + zr^2 + r^3$
71. $y^3 - 3y^2 - 16y + 48$

Exploratory Exercises **Page 120** **1.** $6(a + b)$
3. $a(b + c)$ **5.** $(r + 3)(r - 3)$
7. $(10 - m)(10 + m)$ **9.** $2(x^2 + 3y + 4b)$
11. $3(a^2 + 2a + 3y)$ **13.** $(5a - b)(5a + b)$
15. $5xy(x - 2y)$ **17.** $4m(2m + a + 4y)$
19. $(x + 2)(x^2 - 2x + 4)$ **21.** $(r - 1)(r^2 + r + 1)$

Written Exercises **Page 120**
1. $(b - 12)(b + 12)$ **3.** $(1 + r)(1 - r + r^2)$
5. $(2 - x)(4 + 2x + x^2)$ **7.** $3(d - 4)(d + 4)$
9. $(3 + x)(9 - 3x + x^2)$ **11.** $(2 + x)(4 - 2x + x^2)$
13. $(2a - 3)(2a + 3)$ **15.** $(3y - 8)(3y + 8)$
17. $(2b - 3x)(4b^2 + 6bx + 9x^2)$
19. $ab(1 - a)(1 + a + a^2)$
21. $(r^2 + s^2)(r - s)(r + s)$
23. $(4y - 1)(16y^2 + 4y + 1)$
25. $(y^2 + 5)(y^4 - 5y^2 + 25)$
27. $(1 - 2m^2)(1 + 2m^2 + 4m^4)$
29. $(a + b - m)(a + b + m)$

Exploratory Exercises **Page 123** **1.** $(y + 3)^2$
3. $(k - 4)^2$ **5.** $(a + 2)(a + 3)$ **7.** $(p - 1)(p - 4)$
9. $(m - 5)(m - 2)$

Written Exercises **Page 123** **1.** $(a + 5)(a + 7)$
3. $(f - 9)^2$ **5.** $(k + 6)^2$ **7.** $(3y + 2)(y + 1)$
9. $(2z - 7)(2z - 3)$ **11.** $(a + 2b)^2$ **13.** $(p - 2b)^2$
15. $(2r - 5s)^2$ **17.** $2(2k + 3)(k + 5)$
19. $4(h + 6)(h - 4)$ **21.** $2y(y + 3)(y - 7)$
23. $(9d + 4)(2d - 3)$ **25.** $(4x - 3y)(5x + 8y)$

Exploratory Exercises **Page 126**
1. $(y + 4k)(3y - 2)$ **3.** $(a - c)(y - b)$
5. $(a - 2)(a + b)$ **7.** $(2x^2 + 1)(x - 3)$

9. $\left(x + y - \dfrac{1}{2}\right)\left(x + y + \dfrac{1}{2}\right)$

11. $(m - k + 3)(m + k - 3)$
13. $(k - 3)(k + 3)(k + 4)$ **15.** $(x - y)(x + y - 4)$
17. $(a + b)(6x + 4y + 7)$

Written Exercises **Page 126**
1. $(3y - 2)(y + 4k)$ **3.** $(a - c)(y - b)$
5. $(a - 2)(a + b)$ **7.** $(2x^2 + 1)(x - 3)$
9. $(x + y - r)(x + y + r)$
11. $(m - k + 3)(m + k - 3)$
13. $(k - 3)(k + 3)(k + 4)$ **15.** $(x - y)(x + y - 4)$
17. $(a - b + 4)(a + b - 4)$ **19.** $(2a - 1)(b + m)$
21. $(x + 3 - a)(x + 3 + a)$

23. $\left(a - \dfrac{1}{2} - y\right)\left(a - \dfrac{1}{2} + y\right)$ **25.** $x(x - z)(x + y)$

27. $3(2x - 3)(3x + 1)$
29. $(b - y - p)(b + y + p)$
31. $(b + m)(2a + b - m)$
33. $(2a + 3)(4a^2 - 6a + 9)$
35. $3r(1 - 3r)(1 + 3r + 9r^2)$ **37.** $(x + y)(x - y)^2$
39. $(x - 3)(x + 3)(x - 2)(x + 2)$
41. $(r - p)(r + p)^2$ **43.** $(2x + 7y)(2a - 5b)$
45. $(4a - 3)(2x - 3)$

Exploratory Exercises **Page 130** **1.** $\dfrac{1}{7}$ **3.** g^3

5. 1 **7.** $4a^2b^3$ **9.** $3xy^3$ **11.** $-a^2b + a - \dfrac{2}{b}$

Written Exercises **Page 130**
1. $6p^3q + 4p + 5q^2$ **3.** $2k^2 - 3py + 4p^2y$

5. $5r + \dfrac{23}{3}s + \dfrac{2s^2}{r}$ **7.** $x - 15$ **9.** $3y - 1$

11. $4a + 3 - \dfrac{2}{2a + 7}$ **13.** $4y + 5 + \dfrac{2}{7y - 3}$

15. $a - 12$ **17.** $a - 2b$ **19.** $2z - 4$

21. $a + 10 + \dfrac{44}{a - 6}$ **23.** $8x - 44 + \dfrac{231}{x + 5}$

25. $7m - 8 + \dfrac{3}{8m - 7}$ 27. $2y^2 + 5y + 2$

29. $3a^2 - 2a + 3$ 31. $m^2 + m + 1$

33. $y^2 - 6y + 9 - \dfrac{1}{y - 3}$ 35. $2a^2 - 3a - 2$

37. $m + 3$ 39. $x^2 - 2x + 8 - \dfrac{20}{x + 2}$

41. $x^2 + 2x + 2$ 43. $a^2 - a - 1$ 45. yes

47. $a + 1, a - 1$ 49. Both are 15.

Exploratory Exercises Page 134 1. d 3. e
5. a 7. f

Written Exercises Page 134

1. $2x^2 + x + 5 + \dfrac{6}{x - 2}$ 3. $2a^2 - a - 1 + \dfrac{4}{a + 1}$

5. $x^3 + x - 1$ 7. $6k^2 - k - 2$ 9. $2b^2 - 5b - 3$

11. $y^3 - 11y^2 + 31y - 21$

13. $2x^3 + x^2 + 3x - 1 + \dfrac{5}{x - 3}$

15. $y^3 + 3y^2 - 16y + 55 - \dfrac{166}{y + 3}$

17. $2x^3 + x^2 - 2x + \dfrac{3}{2x - 1}$

19. $2x^2 - 8x + 1 + \dfrac{5}{3x - 2}$

21. $x^4 - 2x^3 + 4x^2 - 8x + 16$

Chapter Review Page 136 1. y^{11} 3. x^6

5. $114a^4b^4$ 7. a^4 9. $\dfrac{n}{2}$ 11. 1

13. $b^3 + 15b^2 - 3b - 2$ 15. $4a^2 + 23a - 35$

17. $y^3 + 4y^2 - 16y + 35$

19. $2m^3 + 15m^2 + 34m + 21$ 21. $(y - 5)(y + 5)$

23. $(m + 2)(m^2 - 2m + 4)$

25. $(2m - 3)(4m^2 + 6m + 9)$ 27. $(x - 2)(x - 5)$

29. $(3p - 5t)^2$ 31. $(5b + a)(b - 4a)$

33. $(7b - 5)(3b + 4)$ 35. $(x - 2y)(x + 1)$

37. $(a + b - 4)(a - b + 4)$

39. $2y^2 - 7y + 4 + \dfrac{3}{4y + 3}$ 41. Since the
remainder upon division is $^-20$, $x + 1$ is not a
factor of $2x^3 + x^2 - 11x - 30$.

43. $2m^2 + 5m + 12 + \dfrac{49}{m - 4}$ 45. Since the
remainder upon division is 0, $2x + 1$ is a factor of
$2x^3 - 11x^2 + 12x + 9$.

CHAPTER 5 ROOTS

Exploratory Exercises Page 142 1. 49
3. 27 5. 16 7. 169 9. 100,000 11. $^-12$

13. 2 15. $^-|y|$ 17. $^-4$ 19. $4|a|b^2$

21. $|x + 3|$ 23. 2601 25. 2.621 27. 148,877

Written Exercises Page 142 1. $^-9$ 3. 15

5. 3 7. $^-1$ 9. 0.7 11. $11|n|$ 13. $9s^2$ 15. 24

17. $8|a|b^2$ 19. ^-2bm 21. $4a^2b$ 23. $|3p + q|$

25. $z + a$ 27. $2m - 3$ 29. $|y + 3|$

31. $|3x + 1|$ 33. $|2x + 3y|$ 35. 9.110

37. 24.01 39. 2.008 41. 110,592 43. 2.6458

45. 4.5826 47. 4.3589

Exploratory Exercises Page 144 1. $2\sqrt{2}$

3. $5|x|\sqrt{2}$ 5. $2\sqrt[3]{2}$ 7. $2\sqrt[4]{3}$ 9. $|b|\sqrt{b}$

11. $|a|\sqrt[4]{a}$ 13. $r\sqrt[5]{r^2}$ 15. $3\sqrt{5}$ 17. $3\sqrt[4]{2}$

19. $5 - \sqrt{15}$

Written Exercises Page 144 1. $15\sqrt{6}$

3. $2\sqrt[3]{3}$ 5. $9\sqrt{2}$ 7. $^-4\sqrt[3]{3}$ 9. $33\sqrt{2}$ 11. $2\sqrt[4]{7}$

13. $48\sqrt{7}$ 15. 22 17. $3\sqrt{2} - 2\sqrt{3}$

19. $7\sqrt{2} + 7\sqrt{3}$ 21. 14 23. $2ab^2\sqrt[3]{ab}$

25. $5rp^2\sqrt{2r}$ 27. $xy\sqrt[3]{3xy}$ 29. $3x^2z^2\sqrt{5}$

31. $5mb^2\sqrt[4]{m}$ 33. $6rs\sqrt[3]{4r^2s}$ 35. $6a^2b\sqrt[4]{4b}$

Exploratory Exercises Page 146 1. $^-\sqrt{7}$

3. $^-7\sqrt[4]{5}$ 5. $3\sqrt[3]{x}$ 7. $5\sqrt[5]{3}$ 9. $3\sqrt{3}$ 11. 0

13. $17 + 7\sqrt{5}$ 15. $37 - 12\sqrt{2}$ 17. 34

19. $19 + 8\sqrt{3}$ 21. $55 + 14\sqrt{6}$

Written Exercises Page 147 1. $8\sqrt{2} - 8$

3. $5\sqrt{5} - 10\sqrt{2}$ 5. $^-7\sqrt{7}$ 7. $11\sqrt[3]{5}$ 9. $\sqrt[3]{6}$

11. $7\sqrt[3]{2} + 6\sqrt[3]{150}$ 13. $14\sqrt{6} + 2\sqrt[3]{3}$ 15. $5\sqrt{2}$

17. $15\sqrt[3]{2}$ 19. $(1 + |x|)\sqrt[4]{x^2}$ 21. $3|yz|\sqrt[4]{z^2}$

23. $|z| + z^2 + z^4$ 25. $17 + 8\sqrt{2}$

27. $25 - 5\sqrt{2} + 5\sqrt{6} - 2\sqrt{3}$ 29. $3 - 5\sqrt{11}$

31. $1 + \sqrt{15}$ 33. $4 - 2\sqrt{3}$ 35. $^-4\sqrt{5}$

37. $16\sqrt[3]{3} - 12$ 39. $x^3 - 3$

41. $(m - \sqrt{11})(m + \sqrt{11})$ 43. $(a + 2\sqrt{5})^2$

45. $r(r - \sqrt{2})(r + \sqrt{2})$

Exploratory Exercises Page 150 1. $\sqrt{2}$

3. $\sqrt[3]{3y}$ 5. $\dfrac{\sqrt{5}}{2}$ 7. $\dfrac{\sqrt[3]{5}}{2}$ 9. $\dfrac{\sqrt{3}}{\sqrt{3}}$ 11. $\dfrac{\sqrt{5}}{\sqrt{5}}$

13. $\dfrac{\sqrt{7}}{\sqrt{7}}$ 15. $\dfrac{\sqrt{5}}{\sqrt{5}}$ 17. $\dfrac{\sqrt[3]{2}}{\sqrt[3]{2}}$ 19. $\dfrac{\sqrt[3]{3}}{\sqrt[3]{3}}$ 21. $1 - \sqrt{3}$

23. $1 + \sqrt{2}$ 25. $3 - \sqrt{5}$ 27. $5 - 3\sqrt{3}$

29. $2\sqrt{2} + 3$ 31. $\sqrt{2} + 5\sqrt{3}$

Written Exercises Page 151 1. $\sqrt{5}$ 3. $\sqrt{7}$

5. $\sqrt[3]{9}$ 7. $\dfrac{\sqrt{5}}{5}$ 9. $\dfrac{2\sqrt{2}}{3}$ 11. $\dfrac{\sqrt[3]{5}}{2}$ 13. $\dfrac{3\sqrt[3]{2}}{5}$

15. $\dfrac{\sqrt[4]{5}}{2}$ 17. $\dfrac{\sqrt{3}}{3}$ 19. $\dfrac{\sqrt{6}}{3}$ 21. $\dfrac{\sqrt{15}}{6}$ 23. $\dfrac{\sqrt[3]{15}}{3}$

25. $\dfrac{\sqrt[4]{54}}{3}$ 27. $\dfrac{3 - \sqrt{5}}{4}$ 29. $\dfrac{3 + \sqrt{5}}{2}$ 31. $\dfrac{5 + 4\sqrt{2}}{7}$

33. $\dfrac{19 - 11\sqrt{3}}{-2}$ **35.** $^-15 - 11\sqrt{2}$ **37.** $\dfrac{16\sqrt{10}}{5}$
39. $\dfrac{3\sqrt[3]{2}}{2}$ **41.** 1.118 **43.** 0.943 **45.** 0.855
47. 0.756 **49.** 2.72 seconds **51.** 7 inches

Exploratory Exercises Page 155 1. 4
3. $7 - 2\sqrt{5}$ **5.** 1 **7.** 29 **9.** $4\sqrt{3}$ **11.** $1 + \sqrt{3}$

Written Exercises Page 155 1. $^-\sqrt{3}$
3. $\dfrac{12 - 4\sqrt{2}}{7}$ **5.** $\dfrac{^-15 - 5\sqrt{3}}{6}$ **7.** $\dfrac{26 + 13\sqrt{11}}{^-7}$

9. 64 **11.** 54 **13.** 7 **15.** 62 **17.** $40\dfrac{1}{2}$

19. 23 **21.** 3 **23.** 23 **25.** $^-13$ **27.** 8
29. $\pm\sqrt{y^2 - s^2}$ if $y \geq s$ **31.** $\dfrac{2mM}{r^3}$ if $r \neq 0$

33. $\dfrac{T}{4v^2 - 1}$ if $4v^2 - 1 \neq 0$

Skills Review Page 155 1. $(6, ^-2)$ **3.** $(7, ^-2)$

5. $\left(\dfrac{7}{10}, \dfrac{7}{15}\right)$

Exploratory Exercises Page 158 1. $6i$
3. $4i\sqrt{2}$ **5.** $^-3$ **7.** $5i$ **9.** $6i$ **11.** $11i$
13. ^-3i **15.** $^-1$

Written Exercises Page 158 1. $9i$ **3.** $5i\sqrt{2}$
5. $\dfrac{2}{3}i$ **7.** $\dfrac{i\sqrt{3}}{3}$ **9.** i **11.** ^-i **13.** ^-i **15.** $^-1$
17. $5i$ **19.** $2i$ **21.** $3i$ **23.** $11i$ **25.** $^-4$
27. $^-7\sqrt{2}$ **29.** $^-3$ **31.** $^-3i\sqrt{3}$ **33.** 24
35. ^-216i **37.** ^-18i **39.** $\pm 4i$ **41.** $\pm 13i$
43. $\pm i\sqrt{3}$ **45.** $\pm 2i$ **47.** $\pm 5i$ **49.** $\pm i\dfrac{\sqrt{5}}{2}$

Exploratory Exercises Page 161 1. $8 + 11i$
3. 3 **5.** 10 **7.** $20 + 12i$ **9.** $7 + (\sqrt{2} + \sqrt{3})i$
11. $x = 5, y = 6$ **13.** $x = 7, y = 2$ **15.** $x = 3$,
$y = 0$ **17.** $^-10 + 10i$ **19.** $14 + 5i$ **21.** 37

Written Exercises Page 161 1. $7 + 7i$
3. $6 + 4i$ **5.** $2 + 9i$ **7.** $8 - 15i$ **9.** $5 - 3i\sqrt{3}$
11. $^-21 - 2i$ **13.** $13 - 13i$ **15.** $32 - 24i$
17. $37 + 2i\sqrt{2}$ **19.** $5 + 12i$ **21.** 3 **23.** 7
25. $20 + 15i$ **27.** $148 - 222i$ **29.** $109 - 37i$
31. $1 - i, ^-1 + 5i, 6 + 2i$ **33.** $14, 4i, 53$
35. $2, 2i, 2$ **37.** $x = 2, y = 3$ **39.** $x = ^-1, y = ^-3$
41. $x = 3, y = 1$

Exploratory Exercises Page 163 1. $2 - i$
3. $5 + 4i$ **5.** ^-4i **7.** $5i$ **9.** 6 **11.** $5 + 6i$
13. 5 **15.** 41 **17.** 16 **19.** 61

21. $(3 + 2i)\dfrac{3 - 2i}{13} = \dfrac{9 - 4i^2}{13} = \dfrac{9 + 4}{14} = \dfrac{13}{13} = 1$

23. $(6 + 8i)\dfrac{3 - 4i}{50} = \dfrac{18 - 24i + 24i - 32i^2}{50}$
$= \dfrac{18 + 32}{50} = \dfrac{50}{50} = 1$

Written Exercises Page 163 1. 58 **3.** 85

5. 13 **7.** 4 **9.** $\dfrac{5 + i}{2}$ **11.** $\dfrac{5 + i}{13}$ **13.** $\dfrac{5 - 3i}{2}$

15. $\dfrac{6 + 5i}{3}$ **17.** $\dfrac{12 + 3i}{17}$ **19.** $\dfrac{4\sqrt{3} - 8i}{7}$

21. $\dfrac{1 + 4i\sqrt{3}}{7}$ **23.** $\dfrac{2 - 3i\sqrt{5}}{7}$ **25.** $\dfrac{16 + 63i}{50}$

27. $\dfrac{^-1 - i}{2}$ **29.** $\dfrac{3 - i}{10}$ **31.** $\dfrac{7 + 3i}{58}$ **33.** $\dfrac{1 - 3i}{4}$

35. $3 + 2i$

Exploratory Exercises page 166 1. no
additive identity, no inverses **3.** not closed
under addition or multiplication, no identities
5. not closed under addition or multiplication, no
identities

Written Exercises Page 166 1–5. Answers
will vary. **7.** $^-5 - 4i, \dfrac{5 - 4i}{41}$ **9.** $^-11 + i, \dfrac{11 + i}{122}$

11. $3 + 2i, \dfrac{^-3 + 2i}{13}$

Chapter Review Page 168 1. $7|a|$ **3.** $2xy^2$
5. 3.391 **7.** 941.192 **9.** $2\sqrt[3]{6a^2}$ **11.** $^-45\sqrt{30}$
13. $5\sqrt{2} + 2\sqrt{5}$ **15.** $2\sqrt[3]{6} + 3$ **17.** $2xy^2\sqrt[3]{9}$
19. $4\sqrt[3]{5}$ **21.** 4 **23.** $2\sqrt[3]{5}$
25. $\dfrac{4\sqrt{3} + 4\sqrt{2} - \sqrt{6} - 3}{13}$ **27.** 62 **29.** $2i\sqrt{2}$
31. ^-i **33.** $^-3$ **35.** $12 - i, 2 + 5i, 41 - 11i$
37. $x = 2, y = 3$ **39.** $\dfrac{^-3 - 7i}{2}$ **41.** commutative
property of addition.

CHAPTER 6 QUADRATIC EQUATIONS
Exploratory Exercises Page 172 1. yes
3. yes **5.** no **7.** yes **9.** no **11.** $4, ^-5$ **13.** $^-6$,
$^-2$ **15.** $0, 1$ **17.** $^-\dfrac{7}{3}, ^-5$ **19.** $^-\dfrac{3}{2}, \dfrac{1}{3}$

Written Exercises Page 172 1. $^-2, ^-4$
3. $4, 5$ **5.** $^-5, 2$ **7.** $^-2$ **9.** $0, ^-3$ **11.** $4, ^-1$

13. $^-6, 5$ **15.** $^-\dfrac{3}{2}, ^-1$ **17.** $^-\dfrac{3}{2}, 3$ **19.** $0, \dfrac{5}{3}$

21. $^-\dfrac{3}{2}, ^-\dfrac{2}{3}$ **23.** $\dfrac{1}{5}, ^-\dfrac{7}{2}$ **25.** $\dfrac{1}{6}, \dfrac{3}{4}$ **27.** $^-\dfrac{1}{4}, 3$

29. $^-8, 5$ **31.** $\dfrac{2}{3}, 4$ **33.** $^-\dfrac{1}{4}, \dfrac{5}{3}$ **35.** $\dfrac{5}{6}, ^-\dfrac{3}{2}$

37. $-\frac{3}{4}, 4$ 39. $\frac{3}{2}$ 41. $\frac{11}{4}, -\frac{11}{4}$ 43. $0, 3, ^-3$
45. $0, -\frac{6}{7}, \frac{2}{5}$ 47. $0, \frac{3}{5}$

Exploratory Exercises Page 175 1. yes
3. no **5.** yes **7.** yes **9.** yes **11.** 1 **13.** 400
15. 81 **17.** $\frac{81}{4}$ **19.** 2500 **21.** $\frac{225}{4}$

Written Exercises Page 176 1. 9 **3.** $\frac{1}{16}$
5. $\frac{1}{4}$ **7.** $\frac{9}{4}$ **9.** $\frac{49}{4}$ **11.** 625 **13.** 6, $^-4$
15. $^-11, 8$ **17.** 3, 5 **19.** $^-10, 2$ **21.** 3, 4
23. 6, $^-14$ **25.** $^-8, 5$ **27.** $4 \pm \sqrt{2}$ **29.** $\frac{7 \pm \sqrt{29}}{2}$
31. $\frac{5 \pm \sqrt{65}}{2}$ **33.** $-\frac{1}{3}, ^-2$ **35.** $-\frac{3}{2}, \frac{1}{3}$ **37.** $\frac{3}{2}, ^-7$
39. $\frac{5}{3}, ^-3$ **41.** $2 \pm \frac{2}{3}\sqrt{6}$ **43.** no real solutions

Skills Review Page 176 1. $x(x-4)(x-3)$
3. $7x(x-2)(x+2)$ **5.** $(2a-5b)(2x+7y)$
7. $(b-3)(b^2+3b+9)$
9. $4m^2(2m+3)(4m^2-6m+9)$

Exploratory Exercises Page 179 1. 5, $^-3$, 7
3. 1, 2, $^-1$ **5.** 1, 1, 0 **7.** 4, 2, $^-7$ **9.** 5, $^-1$, $^-6$
11. 3, $^-2$, 7

Written Exercises Page 179 1. 6, $^-5$
3. $^-5$, 3 **5.** 6, 4 **7.** 4, 1 **9.** 4, $-\frac{5}{3}$ **11.** $\frac{5}{3}, -\frac{3}{2}$
13. $\frac{1}{7}, -\frac{5}{2}$ **15.** $\frac{1}{4}, -\frac{2}{5}$ **17.** $\frac{5}{6}, -\frac{3}{4}$ **19.** 3, $-\frac{5}{2}$
21. $\frac{7}{2}, -\frac{2}{7}$ **23.** 0, 13 **25.** $\frac{4}{3}, -\frac{3}{4}$ **27.** $\frac{8}{7}, ^-4$
29. $\frac{\pm\sqrt{30}}{2}$ **31.** $\frac{^-3 \pm i\sqrt{15}}{4}$ **33.** $\frac{^-7 \pm i\sqrt{11}}{10}$
35. $\frac{9 \pm i\sqrt{3}}{2}$ **37.** $\frac{1 \pm i\sqrt{5}}{6}$ **39.** 0, $-\frac{1}{4}$ **41.** $-\frac{1}{2}$,
$-\frac{1}{4}$ **43.** $^-1 \pm i\sqrt{3}, 2$ **45.** $2 \pm 2i\sqrt{3}, ^-4$
47. $\frac{^-5 \pm 5i\sqrt{3}}{2}, 5$

Exploratory Exercises Page 181 1. 33;
2 real **3.** 1; 2 real **5.** 0; 1 real **7.** 81; 2 real
9. 1; 2 real **11.** $^-16$; 2 imaginary

Written Exercises Page 181 1. 144; 2 real;
7, $^-5$ **3.** 0; 1 real; 2 **5.** 12; 2 real; $2 \pm \sqrt{3}$
7. 16; 2 real; $-\frac{3}{2}, -\frac{1}{2}$ **9.** 73; 2 real; $\frac{^-11 \pm \sqrt{73}}{6}$
11. $^-16$; 2 imaginary; $1 \pm 2i$ **13.** 89; 2 real;
$\frac{^-9 \pm \sqrt{89}}{2}$ **15.** 36; 2 real; 0, 6 **17.** $^-144$;
2 imaginary; $\frac{2 \pm 3i}{2}$ **19.** 289; 2 real; 6, $\frac{1}{3}$ **21.** $^-3$;

2 imaginary; $\frac{1 \pm i\sqrt{3}}{2}$ **23.** 21; 2 real; $\frac{^-1 \pm \sqrt{21}}{2}$

Exploratory Exercises Page 184 1. $^-7, ^-4$
3. 3, 5 **5.** $-\frac{7}{3}, ^-3$ **7.** $\frac{3}{5}, 0$ **9.** $0, -\frac{3}{5}$ **11.** $\frac{2}{3}, \frac{11}{3}$
13. $\frac{1}{4}, \frac{1}{3}$ **15.** $\frac{1}{15}, -\frac{4}{15}$

Written Exercises Page 184 1. $^-6; ^-7; ^-7, 1$
3. $\frac{5}{2}; -\frac{3}{2}; 3, -\frac{1}{2}$ **5.** 3; 1; $\frac{3 \pm \sqrt{5}}{2}$ **7.** $-\frac{21}{4}; -\frac{9}{2}, \frac{3}{4}$,
$^-6$ **9.** 3; $\frac{5}{2}; \frac{3 \pm i}{2}$ **11.** 0; $-\frac{1}{9}; \pm\frac{1}{3}$ **13.** $\frac{7}{2}; -\frac{15}{2}$,
5, $-\frac{3}{2}$ **15.** $\frac{2}{15}; -\frac{8}{15}, \frac{4}{5}, -\frac{2}{3}$ **17.** $^-25; 156; ^-13$,
$^-12$ **19.** $\frac{7}{3}; 1; \frac{7 \pm \sqrt{13}}{6}$ **21.** $-\frac{19}{12}; \frac{1}{3}; -\frac{1}{4}, -\frac{4}{3}$
23. $x^2 - 3x - 10 = 0$ **25.** $x^2 - x - 6 = 0$
27. $x^2 + 13x + 36 = 0$ **29.** $3x^2 - 17x + 10 = 0$
31. $4x^2 + 13x - 12 = 0$ **33.** $25x^2 - 4 = 0$
35. $6x^2 - 5x + 1 = 0$ **37.** $x^2 + 4\sqrt{2}x - 10 = 0$
39. $x^2 - 10x + 23 = 0$ **41.** $x^2 + 36 = 0$
43. $x^2 - 10x + 28 = 0$ **45.** $8x^2 - 20x + 17 = 0$

47. 4 **49.** $-\frac{49}{3}$

Written Exercises Page 187 1. 26, 27 or $^-27$,
$^-26$ **3.** 37, 39 or $^-39, ^-37$ **5.** 15, 17 **7.** 11, 12
or $^-12, ^-11$ **9.** 10 meters **11.** 18 feet by 24 feet
13. 10, 11 or $^-11, ^-10$ **15.** 8 or $^-9$ **17.** $\frac{2}{3}$ or $\frac{1}{3}$
19. 3 or $\frac{1}{3}$ **21.** 2 meters **23.** $\frac{6}{5}$ or $-\frac{5}{6}$ **25.** 6 cm
by 4 cm **27.** 7 or 3 **29.** 0 or 7 **31.** 4 meters

Exploratory Exercises Page 190 1. yes
3. no **5.** yes **7.** no **9.** no **11.** yes **13.** yes
15. yes

Written Exercises Page 190 1. $\pm 2, \pm 1$
3. $\pm 4, \pm 3$ **5.** $\pm\sqrt{5}, \pm i\sqrt{5}$ **7.** $\pm\sqrt{3}, \pm i\sqrt{3}$
9. 0, 5, $^-5$ **11.** $\pm i\sqrt{3}, \pm i\sqrt{6}$ **13.** $\pm 2, \pm\sqrt{2}$
15. 64, 1 **17.** 1 **19.** 0, 4, $^-2 \pm 2i\sqrt{3}$ **21.** 2, $^-1$,
$^-1 \pm i\sqrt{3}, \frac{1 \pm i\sqrt{3}}{2}$ **23.** 2, $\sqrt[3]{2}$, $^-1 \pm i\sqrt{3}$

Chapter Review Page 192 1. $-\frac{3}{2}, \frac{1}{3}$
3. $-\frac{3}{2}, ^-1$ **5.** $-\frac{6}{5}, \frac{1}{3}$ **7.** 49 **9.** 15, 5 **11.** $-\frac{7}{2}, 3$
13. 2, $\frac{5}{3}$ **15.** $\frac{\pm 3\sqrt{2}}{2}$ **17.** 1200; 2 real; $\frac{10 \pm 5\sqrt{3}}{2}$
19. 0; 1 real; 4 **21.** 12; $^-45$; 15, $^-3$ **23.** 0; $-\frac{11}{3}$;
$\frac{\pm\sqrt{33}}{3}$ **25.** $x^2 - 2x - 24 = 0$

27. $x^2 - 10x + 34 = 0$ **29.** 32 or $^-12$ **31.** 3.5 feet (24.5 is not a reasonable answer.) **33.** ±3, $\pm\sqrt{3}$ **35.** no solutions

Cumulative Review   Pages 194–195

1. $10m + n$ **3.** $6x + 18y$ **5.** $45w^2z^{16}$
7. $k^2 + 17k + 8$ **9.** $r^3 + 3r^2s + 3rs^2 + s^3$ **11.** 3
13. $^-7$ **15.** 4 **17.** $x \le ^-1$ **19.** $^-1 < x < 3$
25. $5x - 6y = ^-50$ **27.** (8, 2) **29.** (1, 1)
31. $3ab^2(3a^2 + 4b)$ **33.** $(a + 12)(a - 12)$
35. $(b + 7)^2$ **37.** $(z + 2)(z + 8)$
39. $(2 + t)(r + s)$ **41.** $2a + 5$ **43.** $^-11$
45. $3x^2y$ **47.** $2\sqrt{6}$ **49.** $10\sqrt{7}$ **51.** $\dfrac{5\sqrt{7}}{7}$
53. $4 - 4\sqrt{2}$ **55.** $3r^2s\sqrt[3]{5rs^2}$ **57.** 33
59. $5 + 3\sqrt{3}$ **61.** $^-4\sqrt{3}$ **63.** $2 + 15i$
65. $\dfrac{^-5i + 6}{2}$ **67.** $\dfrac{\sqrt{3}}{3}$ **69.** $^-2, ^-3$ **71.** $^-2 \pm i\sqrt{6}$
73. $\dfrac{1}{2}, ^-1$ **75.** $\dfrac{3 \pm i\sqrt{15}}{12}$ **77.** \$600 **79.** 13, 15 or $^-15, ^-13$ **81.** 6 or $^-6$

CHAPTER 7   QUADRATIC RELATIONS AND FUNCTIONS

Exploratory Exercises   Page 198   **1.** yes

3. no **5.** yes **7.** yes **9.** no **11.** $x^2; 3x; -\dfrac{1}{4}$
13. $x^2; ^-3x; -\dfrac{1}{4}$ **15.** $3a^2; 0; ^-2$ **17.** $x^2; 3x; 0$
19. $x^2; 6x; 9$

Written Exercises   Page 198

1. $f(x) = x^2 - 4x + 4$ **3.** $f(x) = 9x^2 + 12x + 4$
5. $f(x) = 32x^2 + 16x + 2$
7. $f(x) = 3x^2 - 24x + 42$
9. $f(x) = 45x^2 - 60x + 24$
11. $f(x) = 20x^2 - 20x + 13$ **13.** $A = \pi r^2$
15. $x =$ one of the numbers; product $= 40x - x^2$
17. $x =$ the lesser number; product $= 64x + x^2$
19. $x =$ length of rectangle; area $= 10x - x^2$
21. $x =$ first integer; $x(x + 1) = (x + 1)^2 - 9$
23. $p =$ number of \$1.00 price increases; $I = 2400 + 140p - 20p^2$ **25.** $x =$ length of side; area $= 120x - 2x^2$

Skills Review   Page 199   **1.** $\dfrac{3 + 3i}{4}$

3. $^-3 + \dfrac{3i}{2}$ **5.** $\dfrac{9 - 7i}{13}$ **7.** 3 **9.** $\dfrac{6 - 10i}{17}$
11. $\dfrac{1 - 2i\sqrt{6}}{5}$

Exploratory Exercises   Page 202   **1.** $^-72; ^-72;$ $^-32; ^-32; -\dfrac{1}{2}; -\dfrac{1}{2}$

Written Exercises   Page 202

1. **3.**

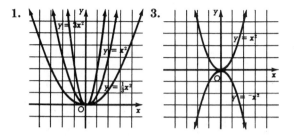

7. $(0, 0); x = 0;$ up **9.** $(0, 0); x = 0;$ down
11. $(0, 0); x = 0;$ up **13.** $(0, 0); x = 0;$ up
15. $(0, 0); x = 0;$ down **17.** $\dfrac{1}{2}$ **19.** 1 **21.** $^-2$
23. $^-4$ **25.** 3 **27.** $\dfrac{2}{3}$ **29.** $f(x) = -\dfrac{1}{4}x^2$

Exploratory Exercises   Page 205   **1.** $(0, 0);$ $x = 0;$ up **3.** $(3, 0); x = 3;$ up **5.** $(^-4, 0); x = ^-4;$ down **7.** $(^-3, 0); x = ^-3;$ up **9.** $(^-2, 0); x = ^-2;$ down **11.** $(2, 0); x = 2;$ up

Written Exercises   Page 206

1. $f(x) = (x - 1)^2; (1, 0); x = 1;$ up
3. $f(x) = \dfrac{2}{5}(x + 2)^2; (^-2, 0); x = ^-2;$ up
5. $f(x) = 6(x + 5)^2; (^-5, 0); x = ^-5;$ up
7. $f(x) = ^-9(x - 1)^2; (1, 0); x = 1;$ down
9. $f(x) = 4\left(x - \dfrac{11}{2}\right)^2; \left(\dfrac{11}{2}, 0\right); x = \dfrac{11}{2};$ up
11. $f(x) = 5(x - 3)^2; (3, 0); x = 3;$ up
13. $f(x) = 2(2x + 3)^2; (-\dfrac{3}{2}, 0); x = -\dfrac{3}{2};$ up
15. $f(x) = 9\left(x - \dfrac{10}{3}\right)^2; \left(\dfrac{10}{3}, 0\right); x = \dfrac{10}{3};$ up

17. **18.**

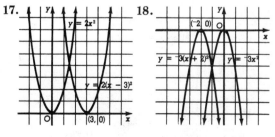

23. $f(x) = (x - 3)^2$ **25.** $f(x) = -\dfrac{1}{4}\left(x + \dfrac{3}{4}\right)^2$

Exploratory Exercises   Page 209   1. $(0, 0)$; $x = 0$; up   **3.** $(8, 0)$; $x = 8$; up   **5.** $(0, 6)$; $x = 0$; down   **7.** $(^-3, ^-1)$; $x = ^-3$; up   **9.** $\left(1, \frac{1}{3}\right)$; $x = 1$; up   **11.** $\left(^-2, -\frac{4}{3}\right)$; $x = ^-2$; down

Written Exercises   Page 209

1. 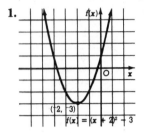   **3.**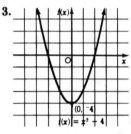

7. 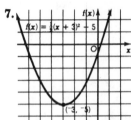   **11.**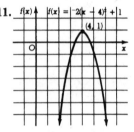

Exploratory Exercises   Page 211
1. $40 + 10x$ **3.** income $= (40 + 10x)$ $(50{,}000 - 5000x)$ **5.** 70¢   **7.** $x(300 - 2x)$ $- (20x + 1000)$ or $^-2x^2 + 280x - 1000$

Written Exercises   Page 212   1. 18, 18
3. $^-24$, 24   **5.** $^-8$, 8   **7.** 28, 28   **9.** 10 cm by 10 cm; 100 cm²   **11.** length = 60 m; width = 30 m
13. $11.50   **15.** 300 ft; 2.5 sec   **17.** length = 300 m; width = 200 m   **19.** 18 cm   **21.** $3.50

Exploratory Exercises   Page 215
1. $y = (x + 2)^2$ **3.** $y = (x + 4)^2 + 1$
5. $y = 3(x - 4)^2 - 44$ **7.** $y = \left(x + \frac{3}{2}\right)^2 - \frac{13}{4}$
9. $y = 2\left(x + \frac{3}{2}\right)^2 - \frac{19}{2}$

Written Exercises   Page 215

7.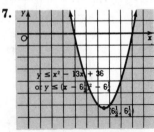

9.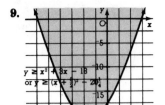

Exploratory Exercises   Page 218   1. one > 0 and one < 0 **3.** both > 0 or both < 0
5. both ≥ 0 or both ≤ 0 **7.** one ≤ 0 and one ≥ 0
9. one ≤ 0 and one ≥ 0

Written Exercises   Page 218
1. $\{x \mid x > 2 \text{ or } x < ^-3\}$ **3.** $\{p \mid p \geq 4 \text{ or } p \leq ^-6\}$
5. $\{b \mid -\frac{3}{2} < b < 2\}$ **7.** $\{x \mid 0 \leq x \leq 4\}$
9. $\{t \mid ^-6 \leq t \leq 6\}$ **11.** $\{r \mid ^-9 \leq r \leq ^-3\}$
13. $\left\{c \mid -\frac{1}{2} < c < 3\right\}$ **15.** all reals
17. $\left\{t \mid \frac{-1 - \sqrt{10}}{2} < t < \frac{-1 + \sqrt{10}}{2}\right\}$

Chapter Review   Page 220   1. x^2, $2x$, 5
3. 0, 0, 16   **5.** $f(x) = 3x^2 + 12x + 5$

7. $f(x) = ^-2x^2 + 12x - 9$

9. 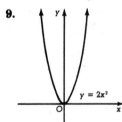   **13.** $\frac{1}{12}$ **15.** $\frac{1}{4}$

17. $(3, 0)$; $x = 3$; up

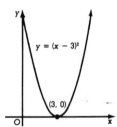

23. $(2, ^-3)$; $x = 2$; up

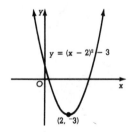

29. 32 and 32

31.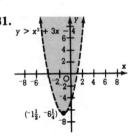

33. $\{x \mid ^-2 < x < 4\}$

614   *Selected Answers*

CHAPTER 8 CONICS

Exploratory Exercises Page 225 1. 2

3. 9 **5.** 11 **7.** 16 **9.** 31.1 **11.** $22\frac{7}{10}$

Written Exercises Page 225 1. $2\sqrt{53}$
3. $\sqrt{58}$ **5.** $\sqrt{53}$ **7.** $\dfrac{\sqrt{4594}}{15}$ **9.** $\dfrac{\sqrt{5}}{10}$
11. $\sqrt{16.85}$ **13.** 1 **15.** $5\sqrt{3}$ **17.** 3 or 11

19. 7.1 or 13.1 **21.** $\left(\dfrac{3}{2}, -\dfrac{5}{2}\right)$ **23.** $\left(\dfrac{2}{3}, -\dfrac{3}{4}\right)$
25. $((3 + \sqrt{2})/2, (3 - \sqrt{2})/2)$ **27.** $2\sqrt{106}$
and $2\sqrt{146}$ **29.** $\overline{AB} = \sqrt{4 + 16}$ or $\sqrt{20}$; $\overline{AC} = \sqrt{16 + 4}$ or $\sqrt{20}$; Thus, $\triangle ABC$ is isosceles.

31. midpoint of hypotenuse $= \left(\dfrac{4 + 0}{2}, \dfrac{1 + 7}{2}\right)$

$$= (2, 4)$$
distance from $(2, 4)$ to $D = \sqrt{4 + 9} = \sqrt{13}$
distance from $(2, 4)$ to $E = \sqrt{4 + 9} = \sqrt{13}$
distance from $(2, 4)$ to $F = \sqrt{4 + 9} = \sqrt{13}$

Exploratory Exercises Page 228 1. 4 **3.** 16

5. $\dfrac{9}{4}$ **7.** $\dfrac{49}{4}$ **9.** 4.2025 **11.** $y = \dfrac{1}{10}x^2$
13. $y = (x - 3)^2 + 24$ **15.** $y = 3(x - 4)^2 + 2$

17. $x = \dfrac{1}{6}y^2$ **19.** $x = (y + 4)^2 + 4$

21. $x = \dfrac{1}{4}(y - 1)^2 - \dfrac{13}{4}$

Written Exercises Page 228 1. $(0, 0)$; $x = 0$;
$\left(0, \dfrac{3}{2}\right)$; $y = -\dfrac{3}{2}$; up; 6 **3.** $(-2, 3)$; $x = -2$; $\left(-2, 3\frac{1}{4}\right)$;
$y = 2\frac{3}{4}$; up; 1 **5.** $(8, -1)$; $x = 8$; $\left(8, -\frac{7}{8}\right)$;
$y = -\dfrac{9}{8}$; up; $\dfrac{1}{2}$ **7.** $(0, 1)$; $x = 0$; $\left(0, \frac{5}{4}\right)$; $y = \dfrac{3}{4}$;
up; 1 **9.** $(2, -3)$; $y = -3$; $(3, -3)$; $x = 1$; right; 4

11. $(3, 24)$; $x = 3$; $\left(3, 24\frac{1}{4}\right)$; $y = 23\frac{3}{4}$; up; 1

13. $(-24, 7)$; $y = 7$; $\left(-23\frac{3}{4}, 7\right)$; $x = -24\frac{1}{4}$;

right; 1 **15.** $\left(-\dfrac{13}{4}, 1\right)$; $y = 1$; $\left(-\dfrac{9}{4}, 1\right)$; $y = -\dfrac{17}{4}$;

right; 4 **17.** $(4, 2)$; $x = 4$; $\left(4, 2\frac{1}{12}\right)$; $y = 1\frac{11}{12}$;

up; $\dfrac{1}{3}$ **19.** $y = -\dfrac{1}{4}(x - 2)^2 + 5$

21. $y = -\dfrac{1}{8}(x - 8)^2 + 2$ **23.** $y = \dfrac{1}{16}(x - 5)^2 + 1$

25. $x = \dfrac{1}{10}(y + 1)^2 + \dfrac{1}{2}$

27. $x = -\dfrac{1}{2}(y - 4)^2 + \dfrac{1}{2}$ **29.** $x = -\dfrac{1}{8}(y + 1)^2 + 5$

31. $y = -\dfrac{1}{6}(x + 7)^2 + 4$

Exploratory Exercises Page 231 1. circle
3. parabola **5.** circle **7.** circle **9.** parabola
11. $(0, 0)$; 4 **13.** $(2, 0)$; 3 **15.** $(10, -10)$; 10

17. $\left(-4, \dfrac{1}{2}\right)$; $\sqrt{6}$ **19.** $(-5, 2)$; $\dfrac{\sqrt{3}}{2}$

Written Exercises Page 232 1. $(2, 0)$; 3
3. $(0, 8)$; 8 **5.** $(0, 0)$; 8 **7.** $(2, 5)$; 4 **9.** $(-8, 3)$; 5
11. $(-1, -9)$; 6 **13.** $(6, -8)$; 4 **15.** $(-4, 3)$; 5

17. $(2, 0)$; $\sqrt{13}$ **19.** $\left(-\dfrac{3}{2}, -1\right)$; $\dfrac{\sqrt{141}}{6}$ **21.** $\left(-\dfrac{9}{2}, 5\right)$;

7 **23.** $(-1, -2)$; $\sqrt{14}$ **25.** $(-1, 0)$; $\sqrt{11}$
27. $(x - 6)^2 + (y - 2)^2 = 25$ **29.** $x^2 + (y - 3)^2$

31. $(x + 6)^2 + (y - 2)^2 = \dfrac{1}{16}$

33. $(x - 1)^2 + (y - 5)^2 = 26$
35. $(x - 2)^2 + (y - 2)^2 = 9$

Exploratory Exercises Page 236 1. $(0, 0)$
3. $(0, 0)$ **5.** $(0, 5)$ **7.** $(2, -5)$ **9.** $(-2, 3)$
11. $(\pm\sqrt{15}, 0)$ **13.** $(0, \pm\sqrt{26})$ **15.** $(1, 0), (-7, 0)$

Written Exercises Page 237 1. $(0, 0)$;
$(0, \pm\sqrt{21})$; 10, 4 **3.** $(0, 0)$; $(\pm 4, 0)$; 10, 6
5. $(0, 0)$; $(\pm\sqrt{7}, 0)$; 8, 6 **7.** $(0, 0)$; $(\pm\sqrt{5}, 0)$; 6, 4
9. $(0, 0)$; $(\pm 3\sqrt{5}, 0)$; 18, 12 **11.** $(0, 0)$; $(0, \pm\sqrt{6})$;
6, $2\sqrt{3}$ **13.** $(-2, -3)$; $(-2, -3 \pm 2\sqrt{5})$; $4\sqrt{10}$, $4\sqrt{5}$
15. $(-2, 3)$; $(-2 \pm \sqrt{3}, 3)$; $2\sqrt{5}$, $2\sqrt{2}$ **17.** $(2, 3)$;
$(2 \pm \sqrt{7}, 3)$; 8, 6 **19.** $(2, 2)$; $(4, 2), (0, 2)$; $2\sqrt{7}$,
$2\sqrt{3}$ **21.** $(-1, 3)$; $(2, 3), (-4, 3)$; 10, 8

23. $\dfrac{x^2}{169} + \dfrac{y^2}{25} = 1$ **25.** $\dfrac{(x + 2)^2}{16} + \dfrac{(y - 3)^2}{36} = 1$

27. $\dfrac{(x - 1)^2}{25} + \dfrac{(y - 4)^2}{9} = 1$

Exploratory Exercises Page 242 1. ellipse
3. hyperbola **5.** hyperbola **7.** ellipse
9. hyperbola

Written Exercises Page 242 1. $(\pm 3, 0)$;
$(\pm\sqrt{34}, 0)$; $y = \pm\dfrac{5}{3}x$ **3.** $(\pm 6, 0)$; $(\pm\sqrt{37}, 0)$;
$y = \pm\dfrac{1}{6}x$ **5.** $(0, \pm 9)$; $(0, \pm\sqrt{106})$; $y = \pm\dfrac{9}{5}x$
7. $(\pm 2, 0)$; $(\pm\sqrt{13}, 0)$; $y = \pm\dfrac{3}{2}x$ **9.** $(\pm 9, 0)$;
$(\pm\sqrt{117}, 0)$; $y = \pm\dfrac{2}{3}x$ **11.** $(\pm 3, 0)$; $(\pm 5, 0)$;
$y = \pm\dfrac{4}{3}x$ **13.** $(\pm 2, 0)$; $(\pm\sqrt{29}, 0)$; $y = \pm\dfrac{5}{2}x$
15. $(\pm\sqrt{2}, 0)$; $(\pm\sqrt{3}, 0)$; $y = \pm\dfrac{\sqrt{2}}{2}x$ **17.** $(0, \pm 6)$;

$(0, \pm3\sqrt{5})$; $y = \pm2x$ **19.** $(0, ^-3)$, $(^-12, ^-3)$,
$(^-6 \pm 3\sqrt{5}, ^-3)$; $y + 3 = \pm\frac{1}{2}(x + 6)$ **21.** $(^-2, 0)$,
$(^-2, 8)$; $(^-2, ^-1)$, $(^-2, 9)$; $y - 4 = \pm\frac{4}{3}(x + 2)$
23. $(4 \pm 2\sqrt{5}, ^-2)$; $(4 \pm 3\sqrt{5}, ^-2)$;
$y + 2 = \pm\frac{\sqrt{5}}{2}(x - 4)$ **25.** $(1, ^-3 \pm 2\sqrt{6})$;
$(1, ^-3 \pm 4\sqrt{2})$; $y + 3 = \pm\sqrt{3}(x - 1)$
27. $\frac{x^2}{1} - \frac{y^2}{16} = 1$ **29.** $\frac{(y - 2)^2}{36} - \frac{(x + 2)^2}{64} = 1$
31. $2, 1, \frac{1}{2}, \frac{1}{4}, ^-2, -\frac{1}{2}, -\frac{1}{4}$
33. $\{y \mid y \text{ is real}, y \neq 0\}$

Exploratory Exercises   Page 245   1. circle
3. ellipse **5.** parabola **7.** hyperbola

Written Exercises   Page 245   1. $y = \frac{1}{8}x^2$;
parabola **3.** $x^2 + y^2 = 27$; circle
5. $\frac{x^2}{4} + \frac{(y + 1)^2}{3} = 1$; ellipse **7.** $\frac{y^2}{16} - \frac{x^2}{8} = 1$;
hyperbola **9.** $x^2 + (y - 4)^2 = 5$; circle
11. $y = -1\left(x - \frac{1}{2}\right)^2 + \frac{9}{4}$; parabola
13. $\frac{(x - 3)^2}{25} + \frac{(y - 1)^2}{9} = 1$; ellipse
15. $\frac{(y + 4)^2}{2} - \frac{(x + 1)^2}{6} = 1$; hyperbola

Skills Review   Page 245   1. $11\sqrt{2}$ **3.** 20
5. $30\sqrt{5}$ **7.** $11\sqrt{2}$ **9.** $\frac{\sqrt{2}}{3}$ **11.** $2\sqrt{14} - 10$

Written Exercises   Page 248   1. $(\pm2\sqrt{3}, 2)$
3. $(2, 2), (^-2, ^-2)$ **5.** $(3, 0), (^-5, ^-4)$ **7.** $(0, ^-1)$,
$(^-3, 2)$ **9.** $(\pm5.2, 6)$ **11.** no solutions **13.** no
solutions **15.** $(^-2, 0), (2, 4)$ **17.** $(3, 3), (^-1, ^-1)$
19. $(3, 7), (8, 4)$ **21.** $(\pm1, 5), (\pm1, -5)$
23. $(\pm2, \sqrt{3}), (\pm2, -\sqrt{3})$ **25.** no solutions
27. no solutions **29.** $(\pm8, 0)$

Written Exercises   Page 251   1. $(\pm2\sqrt{3}, 2)$
3. $(2, 2), (^-2, ^-2)$ **5.** $(3, 0), (^-5, ^-4)$ **7.** $(^-3, 2)$,
$(0, ^-1)$ **9.** $(\pm3\sqrt{3}, 6)$ **11.** no solutions **13.** no
solutions **15.** $(^-2, 0), (2, 4)$ **17.** $(6, 9), (2, 1)$
19. $(3, 7), (8, 4)$ **21.** $(1, \pm 5), (^-1, \pm5)$
23. $(2, \pm\sqrt{3}), (^-2, \pm\sqrt{3})$ **25.** no solutions
27. no solutions

Chapter Review   Page 256   1. $2\sqrt{53}$
3. $\sqrt{16.85}$ **5.** $\left(1, \frac{3}{2}\right)$ **7.** $(0.25, 0.5)$ **9.** $(0, 0)$;

$x = 0$; $(0, 1)$; $y = ^-1$; up; 4 **11.** $(4, 8)$; $y = 8$;
$(3, 8)$; $x = 5$; left; 4 **13.** $(3, ^-7)$; 9 **15.** $(0, 0)$;
$(0, \pm 2\sqrt{2})$; $8, 4\sqrt{2}$ **17.** $(0, 0)$; $(\pm \sqrt{7}, 0)$; $8, 6$
19. $(1, ^-6 \pm 2\sqrt{5})$; $(1, ^-6 \pm 3\sqrt{5})$;
$y + 6 = \pm\frac{2\sqrt{5}}{5}(x - 1)$ **21.** parabola
23. ellipse **25.** $(^-1.6, 2.6), (2.6, ^-1.6)$ **27.** $(^-2, 0)$
$(2, 4)$

CHAPTER 9   POLYNOMIAL FUNCTIONS

Exploratory Exercises   Page 260   1. no
3. no **5.** no **7.** yes **9.** no **11.** yes **13.** yes

Written Exercises   Page 261   1. 4 **3.** 1
5. $^-4$ **7.** $-\frac{11}{2}$ **9.** $\frac{19}{3}$ **11.** $^-5$ **13.** $^-6$ **15.** 28
17. 2 **19.** 13 **21.** 144 **23.** 35 **25.** $^-12$
27. 74 **29.** $x + h$
31. $x^3 + 3x^2h + 3xh^2 + h^3 + 4x + 4h$
33. $\frac{4}{3}x^3 + 4hx^2 + 4h^2x + \frac{4}{3}h^3 - 1$
35. $x^3 + 3hx^2 + 3h^2x + h^3 - 4x^2 - 8hx - 4h^2$
37. $9x + 6$ **39.** $3x^3 - 9x^2 + 9x - 3$
41. $5x^2 - 10x + \frac{5}{2}$ **43.** $^-5x - 12$
45. $^-x^2 + x + 2$ **47.** $-\frac{4}{5}x^3 - \frac{77}{10}x^2 - \frac{51}{5}x - \frac{19}{10}$

Exploratory Exercises   Page 264
1. $x^2 - 3x + 1 = (x - 1)(x - 2) - 1$
3. $x^3 - 8x^2 + 2x - 1 = (x^2 - 9x + 11)(x + 1) - 12$ **5.** $x^5 + x^4 + 2x - 1 = (x^4 + 3x^3 + 6x^2 + 12x + 26)(x - 2) + 51$ **7.** $x^5 + 32 = (x^4 - 2x^3 + 4x^2 - 8x + 16)(x + 2) + 0$

Written Exercises   Page 264
1. $2x^3 + 8x^2 - 3x - 1 = (2x^2 + 12x + 21)(x - 2) + 41$ **3.** $x^4 - 16 = (x^3 + 2x^2 + 4x + 8)(x - 2) + 0$
5. $4x^4 + 3x^3 - 2x^2 + x + 1 = (4x^3 + 7x^2 + 5x + 6)(x - 1) + 7$ **7.** $3x^3 + 2x^2 - 4x - 1 = \left(3x^2 + \frac{1}{2}x - \frac{17}{4}\right)\left(x + \frac{1}{2}\right) + \frac{9}{8}$ **9.** 37 **11.** $^-34$ **13.** 314
15. 461 **17.** $x + 2, x - 2$ **19.** $x + 1, x + 2$
21. $x - 1, x + 2$ **23.** $x - 2, x^2 + 2x + 4$
25. $x - 1, x + 1, x^2 + 1$ **27.** $^-17$ **29.** $\frac{25}{2}$

Exploratory Exercises   Page 269   1. $\pm1, \pm2$
3. $\pm1, \pm2, \pm3, \pm6$ **5.** $\pm1, \pm2, \pm4, \pm8$ **7.** ±1
9. $\pm1, \pm2, \pm4, \pm5, \pm10, \pm20$ **11.** $\pm1, \pm\frac{1}{2}, \pm\frac{1}{3},$

616   *Selected Answers*

$\pm\frac{1}{6}$ **13.** $\pm1, \pm2, \pm4, \pm\frac{1}{3}, \pm\frac{2}{3}, \pm\frac{4}{3}$ **15.** $3, ^-5, -\frac{5}{2}$

17. $3, 3, ^-2, \frac{1}{2}, \frac{2}{3}$

Written Exercises   Page 269   1. $^-2, ^-4, 7$

3. $3, 3, -\frac{1}{2}$ **5.** 3 **7.** $^-2, ^-4$ **9.** $1, ^-1$ **11.** $\frac{1}{2}, \frac{1}{4}$

13. $^-1, ^-2, 5$ **15.** $^-6$ **17.** $0, -\frac{1}{3}, \frac{1}{2}, -\frac{1}{2}$ **19.** $2,$
$^-2$ **21.** height = 2 m, width = 4 m, length = 9 m

Skills Review   Page 269   1. $3, ^-3$ **3.** $^-3, ^-8$

5. $1, 24$ **7.** $^-4, \frac{1}{2}$ **9.** $-\frac{1}{5}, 1$ **11.** $\frac{3 \pm \sqrt{17}}{2}$

Exploratory Exercises   Page 272   1. 3 or 1; 1
3. 4, 2, or 0; 0   **5.** 2 or 0; 2 or 0   **7.** 5, 3, or 1, 1
9. 1; 3 or 1

Written Exercises   Page 272   1. 2 or 0; 2 or 0;
4, 2, or 0   **3.** 1; 0; 2   **5.** 2 or 0; 1; 4 or 2   **7.** 2 or
0; 1; 4 or 2   **9.** 3 or 1; 1; 12 or 10   **11.** $3 + i,$
$3 - i, 4$ **13.** $1 + 2i, 1 - 2i, ^-4$ **15.** $^-2 + 3i,$
$^-2 - 3i, ^-2$ **17.** $x^3 - 4x^2 + 6x - 4$
19. $x^3 - 3x^2 + 4x - 12$
21. $x^4 + 2x^3 + 7x^2 + 30x + 50$ **23.** It has no
positive real roots and only one negative real root.
Thus, there must be two complex roots.

Written Exercises   Page 276   1. $^-1.3$ **3.** 0.6
5. $1.6, ^-1.3, ^-2.4$ **7.** 1.4 **9.** $^-0.7$ **11.** $0.1, 2.5$
13. $1, 0.8, ^-1.4$ **15.** $^-1$ **17.** $^-2.4$

Written Exercises   Page 279

3.
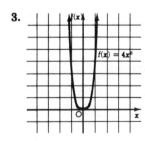

7.
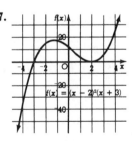

11.
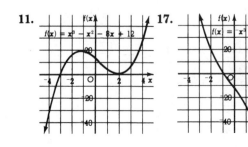

17.

Exploratory Exercises   Page 282   1. $^-1, ^-5,$
$^-3$ **3.** 1, 9, 1   **5.** 4, 4, 2   **7.** 10, 10, $^-6$ **9.** 30,
$^-34, 2$ **11.** 4, 9, 3

Written Exercises   Page 282   1. 4, 4   **3.** 63,
27   **5.** 129, 360   **7.** $2x - 5, 2x - 2$
9. $4x^2 - 4x + 4, 2x^2 + 5$ **11.** $^-x^4 + 2x^2 - 9,$
$x^4 + 16x^2 + 63$ **13.** $^-1, ^-1$ **15.** 50, 2   **17.** $^-7, 9$

19. 9   **21.** 8   **23.** 12   **25.** $^-9$ **27.** $\frac{9}{4}$

29. $6 + 4\sqrt{2}$ **31.** $9x^2$ **33.** $9x^2 - 18x + 9$
35. $\{(3, 6), (4, 4), (6, 6), (7, ^-8)\}$; does not exist
37. $\{(1, 8), (^-1, ^-2), (5, ^-8), (9, ^-3)\}$; does not exist

Exploratory Exercises   Page 285   1. $\{(1, 3),$
$(4, 2), (5, 1)\}$; yes   **3.** $\{(8, 3), (^-2, 4), (^-3, 5)\}$; yes
5. $\{(1, ^-3), (4, 2), (8, 7)\}$; yes

Written Exercises   Page 285   1. $y = \frac{1}{2}x$

3. $f^{-1}(x) = -\frac{1}{6}x - \frac{5}{6}$ **5.** $x = 3$ **7.** $f^{-1}(x) = 0$
9. $y = \pm\sqrt{x}$

11.
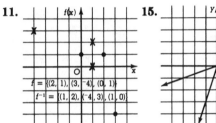

15.
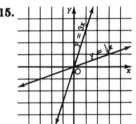

21. yes   **23.** yes   **25.** no   **27.** yes   **29.** yes
31. yes   **33.** no   **35.** 3   **37.** a **39.** $a + 1$

Chapter Review   Page 288   1. $^-13$
3. $m^2 + 7m + 3$ **5.** 2   **7.** $^-94$
9. $(x + 2)(x - 1)(x + 1)$ **11.** $(x + 2)(x - 1)^2$

13. $1, 1, \frac{3}{2}, \frac{3}{2}$ **15.** $5, \frac{1}{3}, \frac{3}{2}$ **17.** 3 or 1; 1; 2 or 0
19. 1; 0; 2   **21.** $2 + i, 2 - i, 3$ **23.** $^-1, 0.7$
25. 1.6   **29.** 324, 1249, $4x^4$
31. $1, 4, |2|x - 3| + 1|$

34.
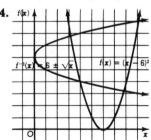

Cumulative Review   Page 290   1. $\frac{9}{2}$ **3.** 12

5. 2   **7.** $^-3, 0$ **9.** $x \geq \frac{5}{2}$ **11.** $b > \frac{8}{3}$ **23.** $(4, 6)$

27. $^-10a^3$ **29.** $x^2 + 2x - 15$ **31.** $^-a^2$

33. $x(3x - 3y + 1)$ **35.** $9(x - 2)(x + 2)$

37. $(y - 4)^2$ **39.** $6\sqrt{2}x$ **41.** $\frac{\sqrt{6}}{3}$ **43.** $\sqrt{5}$

45. $^-4 - i$ **47.** $2\sqrt{5}(i + 1) - 3i - 16$ **49.** $0, 4$

51. $4 \pm \sqrt{21}$ **53.** $\frac{1}{2}, ^-2$ **55.** $\frac{5 \pm \sqrt{37}}{6}$

57. $(2, ^-4); x = 2;$ up   **59.** $(1, ^-1); x = 1;$ down

63. hyperbola   **65.** ellipse   **67.** circle   **69.** 5, 14

71. $^-1, 3, \frac{5}{2}$ **73.** $-\frac{3}{2}, 4, ^-6$ **75.** 7   **77.** 0

79. 34, 35, 36   **81.** 38, 14

CHAPTER 10   RATIONAL POLYNOMIAL EXPRESSIONS

Exploratory Exercises   Page 294   1. $24; \frac{1}{3}$

3. $3; \frac{11}{101}$ **5.** $13x; \frac{1}{3x}$ **7.** $2x^2; \frac{17}{21x^3}$ **9.** $2a; \frac{19a}{21b}$

11. $3x^2y^2; -\frac{y^3}{6x^3}$ **13.** $4x^5y; ^-2xy^2$ **15.** $x^4y^2; 16y^2$

17. $m + 5; \frac{1}{2}$ **19.** $a + b; \frac{1}{a - b}$ **21.** $8 - x; \frac{x^2}{2}$

23. $y + 3; \frac{y - 3}{y + 3}$ **25.** $\frac{2(x + 4)}{x - 11}$ **27.** $x + 4;$

$\frac{x - 5}{x + 3}$ **29.** $a + 1; \frac{a + 1}{2a + 1}$

Written Exercises   Page 295   1. $\frac{6}{7}$ **3.** $\frac{x^2}{4yz}$

5. $3b$ **7.** $-\frac{yz}{12x}$ **9.** $\frac{9abc^2}{2}$ **11.** $-\frac{7}{54c}$ **13.** cd^2x

15. $\frac{5x^3}{3y^2}$ **17.** $\frac{x}{y + 2}$ **19.** $\frac{x - 3}{2}$ **21.** 4   **23.** x

25. $^-y(x + y)$ **27.** $^-1$ **29.** $\frac{5(a - b)}{2}$ **31.** $\frac{12}{x - 1}$

33. $^-1$ **35.** $\frac{(3m - 1)(2 - m)}{30}$ **37.** $\frac{x(x + 4)}{2y(x - 3)}$

39. $\frac{x - 2}{x + 2}$ **41.** $(x + 1)^2(x - 5)$ **43.** $(a - b)^2$

45. $\frac{w - 3}{w - 4}$

Exploratory Exercises   Page 297   1. $\frac{8}{3}$

3. $\frac{9y}{7x}$ **5.** $\frac{1}{16}$ **7.** $\frac{2}{x + y}$ **9.** $\frac{(x - 3)^2}{(x + 4)^2}$ **11.** $x - y$

13. $\frac{3}{8} \cdot \frac{2}{1}$ **15.** $\frac{a^2}{b^2} \cdot \frac{a^2}{b^2}$ **17.** $\frac{3m}{m + 1} \cdot \frac{1}{m - 2}$

Written Exercises   Page 298   1. $\frac{a^2}{14}$ **3.** $\frac{ab}{x + y}$

5. $\frac{a^2 - b^2}{a^2 + ab + b^2}$ **7.** $\frac{x^2 + 2x - 3}{3x + 3}$ **9.** $-\frac{2}{9}$ **11.** $\frac{a}{2}$

13. $-\frac{x}{3}$ **15.** $\frac{c}{2b}$ **17.** $\frac{ac^4d}{b}$ **19.** $b(x + y)$ **21.** $\frac{1}{2}$

23. $3(a + b)$ **25.** $\frac{2(x - 1)}{3(x + 2)}$ **27.** $\frac{2(a + 5)}{(a - 2)(a + 2)}$

29. $2(x + y)$ **31.** $\frac{a(a + 2)}{a + 1}$ **33.** $\frac{2y(y - 2)}{3(y + 2)}$

35. $^-1$ **37.** 1

Exploratory Exercises   Page 302   1. 756

3. 2000   **5.** $14a^2b$ **7.** $x(x - 2)(x + 2)$

9. $(x + 1)^2(x - 3)(x + 3)$ **11.** $xy(x - 8)(y - 8)$

Written Exercises   Page 302   1. $\frac{31}{12a}$

3. $\frac{5 + 7a}{a}$ **5.** $\frac{x}{y - x}$ **7.** $\frac{7y - 4}{2xy}$ **9.** $\frac{3(x - 1)}{2(x - 3)(x + 3)}$

11. $\frac{5a - 13}{(a - 2)(a - 3)}$ **13.** $\frac{3(2x + 11)}{(x - 5)(x + 5)}$

15. $\frac{7x + 38}{2(x - 7)(x + 4)}$ **17.** $\frac{7y + 11}{(y - 5)(y + 1)(y + 3)}$

19. 0   **21.** $\frac{2x^2 + x - 4}{(x - 1)(x - 2)}$ **23.** $\frac{110a - 423}{90a}$

25. $\frac{13}{y - 8}$ **27.** $\frac{y + 4}{y - 8}$ **29.** $\frac{x(x - 9)}{(x + 3)(x - 3)}$

31. $\frac{6}{y - 4}$ **33.** $\frac{^-x^2 - 2x - 2}{(x + 1)^2}$ **35.** $\frac{m(m + 11)}{(m - 3)(m + 3)}$

37. $\frac{3}{10}$ **39.** y **41.** $\frac{2(x + 5)}{x^2(2x + 1)}$ **43.** $\frac{a + 7}{a + 2}$

Exploratory Exercises   Page 305   1. $2x$

3. $10y$ **5.** x^2 **7.** $(x - 3)(x - 2)$ **9.** $6(m - 5)$

11. $7(2 + m)$

Written Exercises   Page 306   1. 3   **3.** $^-3, \frac{1}{6}$

5. 2   **7.** 4   **9.** 5   **11.** 54   **13.** $^-6, 1$ **15.** 0

17. 2, 6   **19.** 3   **21.** 10   **23.** 5   **25.** $\frac{2}{3}$ **27.** $^-2$

29. $^-6, ^-2$ **31.** 11   **33.** $\frac{5}{3}$ **35.** $^-17$ **37.** $\frac{1}{7}$

39. $\frac{3}{2}$ **41.** $^-6, 2$ **43.** $\frac{7}{3}$

Written Exercises   Page 309   1. $2\frac{2}{9}$ hours

3. $25\frac{1}{5}$ hours   **5.** 20 days   **7.** $\frac{7}{13}$ **9.** 19

11. 3 km/h   **13.** 52 km/h   **15.** $3\frac{3}{4}$ **17.** 5 tons

19. 5:27 plus 16 seconds

Skills Review   Page 310   1. $(3, 0); x = 3;$ up

3. $(3, ^-1); x = 3;$ down   **5.** $(^-2, ^-1); x = ^-2;$ up

Exploratory Exercises   Page 313   1. $x = 1,$

$y = 0$ **3.** $x = 3, y = 0$ **5.** $x = 6, y = 0$

7. $x = 1, x = ^-5, y = 0$ **9.** $x = 1, x = 4, y = 0$

Exploratory Exercises   Page 316   1. direct; $\frac{1}{4}$

3. direct; $^-4$ **5.** direct; 5   **7.** direct; $\frac{4}{3}$

9. indirect; 9 11. direct; 4

Written Exercises **Page 316** 1. 36 3. 1.125

5. $\frac{84}{11}$ 7. $\frac{121}{10}$ 9. 24 11. 118.5 km

13. $11\frac{2}{3}$ kg 15. $3\frac{23}{55}$ hours 17. 42 pounds

19. $\frac{343}{81}$

Chapter Review **Page 317** 1. $\frac{5a}{16}$ 3. $\frac{2y^2}{y-3}$

5. $\frac{ay-2a-3y+6}{a-x}$ 7. a^2 9. $(y+3)(y-6)$

11. $\frac{5y(x+y)}{2x}$ 13. $\frac{28a-27b}{12ab}$ 15. $\frac{7(x-4)}{x-5}$

17. $\frac{18}{y-2}$ 19. $\frac{25b+16}{24b}$ 21. $\frac{a(a+2)}{3a^2+1}$ 23. 31

25. 0 27. $8\frac{4}{7}$ hours 33. $-\frac{5}{3}$

CHAPTER 11 EXPONENTS

Exploratory Exercises **Page 322** 1. $\frac{1}{4^3}$ 3. 4

5. $\frac{1}{8^9}$ 7. y^3 9. $\frac{x^5}{7^5}$ 11. m^2 13. r^6 15. y^4

17. x^{5-y} 19. a^5 21. 1 23. $\frac{1}{36}$ 25. $\frac{1}{4}$ 27. $\frac{1}{64}$

29. $\frac{1}{27}$ 31. 4

Written Exercises **Page 322** 1. 9 3. $\frac{4}{9}$

5. 3 7. $\frac{1}{16}$ 9. 36 11. 12 13. 16 15. 29

17. y^5 19. r^3 21. $\frac{b^7}{2^7}$ 23. $\frac{4^2}{x^2}$ 25. $\frac{1}{8x^4}$

27. $^-12s^3$ 29. $\frac{1}{(x+4)^4}$ 31. $\frac{(x+3)^2}{5}$ 33. $\frac{1}{x^3y^2}$

35. $\frac{b^3x^4}{5^3y}$ 37. $\frac{1}{2}$ 39. $2mn$ 41. $\frac{1}{25}$ 43. r^3

45. $\frac{12}{m^2}$ 47. $\frac{4}{9y^4}$ 49. $\frac{1}{d^2}$ 51. $4r^{14}$ 53. $27m^8$

55. $\frac{1}{(p+q)^5}$ 57. $a+\frac{1}{a^2}+a^4$ 59. $2ab$

61. $\frac{a^2+ab+b^2}{a-b}$

Exploratory Exercises **Page 327** 1. 4 3. $^-5$
5. 6.753×10^4 7. 7.5×10^{-5} 9. 58,000
11. 0.0054 13. 3.6×10^7; 36,000,000
15. 6.0×10^{-5}; 0.00006

Written Exercises **Page 327** 1. 6.18×10^2
3. 2.1×10^{-3} 5. 8.104×10^2 7. 9×10^9
9. 1.6×10^{-4} 11. 7.21×10^{-7} 13. 6,000
15. 0.00057 17. 0.000072 19. 5.832×10^9;

5,832,000,000 21. $5 \times 10^\circ$; 5 23. 8.6×10^1; 86
25. 3.27×10^{-4}; 0.000327 27. 3.1×10^7;
31,000,000 29. 2.592×10^{10} km/day
31. 1.9663×10^6 33. 15.4 cm

Exploratory Exercises **Page 331** 1. 8 3. $\frac{1}{2}$

5. $\frac{1}{2}$ 7. 32 9. 4 11. 3 13. 36 15. 6

17. $\sqrt{6}$ 19. $\sqrt[3]{9}$

Written Exercises **Page 331** 1. $21^{\frac{1}{2}}$ 3. $32^{\frac{1}{6}}$
5. $y^{\frac{1}{3}}$ 7. $2mr^2$ 9. $27^{\frac{1}{4}}$ 11. $n^{\frac{2}{3}}$ 13. $\sqrt[3]{8}$
15. $\sqrt[3]{6}$ 17. $ab^2\sqrt{ab}$ 19. $2x^2\sqrt[3]{4x}$ 21. $\sqrt[3]{5p^2q}$
23. $r^2\sqrt[4]{r^2q^3}$ 25. $\sqrt[6]{x^2y^3}$ 27. $25\sqrt[4]{b^2c}$ 29. $\sqrt{3}$
31. $\sqrt{2}$ 33. 11 35. 12 37. $\frac{7}{4}$ 39. 36
41. 0.25 43. 0.3

Exploratory Exercises **Page 334** 1. $\frac{3^{\frac{1}{2}}}{3^{\frac{1}{2}}}$

3. $\frac{4^{\frac{1}{2}}}{4^{\frac{1}{2}}}$ 5. $\frac{x^{\frac{1}{3}}}{x^{\frac{2}{3}}}$ 7. $\frac{m^{\frac{1}{4}}}{m^{\frac{1}{4}}}$ 9. $\frac{a^{\frac{1}{5}}}{a^{\frac{4}{5}}}$ 11. $\frac{x^{\frac{1}{2}}-1}{x^{\frac{1}{2}}-1}$

13. $\frac{r^{\frac{1}{2}}+s^{\frac{1}{2}}}{r^{\frac{1}{2}}+s^{\frac{1}{2}}}$ 15. $\frac{b^{\frac{3}{2}}-b^{\frac{1}{2}}}{b^{\frac{3}{2}}-b^{\frac{1}{2}}}$

Written Exercises **Page 334** 1. $2 \cdot 3^{\frac{1}{2}}$ 3. 2

5. $\frac{x^{\frac{2}{3}}}{x}$ 7. $\frac{2m^{\frac{1}{4}}}{m}$ 9. $\frac{a^{\frac{4}{5}}}{a}$ 11. $\frac{x^{\frac{1}{2}}-1}{x-1}$

13. $\frac{r^{\frac{3}{2}}+rs^{\frac{1}{2}}}{r-s}$ 15. $\frac{b^{\frac{3}{2}}-b^{\frac{1}{2}}}{b^3-b}$ 17. $\frac{3r^{\frac{1}{5}}}{r}$ 19. $\frac{m^{\frac{1}{6}}}{m}$

21. $4 \cdot 6^{\frac{1}{3}}$ 23. $\frac{pqa^{\frac{2}{3}}}{a}$ 25. $\frac{a^2m+3}{a}$ 27. $\frac{3mb^{\frac{3}{2}}a^{\frac{2}{3}}}{a}$

29. $\frac{y^{\frac{3}{4}}}{y}$ 31. $\frac{x+2x^{\frac{1}{2}}y^{\frac{1}{2}}+y}{x-y}$ 33. $\frac{x+2x^{\frac{1}{2}}+1}{x-1}$

35. $\frac{x^{\frac{2}{3}}}{x-1}$ 37. $\frac{b^2}{a}$ 39. $\frac{z^2}{25}$ 41. $2\sqrt{6}-5$

43. $a-a^{\frac{1}{3}}b^{\frac{2}{3}}$ 45. 34

Exploratory Exercises **Page 338** 1. 8 3. 25

5. $\frac{1}{5}$ 7. 4 9. $\frac{1}{13}$ 11. 64

13. $1(x^{\frac{2}{3}})^2 - 7(x^{\frac{2}{3}}) + 12 = 0$

15. $1(x^{\frac{1}{2}})^2 - 10(x^{\frac{1}{2}}) + 25 = 0$

17. $1(x^{\frac{1}{4}})^2 - 8(x^{\frac{1}{4}}) + 15 = 0$

19. $1(r^{\frac{1}{3}})^2 - 5(r^{\frac{1}{3}}) + 6 = 0$

21. $1(a^{-\frac{1}{3}})^2 - 11(a^{-\frac{1}{3}}) + 28 = 0$

23. $2(m^{\frac{1}{2}})^2 + 5(m^{\frac{1}{2}}) + 3 = 0$

Written Exercises **Page 338** 1. 4096, 16

3. 8, 1000 5. 25, 36 7. 8 9. $\frac{1}{343}, \frac{1}{27}$ 11. $\frac{1}{9}, \frac{1}{4}$

13. $8, 3\sqrt{3}$ 15. 25 17. 81, 625 19. 8, 27

21. $\dfrac{1}{64}, \dfrac{1}{363}$ **23.** no solutions **25.** $8, \dfrac{64}{27}$

27. $\dfrac{9}{4}, \dfrac{25}{9}$ **29.** $\dfrac{625}{16}$

Exploratory Exercises Page 341 1. 51
3. 25 **5.** 0, 7 **7.** $^-3$ **9.** $^-1$

Written Exercises Page 341 1. $^-2, ^-3$ **3.** 7
5. 7 **7.** 9 **9.** 6 **11.** 9 **13.** 0, $^-1$ **15.** 10
17. 3 **19.** no solution **21.** 5 **23.** 1 **25.** 1, 6

27. $\dfrac{25}{3}, ^-3$ **29.** 2 **31.** 6, 2 **33.** 2 **35.** $^-1, 3$

37. 2

Skills Review Page 341 1. ellipse
3. hyperbola **5.** parabola

Exploratory Exercises Page 345 1. 1.6
3. 0.8 **5.** 2.6 **7.** 83.2 **9.** $2^{4\sqrt{5}}$ **11.** 2^3 **13.** 3
15. $^-5$ **17.** $^-2$

Written Exercises Page 345 1. 64 **3.** $5^{4\sqrt{3}}$
5. $2^{3\sqrt{7}}$ **7.** $2^{3\sqrt{3}+4\sqrt{5}}$ **9.** $y^{4\sqrt{5}}$ **11.** y^9 **13.** $m^2 p^2$
15. $x^{2\sqrt{3}} + 2x^{\sqrt{3}}y^{\sqrt{2}} + y^{2\sqrt{2}}$ **17.** 3 **19.** $^-2$
21. 2 **23.** $^-22$ **25.** $^-7$ **27.** $^-9$ **33.** The graphs
are reflections over the y-axis.

Chapter Review Page 348 1. $\dfrac{1}{9}$ **3.** $\dfrac{9}{16}$

5. $\dfrac{125}{343}$ **7.** $\dfrac{1}{256}$ **9.** $\dfrac{1}{y^3}$ **11.** $\dfrac{1}{s^5}$ **13.** m^6 **15.** $\dfrac{1}{r^5}$
17. 1215 **19.** 0.0001592 **21.** 8.3215×10^7
23. 36 **25.** 0.04 **27.** $xy^{\frac{3}{4}}$ **29.** $2w^2 r$ **31.** $\sqrt{3}$

33. $\dfrac{z^{\frac{2}{5}}}{z}$ **35.** $\dfrac{z^{\frac{2}{3}}}{z-1}$ **37.** $-\dfrac{464}{3}$ **39.** $\dfrac{1}{32}$

41. $\dfrac{1}{343}, \dfrac{1}{64}$ **43.** 7 **45.** $^-1$ **47.** $-\dfrac{7}{4}$

49. 81

CHAPTER 12 EXPONENTIAL AND LOGARITHMIC FUNCTIONS
Exploratory Exercises Page 352

1. $\log_3 27 = 3$ **3.** $\log_2\left(\dfrac{1}{8}\right) = ^-3$

5. $\log_{10} 1000 = 3$ **7.** $4^3 = 64$ **9.** $9^{\frac{3}{2}} = 27$
11. $10^{-1} = 0.1$ **13.** 2 **15.** 4 **17.** $^-3$ **19.** $^-3$

Written Exercises Page 353 1. $\log_3 81 = 4$

3. $\log_5 125 = 3$ **5.** $\log_4\left(\dfrac{1}{16}\right) = ^-2$

7. $\log_2\left(\dfrac{1}{16}\right) = ^-4$ **9.** $\log_3 \sqrt{3} = \dfrac{1}{2}$

11. $\log_{36} 216 = \dfrac{3}{2}$ **13.** $2^5 = 32$ **15.** $11^2 = 121$

17. $5^0 = 1$ **19.** $\left(\dfrac{1}{2}\right)^{-4} = 16$ **21.** $10^{-1} = \dfrac{1}{10}$

23. $\left(\dfrac{1}{3}\right)^{-4} = 81$ **25.** 3 **27.** 2 **29.** $^-3$ **31.** $\dfrac{3}{2}$

33. $^-3$ **35.** 7 **37.** 36 **39.** $^-4$ **41.** 3 **43.** $\dfrac{1}{25}$

45. $\dfrac{1}{2}$ **47.** 3 **49.** 64 **51.** $\dfrac{1}{16}$ **53.** 6 **55.** 7

Exploratory Exercises Page 355 1. 2 **3.** 2
5. 4 **7.** 5 **9.** 4 **11.** 1

Written Exercises Page 356 1. 3 **3.** 7
5. 5 **7.** 7 **9.** 1 **11.** 2.5 **13.** ± 8 **15.** 1 or $^-10$
21. $\log_4 4 + \log_4 16 \overset{?}{=} \log_4 64$
$\quad\quad 1 + 2 \quad\quad = 3$
$\quad\quad\quad 3 = 3$

23. $\log_2 32 - \log_2 4 \overset{?}{=} \log_2 8$
$\quad\quad 5 - 2 \quad\quad = 3$
$\quad\quad\quad 3 = 3$

25. $\log_3 27 \overset{?}{=} 3\log_3 3$ **27.** $\dfrac{1}{2}\log_3 81 \overset{?}{=} \log_3 9$
$\quad\quad 3 \overset{?}{=} 3(1)$ $\quad\quad\quad\quad \dfrac{1}{2}(4) \overset{?}{=} 2$
$\quad\quad 3 = 3$ $\quad\quad\quad\quad\quad\quad 2 = 2$

29. $\log_2 8 \cdot \log_8 2 \overset{?}{=} 1$ **33.** $\log_3 81 \overset{?}{=} \dfrac{4}{3}\log_2 8$
$\quad\quad 3 \cdot \dfrac{1}{3} \quad\quad \overset{?}{=} 1$ $\quad\quad\quad\quad 4 \overset{?}{=} \dfrac{4}{3}(3)$
$\quad\quad 1 \quad\quad\quad = 1$ $\quad\quad\quad\quad\quad 4 = 4$

35. 6, $^-5$ **37.** 9

Skills Review Page 356 1. $^-4, 2, ^-1$

3. $\dfrac{13}{4}, \dfrac{11}{4}, 3$ **5.** $^-4, ^-2, ^-2$ **7.** $f^{-1}(x) = \dfrac{(x+5)}{^-7}$

9. $f^{-1}(x) = \pm\sqrt{x+16}$ **11.** $y = \dfrac{x}{3}$

Exploratory Exercises Page 360 1. 21
3. 3 **5.** 72 **7.** $\log_3 x + \log_3 y$

9. $4\log_2 m + \log_2 y$ **11.** $\dfrac{1}{2}\log_b x - \log_b p$

13. $\log_3 5 + \dfrac{1}{3}\log_3 a$ **15.** $\log_2 a + \dfrac{1}{2}\log_2 x$

17. 2

Written Exercises Page 360 1. 1.3222
3. 1.4313 **5.** 1.4771 **7.** 2.3222 **9.** 2.8451
11. 0.5229 **13.** 2 **15.** 24 **17.** 343 **19.** 6
21. 14 **23.** 3 **25.** 2 **27.** 6 **29.** 3 **31.** 5

33. $\dfrac{1}{3}$

Exploratory Exercises Page 363 1. 2
3. 1.6839 **5.** $0.6839 - 3$ **7.** 483,000
9. 1; 1.6767 **11.** 0; 0.6637 **13.** $^-1; 0.3201 - 1$
15. 1; 1.7404 **17.** 1; 35.70 **19.** $^-2; 0.0688$
21. 4; 39,400 **23.** $^-1; 0.618$

Written Exercises Page 364 1. 1.7649
3. 0.9814 **5.** 3.8704 **7.** 0.3243 − 3
9. 0.5855 − 2 **11.** 4.7973 **13.** 12.3 **15.** 9080
17. 0.09 **19.** 0.159 **21.** 521,000 **23.** 4630

Exploratory Exercises Page 366 1. 7.41,
7.42 **3.** 0.000746, 0.000747 **5.** 4.17, 4.18
7. 9,520, 9,530

Written Exercises Page 367 1. 0.7221
3. 1.4398 **5.** 0.2905 − 1 **7.** 0.4980 − 3
9. 3.6198 **11.** 2.5177 **13.** 0.6748 − 2
15. 0.6997 **17.** 1.9035 **19.** 6.3320
21. 0.2193 − 1 **23.** 3.553 **25.** 601.4
27. 0.004143 **29.** 0.002754 **31.** 16,493
33. 0.004762 **35.** 0.07563 **37.** 394,273
39. 2,612 **41.** 0.0003705

Exploratory Exercises Page 370 1. 3 log
63.9 **3.** 4 log 0.7425 **5.** 3 log 4173

7. $\frac{1}{4}$ log 594 **9.** $\frac{1}{4}$ log 9.813 **11.** $\frac{2}{3}$ log 46

13. 0 − 3 **15.** 2 − 5 **17.** 0 − 4 **19.** 2 − 3

Written Exercises Page 370 1. 260,900
3. 0.3039 **5.** 7.267×10^{10} **7.** 4.937 **9.** 1.770
11. 12.84 **13.** 0.1197 **15.** 0.05185 **17.** 0.1495
19. ⁻0.6649 **21.** 0.03677 **23.** 7.415
25. 0.8641 **27.** $180.30 **29.** $3367 **31.** The
first way yields more; first way ($1147.63); second
way ($930.89)

Exploratory Exercises Page 374 1. $\frac{\log 55}{\log 3}$

3. $\frac{\log 74}{2 \log 7}$ **5.** $\frac{\log 144}{\log 6}$ **7.** $\frac{\log 12}{\log 3}$ **9.** $\frac{-1}{\log 2}$

11. $\frac{\frac{1}{2} \log 13}{\log 3}$ or $\frac{\log 13}{2 \log 3}$

Written Exercises Page 374 1. 3.6479
3. 1.1059 **5.** 2.7736 **7.** 2.2619 **9.** ⁻3.3222
11. 1.1674 **13.** 1.771 **15.** 2.230 **17.** 1.338
19. 2.387 **21.** 3.9839 **23.** 3.8394 **25.** 4.8363
27. 2.8446 **29.** 38.619 **31.** 3.1501
33. ⁻2.1507 **35.** 2.4527 **37.** 3.2618
39. 2.9169 **41.** 794.8771

Exploratory Exercises Page 377 1. 1.3863
3. 18.2797 years

Written Exercises Page 377 1. ⁻0.0770
3. 2.9403 hours **5.** 3.0762 years **7.** ⁻0.000385
9. $650.13 **11.** 32.8947 years; 65.7895 years
13. 58.98 or 6 weeks

Chapter Review Page 379 1. $\log_7 343 = 3$

3. $\log_4 1 = 0$ **5.** $4^3 = 64$ **7.** $6^{-2} = \frac{1}{36}$ **9.** 3

11. $\frac{1}{4}$ **13.** 7 **15.** 3 **17.** 3 **19.** 7 **21.** 8

23. ⁻4, 3 **25.** 0.243 **27.** 0.6021 − 3 **29.** 48
31. 3 **33.** 14 **35.** 4 **37.** 0.4232
39. 0.8904 − 2 **41.** 5.45 **43.** 0.0276
45. 0.5334 **47.** 0.6139 − 2 **49.** 2.165
51. 11.82 **53.** 2.4496 **55.** 1.5617 **57.** 5.7273
59. 5.7286 **61.** 1.7426 **63.** 4.2448 **65.** 69.23
67. 6.7471 years

Cumulative Review Page 382

3. $y = -\frac{2}{3}x + 4$ **5.** (3, 2) **7.** 14
9. $4y^3 - 15y^2 + 17y - 6$
11. $(2a - 1)(2a + 1)(4a^2 + 1)$ **13.** $6|x|$
15. $1 - i$ **17.** $\frac{1 \pm \sqrt{7}}{3}$ **19.** ⁻56; two imaginary
solutions **21.** (0, 0); $x = 0$; down **23.** each
number is $\frac{81}{2}$ **25.** hyperbola **27.** circle
29. $(x + 1)(x + 4)(x - 3)^2$ **31.** 0 positive real
zeros; 0 negative real zeros, 4 imaginary zeros
33. $x^4 + x^2 - 10$; $x^4 + 6x^3 - 7x^2 - 48x + 63$
35. 2 **37.** $\frac{x^{\frac{1}{3}}}{x}$ **39.** $\frac{x^{\frac{3}{2}} + x^{\frac{1}{2}}y + xy^{\frac{1}{2}} + y^{\frac{3}{2}}}{x - y}$
41. 1.1844×10^{19} **43.** $x^{\frac{2}{3}}yz^{\frac{4}{3}}$ **45.** 8 **47.** 4.4031
49. 26,497.2

CHAPTER 13 SEQUENCES AND SERIES
Exploratory Exercises Page 387 1. 4, 7, 10,
13, 16 **3.** 16, 14, 12, 10, 8 **5.** $\frac{3}{4}, \frac{1}{2}, \frac{1}{4}, 0, -\frac{1}{4}$
7. 2.3, 3.9, 5.5, 7.1, 8.7 **9.** $-\frac{1}{3}, ⁻1, -\frac{5}{3}, -\frac{7}{3}, ⁻3$
11. ⁻4.2, ⁻5.5, ⁻6.8, ⁻8.1, ⁻9.4 **13.** 17, 21, 25, 29
15. ⁻13, ⁻18, ⁻23, ⁻28 **17.** $\frac{7}{2}, \frac{9}{2}, \frac{11}{2}, \frac{13}{2}$ **19.** $-\frac{11}{4},$
$-\frac{13}{4}, -\frac{15}{4}, -\frac{17}{4}$ **21.** 6.84, 9.14, 11.44, 13.74

Written Exercises Page 388 1. 46 **3.** ⁻241
5. $\frac{11}{2}$ **7.** 416 **9.** 379 **11.** $\sqrt{3} - 10\sqrt{2}$ **13.** 27
15. 97 **17.** 9 **19.** 19 **21.** 8 **23.** 70, 85, 100
25. $-\frac{38}{5}, -\frac{26}{5}, -\frac{14}{5}, -\frac{2}{5}$ **27.** ⁻13, 1, 8, 22
29. 168 **31.** 54 **33.** 304

Exploratory Exercises   Page 392   1. 116
3. 10,100   **5.** 375   **7.** 240   **9.** 5050

Written Exercises   Page 392   1. 632.5
3. 702   **5.** 135   **7.** 1210   **9.** 287   **11.** ⁻420

13. 735   **15.** ⁻220   **17.** 387   **19.** $\frac{45}{2}$ **21.** 6, 36,

66   **23.** 1, 5, 9   **25.** 2500   **27.** 231   **29.** 1065

Exploratory Exercises   Page 396   1. yes, 5

3. yes, $\frac{3}{2}$ **5.** no   **7.** 135, 405   **9.** $\frac{1}{3}$, 1

Written Exercises   Page 396   1. 54, 162

3. 67.5, 101.25   **5.** 1, 3   **7.** $\frac{3}{2}$, 3, 6, 12   **9.** 12, 6,

3, $\frac{3}{2}$ **11.** $a_4 = 56$ **13.** $a_5 = 32$ **15.** $a_6 = {}^-4$

17. 6, 12, 24 or ⁻6, 12, ⁻24   **19.** 4, 2, 1, $\frac{1}{2}$

21. 10, 20, 40 or ⁻10, 20, ⁻40   **23.** ⁻3, 6, 24, ⁻48
25. ≈65.6%   **27.** $10,486

Skills Review   Page 397   1. $-\frac{1}{4x^2y}$ **3.** $\frac{3x^2}{x+3}$

5. $\frac{3x^2 + 20b}{5x}$ **7.** $\frac{y+9}{x-y}$ **9.** $b - a$

Exploratory Exercises   Page 400   1. 9; ⁻2;

144; 5   **3.** 20; $-\frac{1}{4}$, $\frac{5}{64}$; 5   **5.** 2; 4; 512; 5   **7.** ±4;
±3; ⁻972; 6

Written Exercises   Page 400   1. ⁻364   **3.** $15\frac{3}{4}$

5. 1111   **7.** $93\frac{18}{25}$ **9.** 105   **11.** 732   **13.** 165

15. 1441   **17.** $\frac{63}{8}$ **19.** $\frac{781}{5}$ **21.** $\frac{189}{32}$ **23.** $\frac{4095}{256}$

25. $\frac{32}{63}$ **27.** 4   **29.** 2   **31.** $\frac{196820}{27}$ **33.** 127

Exploratory Exercises   Page 403   1. $\frac{1}{2}$; $\frac{2}{3}$;

$\frac{3}{2}$ **3.** 1; $-\frac{1}{3}$; $\frac{3}{4}$ **5.** 1; $\frac{3}{2}$; no sum

7. $\frac{7}{10} + \frac{7}{100} + \frac{7}{1000} + \cdots = \frac{7}{9}$

9. $\frac{73}{100} + \frac{73}{10,000} + \frac{73}{1,000,000} + \cdots = \frac{73}{99}$

11. $\frac{152}{1000} + \frac{152}{100,000} + \frac{152}{100,000,000} + \cdots = \frac{152}{999}$

13. $\frac{93}{100} + \frac{93}{10,000} + \frac{93}{1,000,000} + \cdots = \frac{31}{33}$

Written Exercises   Page 404   1. 72   **3.** 4

5. 27   **7.** $\frac{9}{5}$ **9.** 9   **11.** 8   **13.** no sum   **15.** $\frac{100}{11}$

17. $\frac{1}{3}$ **19.** $\frac{5}{33}$ **21.** $\frac{25}{333}$ **23.** $\frac{17}{45}$ **25.** $6 + 2 + \frac{2}{3}$

27. $36 + \left(-\frac{72}{7}\right) + \frac{144}{49}$ **29.** 500 cm   **31.** 68 feet

Exploratory Exercises   Page 406   1. j; 4;
$3 + 4 + 5 + 6$ **3.** r; 3; $0 + 1 + 2$ **5.** i; 5;
$0 + 2 + 4 + 6 + 8$ **7.** p; 4; $6 + 7 + 8 + 9$

Written Exercises   Page 407
1. $13 + 20 + 27 + 34 + 41 = 135$
3. $5 + 7 + 9 + 11 + 13 = 45$
5. $5 + 7 + 9 + 11 + 13 = 45$
7. $2 + 4 + 6 + 8 + 10 + 12 + 14 = 56$
9. $9 + 8 + 7 + 6 + 5 + 4 + 3 + 2 + 1 = 45$
11. $10 + 11 + 12 + 13 + 14 = 60$
13. $256 + 1024 + 4096 + 16,384 + 65,536 = 87,296$

15. ${}^-12 + 6 + ({}^-3) + \frac{3}{2} = {}^-7\frac{1}{2}$ **17.** 900

19. 3649   **21.** 42   **23.** $\frac{42753}{100000}$ **25.** $\sum_{n=1}^{5} (3n + 4)$

27. $\sum_{n=1}^{5} ({}^-4n + 19)$ **29.** $\sum_{n=1}^{13} (2n - 1)$

31. $\sum_{n=1}^{6} 2^{4-n}$ **33.** $\sum_{n=1}^{6} 243\left(-\frac{2}{3}\right)^{n-1}$ **35.** $\sum_{n=1}^{5} n^2$

Exploratory Exercises   Page 409   1. 99, 120
3. 80, 99   **5.** 8, 7, 6, 5   **7.** ⁻2, ⁻6, ⁻18, ⁻54
9. ⁻4, ⁻4, 4, 4   **11.** 3, 1, 4, 5   **13.** $a_n = 2n$

15. $a_n = \frac{n+1}{n}$ **17.** $a_{n+1} = \frac{1}{3}a_n$, $a_1 = 1$
19. $a_{n+1} = ({}^-1)a_n$, $a_1 = 1$

Written Exercises   Page 410   1. 29, 33, 37

3. $\frac{17}{10}, \frac{19}{11}, \frac{21}{12}$ **5.** $\frac{1}{4}, \frac{2}{9}, \frac{1}{5}$ **7.** ⁻16, 18, ⁻20   **9.** 81,
100, 121   **11.** 2, 6, 18, 54, 162, 486   **13.** 3, 5, 8,
13, 21, 34   **15.** 2, 3, 7, 13, 27, 53
17. $a_{n+1} = a_n + 4$, $a_1 = 3$; $a_n = 4n - 1$
19. $a_{n+1} = 5a_n$, $a_1 = 3$; $a_n = 3(5)^{n-1}$
21. $a_{n+1} = a_n + 5$, $a_1 = 5$; $a_n = 5n$

23. $\sum_{n=1}^{5} (7n - 4)$ **25.** $\sum_{n=1}^{5} \frac{3n}{n+2}$ **27.** $\sum_{n=1}^{6} \frac{3}{4}n$

29. $\sum_{n=1}^{5} 2n(2n + 3)$

Written Exercises   Page 414   1. 1404, 4212
3. 2.875   **5.** 31, 43   **7.** 91, 140   **9.** 18, 29, 47
11. 1, 1, 2, 3, 5, 8, 13, 21, 34, 55, 89, 144, 233, 377,
610, 987, 1597, 2584, 4181, 6765   **13.** 0.6928
15. $L_n = F_{n+1} + F_{n-1}$ for $n \geq 2$

Exploratory Exercises   Page 417   1. 5040
3. 3,628,800   5. 90   7. 120   9. 5; $4rs^3$ 11. 8;
$-35k^4m^3$ 13. 6; $-80x^2$

Written Exercises   Page 417
1. $x^4 + 4x^3m + 6x^2m^2 + 4xm^3 + m^4$
3. $y^7 + 7y^6p + 21y^5p^2 + 35y^4p^3 + 35y^3p^4 +$
$21y^2p^5 + 7yp^6 + p^7$
5. $b^5 - 5b^4z + 10b^3z^2 - 10b^2z^3 + 5bz^4 - z^5$
7. $32m^5 + 80m^4y + 80m^3y^2 + 40m^2y^3 + 10my^4 +$
y^5 9. $64b^6 + 192b^5x + 240b^4x^2 + 160b^3x^3 +$
$60b^2x^4 + 12bx^5 + x^6$ 11. $243x^5 - 810x^4y +$
$1080x^3y^2 - 720x^2y^3 + 240xy^4 - 32y^5$
13. $32y^5 + 80y^4 + 80y^3 + 40y^2 + 10y + 1$

15. $\frac{1}{729}y^6 + \frac{2}{27}y^5 + \frac{5}{3}y^4 + 20y^3 + 135y^2 + 486y +$
729   17. $145{,}152x^6y^3$ 19. $3360x^6$
21. $2{,}088{,}281{,}250a^4b^7$ 23. $17{,}715.61

Chapter Review   Page 420   1. 6, 14, 22, 30, 38
3. 234   5. 22   7. 2322   9. 1612   11. 60, 120

13. 12, 36, 108   15. 1031   17. 625   19. $\frac{4}{9}$
21. $20 + 23 + 26 + 29$ 23. 1, 3, 5, 11, 21
25. $a_n = a_{n-1} + (a_{n-1} - a_{n+2} + 1)$; 33, 42, 52, 63
27. $243a^5 + 405a^4b + 270a^3b^2 + 90a^2b^3 + 15ab^4$
$+ b^5$

CHAPTER 14   PROBABILITY

Exploratory Exercises   Page 425
1. independent   3. not independent
5. independent

Written Exercises   Page 425   1. 3125   3. 90
5. 60   7. 16   9. 720   11. 840   13. 5040
15. 480

Exploratory Exercises   Page 428   1. false
3. false   5. true   7. true   9. true

Written Exercises   Page 428   1. 720   3. 3
5. 60   7. 34,650   9. 2520   11. 90,720   13. 6
15. 72   17. 42   19. 8   21. 27,720   23. 151,200
25. 56   27. 126

Exploratory Exercises   Page 432
1. reflective, circular   3. not reflective, circular
5. not reflective, linear   7. not reflective,
circular   9. not reflective, linear   11. not
reflective, circular

Written Exercises   Page 432   1. 39,600
3. 30   5. 840   7. 6720   9. 311,040   11. 60
13. 9   15. 60   17. 2520   19. 24   21. 12
23. 5040

Exploratory Exercises   Page 435
1. combination   3. combination
5. permutation   7. combination

Written Exercises   Page 435   1. 56   3. 21
5. 11   7. 30   9. 792   11. 126   13. 351
15. 5148   17. 6   19. 0   21. 4320   23. 56
25. 1680

Exploratory Exercises   Page 438   1. 1 to 1

3. 1 to 6   5. 7 to 8   7. 4 to 5   9. $\frac{3}{7}$ 11. $\frac{6}{11}$

13. $\frac{7}{10}$ 15. $\frac{5}{16}$ 17. $\frac{1}{7}$

Written Exercises   Page 438   1. $\frac{1}{16}$ 3. $\frac{1}{56}$

5. $\frac{1}{4}$ 7. $\frac{1}{19}$ 9. $\frac{9}{38}$ 11. $\frac{5}{39}$ 13. $\frac{4}{7}$ 15. $\frac{2}{7}$

17. $\frac{9}{170}$ 19. $\frac{18}{85}$ 21. 33 to 108,257   23. 429 to
7901

Exploratory Exercises   Page 440
1. dependent   3. independent

Written Exercises   Page 441   1. $\frac{1}{28}$ 3. $\frac{25}{81}$

5. $\frac{1}{26}$ 7. $\frac{3}{13}$ 9. $\frac{1}{32}$ 11. $\frac{1}{94{,}109{,}400}$ 13. $\frac{9}{49}$

15. $\frac{1}{8}$ 17. $\frac{5}{48}$ 19. $\frac{1}{36}$ 21. $\frac{1}{36}$ 23. $\frac{1}{6}$

Exploratory Exercises   Page 444
1. exclusive   3. exclusive   5. exclusive
7. inclusive

Written Exercises   Page 444   1. $\frac{4}{15}$ 3. $\frac{9}{91}$

5. $\frac{34}{55}$ 7. $\frac{2}{3}$ 9. $\frac{2}{11}$ 11. $\frac{14}{33}$ 13. $\frac{12}{221}$ 15. $\frac{55}{221}$

17. $\frac{7}{16}$ 19. $\frac{35}{64}$ 21. $\frac{29}{3003}$ 23. $\frac{160}{429}$ 25. $\frac{1}{525}$

27. $\frac{3}{5}$

Exploratory Exercises   Page 447

1. binomial; $\frac{3}{8}$ 3. not binomial   5. binomial; $\frac{4}{81}$

7. not binomial   9. not binomial

Written Exercises   Page 448   1. $\frac{1}{4}$ 3. $\frac{3}{8}$

5. $\frac{3125}{7776}$ 7. $\frac{1875}{1944}$ 9. $\frac{1}{81}$ 11. $\frac{48}{81}$ 13. $\frac{15}{128}$

15. $\frac{1}{1024}$ **17.** $\frac{256}{625}$ **19.** $\frac{21}{3125}$ **21.** $\frac{1}{8}$ **23.** $\frac{1}{2}$

25. $\frac{1024}{9,765,625}$ **27.** $\frac{1,959,552}{9,765,625}$ **29.** $\left(\frac{1}{10}\right)^{12}$

31. $\left(\frac{9}{10}\right)^{12}$

Chapter Review   Page 450   1. 125
3. 1,625,702,400 **5.** 5.6 **7.** 5040 **9.** 1485
11. $\frac{1}{13}$ **13.** $\frac{3}{91}$ **15.** $\frac{4}{13}$ **17.** $\frac{1}{4}$

CHAPTER 15   STATISTICS

Exploratory Exercises   Page 454
1. \$38,448,000,000,000 **3.** \$2,350,000,000,000
5. \$43,615,000,000,000 **7.** 11,012; 18,672;
$^-$1112; $^-$5628; 7725; $^-$552

Written Exercises   Page 455   3. 12 **5.** 28.0%
7. 27.3% **9.** General Motors Corporation
11. 1970 **13.** 6,377,600 **15.** 27 **17.** 46
21. 16

Exploratory Exercises   Page 459   1. 18.2%
3. 7.4% **5.** 1970 **7.** Health & Hospitals

Exploratory Exercises   Page 463   1. 3 **3.** 1
5. 43 **7.** 2.1 **9.** 12 **11.** none **13.** 1
15. none **17.** 2.1 **19.** 12, 13 **21.** 3 **23.** 1.8
25. 30.6 **27.** about 3.4 **29.** about 12.3

Written Exercises   Page 463   1. 4, 6, about
3.7 **3.** 18,590.5, none, about 18,939 **5.** answers
may vary. A, 1; B, 13; C, 50; D, 60; E, 74; F, 53;
G, 39; H, 11; I, 1

Exploratory Exercises   Page 467   1. 10
3. 22 **5.** 48 **7.** 150 **9.** 34

Written Exercises   Page 468   1. 3.6 **3.** 6.3
5. 13.6 **7.** 50 **9.** 7.0 **11.** 90 **13.** 200 **15.** 27
17. 22 **19.** 22.1 **21.** 6.7 **23.** 8 **25.** about 4.9
27. about 1.6 **29.** A

Exploratory Exercises   Page 471   1. 340
3. 495 **5.** 170 **7.** 1360 **9.** 1980 **11.** 680
13. 10,880 **15.** 15,840 **17.** 5440

Written Exercises   Page 471   1. 6800
3. 5000 **5.** 250 **7.** 68% **9.** 47.5% **11.** 50%
13. 0.5% **15.** 50% **17.** 2.5%

Exploratory Exercises   Page 473   1. 1.0
3. 3.0 **5.** 5.0 **7.** 6.5 **9.** 160 **11.** 130
13. 110 **15.** 80

Written Exercises   Page 474   1. 400

3. $y = 400x + 2,000,000$ **5.** \$8,000,000 **7.** $-\frac{1}{10}$

9. $y = -\frac{1}{10}x + 28$ **11.** 3 **15.** \$10,666 **19.** 75

Chapter Review   Page 476   1. \$13,719
3. +\$851 **5.** +\$1239 **7.** +\$1631 **11.** 25
plants per plot **13.** 17 plants per plot **15.** 1600
17. $\frac{19}{20}$ **19.** $y = \frac{19}{20}x - 95$

CHAPTER 16   TRIGONOMETRIC FUNCTIONS AND IDENTITIES

Exploratory Exercises   Page 481   1. III **3.** I
5. I **7.** IV **9.** II **11.** I **13.** IV **15.** III
17. III **19.** III **21.** IV **23.** II

Written Exercises   Page 481   1. $\frac{\pi}{2}$ **3.** $-\frac{\pi}{4}$
5. $\frac{5\pi}{2}$ **7.** $\frac{5\pi}{6}$ **9.** $\frac{\pi}{4}$ **11.** $\frac{11\pi}{6}$ **13.** $\frac{3\pi}{2}$ **15.** π
17. $\frac{9\pi}{4}$ **19.** $-\frac{7\pi}{4}$ **21.** 180° **23.** 45° **25.** 540°
27. $^-$480° **29.** 30° **31.** $^-$45° **33.** 330°
35. $\frac{900°}{\pi}$ **37.** 990° **39.** $\frac{1170°}{\pi}$

Exploratory Exercises   Page 485   1. $-$ **3.** $-$
5. $-$ **7.** $+$ **9.** $+$ **11.** $+$

Written Exercises   Page 485   1. 60° **3.** 300°
5. π **7.** $\frac{\pi}{2}$ **9.** $\frac{7\pi}{4}$ **11.** 120° **13.** $\frac{\pi}{3}$ **15.** $\frac{3\pi}{4}$
17. 120° **19.** $\frac{10\pi}{9}$ **21.** $\frac{\pi}{4}$ **23.** $\frac{4\pi}{3}$ **25.** 240°
27. 320° **29.** $-\frac{\sqrt{3}}{2}$ **31.** $\frac{1}{2}$ **33.** $-\frac{\sqrt{2}}{2}$ **35.** $^-$1
37. $\frac{\sqrt{3}}{2}$ **39.** $\frac{\sqrt{2}}{2}$ **41.** $-\frac{\sqrt{3}}{2}$ **43.** $\frac{\sqrt{3}}{2}$ **45.** $\frac{1}{2}$
47. $-\frac{\sqrt{3}}{2}$ **49.** $\frac{1}{2}$ **51.** 1 **53.** 1 **55.** $\frac{-1 - \sqrt{3}}{2}$

Exploratory Exercises   Page 489   1. 1, 2π
3. $\frac{2}{3}, 2\pi$ **5.** 6, 3π **7.** 4, $\frac{8\pi}{3}$ **9.** 5, 2π
11. 1, $\frac{2\pi}{3}$ **13.** 4, 4π **15.** 3, 3π **17.** $\frac{1}{2}, \frac{8\pi}{3}$
19. 6, π

Written Exercises   Page 489

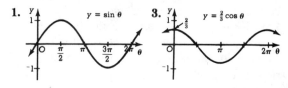

1. $y = \sin\theta$ **3.** $y = \frac{2}{3}\cos\theta$

7.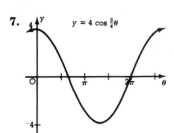

$y = 4 \cos \frac{3}{4}\theta$

11.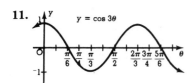

$y = \cos 3\theta$

15.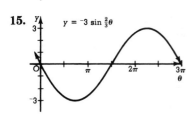

$y = {}^-3 \sin \frac{2}{3}\theta$

17.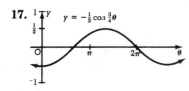

$y = -\frac{1}{2}\cos \frac{3}{4}\theta$

Exploratory Exercises   Page 491   1. none
3. 90°, 270°   **5.** 90°, 270°   **7.** 2π **9.** π **11.** $\frac{\pi}{3}$

13. $\frac{8\pi}{3}$ **15.** π **17.** 3π

Written Exercises   Page 492   1. I,
increasing; II, decreasing; III, decreasing; IV,
increasing   **3.** I, increasing; II, increasing; III,
increasing; IV, increasing   **5.** I, increasing; II,
increasing; III, decreasing; IV, decreasing   **7.** 2
9. $^-1$ **11.** $^-\sqrt{3}$ **13.** 2   **15.** $^-2$ **17.** $^-2$ **19.** $^-1$
21. $^-2$ **23.** undefined   **25.** 1   **27.** $\frac{\sqrt{3}}{3}$ **29.** 0

31. $-\frac{\sqrt{3}}{3}$ **33.** 1   **37.**

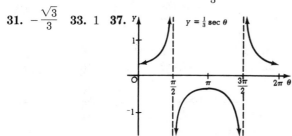

$y = \frac{1}{3}\sec \theta$

40.

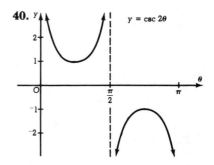

$y = \csc 2\theta$

Exploratory Exercises   Page 496   1. yes
3. yes   **5.** yes

Written Exercises   Page 496   1. $\frac{\sqrt{3}}{2}$ **3.** $\frac{3}{5}$
5. $\frac{3\sqrt{5}}{5}$ **7.** $\frac{4\sqrt{17}}{17}$ **9.** $-\frac{4}{5}$ **11.** $\frac{5}{4}$ **13.** $-\frac{\sqrt{17}}{4}$
15. $-\frac{\sqrt{3}}{2}$ **17.** $-\frac{12}{13}$ **19.** $\frac{3}{5}$ **21.** 1   **23.** $2 \sin x$
25. 2
27. $1 + \cot^2 \theta \stackrel{?}{=} \csc^2 \theta$ **29.** $\sin x \sec x \stackrel{?}{=} \tan x$

$$\frac{\sin^2 \theta + \cos^2 \theta}{\sin^2 \theta} \stackrel{?}{=} \csc^2 \theta \qquad \sin x \cdot \frac{1}{\cos x} \stackrel{?}{=} \tan x$$

$$\frac{1}{\sin^2 \theta} \stackrel{?}{=} \csc^2 \theta \qquad \frac{\sin x}{\cos x} \stackrel{?}{=} \tan x$$

$$\csc^2 \theta = \csc^2 \theta \qquad \tan x = \tan x$$

Exploratory Exercises   Page 499   1. 1
3. $\csc^2 \theta$ **5.** 1   **7.** $\cos \theta$ **9.** $\tan^2 \theta$

Written Exercises   Page 499
1. $\tan \beta \, (\cot \beta + \tan \beta) \stackrel{?}{=} \sec^2 \beta$

$$\tan \beta \left(\frac{1}{\tan \beta} + \tan \beta \right) \stackrel{?}{=} \sec^2 \beta$$
$$1 + \tan^2 \beta \stackrel{?}{=} \sec^2 \beta$$
$$\sec^2 \beta = \sec^2 \beta$$

3. $\csc x \sec x \stackrel{?}{=} \cot x + \tan x$

$$\frac{1}{\sin x} \cdot \frac{1}{\cos x} \stackrel{?}{=} \frac{\cos x}{\sin x} + \frac{\sin x}{\cos x}$$
$$\frac{1}{\sin x} \cdot \frac{1}{\cos x} \stackrel{?}{=} \frac{\cos^2 x + \sin^2 x}{\sin x \cos x}$$
$$\frac{1}{\sin x \cos x} = \frac{1}{\sin x \cos x}$$

5. $\dfrac{\sec \theta}{\sin \theta} - \dfrac{\sin \theta}{\cos \theta} \stackrel{?}{=} \cot \theta$

$$\frac{1}{\cos \theta \sin \theta} - \frac{\sin \theta}{\cos \theta} \stackrel{?}{=} \cot \theta$$
$$\frac{1 - \sin^2 \theta}{\cos \theta \sin \theta} \stackrel{?}{=} \cot \theta$$
$$\frac{\cos^2 \theta}{\cos \theta \sin \theta} \stackrel{?}{=} \cot \theta$$

$$\frac{\cos\theta}{\sin\theta} \stackrel{?}{=} \cot\theta$$

$$\cot\theta = \cot\theta$$

7. $\quad \dfrac{\sin\alpha}{1-\cos\alpha} + \dfrac{1-\cos\alpha}{\sin\alpha} \stackrel{?}{=} 2\csc\alpha$

$$\frac{\sin^2\alpha + (1-\cos\alpha)}{(1-\cos\alpha)(\sin\alpha)} \stackrel{?}{=} \frac{1}{\sin\alpha}$$

$$\frac{\sin^2\alpha + 1 - 2\cos\alpha + \cos^2\alpha}{(1-\cos\alpha)\sin\alpha} \stackrel{?}{=} \frac{2}{\sin\alpha}$$

$$\frac{2 - 2\cos\alpha}{(1-\cos\alpha)\sin\alpha} \stackrel{?}{=} \frac{2}{\sin\alpha}$$

$$\frac{2(1-\cos\alpha)}{(1-\cos\alpha)\sin\alpha} \stackrel{?}{=} \frac{2}{\sin\alpha}$$

$$\frac{2}{\sin\alpha} = \frac{2}{\sin\alpha}$$

9. $\quad \dfrac{\cos^2 x}{1-\sin x} \stackrel{?}{=} 1 + \sin x$

$$\frac{\cos^2 x}{1-\sin x} \cdot \frac{1+\sin x}{1+\sin x} \stackrel{?}{=} 1 + \sin x$$

$$\frac{\cos^2 x\,(1+\sin x)}{1-\sin^2 x} \stackrel{?}{=} 1 + \sin x$$

$$\frac{\cos^2 x\,(1+\sin x)}{\cos^2 x} \stackrel{?}{=} 1 + \sin x$$

$$1 + \sin x = 1 + \sin x$$

11. $\quad \dfrac{\sin\theta}{\sec\theta} \stackrel{?}{=} \dfrac{1}{\tan\theta + \cot\theta}$

$$\frac{\sin\theta}{\dfrac{1}{\cos\theta}} \stackrel{?}{=} \frac{1}{\dfrac{\sin\theta}{\cos\theta} + \dfrac{\cos\theta}{\sin\theta}}$$

$$\sin\theta\cdot\cos\theta \stackrel{?}{=} \frac{1}{\dfrac{\sin^2\theta + \cos^2\theta}{\cos\theta\cdot\sin\theta}}$$

$$\sin\theta\cdot\cos\theta \stackrel{?}{=} \frac{1}{\dfrac{1}{\cos\theta\cdot\sin\theta}}$$

$$\sin\theta\cdot\cos\theta = \cos\theta\cdot\sin\theta$$

15. $\quad \cos^2 x + \tan^2 x\cos^2 x \stackrel{?}{=} 1$

$$\cos^2 x + \frac{\sin^2 x}{\cos^2 x}\cdot\cos^2 x \stackrel{?}{=} 1$$

$$\cos^2 x + \sin^2 x \stackrel{?}{=} 1$$

$$1 = 1$$

17. $\quad \dfrac{1+\tan^2\theta}{\csc^2\theta} \stackrel{?}{=} \tan^2\theta$

$$\frac{\sec^2\theta}{\csc^2\theta} \stackrel{?}{=} \tan^2\theta$$

$$\frac{\dfrac{1}{\cos^2\theta}}{\dfrac{1}{\sin^2\theta}} \stackrel{?}{=} \tan^2\theta$$

$$\frac{1}{\cos^2\theta}\cdot\frac{\sin^2\theta}{1} \stackrel{?}{=} \tan^2\theta$$

$$\frac{\sin^2\theta}{\cos^2\theta} = \tan^2\theta$$

$$\tan^2\theta = \tan^2\theta$$

21. $\qquad \cos^4 x - \sin^4 x \stackrel{?}{=} \cos^2 x - \sin^2 x$

$$(\cos^2 x + \sin^2 x)(\cos^2 x - \sin^2 x) \stackrel{?}{=} \cos^2 x - \sin^2 x$$

$$1(\cos^2 x - \sin^2 x) \stackrel{?}{=} \cos^2 x - \sin^2 x$$

$$\cos^2 x - \sin^2 x = \cos^2 x - \sin^2 x$$

23. $\qquad \dfrac{\tan^2 x}{\sec x - 1} \stackrel{?}{=} 1 + \dfrac{1}{\cos x}$

$$\frac{\tan^2 x(\sec x + 1)}{(\sec x - 1)(\sec x + 1)} \stackrel{?}{=} 1 + \frac{1}{\cos x}$$

$$\frac{\tan^2 x(\sec x + 1)}{\tan^2 x} \stackrel{?}{=} 1 + \frac{1}{\cos x}$$

$$\frac{1}{\cos x} + 1 = 1 + \frac{1}{\cos x}$$

25. $\quad \dfrac{1+\sin x}{\sin x} \stackrel{?}{=} \dfrac{\cot^2 x}{\csc x - 1}$

$$\frac{1+\sin x}{\sin x} \stackrel{?}{=} \frac{\csc^2 x - 1}{\csc x - 1}$$

$$\frac{1+\sin x}{\sin x} \stackrel{?}{=} \frac{(\csc x - 1)(\csc x + 1)}{\csc x - 1}$$

$$\frac{1+\sin x}{\sin x} \stackrel{?}{=} \csc x + 1$$

$$\frac{1+\sin x}{\sin x} \stackrel{?}{=} \frac{1}{\sin x} + 1$$

$$\frac{1+\sin x}{\sin x} = \frac{1+\sin x}{\sin x}$$

Exploratory Exercises   Page 502
1. $45° + 60°$ **3.** $^{-}135° - 30°$ **5.** $30° + 45°$
7. $225° + 60°$

Written Exercises   Page 502   1. $\dfrac{\sqrt{6} + \sqrt{2}}{4}$

3. $\dfrac{^{-}\sqrt{2} - \sqrt{6}}{4}$ **5.** $\dfrac{^{-}\sqrt{6} - \sqrt{2}}{4}$ **7.** $\dfrac{\sqrt{6} + \sqrt{2}}{4}$

9. $\dfrac{^{-}\sqrt{6} - \sqrt{2}}{4}$

11. $\sin(270 - \theta) = \sin 270\cos\theta - \cos 270\sin\theta$
$$= \,^{-}1\cdot\cos\theta - 0\cdot\sin\theta$$
$$= \,^{-}\cos\theta$$

13. $\sin(180 + \theta) = \sin 180\cos\theta + \cos 180\sin\theta$
$$= 0 - 1\cdot\sin\theta$$
$$= \,^{-}\sin\theta$$

15. $\sin(90 + \theta) = \sin 90\cos\theta + \cos 90\sin\theta$
$$= 1\cdot\cos\theta + 0$$
$$= \cos\theta$$

17. $\dfrac{\sqrt{3}}{2}$ **19.** $\dfrac{1}{2}$

29. $^{-}2 - \sqrt{3}$ **31.** $^{-}2 + \sqrt{3}$ **33.** $\sqrt{3}$
35. $^{-}2 - \sqrt{3}$ **37.** $^{-}2 + \sqrt{3}$ **39.** $^{-}\tan\theta$

Exploratory Exercises   Page 506   1. I or II
3. I or II   **5.** I   **7.** II   **9.** I or II   **11.** I or II
13. I   **15.** II

Written Exercises **Page 506** **1.** $\frac{\sqrt{3}}{2}$; $\frac{1}{2}$;

$\frac{\sqrt{2-\sqrt{3}}}{2}$; $\frac{\sqrt{2+\sqrt{3}}}{2}$ **3.** $\frac{4}{9}\sqrt{5}$; $-\frac{1}{9}$; $\frac{\sqrt{30}}{6}$; $-\frac{\sqrt{6}}{6}$

5. $-\frac{120}{169}$; $\frac{119}{169}$; $\frac{5\sqrt{26}}{26}$; $\frac{\sqrt{26}}{26}$ **7.** $\frac{3\sqrt{7}}{8}$; $-\frac{1}{8}$; $\frac{\sqrt{8-2\sqrt{7}}}{4}$;

$\frac{-\sqrt{8+2\sqrt{7}}}{4}$ **9.** $-\frac{\sqrt{15}}{8}$; $-\frac{7}{8}$; $\frac{\sqrt{10}}{4}$; $\frac{\sqrt{6}}{4}$

11. $-\frac{3\sqrt{55}}{32}$; $\frac{23}{32}$; $\frac{\sqrt{8-\sqrt{55}}}{4}$; $\frac{-\sqrt{8+\sqrt{55}}}{4}$ **13.** $\frac{\sqrt{15}}{8}$;

$\frac{7}{8}$; $\frac{\sqrt{8+2\sqrt{15}}}{4}$; $\frac{-\sqrt{8-2\sqrt{15}}}{4}$

15. $\cos^2 2x + 4\sin^2 x \cos^2 x \overset{?}{=} 1$
$$\cos^2 2x + \sin^2 2x \overset{?}{=} 1$$
$$1 = 1$$

17.
$$\sin^4 x - \cos^4 x \overset{?}{=} 2\sin^2 x - 1$$
$$(\sin^2 x - \cos^2 x)(\sin^2 x + \cos^2 x) \overset{?}{=} 2\sin^2 x - 1$$
$$(\sin^2 x - \cos^2 x) \cdot 1 \overset{?}{=} 2\sin^2 x - 1$$
$$[\sin^2 x \cdot (1 - \sin^2 x)] \cdot 1 \overset{?}{=} 2\sin^2 x - 1$$
$$\sin^2 x - 1 + \sin^2 x \overset{?}{=} 2\sin^2 x - 1$$
$$2\sin^2 x - 1 = 2\sin^2 x - 1$$

19. $\sin^2 \theta \overset{?}{=} \frac{1}{2}(1 - \cos 2\theta)$
$$\overset{?}{=} \frac{1}{2}[1 - (1 - 2\sin^2 \theta)]$$
$$\overset{?}{=} \frac{1}{2}[2\sin^2 \theta)]$$
$$= \sin^2 0$$

Exploratory Exercises **Page 509** **1.** 1 **3.** 2
5. 2 **7.** 4 **9.** 4 **11.** 0

Written Exercises **Page 509** **1.** 45°, 135°,
225°, 315° **3.** 0°, 180°, 210°, 330° **5.** 0°, 90°, 270°
7. 30°, 90°, 150°, 270° **9.** 30°, 150°
11. 0° + $n \cdot 120$° where n is any integer
13. 45° + $n \cdot 180$° where n is any integer
15. 120° + $n \cdot 360$° where n is any integer,
240° + $n \cdot 360$° where n is any integer
17. 90° + $n \cdot 360$° where n is any integer,
180° + $n \cdot 360$° where n is any integer
19. 0° + $n \cdot 360$° where n is any integer,
60° + $n \cdot 360$° where n is any integer,
300° + $n \cdot 360$° where n is any integer

Skills Review **Page 509** **1.** yes **3.** no

Exploratory Exercises **Page 513** **1.** $\frac{1}{2}$

3. ⁻60° **5.** undefined **7.** 1 **9.** 150° **11.** 45°

13. undefined **15.** 60° **17.** $\frac{\sqrt{2}}{2}$ **19.** ⁻90°

21. 90° **23.** 0

Written Exercises **Page 513** **1.** $\frac{1}{2}$ **3.** 90°

5. $\frac{1}{2}$ **7.** $\frac{1}{2}$ **9.** $\frac{5}{12}$ **11.** $\frac{24}{25}$ **13.** $\frac{\sqrt{3}}{2}$ **15.** $\frac{\sqrt{2}}{2}$

17. $-\frac{4}{3}$ **19.** $\frac{1}{2}$ **21.** $\frac{\sqrt{2}}{2}$ **23.** $-\frac{1}{2}$ **25.** $\frac{1}{2}$

27. $\frac{\sqrt{3}}{2}$ **29.** $\frac{\sqrt{2}}{2}$

Chapter Review **Page 515** **1.** $\frac{2\pi}{3}$ **3.** $\frac{3\pi}{2}$

5. 60° **7.** $\left(\frac{240}{\pi}\right)^{\circ}$ **9.** 205° **11.** 180° **13.** $\frac{2\pi}{3}$

15. $\frac{16\pi}{9}$ **17.** $\frac{\sqrt{3}}{2}$ **19.** ⁻1 **21.** $-\frac{1}{2}$ **23.** $-\frac{\sqrt{2}}{2}$

25. 1 **27.** 1; 2π **29.** 4; π **31.** $\frac{2\sqrt{3}}{3}$ **33.** $-\frac{1}{2}$

35. $\sqrt{3}$ **37.** 2 **39.** $-\frac{4}{5}$ **41.** $\frac{\sqrt{17}}{4}$ **43.** 0

45. $\frac{2\sqrt{3}}{3}$

47. $\frac{\sin \theta}{\tan \theta} + \frac{\cos \theta}{\cot \theta}$ $\quad \overset{?}{=} \cos \theta + \sin \theta$

$\frac{\sin \theta}{\frac{\sin \theta}{\cos \theta}} + \frac{\cos \theta}{\frac{\cos \theta}{\sin \theta}}$ $\quad \overset{?}{=} \cos \theta + \sin \theta$

$\sin \theta \cdot \frac{\cos \theta}{\sin \theta} + \cos \theta \cdot \frac{\sin \theta}{\cos \theta} \overset{?}{=} \cos \theta + \sin \theta$

$\cos \theta + \sin \theta = \cos \theta \sin \theta$

49. $\tan x + \cot x \overset{?}{=} \sec x \csc x$

$\frac{\sin x}{\cos x} + \frac{\cos x}{\sin x} \overset{?}{=} \sec x \csc x$

$\frac{\sin^2 x + \cos^2 x}{\cos x \sin x} \overset{?}{=} \sec x \csc x$

$\frac{1}{\cos x \sin x} \overset{?}{=} \sec x \csc x$

$\frac{1}{\cos x} \cdot \frac{1}{\sin x} \overset{?}{=} \sec x \csc x$

$\sec x \csc x = \sec x \csc x$

51. $-\frac{1}{2}$ **53.** $\frac{(\sqrt{2} + \sqrt{6})}{4}$ **57.** $\frac{7}{8}$ **59.** 0°

61. 270° **63.** 15°, 75°, 195°, 255° **65.** 30°
67. 60° **69.** 0

CHAPTER 17 RIGHT TRIANGLE TRIGONOMETRY

Exploratory Exercises **Page 521**
1. $\sin A = \frac{5}{13}$; $\sin B = \frac{12}{13}$ **3.** $\sin A = 3\sqrt{13}/13$;
$\sin B = 2\sqrt{13}/13$ **5.** $\cos A = \sqrt{5}/5$;
$\cos B = 2\sqrt{5}/5$ **7.** $\tan A = \frac{5}{12}$; $\tan B = \frac{12}{5}$
9. $\tan A = \frac{3}{2}$; $\tan B = \frac{2}{3}$

Written Exercises   Page 521   1. 0.8000
3. 1.3333 **5.** 0.8000 **7.** 0.4706 **9.** 0.8824
11. 0.5333 **13.** 0.3492 **15.** 0.9370 **17.** 0.3727
19. 1.3333 **21.** 2.8636 **23.** 2.1250
25. sin A = 0.9428; cos A = 0.3333; tan
A = 2.8284 **27.** sin A = 0.4545; cos A = 0.8907;
tan A = 0.5103 **29.** $-\dfrac{\sqrt{3}}{2}$ **31.** $\dfrac{\sqrt{3}}{2}$ **33.** $-\dfrac{1}{2}$
35. $2 + \sqrt{3}$

Exploratory Exercises   Page 525   1. 0.6691
3. 0.9272 **5.** 343.8 **7.** 1.171 **9.** 0.4488
11. 0.9605 **13.** 0.9511 **15.** 0.4592

Written Exercises   Page 525   1. 0.7880
3. 0.9272 **5.** 0.2812 **7.** 4.511 **9.** 0.5125
11. 50.54 **13.** 1.809 **15.** ⁻2.616 **17.** ⁻0.2518
19. 0.9228 **21.** 59°7′ **23.** 19°13′ **25.** 44°00′
27. 12°32′ **29.** 53°55′ **31.** 45°5′ **33.** 40°42′
35. 35°51′

Exploratory Exercises   Page 527

1. $\sin 15° = \dfrac{a}{37}$ **3.** $\sin 49°13' = \dfrac{10}{c}$

5. $\cos 16° = \dfrac{13}{c}$ **7.** $7^2 + b^2 = 16^2$

9. $\tan A = \dfrac{7}{12}$

Written Exercises   Page 527   1. $c = \sqrt{53}$,
$A = 15°57'$, $B = 74°04'$ **3.** $b = 5$, $A = 67°23'$,
$B = 22°37'$ **5.** $a = \sqrt{133}$, $A = 62°31'$,
$B = 27°29'$ **7.** $a = 3.86$, $b = 13.46$, $B = 74°$
9. $B = 52°45'$, $c = 13.82$, $a = 8.36$
11. $A = 47°50'$, $c = 12.14$, $b = 8.15$
13. $A = 77°$, $a = 5.85$, $b = 1.35$ **15.** $B = 13°$,
$a = 181.92$, $c = 186.71$ **17.** $A = 57°$, $c = 39.35$,
$b = 21.43$ **19.** $B = 34°5'$, $a = 13.25$, $b = 8.97$
21. $B = 45°$, $b = 7$, $a = 7$ **23.** $B = 75°$, $a = 6.47$,
$b = 24.15$

Skills Review   Page 527   1. $3 \pm \sqrt{21}$ **3.** $4, \dfrac{2}{3}$
5. $1, 64$

Written Exercises   Page 529   1. 64.35 m
3. 1119.36 ft **5.** 7.42 ft **7.** 22.07 m **9.** 9°36′
11. 22°48′ **13.** $x = 63°26'$, $y = 26°34'$,
$z = 63°26'$ **15.** 100 ft, 300 ft **17.** 102.25 ft
19. 4.05 cm **21.** 164.92 km

Exploratory Exercises   Page 534

1. area $= \left(\dfrac{1}{2}\right)(10)(17)(\sin 46°)$

3. area $= \left(\dfrac{1}{2}\right)(15)(30)(\sin 90°)$

5. $\dfrac{\sin 50°}{14} = \dfrac{\sin B}{10}$ **7.** $\dfrac{\sin 53°}{a} = \dfrac{\sin 61°}{2.8}$

Written Exercises   Page 535   1. 55.152
3. 27.531 **5.** 37.001 **7.** 63.2089 **9.** $c = 74°$,
$b = 8.8904$, $c = 10.19$ **11.** $B = 60°19'$,
$c = 36°31'$, $c = 47.95$ **13.** $A = 52°$, $b = 100.17$,
$c = 90.40$ **15.** $B = 52°53'$, $A = 62°27'$
$a = 16.68$ **17.** $A = 24°24'$, $a = 5.54$, $c = 11.74$

Exploratory Exercises   Page 538   1. Law of
Cosines **3.** Law of Cosines **5.** Law of Cosines
7. Law of Cosines **9.** Law of Cosines

Written Exercises   Page 538   1. $A = 46°37'$,
$B = 73°50'$, $C = 59°33'$ **3.** $A = 44°25'$,
$B = 57°07'$, $C = 78°28'$ **5.** $b = 17.92$,
$A = 54°42'$, $C = 78°18'$ **7.** $C = 81°$, $a = 9.11$,
$b = 12.15$ **9.** $A = 29°58'$, $B = 69°45'$, $c = 80°17'$
11. $P = 1434.26$ ft; $A = 86{,}804.28$ ft²
13. 228.38 mi; 19°53′ **15.** 183.03 mi
17. 35°41′

21.
$$a^2 = b^2 + c^2 - 2bc \cos A$$
$$-2bx \cos A = a^2 - b^2 - c^2$$
$$2bc - 2bc \cos A = a^2 - b^2 - c^2 + 2bc$$
$$2bc - 2bc \cos A = (a - b + c)(a + b - c)$$
$$1 - \cos A = \frac{(a - b + c)(a + b - c)}{2bc}$$

Exploratory Exercises   Page 541   1. no
triangle **3.** 1 triangle **5.** 1 triangle

Written Exercises   Page 541   1. 1; $B = 90°$
$C = 53°08'$, $c = 8$ **3.** none **5.** 1; $A = 44°46'$
$B = 37°14'$, $b = 54.99$ **7.** none **9.** none
11. none **13.** none **15.** none

Chapter Review   Page 543   1. 0.6000
3. 0.8000 **5.** 0.7500 **7.** 1.6667 **9.** 0.7500
11. $\sqrt{3}$ **13.** 0.9397 **15.** 0.8192 **17.** 1.0724
19. 68°00′ **21.** 23°30′ **23.** 19°10′
25. $B = 65°$, $a = 2.54$, $b = 5.44$ **27.** $A = 5°$,
$b = 70.98$, $c = 71.25$ **29.** $c = 3.16$, $A = 18°26'$,
$B = 71°34'$ **31.** $a = 7.14$, $A = 45°34'$,
$B = 44°26'$ **33.** 55.53 m **35.** 38°39′
37. $c = 11.65$, $C = 63°11'$, $B = 66°49'$
39. $A = 51°$, $a = 70.22$, $c = 89.69$ **41.** $a = 4.36$,
$B = 23°24'$, $C = 96°35'$ **43.** $c = 4.54$,
$A = 58°05'$, $B = 81°55'$ **45.** no solution
47. $B = 35°08'$, $C = 98°52'$, $c = 13.74$